Ideas on Human Evolution

Selected Essays, 1949-1961

Ideas on Human Evolution

Selected Essays, 1949–1961

Edited by
WILLIAM HOWELLS

∿∿∿

HARVARD UNIVERSITY PRESS
Cambridge
1962

© *Copyright, 1962, by the President and Fellows of Harvard College*

Distributed in Great Britain by
Oxford University Press, London

Library of Congress Catalog Card Number 62–11399

Printed in the United States of America

Preface

〜〜〜

Ideas on human evolution have changed largely because of two things: new fossils and new theoretical understandings. Effects of both will be seen in papers in this volume.

Evolutionary theory, as it makes a background for human origins, got its first impulse from Darwin, but has had its broad development only during the second quarter of this century, culminating in the emergence of the so-called synthetic theory of evolution and the development of "population thinking" (see Mayr, 1959, for a succinct statement of the nature of these changes). Important in this period were the loosening of the grip of certain older ideas. Some of these orthodoxies were: a Mendelian genetics based on genes of major effect and a reliance on mutation as the one important source of change; a simplistic natural selection saving "good" genes and mutations and eliminating "bad" ones; a too strict adherence to certain otherwise suggestive principles, such as "irreversibility of evolution"; and a feeling that the fossil record revealed transformations too profound to be explained by what fruit flies could tell us, so that sympathy for "orthogenesis," overt or covert, was difficult to exorcise. The final surmounting of these scruples, and the change of charge between palaeontologists and geneticists from repulsion to attraction, have been too recent indeed. In general evolutionary circles, they were signalized by the well known 1947 symposium, *Genetics, Palaeontology and Evolution* (Jepson, Simpson and Mayr, 1949), and by a series of influential books by individuals, for example, *Genetics and the Origin of Species* (Dobzhansky, 1937), *Systematics and the Origin of Species* (Mayr, 1942), and *Tempo and Mode in Evolution* (Simpson, 1944). These, at any rate, exemplify the writings which had a marked effect on the study of the evolution of man. The groundwork for all this had of course been laid earlier, in the work of the men cited and in that of such theoretical geneticists as Fisher and Sewall Wright.

Recent ideas of human history also strongly reflect the history of fossil

finds. The first phase of this history was Neanderthal Man's. To him fell
the job of proving the existence of fossil man: earlier *Homo sapiens* skulls,
and even the Engis Neanderthal child of 1829, had been unable to assure
everyone that they were not chance burials among Pleistocene animals.
After 1856, however, there followed a series of finds, both of Neanderthals
and of sapiens men of the Upper Palaeolithic and later times, making it
clear that these two populations had indeed existed anciently.

But they long remained the only known fossil men. A second period
may be considered to have started with the finding of Java Man in the
1890's, and to have run on until about 1930. It was a period in which
spectacular discoveries were made of single specimens, each one different
from the others, and all poorly dated, relatively or absolutely. Java Man,
however, suggested a simple chimpanzee—Pithecanthropus—Neanderthal—sapiens sequence, and family trees began to sprout. The Heidelberg
jaw followed in 1907, the Piltdown remains in 1912, the Rhodesian skull
from Broken Hill in 1921, the first Pekin calvarium in 1929, and of course
the then highly suspect *Australopithecus* in 1924. Piltdown Man belongs
fairly in this list since, regardless of what happened to his reputation in
1953, he made a perfectly good member of the series of new kinds of men
in the early part of the century. In fact, he is a very good sign of the times,
since he shows how acceptable seemingly widely divergent lines of human development then were, to the minds of the anthropologists. The
fact that some of them did not accept him on the evidence does not deny
the existence of such a state of mind.

Toward the end of this period a number of general books were published, which reflect how the limited information stifled interpretation. I
am thinking of the first edition of Boule's *Les Hommes Fossiles,* 1921;
MacCurdy's *Human Origins,* 1924; Elliot Smith's *Essays on the Evolution
of Man,* 1924; Keith's 1925 edition of *The Antiquity of Man;* Hrdlička's
Skeletal Remains of Early Man, 1930; and the first (1931) edition of
Hooton's *Up From the Ape.* Others could be added, and in fact the time
since then, excepting possibly the present moment, has seen no such spate
of books devoted to fossil man, disregarding rank popularizations. These
are famous and justly honored works. Although they differ in style, the
treatment comes down to the same thing in each: separate descriptions of
the individual fossil types. Family trees were usually attempted as well,
and these also had the same pattern: Something labeled the human or
"humanoid" stem came from a fork with the anthropoid apes and rose like
a sturdy trunk, straight toward the sun, splitting at the top into the
modern races; from the sides, lateral branches thrust out, labeled Java
Man, Piltdown Man, Pekin Man, Rhodesian Man, Neanderthal Man. (For
a review of such phylogenies, see Kennedy, 1960; also Vallois, 1958, in

this volume). There were, of course, exceptions, discussed in the papers which follow.

We can see now what the limiting factors were: various *kinds* of men were known, but next to nothing about populations, distributions, or dates. Consequently, discerning logical connections or making judgments as to how one form might have led into another, or have become separate from another, was out of the question. Small wonder that there was an unabashed proliferation of spurious species and genera, something frequently referred to in this book.

From 1930 on, however, things have been very different. In this third phase, variation, distribution, and sequences began to be evident, in a rapid increase in material. The Chou Kou Tien finds, straddling this date, changed from a couple of specimens to a whole population. Von Koenigswald produced more Java skulls, from different time levels. He also, in 1931 and 1932, participated in the recovery of another "population"— eleven crania—of Solo men. Another Rhodesian skull was found (1953) at Hopefield, Cape Colony. A critical group of "intermediate" forms came to light, now well dated: Mt. Carmel, Steinheim, Swanscombe, Florisbad, Fontéchevade. The australopithecines were transformed from a single juvenile specimen into a whole phase of human development, richly documented. Two important Tertiary hominoids became known—*Proconsul* and *Oreopithecus*—with skulls and postcranial parts, a contrast with the dryopithecine material existing before, which consisted almost entirely of teeth and mandibular body fragments. Finally, these thirty years have seen the erasing, not only of the Piltdown bugaboo, but also of a list of older finds, headed by Galley Hill, which had been false buttresses of the hypothesis that *Homo sapiens* had a considerable Pleistocene antiquity as a separate line. The emergence of sapiens man, of course, is still a crucial problem in unraveling human phylogeny, but it can be better attacked if the stage is cleared of elements not really related to the plot.

By the end of World War II, and especially in the 1950's, a new level of understanding had been reached, as a result of the above advances in theory and fact; and writings on human evolution were decidedly more sophisticated than they had been before. It has seemed to me that university students would benefit from a sampling of these recent writings, and possibly even professional anthropologists of the nonphysical variety as well.

The principal aim of this book is to present ideas, not data—views and thoughts rather than facts. The latter are assumed; they may be found in texts, or in course lectures. The body of fact grows rapidly, and in paleoanthropology the "facts" themselves have a way of changing: redating may have critical effects, or it may turn out that a long-established "fact" is actually a misinterpretation of structure or of restoration. Thus, no attempt is made to be up-to-date in reference to information, and the reader should understand clearly, for the sake of the authors concerned, that these articles relate to their dates of writing. There has been a series of most important developments in the last ten years (and there will be others even before this book gets through the press), some obvious ones being: exposure of the Piltdown fraud, 1953; findings of more *Oreopithecus* material, and re-interpretation by Hürzeler and others, especially from 1954 to the present; finding of *Gigantopithecus* jaws and more teeth, 1955 on; questions as to the status of *Parapithecus* as an Oligocene hominoid, 1957 on; and discovery of "Zinjanthropus" and other hominids at Olduvai and more finds of stone implements at australopithecine sites, 1956 on. There were other supplementary finds (for example, Shanidar Neanderthals, South China fossils) and re-datings by technical means or by geological refinements, too numerous to specify.

None of this affects the principal purpose of this volume, which is to present lines of thought, representative for date of publication and generally valid now. Authors have been encouraged (on the above understanding) to make such corrections, addenda, or footnotes to their original articles as they wished, although such last-minute observations are just as exposed to still later modifications by discovery as the original text, if not more so. In a few cases the editor has deleted sentences or paragraphs which have become totally irrelevant today, but only where this had no effect on the actual train of thought of the author. But such correction is secondary, and the aim remains that stated: to offer a sampling of interpretative and methodological writing of the last ten or a dozen years, by significant writers. The book should serve, for a short generation, as a source for recent ideas, current varieties of thinking, and then should become an item for historical reference, as the weight of new finds, new applications of biological theory, and a new generation of writers bring a new literature to succeed the present one.

A point of interest. Many of the papers refer to variety within populations of fossil man. Only Gregory touches on variety within the anthropologists. This collection may reveal how much individual temperaments and attitudes have to do with interpretations, and thus eventually with the whole current of thinking of a period. One student sees broad outlines, and evidently has a temperamental feeling for fluidity, dynamism, suggestive speculation; another moves relentlessly through statistical investigations of particular phenomena, permitting himself only the most chary and solidly grounded final observations. The continental Europeans have readily coined new terms and group designations; writers in English on the other hand seem to have a distaste for this, with Gregory even using it in a vein of gentle humor.

The criteria for selection of papers have been several, but especially these: to represent leading writers and varied points of view on human evolution in its historical aspects, and to make papers accessible which are otherwise not so, at least for many student readers. Actually, these principles are honored as often in the breach. Many authors who should be on such a list—it is easy to think of names—do not happen to have written something which seemed to me to fit into the framework of the book as I have proportioned it. Of those authors selected, other papers of theirs may have been more influential in the past, but such papers seemed to me no longer to represent the author's more recent point of view—and I have wanted to be at least this much up-to-date. Some stimulating papers, which might have been used with profit, appeared in a publication or symposium which is already a useful collection of such papers, and in any case easily accessible to students of anthropology in this country. Many that I have included would seem to be similarly accessible, having even in some cases been reprinted since publication; they are, however, to be found in journals or volumes not usable by considerable numbers of students, and are also articles which are too central to the volume as a whole to be omitted.

My choice of papers does not mean that I favor the views expressed more than those in papers not chosen, or that I consider the emphases of certain schools of thought relative to others as necessarily a fair picture of present weight of opinion generally. All such considerations are overruled by the wish to choose writers who have expressed themselves clearly and usefully, in a compass suitable for this book, either in interpretation, in exposition of theory, or in illustration of some special comparative method.

On one subject in particular—hominid phylogeny in the Pleistocene—there will be noticed a good deal of overlap among a number of papers. This is not accidental, since one of my purposes has been to show a breadth of different views and different treatment at the present time. A single book by a single author should avoid such repetition and variety of statement as far as possible; it should edit and confine to a smaller space the content of other technical works and full-fledged discussions; and it should either argue a single coherent point of view, the author's, or offer a fair consensus, rather than a lengthy discussion of the same facts from a series of different points of view. This might result in a considerable dehydration of the subject matter. The present volume is not a text or general book (nor yet a symposium), but rather an attempt to put forth some of these matters at their normal hydration, that is, in the fullness of exposition of views which must be allowed if the matter discussed is to be properly comprehended by the interested reader on human evolution, and not merely comfortably absorbed in digest form from a more succinct statement in a shorter work.

Two final editorial notes. Different authors have used different systems of nomenclature, and in somewhat different systems of groupings, both for fossil men and for hominoids generally, so that a word like "prehominid" may mean various things. The editor can do nothing to eliminate this and can only put the reader on his guard. If he has the basic knowledge of the material, the above disagreements should be obvious as they are come to. (For the above reasons I have thought it unwise to attempt a glossary, in which my definitions might misrepresent the meaning intended by an author. Nor have I furnished an index, since these writings are essays rather than expositions of fact.)

Also, the spelling of Neanderthal. At the turn of the century, German spelling officially dropped the "h" from "thal" and a number of other words in which it had followed the "t," for example, "theil," "thor." Although it must be retained, by the rules of nomenclature, in *Homo neanderthalensis*, the Germans and the French now use the spelling Neandertal in all other references. It is English-speaking writers only who have retained the "h,"—unfortunately, since unlike French and German, English has a genuine "th" sound for beginning anthropology students to employ in mispronouncing Neanderthal. In spite of a few mild protests, the usage persists, and so I have followed it in making translations from French and German, though I have changed no orthography in any article already published in English.

The separate lists of references have been consolidated into a single bibliography, for ease of reference and because such a bibliography should be useful in itself. Errors and incomplete citations have been eliminated as far as possible; this arduous work was done by Peter Sindell, a Harvard undergraduate, with a care and intelligence praiseworthy even for that species.

It remains to thank all the authors whose articles I have used, as warmly as I can. Each one promptly and heartily gave his consent for the use of his writing, and all have been extremely helpful in furnishing illustrations as best they could, and in responding to queries, checking translations, etc. The latter are my responsibility, and errors which may have escaped both me and the original author are obviously chargeable to me. I am most grateful to the staff of the Harvard University Press, and also to Mrs. Elinor Dannay, Mrs. Cynthia Black, and Mrs. Edith Gray, for their help in preparing the text and attending to correspondence.

Cambridge, 1961   William Howells

Contents

wwwwwwwwwwwwwwwwwwwwwwwwwwwwwwwwwwwwwwwwwwwwwwwwwwwwwwwwwwwwwwwwwwwwwwwwwwww

Contents

Ideas on Human Evolution

Selected Essays, 1949-1961

The Study of Evolution:
Methods and Present Status of Theory

George Gaylord Simpson   1958

Samuel Butler said that a hen is an egg's way of producing another egg. Thus in the Darwinian epoch he foreshadowed a reorientation of evolutionary studies that did later occur. Without expressing it in that way, the evolutionary scientists of Butler's and earlier times held the common-sense view that an egg is a hen's way of producing another hen. They were trying to explain the evolution of the hen, not of the egg. It was the geneticists, after 1900, who came around to Butler's view that the essence of the matter is in the egg, not in the hen.[1]

Those contrasting points of view reflect different ideas as to the involvement of behavior in evolution. The 19th-century evolutionary theories of the naturalists were largely, if not primarily, behavioral. The behavioral element tended at first to be minimized in the 20th-century evolutionary theories of the geneticists, who might in some cases be accused of leaving the hen out of the picture altogether except as a means of learning what the egg "knows."

The first great issue in naturalistic evolutionary theory was between the neo-Lamarckians and the Darwinians. (There were and are non-

[1] Without, indeed, any real debt to Butler. That an egg somehow "knows" how to produce a hen and thus produces another egg that "knows" just a little more seems brilliantly apt in retrospect. But, like other flashes of Butler's peculiar genius, this bit of insight was so embedded in nonsense that it was not really helpful at the time and had no useful outcome.

FROM Behavior and Evolution, *1958, edited by Anne Roe and George Gaylord Simpson; reprinted by permission of the author and of the Yale University Press. The book is the publication of a conference held April 30–May 5, 1956, at Princeton. This chapter is a brief and simple review of certain main points of the modern synthetic theory of evolution, written by one of its principal architects. Dr. Simpson is Alexander Agassiz Professor of Vertebrate Paleontology at Harvard University.*

naturalistic alternative schools, such as those of vitalism or of finalism, but their metaphysics can legitimately be omitted from this brief account.) Lamarck, himself, stressed behavior almost to the point of considering it the sole effective cause of evolution. It is, he taught, the habitual actions of organisms—in other words, their behavior—that modify their morphology, and these modifications accumulated through the generations *are* evolution. It is true that Lamarck also believed in a perfecting principle that somehow has driven organisms up the *scala naturae*, but the neo-Lamarckians discarded that essentially nonnaturalistic element in his theory. The neo-Lamarckians also incorporated into their views the accumulation of direct results of the action of the environment on organisms, a hypothesis that is non-Lamarckian and nonbehavioral.

Darwin's theory of evolution was hardly less behavioral than Lamarck's. Darwin saw no reason to question the Lamarckian belief in the direct influence of behavior on evolution, through the induction of heritable modifications. Darwin's own main contribution, the theory of natural selection, also involved essential relationships beween behavior and evolution. He saw and illustrated with many examples that the behavior of animals is often determined and always circumscribed by their heredity, although he knew even less than we do about the mechanisms involved. The behavior of animals is also obviously and crucially involved in their survival and success in reproduction. Thus natural selection provides another way, less direct but truer than the supposed Lamarckian way, in which behavior is bound in with the changes in heredity that constitute evolution.

Few now doubt that the Lamarckian and neo-Lamarckian views are essentially false, and we need pay no further attention to them here. The point is that Lamarck, Darwin, and their many colleagues and followers were all primarily interested in the behaving animal, the hen, rather than in the egg, which has no behavior in usual senses of the word, and that one of the things they sought and stressed was a relationship between behavior and evolution. It is a pity, in a way, that we cannot accept a direct and simple relationship, but Darwin pointed out a relationship that is surely present, in some degree, and that is all the more effective for being indirect and subtle.

Then came the shift of emphasis to the egg by the geneticists from about 1900 onward. In extreme form, their views practically eliminated behavior as an essential element in evolution. What a hen is and does depends on the egg, that is, on the mechanism of heredity complete within the fertilized egg. Evolutionary changes in the hen, so some of the early geneticists submitted and a dwindling few still hold, arise without any prior relationship to the hen and its behavior. Evolution is reduced to processes in the precursor cells of the gametes and in the confluence of gametes in the fertilized egg (zygote). The hen (the man, the tree) is largely irrelevant except, as Butler said, as a device for producing another egg.

The most widely held modern theory of evolution may be presented as a reconciliation between the naturalists' hen-evolution and the geneticists' egg-evolution. It reinstates behavior not merely as something to which evolution has happened but as something that is itself one of the essential determinants of evolution. Accepting the geneticists' knowledge of egg-processes, it shows that these are not autonomous but are strongly influenced by hen-processes. The means of that influence is, as Darwin thought, natural selection. In the course of this theoretical synthesis natural selection has turned out to be something broader than and in some respects different from Darwin's concept.[2]

METHODS OF EVOLUTIONARY STUDY

The topic assigned for this chapter requires some notice of methods before proceeding to summarize the present status of evolutionary theory. Methods are, indeed, so numerous and diverse that a catalogue of them would be redundant to those who are using them, confusing to those who are not, and of little interest or usefulness in either case. It will be best to avoid detail and to present only a few broad considerations as to aims, the ways of achieving them, and implications or criteria involved in those ways.

In the first place, most of the aims of evolutionary study involve either events or processes. The study of events is historical; it seeks to reconstruct the whole history of organisms on this planet. That (unattainable) goal is of course approached by accumulation of restricted studies of the histories of particular groups of organisms, of particular anatomical or physiological features, and the like. The procedure is by levels: comparative descriptive studies, then inferential placing of the units of description in phylogenetic sequences, and finally, generalizations as to the kinds of sequences that have most frequently occurred and the conditions that accompany and therefore may determine a particular kind of sequence.

The objective data for historical study, the things described at the first level of research, are characteristics of (1) organisms or parts thereof, (2) their activities, (3) the conditions surrounding and influencing them,

[2] In justice, however, it should be emphasized that practically nothing that Darwin wrote about natural selection is invalidated by the modern concept. Darwinian selection still stands, but its complexities and bearings are better understood and it becomes part of a more inclusive principle.

and (4) the temporal sequence of the items observed.[3] It is especially pertinent to the subject of this book that all four kinds of data are only very exceptionally available in any one study. There are in this respect two quite different cases, each with its distinct methodological problems. A temporal sequence long enough to involve marked evolutionary change usually extends into geological time, and the organisms involved are, or include, fossils. Then the documents are directly historical in nature, but their data are primarily of classes (1), mainly morphological, and (4), sequential. Observations of class (3), environmental, are limited and more often involve inferences than direct observation. Direct observations of class (2), including behavior, are almost entirely lacking.[4] Morphological evolution of, for instance, a bone in the lower jaw of a group of reptiles can sometimes be observed without the slightest ambiguity in a directly historical record. Behavioral evolution cannot be so observed. Inferences as to behavior can be based on the morphology of fossils and analogy with living animals. That can, for instance, usually be done for food habits and locomotion, but such possible inferences include little beyond what might be called elemental or first-order behavior. For example, practically all of the habitual or possible movements of a bird may be inferred from its fossilized skeleton, and those movements are the elements from which the bird's total behavior was necessarily compounded. But it would be impossible to infer just what series of movements occurred in courtship, an example of compound or second-order behavior. The evolution of first-order behavior is important and interesting, and we have some good examples documented by the fossil record, such as the evolution of locomotion in the horse family. Nevertheless, the evolution of second-order behavior is even more important and more interesting, and this is quite properly the principal preoccupation of the evolutionary psychologist. In that field the fossil record is of almost no direct (although it is of some indirect) help.

In the second main sort of historical study the documents are essentially contemporaneous. If the organisms under study are dead (fossils; the usual taxonomic collections of recent organisms; specimens for post-mortem dissection) the limitations are even greater than for fossil sequences, and data for the study of behavioral evolution are few, indeed. If, however, the subjects of study are living, data of classes (1), (2), and

---

[3] The temporal order of a really long sequence is rarely directly observed but it is commonly on so factual a basis that it may be considered an objective datum.

[4] There are, to be sure, surprisingly numerous examples of what may be called "fossilized behavior"; tracks, burrows, wounds, and tooth marks, even animals fossilized in the act of parturition or copulation. Nevertheless I know of only one or two rather unimportant examples in which change, actual evolution, of behavior can be observed in such materials.

(3) are freely available. This is the source of practically all of our observational information on behavior. That is almost too obvious to require statement, but the point to be emphasized is that *such information is in itself completely nonhistorical;* it includes no data of class (4). Almost all students agree with that statement when it is made, but many of them do not really keep it in mind in their own work. In comparative anatomy some such sequence as dogfish-frog-cat-man is still frequently taught as "evolutionary," i.e., historical. In fact the anatomical differences among those organisms are in large part ecologically and behaviorally determined, are divergent and not sequential, and do not in any useful sense form a historical series. The same objection applies with perhaps even greater force to studies of behavior which state or assume an evolutionary (historical) sequence in, for instance, comparison of an insect[5] ("invertebrate level"), a rat[5] ("primitive mammalian level"), and a man.

The three main bases for inference from contemporaneous data to historical sequence are well known. (1) Related lineages often evolve more or less in parallel but some faster than others; at any one time, then, the contemporaneous representatives of the various lineages may form a series that approximates the historical sequence leading to the more advanced members of the group. (2) Certain historical trends (e.g., from smaller to larger size, from simpler to more complex behavior) are so frequent or logical that they may be assumed to have occurred in a given case. (3) Characteristics shared by contemporaneous organisms are likely to have been present in their common ancestry. There is no reason to doubt that methods based on these principles, long used in comparative anatomy, are equally pertinent for the historical study of behavior. There are, however, many pitfalls in these methods, and these are probably (at least in the present state of the subject) even more serious for behavioral studies than they have proved to be for morphological studies. Problems and precautions cannot be further discussed here than to indicate the general nature of a few of the more serious in each category. (1) Divergence is more common than parallelism, and a contemporaneous series may not at all resemble an ancestral sequence; different characteristics commonly evolve at different rates so that the animal most primitive in one respect may be most advanced in another; truly ancestral stages are liable to complete replacement and are frequently totally unrepresented

[5] Apart from the point that there are hundreds of thousands of different kinds of insects, with almost incredibly diverse behavior patterns, and hundreds of kinds of rats, with much less but still important behavioral differences. In the conferences on which this symposium is based, the naturalists present repeatedly had occasion to call attention to the absurdity of speaking of "the insect," "the rat," or "the monkey" in studies of behavior, as if there were only one insect, rat, or monkey, or as if all insects, rats, or monkeys behaved alike.

at the present time. (2) No trends have been universal and comparatively few are established as usual; trends may go in either direction, or both ways from the middle, and data without an objective time factor provide no directional signpost; any array of data can be arranged in a logical sequence, but if the data are contemporaneous the logical sequence may have no relationship to a true historical sequence. (3) Parallelism and convergence in evolution have been extremely common and they produce resemblances not present in a common ancestor; homoplasy is, therefore, widespread and is difficult to distinguish from homology, especially when, as in most studies of behavior, direct historical evidence is lacking.

The second main class of evolutionary studies involves processes rather than (historical) events. Study of a process necessarily includes study of the mechanism that performs it; joint study of genetic mechanisms and processes is an example more or less familiar to everyone with any interest in biology or evolution. The methods are for the most part experimental, and it is really not necessary to discuss them here: they are most familiar to the students least familiar with the matter of the present chapter, and they are richly exemplified in other chapters of this book. It is perhaps well just to point out that there is no natural, deep cleavage between the study of events and that of processes, or between the observational methods characteristic of the former and the experimental methods usual in the latter. Both sorts of methods are used to some extent in both fields, and the two can sometimes hardly be distinguished. Processes can to some extent be inferred from the historical record, and prior events lie implicitly behind existing processes. The importance and long-range effects of processes established by experimentation are best judged in the light of the historical record. Alternative possible interpretations of historical sequences must be judged by compatibility with known processes.

Elements of the Synthetic Theory of Evolution

Among students of evolution the world around there are still neo-Lamarckians, old-line Darwinians, vitalists, finalists, orthogeneticists, hologeneticists, mutationists, even spiritualists, not to mention theories so particular to certain individuals that they hardly fall into an -ism. All those now heterodox views are interesting, and many of them have points of emphasis, at least, that still should be kept in mind. Nevertheless, in a brief review of the present status of evolutionary theory it is now possible and proper to concentrate on a single school of theory. No one would maintain either that this theory is complete or that it is correct in all details. An overwhelming majority of students really familiar with the evidence do maintain that the theory has a sound basis and is proving most fertile in increasing understanding of the tremendously intricate course and process of evolution. This strong consensus, if not near unanimity, is a comparatively recent development. The name here preferred is the *synthetic theory*,[6] so-called because it is a new synthesis from all fields of biology and not the offspring exclusively of any one of the numerous preceding theories. Works cited at the end of this chapter consider various aspects of the synthetic theory in more detail, and several of them discuss and give references to various alternative theories not considered here.

Genetic Mechanisms

The medium of evolution, the thing in which the processes of evolution occur and hence the thing that is actually evolving, is a population. A population, in this sense, is a group of organisms, similar among themselves and dissimilar from other organisms with which they live, descended from a not remote common ancestry, living in the same general region and environment, and with a continuity of many generations through time. The inclusiveness of the term is vague and necessarily variable. At its least inclusive it is synonymous with the deme or local population of the biogeographers and systematists or (in a biparental population) the so-called Mendelian population of the geneticists. At its most inclusive it is practically synonymous with the species of most modern students. In the usual case of biparental organisms, the population is also characterized and unified by interbreeding among its actively sexual members. In the less common case of uniparental (asexual, apomictic, etc.) organisms, the unity of the population is still real but is looser and the evolutionary mechanisms are simpler but less flexible and potent.

The characteristics of any individual organism within a population are determined by interaction of its heredity with its environment, in the broadest sense, as the organism develops and, to less extent, thereafter as long as it lives. Heredity may be determined in part by the nature and organization of directly inherited cytoplasm (in metazoans mostly or entirely maternal, in the egg) and sometimes by extranuclear bodies

---

[6] Numerous other tags have been applied, especially "neo-Darwinian," because of the large role assigned to natural selection in the theory. But "neo-Darwinian" in this application is misleading on two important counts. First, natural selection (itself no longer purely Darwinian) is here synthesized with equally important factors unknown to Darwin and even in strong contradictions with his views, especially on heredity. Second, the label "neo-Darwinian" historically belongs to a school that was literally neo-Darwinian, quite distinct from the present synthetic theory and only one of the several forerunners incorporated in the synthesis.

(plastids in plants, etc.), but to far greater degree it is determined by the chromosomes in the nucleus. Chromosomes are differentiated longitudinally, and the irreducible (or at least experimentally unreduced) units of that differentiation are called genes. Different genes have different effects (necessarily, in practice, because the genes are disinguishable or recognizable in no other way), but the whole chromosomal complement acts and interacts, and it is that complement as a complex unit that is the main determinant of heredity. It may be considered as setting a reaction range, sometimes rigidly narrow and sometimes very broad, within which the characteristics of the developing organism must lie. The characteristics actually arising at one point or another of the reaction range, for instance the exact size of an organism when the range permits much variation in size, depend for the most part on environmental influences during development.

The population as a whole has characteristics likewise determined by the interaction of the genetic mechanism and of the environment. Its total genetic structure at any one time usually depends almost entirely on the kinds and combinations of chromosomes and genes present and their relative frequencies. Continuity of the population depends on the processes of reproduction in which sets of chromosomes are passed on from parent to offspring. In asexual reproduction the parental set (generally double) is simply passed on, usually unchanged. In sexual, biparental reproduction two homologous sets (each usually single) are received, one from each parent. Then there is reduction of a parental double set to a single set in the gamete, and this involves the mechanism of meiosis, with two concomitants of special importance for evolution: (1) the single chromosome set of the gamete is a random assortment from each of the two sets of the parent, and (2) occasional crossing over from one homologous parental chromosome to the other produces different combinations of genes in the chromosomes received by the offspring. Fusion of gametes into a zygote brings together sets of homologous chromosomes from different sources. That factor means that the combinations actually realized will be influenced by breeding structure and habits in the population. The extent to which breeding is random or promiscuous, monogamous, polygamous, etc., becomes important, and above all any influence which makes individuals with certain genetic characteristics more likely than others to have offspring. Also important is the likelihood of hybridization between different populations or, much less commonly, different species.

Changes in characteristics induced by changing environmental influences on identical genetic reaction ranges are not heritable. Such changes may affect evolution quite indirectly, but they cannot in themselves constitute secular evolutionary change. True evolutionary change involves changes in the genetics of the population, which are almost always changes in the relative frequencies of the various kinds of genes and of chromosomes and of their combinations. In sexual, biparental populations constant changes in individual combinations are guaranteed by the mechanisms already mentioned: random assortment of chromosomes and crossing over in meiosis, and biparental origin of chromosomes. These may but, as will be seen, usually do not in themselves bring about changes in relative frequencies in the population as a whole.

The mechanisms hitherto mentioned make for constant and radical individual rearrangements of genetic factors already present in any biparental population. The appearance of new factors in both biparental and uniparental populations is due to mutations which, broadly speaking, include changes in the numbers of chromosomes, in the internal structure of chromosomes (other than by simple crossing over), and in genes. It is the past occurrence of mutations that guarantees that homologous chromosomes rarely have exactly the same forms (alleles) of homologous genes and often are structurally different (have, for instance, the genes arranged in different sequence). Occurrence of new mutations, unless counteracted in various ways, further tends slowly but steadily to change the genetics of a population.

Random Processes and Evolution

It is an extraordinary fact that most of the processes inherent in the genetic mechanism of evolution occur at random. It must be understood that the word "random" in this connection (and, indeed, etymologically) does *not* mean that all of a number of possible outcomes are equally probable. It means that the results of the processes are not oriented toward some end external to the processes themselves. In evolution the relevant end is the adaptedness of the population as a whole, its capacity to continue through future generations within an available environment. The random genetic processes are those that are not inherently adaptive for the population. Assortment of chromosomes in meiosis does seem normally to be random not only in this sense but also in the fullest possible sense that all combinations are about equally probable. Crossing over, as it affects association of any two genes, has probabilities almost directly proportional to the distance (along the chromosome) between the genes, but still is random as regards adaptation. For reasons yet unknown, different genes mutate at quite different rates and mutations of a given gene to (or from) different alleles also have decidedly different rates, so that possible gene mutation—and the same is true also of chromosome mutations—have very diverse probabilities, but these processes are still random by the pertinent definition of that word. Mating or more broadly reproduction is usually not entirely random, a fact to be stressed in the next section, but it may be at least approximately so. Here randomness involves likelihood that parents of given genetic types occurring with given frequencies in the population tend to produce offspring in about the same frequencies, or, what comes to the same thing, that relatively higher production of offspring is not significantly correlated with genetic factors in the parents.[7]

If reproduction is random, in combination with the inherently random processes in meiosis, there is no statistical tendency for change in frequencies of genetic factors within a population; in other words there is no tendency for directional evolutionary change to occur. That is the so-called Hardy-Weinberg law, the mathematical expression and derivation of which are given in most textbooks of genetics. Even if mutation is taken into account, there is a point of equilibrium where a given mutation is balanced by back-mutation and random loss (see below), and there is no (or no further) tendency toward evolutionary change in the population. Thus the random genetic processes, all together, do *not* tend statistically to produce evolution. That statement applies equally to sexual populations with mutation, meiosis, and fertilization and to asexual populations with mutation and mitosis, only.

Although the random processes noted do not tend systematically to change the mean frequencies of genetic factors in a population, those frequencies through the generations do tend to fluctuate around the mean. Populations of organisms are of course always finite, and each generation is in effect a sample drawn from the long-range total population of all generations or from the purely theoretical infinite population of statistical estimation. The genetical constitution of each generation is thus subject to statistical sampling error, which is its departure from the mean of the long-range or infinite population. Such departures or statistical sampling errors also occur, and may be quite radical, when a new area is populated by a few individuals spreading from a larger population elsewhere, or when for any reason a segment of a large population becomes reproductively isolated from the rest of that population. Sampling errors are larger the smaller the population. In very large populations they are so small as to be negligible, at least in comparison with effects of selection (below), but they are never reduced to zero in populations of finite size.

[7] Because of doubts or equivocation as to the precise meanings of "random" in application to these various processes, they are sometimes called "stochastic." Appropriate definition may, nevertheless, be as readily made for "random" as for "stochastic."

Under the influence of random sampling error, commonly called "genetic drift" in this connection, the frequency of a given chromosome number or arrangement or of a given gene allele may increase, even to 100 per cent, or decrease, even to zero. Evolution has then obviously occurred, and as far as now known this is the *only* process by which random (unoriented with respect to adaptation) evolution can occur. That it does occur, for instance in the colonization of an oceanic island from a mainland, is beyond any question. How commonly it occurs and how important it is in the over-all picture of evolution are still strongly disputed questions. The present consensus seems to be that it is rather common but that its importance in long evolutionary sequences or radical evolutionary transformations is largely, or almost completely, overshadowed by the nonrandom effects of selection. One special case of completely demonstrated reality has evidently played an important role in the diversification of plants, at least, on lower taxonomic levels. Polyploid mutants or hybrids, with increased (usually doubled) numbers of chromosomes, may be unable to breed back with a parental stock. If they do survive and increase to become populations, they are thus genetically distinct samples isolated forthwith from their ancestral populations.[8]

Oriented Processes and Adaptation

Thus the usual random processes of the genetic mechanism tend to produce either no evolutionary changes at all or changes that are sampling errors and that are nonadaptive or, so to speak, only accidentally adaptive. Yet it is perfectly clear that evolution does occur and that it is, to say the least, often adaptive and not entirely random. It was often urged against Darwin and, with more basis, against De Vries and other early geneticists who assigned too exclusive a role to mutation that evolution cannot have occurred "by accident." The fairly obvious answer, which was in fact already emphasized and soundly established by Darwin, is that the adaptive orientation of evolution must involve the one genetic process that is not necessarily or, as a matter of conclusive observation, usually random: reproduction. If reproduction is differential, if there is a correlation between distinctive genetic factors in the parents and their relatively greater success in reproduction, then there will be an increase in the frequencies of those genetic factors (and combinations of them) within the population from one generation to another. Evolution will occur, and it will be oriented, not random. That, in brief and

[8] It is not usual to consider the origin of a polyploid species as an example of sampling error, but it does seem logically to fall into that category as an example of random evolutionary change.

shorn of numerous complications, is the modern concept of natural selection. Natural selection, as defined, is known really to exist and to be effective, both by observation in nature and by experimentation. No other nonrandom genetic factor has been objectively demonstrated, even though several have been postulated (e.g., Lamarckian influence of use or disuse, nonrandom mutation, inherent tendency—whatever that may mean —to progress toward a goal). Most students now believe that this only demonstrably real nonrandom process is also sufficient to account for all the observed nonrandom events in the course of evolution. *Proving* sufficiency amounts to proving a negative, which is generally deemed impossible; but sufficiency is the stand of the synthetic theory, and the burden of proof would seem to lie with its (now few) opponents.

Reproductive success may be comparatively simple in asexual organisms. It often amounts only to this: a genetic difference arises by mutation, there is direct competition between mutant and nonmutant forms, members of one group or the other survive more often to reproduce, and the less successful group eventually disappears. Even there complications are ignored, and in biparental populations the matter becomes highly intricate. (1) Male and female must occur in proximity or must find each other. (2) In many, especially the more complex, animals they must be sexually acceptable to each other and must mate. (3) Fertilization must occur. (4) The gametes must be genetically compatible. (5) Normal embryological development must occur. (6) Offspring must survive to breeding age and become sucessful reproducers in their turn. Relatively greater or less success may occur at any one of these stages, and at substages within them, and selection depends on the total outcome.

Darwin was aware of the selective possibilities of all the listed stages, but he stressed (6) above all others, and some of his followers did so almost to the exclusion of any others. Thus Darwinian natural selection was based mainly on differential mortality, and the Darwinians and neo-Darwinians hardly grasped the whole process as one of differential reproduction. Darwin also devoted much attention to stage (2) as involving sexual selection, which he distinguished from natural selection.

Until quite recently it was generally implied or assumed that selection always favors individual survival or, more in the spirit of the modern theory, individual success in reproduction. Now it is evident that selection favors successful reproduction of the population and not necessarily of any or of all particular individuals within it. A striking, although rather exceptional, example of that fact is provided by the social insects, among which only a very small fraction actually reproduce although their success in reproduction is completely dependent on the nonreproducing individuals. Of more general import is the recently accumulating evidence that the most successful populations usually have considerable genetic heterogeneity and much heterozygosity in individuals. But that favored characteristic of a population can be maintained only at the expense of constantly producing a certain proportion of definitely inferior, less heterozygous individuals.

A central problem of evolutionary theory has always been the explanation of adaptation, and the synthetic theory maintains (as did Darwin, but with a different understanding of the mechanism) that adaptation is a result of natural selection. But it also demonstrates that natural selection always favors reproductive success of a population, and nothing else. It might be suitable to redefine adaptation as such reproductive success, but some confusion might arise from the fact that most of the characteristics generally considered adaptive seem to be so in the old Darwinian sense of promoting survival of the individual and seem to have little or nothing to do with population reproduction *per se*. The anomaly is only apparent, however, for clearly reproductive success of the population involves all phases of individual life cycles and will incomparably more often than not be favored by individual adaptation to the environment. Such adaptation will therefore almost always be favored by natural selection. Nevertheless the possibility remains that selection, as here defined, could favor population reproduction at the expense of individual adaptation. We have already noted that it does so, indeed, in the cases of homozygous individuals in heterotic populations. It has also been variously claimed that a species may become so specialized for reproductive ends, for example in development of sexual weapons and competition, as to put the whole population at a disadvantage in competition with other species. The reality or importance of such possible phenomena are not, however, clearly established.

An aspect of the synthetic theory especially pertinent here is that it again brings in behavior as a central element. It not only points the way to evolutionary, historical explanations of existing behavior patterns but also involves behavior as one of the factors that produce or guide evolution. Some phases of selection, as in zygote and embryo, are not directly behavioral, but aspects of breeding, care of young, and subsequent survival are pre-eminently so and are obviously crucial elements in selection.

SOME HISTORICAL GENERALIZATIONS AND PRINCIPLES

Those, in brief, are the most essential features of the mechanisms and processes now believed to underlie the phenomena of evolution. An understanding of comparative behavior, or other biological aspects of our contemporary world, further involves consideration of what those phenomena have, in fact, been, of how the processes have worked out in the prodigious history of life. A review of the vast body of information and theory on this subject is of course beyond the present scope. There are, however, certain generalizations and principles that stand out from that record and that can be particularly useful in any reconstruction of behavioral (or other) evolution. Just a few of the most important of these will be mentioned.

Irrevocability, Opportunism, and Transformation

From a certain point of view all study and knowledge of nature can be divided into processes, immanent and changeless characteristics of the universe, and configurations that result from those processes, transient and historically cumulative states of the universe. The difference is that between gravity, a timeless structural feature of our world, and a falling stone, acted on by gravity but determined as to time, place, and condition by the whole previous history of the matter in the stone. The configuration of the living, as of any other, world depends from instant to instant on its last previous configuration and on how the immanent processes, the "laws" of nature, tend to act on any given configuration. Involved is historical causation, which includes everything that has ever happened and which is thus an inherently nonrepeatable accumulation.

In application to evolution, those rather abstract considerations mean that the actual course of evolution is determined not only by its processes but also by the cumulative total of *all* previous events. It follows that evolution is irrevocable. That law (it seems to be about as near to a true law as anything in the realm of biology) has two major corollaries. One is the famous doctrine of the irreversibility of evolution. No organism, no population, no community returns precisely to any antecedent structure or state. A gross but impressive example: whales are descended from fishes; they have returned to the water and resumed the ecological status of fishes; but they have not again become fishes, and every system, organ, tissue, or cell of a whale is radically distinct from that of any fish that is or ever was. The other corollary of irrevocability is that the effects of previous conditions are never wholly lost. A whale, again, carries not only in general but also in detail down to the last cell unmistakable effects of its ancestors' sojourn on the land.[9]

[9] Exceptions to both aspects of irrevocability are conceivable, but none are known or likely. The genetic processes of evolution are all reversible, but that all should reverse to just the same extent in conjunction and within an intricate and changing environmental framework is so improbable that it is not likely to have happened in only a few billion years. An event such as a mutation may seem to be quite canceled out if the mutant allele is subsequently eliminated from the population, but again the probability that even the transient presence of the allele left no effects at all is infinitesimal.

As each configuration is derived from the last, and from all previous ones, each can only be a modification of or an addition to what was already there. This gives evolution an opportunistic aspect. Changes take place on the basis of the previous condition and not as a wholly new construction most efficiently adapted to new conditions. Early fishes had lungs. In many later fishes the pre-existing lungs evolved into hydrostatic organs, which, in spite of their radically different function, did not arise *de novo*. In land animals the lungs retained and considerably perfected their respiratory structure and function. Land snails, requiring an organ for the same function, had no lungs in their ancestry and did not evolve lungs, but a structure that was pre-existent, the mantle cavity, could and did evolve to serve that function.

When a way of life is changing in the course of evolution it is evidently simpler, that is, it is genetically more likely, to remodel the existing than to introduce something completely new. That is the principle of transformation. The evolution of lung to swim bladder, already mentioned, is an example. Another striking and widely familiar example is the incorporation of the bones hinging skull and jaw in early reptiles (quadrate and articular) into the middle ear of mammals (where they are renamed incus and malleus).

The principles of irrevocability, opportunism, and transformation are based mainly on anatomical and physiological data, but in the nature of things they must also apply, *mutatis mutandis*, to the evolution of behavior.

Trends and Orthogenesis

It is a common observation, backed by hundreds of concrete examples in the fossil record, that evolutionary change in a given direction once started may tend to continue for a long time. In terms of years, as nearly as highly inaccurate approximations permit conclusion, it is the rule for trending changes to continue for more than 10^6 years and common for them to last on the order of 10^7 years. Much longer trends, however, as of the order of 10^8 years without stop or pronounced change of direction, have apparently not been substantiated. For instance the recorded history of the horse family shows several well-marked trends, as has become common knowledge, but it is less widely known by nonspecialists that no single recognized trend in that family was continuous throughout the 6×10^7 years of its known history. The longest of the known trends did not continue with even approximate constancy for more than about 2×10^7 years. Some trends reached an inherent limit, for instance the premolars (all but the first) once fully molarized could not become more so. Other trends stopped without having reached such an apparent limit; for instance increase in size stopped far short of any mechanical limit.

Similar trends often appear simultaneously or successively in multiple related lines, such as a tendency for the shells to become coiled in relatives of the oyster. Others may appear over and over again in widely diverse groups, for example increase in individual size. Yet there has been no universal trend, no trend that did not stop or change before about 10^8 years and usually much less, and even no trend that was not on occasion reversed.[10] The trend toward larger size noted above for some of the horses and here in a more general sense is probably the most widespread to be detected among animals. It has occurred repeatedly in groups as diverse as protozoans and primates. Yet it has obviously been neither universal nor, in any one group, constant. If it had been, all animals would by now be elephantine or cetacean in bulk. The opposite trend, toward smaller size, has evidently been less frequent but has certainly occurred many times, and absence of trend, maintenance of about the same size, has probably been the rule.

The foregoing and many other facts about trends lead to the essential conclusion that there is no mysterious, inherent tendency for evolution to proceed indefinitely in straight lines. It accords with everything really known about trends, to the limited extent that they do characterize evolution, to conclude that they occur only when and only as long as they are adaptive. This pre-eminently oriented feature of evolutionary history is adequately explained by the known orienting (nonrandom or anti-chance) process of evolution: natural selection. The opposite view, that trends may or do occur without relationship to natural selection generally is labeled as "orthogenesis," and there has been widespread belief that the fossil record supports or even proves the postulate of orthogenesis. That idea has always been most widespread among those least familiar with the fossil record. Most paleontologists have long since rejected it.

The facts that trends are adaptive, begin and end at fairly definite times, and rarely persist long, geologically speaking, have another bearing, harking back to methods of inference mentioned early in this chapter. In the absence of really historical documents, it is generally impossible to extrapolate far and accurately from brief sequences or by postulating a previous trend on the basis of comparative data on living animals. It is, for instance, unjustified to conclude that a behavioral sequence from simple to complex among recent primates can be correctly superimposed as a continuing historical trend from Paleocene prosimian to Recent man.

---

[10] There has been some confusion on the subject of trends and the irreversibility of evolution, with the argument that either trends do not become reversed or else evolution is reversible. The difficulty is semantic, only. A lineage that becomes smaller and to that degree more like an ancestral stage has not except in this one artificially segregated characteristic returned to the ancestral condition.

Patterns of Evolution

The fabric of evolution is phylogeny, and above the level of interbreeding and hybridization it has only two elements: splitting and succession. The basic process of evolutionary splitting is speciation, the rise of two or more species from a single species. Isolation of a segment of the population is accompanied or followed by genetic divergence, with more or less divergence also in morphology, physiology, and behavior. In uniparental populations no genetic nexus unites the individuals and speciation is a comparatively simple result of mutation and selection. In biparental populations the crucial feature is the breaking of the nexus of interbreeding. Usually (some would say "always") an initial requirement is some degree of geographic separation. Isolating mechanisms that then reduce and finally stop interbreeding, even if the incipient species do come into contact, are almost innumerable. Many of them are behavioral, for instance in decreasing willingness to mate or success in mating. The eventual and complete barrier, which always does arise finally if the now separate species survive but which may be long delayed, is genetic divergence that makes the gametes so incompatible that hybrid zygotes cannot develop.

The significance of phylogenetic splitting in over-all evolutionary history is increase in diversity, with the occupation of new regions and environments and, within each area of occupation, a parceling out into increasingly numerous and narrow ecological niches, each occupied by a distinctive species. If we had no fossil record, it would be irresistible to visualize a single, broadly adapted, primordial marine species the descendants of which expanded to occupy all the waters and lands and specialized for close fit in each available niche. Expansion and diversification complete, evolution would end. Expansion and diversification are, of course, the main motifs in the rich fabric of life's history, but the whole pattern is astonishingly more complex. Most species, even though already well fitted into a niche or adaptive zone, continue to change. The overwhelming majority finally became extinct without issue and are replaced by other, perhaps quite different organisms.

A few organisms have reached a sort of evolutionary stasis, adequate adaptation to a sufficiently constant environment, and have continued without marked change thereafter to become "living fossils": the horseshoe crab, the opossum, and others. Most environments change enough so that the organisms in them must do so, too. The mere fact that some one species in a community changes, for any reason, means that the environment of all the others is different to some degree. The environmental change requiring adaptive adjustment for a species may even reside within the species, itself—that is probably true of many of the trends toward larger size, the smaller animals of a population always being at a slight competitive disadvantage compared with the larger. Such usually slow shifts of environment and adaptation are nearly, but not quite, universal and they account for the commonest trends in evolution.

Rarer but more sriking events result from not merely maintaining adaptation in a changing world but also changing or improving the quality of adaptation. Then there is likely to occur on a smaller or larger scale what has been aptly called a break-through. Increased competitive efficiency may permit expansion into already occupied adaptive zones, with extinction for their former occupants, as among the fishes the teleosts have ousted all but a tithe of their ancient competitors. Or new ways of life may be achieved, as the reptiles spread over the lands then effectively empty of competitors. In such episodes more or less radical changes in structure, physiology, and behavior are involved. Selection is then particularly intense, and change is correspondingly rapid. The changes do usually take an appreciable time, apparently as a rule on the order of 10^6 years and upward, but the effect in the over-all picture is steplike, not a trend but a steep transition from one level to another. The behavioral change when man became adept with tools—supposing, as one must, that this was accompanied by a biological and not entirely a cultural evolutionary advance—was such an event, probably one of exceptional rapidity and certainly one of exceptional portent.

. . . The following recommended books cover the subject of evolution, or aspects of it, in greater detail and with many citations of original studies.

Carter (1951)   Mayr (1942)
Dobzhansky (1951)   Moody (1953)
Dobzhansky (1955)   Simpson (1953)
Huxley (1942)   Simpson, Pittendrigh, and Tiffany (1957)
Lerner (1954)   Stebbins (1949)

Evolution at Work

Theodosius Dobzhansky   1958

When hunger and other elemental needs are satisfied, people are apt to ask questions about human nature, about man's origins, and about his place in the scheme of things. Some people ask such questions even when hungry and suffering. It would be naive to claim that an evolutionary approach supplies all the answers, but it is relevant to these questions and may profitably be used as a guiding light in the quest for some of the answers. Accordingly, the two short papers by Darwin and by Wallace, read before the Linnean Society of London in 1858, mark a watershed in the intellectual history of mankind. These papers contained the essentials of the theory of biological evolution. They did not explicitly deal with man; but, in 1871, Darwin showed that man is a part of nature and a product of the evolutionary process.

The theory of evolution has not only become a focus of biology but has influenced human thought in much wider domains. Many people who are not biologists are at least dimly aware of this. By way of illustration, permit me to recount some reminiscences. A few years ago, as I stepped ashore from a small launch in a village on one of the tributaries of the Amazon River, I was met by a man who proved to be the local agronomist. His first question was, what influence might Lysenko's discoveries (of the spurious nature of which he was, of course, unaware) have on our ideas about evolution. In Egypt, a friend translated for me parts of a book recently written by a Coptic hermit who lived for many years in one of the desert monasteries. The book contained a very fair exposition of evolutionism, followed by a refutation on what, to the author, seemed

FROM Science, vol. 127, 1958, pp. 1091–1098, adapted from a paper originally delivered December 27, 1957, at meetings of the American Association for the Advancement of Science; reprinted by permission of the author and of the Association. The paper illustrates the mechanism of natural selection in operation in Drosophila, the fruit fly, to which Dr. Dobzhansky has devoted much of his research. He is Da Costa Professor of Zoology at Columbia University.

sufficient theological grounds. Punta Arenas claims to be the southernmost city in the world; the region of the Straits of Magellan where it is located is sometimes described as the "Uttermost Part of the Earth." A Chilean friend and I were asked to give public lectures on evolution in the hall of the Punta Arenas City Library. We complied, and found that a part of the audience was not unfamiliar with the topic.

HISTORICAL BACKGROUND

The idea of evolution in the broadest sense of universal and all-pervading change and development is with many of us a habit of thought. We take it for granted because in our lifetimes we have seen so many innovations—telephones and radios, automobiles and airplanes, plastics and antibiotics, atomic bombs and artificial satellites. Things were not always changing so fast. Lucretius, one of the most lucid thinkers of antiquity, was able to write that "all things remain the same even if you should outlast all the ages in living; and still more would you see them the same if you should never come to die."

Christianity is implicitly evolutionistic; it posits a historical process which moves from the Creation to the Fall, the Redemption, the City of God. However, it took some fourteen centuries to make it explicitly evolutionistic—from Saint Augustine in the 5th century to Vico in 1725, Condorcet in 1793, Darwin and Wallace in 1858, 1859, and 1871, and Marx in 1859 and 1867. Condorcet held that the history of mankind was a gradual but steady ascent from a primitive savagery to ever higher states: man is bound to reach perfection in a not too distant future. This cheerful view might sound almost too smug did we not know that it was written while its author awaited execution as a counterrevolutionary.

The idea of progressive evolution in human affairs reached the acme of popularity during the Victorian era. Civilization was supposed to bring ever more material and spiritual comforts, very quickly to some but, in the long run, to almost everybody. Those who were receiving the comforts readily believed that this admirable prospect would be realized most expeditiously through private enterprise and free competition. Marx recommended rather different methods, which he believed to be somehow deducible from Darwin's discoveries. He proposed to acknowledge his indebtedness by dedicating *Das Kapital* to Darwin—an honor which Darwin politely declined. Marxism is sometimes dubbed a Christian heresy; it promises a socialist City of God but is curiously vague about just what this blessed state will be like.

The favorable intellectual climate of the last century speeded up the acceptance of the discoveries of Darwin and Wallace. In turn, biological evolutionism exerted ever-widening influences on the natural and social sciences, as well as on philosophy and even on politics. Not all of these extrabiological repercussions were either sound or commendable. Suffice it to mention the so-called social Darwinism (Hofstadter, 1955), which often sought to justify the inhumanity of man to man, and the biological racism which furnished a fraudulent scientific sanction for the atrocities committed in Hitler's Germany and elsewhere. But these are merely perversions of Darwinism. In the words of Paul Sears (1950), "Charles Darwin did not kill the faith of mankind. He wrought mightily, and others with him, for a newer and greater faith—faith in universal order, whose secrets open themselves to men truly free to question, to communicate, and to arrive at agreement as to what they have seen."

One problem took precedence in biology during the latter part of the 19th and the early years of the current century. This was the validation of the evolutionary interpretations of the facts of zoology, botany, and anthropology. I have no wish to dogmatize, but this problem appears to have been definitively settled. The occurrence of the evolution of life in the history of the earth is established about as well as events not witnessed by human observers can be. The evidence has not satisfied quite everybody; a few people who are not ignorant of the pertinent facts are nevertheless antievolutionists. However, biological research directed towards producing more evidence that evolution has taken place is no longer urgent.

Guessing where new discoveries are likely to be made is a risky venture in science. And yet, a scientist is constantly forced to take this risk; the success of his work depends on the perspicuity of his guesses. With this reservation, it may be said that the most pressing problems of evolutionary biology seem at present to belong to two groups—those concerned with the mechanisms of evolution and those dealing with the biological uniqueness of man.

Factors of Evolution

Darwin did not eschew making hypotheses concerning the forces which bring evolution about. Without a plausible explanation of how evolution might happen it would be hard to accept the idea that it did happen. The theory of natural selection was Darwin's answer, and from the vantage point of modern knowledge it can be seen that the answer was substantially correct. But Darwin was fully aware that, given the state of biology in his day, a causal analysis of the evolutionary process was unattainable. A number of discoveries in our time made possible at least a start in this direction. The chief one was the discovery and the rediscovery of Mendel's laws; then came the unraveling of the chromosome behavior in cell division, fertilization, and meiosis; the finding of mutations by de Vries

and their study by Morgan and his school; the induction of mutations by
x-rays and other agents, first revealed by Muller; and the foundation of
population genetics by Hardy, Weinberg, and Chetverikov.

The dates of most of these discoveries fall between 1900 and 1930.
Strange to say, it was during this period that some biologists professed
much skepticism about the feasibility of explaining evolution in terms
of the processes then being discovered. Bateson, one of the leaders of
genetics in its formative years, was the foremost skeptic. This attitude is
still lingering in some places, especially in continental Europe. New and
unassimilated information has evidently acted like the proverbial trees
which hid the forest.

A most creative phase of modern evolutionism opened around 1930.
Perhaps for the first time in the history of biology, the leading roles in the
development of a field passed to theoreticians using the tools of mathematical analysis, and their analysis far outdistanced the observational and
experimental work. Fisher, Wright, and Haldane developed, almost
simultaneously, a mathematical theory of Mendelian populations. The
fundamental component of evolutionary changes was perceived to be the
alteration of the frequencies of genic and chromosomal variants in living
populations. Mutation, natural and artificial selection, random drift, and
gene diffusion between populations are the agents known to bring about
such alterations. These are, then, the causative factors of evolution.

The logical step towards a satisfactory theory of evolution should now
be to study quantitatively the factors of evolution and their interactions
in free-living, domesticated, and experimental populations. This is an
exciting but difficult task; so great is the complexity of most evolutionary
patterns that precise measurement is rarely attainable. Determination of
the orders of magnitude of some of the forces may, however, be within
the range of what is possible; even such rough approximations will shed
needed light on the mechanisms of evolution.

NATURAL SELECTION AND BALANCED POLYMORPHISM

It is not my purpose here to review the field of quantitative studies on
the factors of evolution. I choose rather to consider some illustrative
examples.

For many years natural selection was something which biologists frequently discussed but seldom did anything about. To Darwin, natural
selection was an inference from a mass of indirect evidence; he argued
that it should occur, but he did not claim to have directly observed
natural selection acting to produce changes in free-living populations.
This he could not do because the selective advantages and disadvantages
which slowly change natural populations are mostly too small to be

readily detectable. To be sure, one can observe elimination of victims of heritable malformations and diseases. Natural selection is, accordingly, often compared to a sieve, which lets some particles pass but sequesters others. Such a process can prevent the accumulation of hereditary diseases and consequent degeneration of a species. It is less easy to see how it may lead to adaptive improvements.

Studies on microorganisms have changed the situation considerably. In 1943, Luria and Delbruck (1943) analyzed the origin of bacterial strains resistant to destruction by bacteriophages, and their type of analysis was rapidly extended to explain the origin of bacterial resistance to antibiotics and similar phenomena. Mutants which confer upon the bacteria their resistance to phages, or to antibiotics, arise from time to time in most or in all cultures. However, such mutants are too rare to be noticed unless a selective or screening agent is applied. When a suspension of phages is added to a bacterial culture, all the bacteria except for the few phage-resistant mutants are killed; when an antibiotic is added, only the resistant mutants survive. Ingenious methods have been devised for estimating how often the resistant mutants arise. For example, the frequency of the mutation for the phage resistance in the colon bacteria, *Escherichia coli*, is of the order of 10^{-7} to 10^{-8} per cell generation.

The selection of resistant mutants in bacteria is a process which resembles the sieve in the above analogy too closely to be a good model of the selective processes in higher, sexually reproducing, organisms, including man. Materials more suitable for the study of these processes have been found. Fisher (1930) showed in 1930 that if the heterozygote for two genetic variants, A_1A_2, is superior in fitness to both corresponding homozygotes, A_1A_1 and A_2A_2, the natural selection will, in an outbreeding sexual population, act to maintain both A_1 and A_2 with frequencies that may readily be computed. Some twenty years ago, Ford (1937) discovered this situation, known as balanced polymorphism, in nature in some butterflies. More recent studies show that balanced polymorphism is more frequent than was formerly suspected. Natural populations of the flies *Drosophila* have yielded some beautifully clear examples. Moreover, the selective pressures acting on some polymorphic natural populations are, as will be shown below, astonishingly great. This is a boon to the experimental evolutionist, for natural selection becomes at last observable and its magnitude measurable.

Here we may digress to consider the possibility that balanced polymorphism may occur in human populations. The problem is of more than academic interest, since balanced polymorphism has a property which is at first sight astonishing. Provided that the heterozygous carriers of hereditary defects or diseases are superior in fitness to the noncarriers, natural selection will maintain these defects in the populations. The work of Allison (1954) on the sickle-cell anemia, and that of Ceppellini on the Mediterranean anemia, have yielded at least presumptive evidence of balanced polymorphism. The homozygotes for the respective mutant genes usually die of severe anemias, but the heterozygotes may not only be healthy but, at least under certain conditions, may be relatively immune to some malarial fevers as compared with the normal homozygotes. Carter, Penrose, and Wallace (World Health Organization, 1957), among others, have considered the possibility that many genetic variants in man which are deleterious when homozygous may be beneficial when heterozygous. This possibility has often been studiously ignored or dismissed on insufficient grounds. It would greatly complicate several important issues, among them that of the genetic effects of atomic radiations on human and other populations. However, it is becoming evident that the oversimplified models of the genetic population structure are proving inadequate if not positively misleading. Since I recently had an opportunity to discuss this matter in *Science* (1957), I leave it here with the remark that the need for a better understanding of the genetic processes taking place in living populations is now felt more keenly than ever.

NATURAL SELECTION IN EXPERIMENTAL POPULATIONS OF DROSOPHILA

The trait which proved to be highly favorable for experimental studies on evolution is a cryptic one. Many natural populations of most species of *Drosophila* are polymorphic for variations in the structure of certain chromosomes, due to so-called inversions of blocks of genes. These variants of the chromosome structure are inherited as simply as are the genes that determine the blood groups for which human populations are polymorphic. A further similarity is that the flies which carry different chromosomal types are externally as indistinguishable as are people with different blood groups. The chromosomal types may, however, be diagnosed easily and precisely in stained preparations of the salivary glands of the fly larvae. Every race or population of a given species of *Drosophila* may be characterized in terms of the relative frequencies of the different chromosomal types which it contains (Dobzhansky, 1947, 1949), just as human populations can be described in terms of the relative frequencies of the different blood group genes.

But here the analogy ends, since the chromosomal types which a *Drosophila* carries may easily be shown to influence its fitness, while the problem of the functional significance of the blood groups in man is still full of uncertainties. The experiments with *Drosophila* are arranged as follows. We collect a sample of the population in some natural locality where the flies occur; place the females singly in laboratory culture bottles and allow them to produce progenies; examine the chromosomes in these progenies and pick out the strains which carry the desired chromosome types; and make up a mixture of flies carrying certain chromosome types in known proportions. This mixture is placed in specially constructed population cages in which the flies will breed freely for as many generations as the experimenter may allow. These populations are kept under controlled conditions which can be varied at will, and at desired time intervals we take samples of eggs which the flies in the cages deposit and investigate the chromosomes in the larvae which grow from these eggs.

Such experiments show that the fly which is fittest in most environments usually turns out to be a heterozygote. A fly in which the two chromosomes of a pair differ in structure, say A_1A_2, enjoys hybrid vigor, heterosis, as compared with the homozygotes, A_1A_1 and A_2A_2. There is every reason to think that this heterosis occurs in the environments in which the flies live in nature as well as in the laboratory. The chromosomal polymorphism is balanced polymorphism. Furthermore, at least some of the chromosomal heterozygotes are favored by amazingly powerful selective forces. The magnitude of the selection can be estimated from the speed with which the frequencies of the different chromosomal types undergo changes in the experimental populations, and from the equilibrium proportions that are eventually reached. Thus, in a certain experiment with *Drosophila pseudoobscura*, the following situation was observed: Taking the fitness of a heterozygote, A_1A_2, to be unity, the fitnesses of the homozygotes, A_1A_1 and A_2A_2, proved to be 0.90 and 0.41, respectively (Dobzhansky, 1947, 1949).

Consider the meaning of these figures. The adaptive value of the homozygote A_2A_2 is less than one-half of that of the heterotic type, A_1A_2. Taking the heterozygote as the standard of fitness, the homozygote, A_2A_2, having less than 50 percent of the standard fitness, must technically be classed as a semilethal. Or one may say that the homozygote A_2A_2 is afflicted with a hereditary disease, or a constitutional weakness. Now, this would not greatly surprise us if A_2 were a mutant obtained in the laboratory, under the influence of, say, x-ray treatments. But A_2 is a permanent component of many flourishing populations of *Drosophila* in nature. The A_2A_2 homozygotes are not laboratory artifacts: they occur abundantly in nature.

SEASONAL GENETIC CHANGES IN THE MAKE-UP OF DROSOPHILA POPULATIONS

Not enough is known about the adaptive functions which the chromosomal polymorphism performs in nature. Quite possibly these functions are different in different species of *Drosophila*. Observations on populations of *Drosophila pseudoobscura* in some parts of California furnish a clue for this species. In these populations, the relative frequencies of different chromosomal types change with the seasons; some chromosomes are more common in spring than in summer or in fall, while other chromosomes show the reverse seasonal trends (Figure 1). *Drosophila* produces in nature several generations per year—we do not know just how many. At any rate, natural selection is so intense that the populations undergo genetic reconstructions which fit them to seasonal changes in their environments. Here, then, are evolutionary changes, microevolutionary ones to be sure, which are observable directly in nature in a free-living animal species.

Further light on these evolutionary changes comes from laboratory experiments. The seasonal genetic changes indicate that the adaptive values of the chromosomal types vary in different environments. The carriers of some of the chromosomes are relatively fitter in spring and those of others are superior in summer or in fall. Experiments bear this out; the adaptive values of the chromosomal types are exquisitely sensitive to environmental modification. The series of adaptive values of three chromosomal types cited above (1:0.90:0.41) was observed in experimental populations kept at 25°C. Lowering the temperature by 9°, to 16°C, makes the adaptive values uniform, or so nearly so that no differences can be detected in our experiments within the limits of resolution. The genotype which causes a hereditary infirmity at 25° is completely "cured" at 16°C. This emphasizes how meaningless may be the distinctions between "superior" and "inferior" hereditary endowments if the environment is not specified.

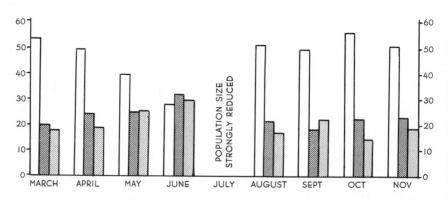

FIGURE 1. Seasonal genetic changes in a population of *Drosophila pseudoobscura* inhabiting a certain locality in California (Piñon Flats on Mount San Jacinto). The heights of the columns indicate the average percentages of three different chromosomal types in different months in samples taken from 1939 to 1954. (Data of Dobzhansky, Epling, *et al.*)

The seasonal genetic changes in *Drosophila pseudoobscura*, observed in nature in the population of Piñon Flats, Mount San Jacinto, California, have been reproduced rather fully in experiments (Dobzhansky, 1947, 1949). In nature, a certain chromosome type increases in frequency at the expense of another type between March and June, the changes are reversed between June and September, and the frequencies remain static from September to March. The kind of genetic changes which occur in nature during the summer months have been easily imitated in experimental population cages kept at 25°C. The winter stability is reproduced if the same population cages are kept at 16°C. All attempts to duplicate the spring situation in population cages were unsuccessful. The experiments of Birch (1955) showed why this should be so; the changes which occur in nature during spring can be copied experimentally only if the fly larvae do not live in crowded conditions (as they always do in population cages).

ALTERATION OF DROSOPHILA POPULATIONS IN CALIFORNIA (1940–1957)

The seasonal genetic changes observed in nature in *Drosophila pseudoobscura* are evolutionary changes by definition. However, because of their cyclic character, the alterations induced at one season are reversed at the next season. The biological significance of the chromosomal polymorphism lies evidently in that it confers a marvelous adaptive plasticity upon the populations. The populations are able to respond by adaptive genetic changes to temporary, and even to seasonal, shifts in their environments. This is, of course, a kind of evolutionary luxury which only a rapidly breeding animal, like *Drosophila*, is able to afford.

The genetic plasticity also permits, however, rapid modifications in response to more lasting alterations in the environment. This creates an opportunity for the direct observation of these evolutionary changes in nature. Changes in the relative frequencies of chromosomal types lasting for several years have been recorded in some populations of *Drosophila pseudoobscura*. Some of these changes may have been caused by succession of droughty and wet years, but this is not established securely. Recently it was discovered that still another, and apparently more enduring, change is going on in certain populations of the same species.

Reference has been made above to the fact that populations or races of a *Drosophila* species may be described in terms of relative frequencies of different types of chromosomes in their chromosome pools. Such a description was made in 1944 for *Drosophila pseudoobscura*, on the basis of samples of the populations of this species collected in western United States and in Mexico, chiefly during the period 1938 to 1940. This study

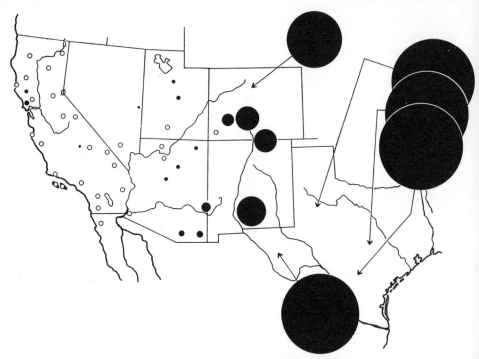

FIGURE 2. The status of populations of *Drosophila pseudoobscura* in the south-western United States according to samplings made chiefly in 1940 and earlier. The diameters of the black circles are proportional to the frequencies of a certain type of chromosome (PP) in the populations of different localities. Open circles indicate populations in which this type of chromosome was not encountered.

showed that a chromosome type, denoted as PP, is the dominant form (occurring in more than 50 percent of the chromosomes) in Texas and also along the eastern face of the Rocky Mountains. The PP chromosomes wane in frequency as one proceeds westward. Among the approximately 20,000 chromosomes scored from populations of California, only four PP chromosomes were found, in three different localities. This is a very low frequency, 0.02 percent (Figure 2).

The first intimation that the populations were changing came in 1946 and 1947, when the population of Mather, in the Sierra Nevada of California, was found to contain about 0.5 percent of PP chromosomes. None were found there in 1945. However, in 1950 the frequency of PP stood at 2.8 percent, in 1951 at 4.5 percent, in 1954 at 11.1 percent, and in 1957 at 10.0 percent. Similar changes took place on Mount San Jacinto, where C. Epling found the first PP chromosome in 1951. By 1955 the frequency had risen to 7.7 percent.

In an attempt to elucidate the nature of these changes, in the summer

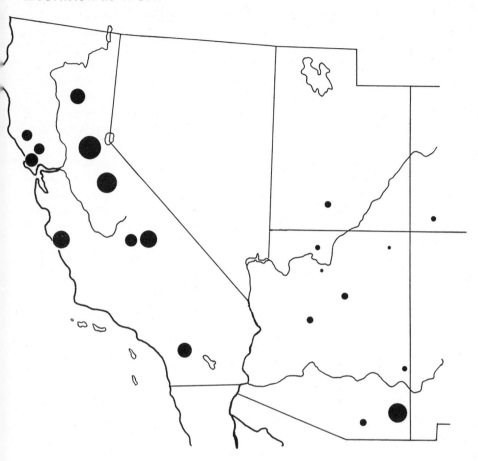

FIGURE 3. The status of populations of *Drosophila pseudoobscura* in the south-western United States in 1957. The diameters of the black circles are proportional to the frequencies of a certain type of chromosome (PP). Although the scale of the map is larger than that of the map in Figure 2, the scale of the black circles is the same in both figures.

of 1957 I sampled the populations of ten localities in California and of ten in Arizona and Utah (Dobzhansky, 1958). More or less adequate population samples had been taken in or near all these localities in 1940, 1941, or earlier. The striking fact which this study has revealed is that, between 1940 and 1957, the PP chromosomes have become fairly common in every one of the California populations sampled. Their frequencies now range between 5.0 and 12.0 percent (Figure 3). Furthermore, the waxing of PP chromosomes has taken place chiefly at the expense of another chromosome type, denoted CH, the frequencies of which have markedly waned in most California populations.

In contrast to the genetic upheaval in the California populations, no spectacular changes were found in Arizona and Utah. In 1940 as well as in 1957, some PP chromosomes (fewer than were found in California in 1957 but more than in 1940) and some CH chromosomes (fewer than in California) occurred in the populations of Arizona and Utah. This is important, since a conjecture which had to be excluded was that the sharp rise of PP in California might have been due to a westward migration of the eastern (Texan) populations, in which PP chromosomes are predominant.

The rise of PP chromosomes in California represents a more impressive evolutionary change than appears at first sight. The average frequency of PP in California populations was close to 0.02 percent in 1940 and 8 percent in 1957. This is a 400-fold increase. The estimated mean number of fly generations in natural habitats over a period of 17 years is probably of the order of 100 (more than twice this number could be obtained in the laboratory). A 400-fold increase in the frequency of a genetic variant in 100 generations bespeaks a quite considerable magnitude of the adaptive advantage, and hence of natural selection.

In fact, the only comparable evolutionary change ever observed in free-living animals is the development of the so-called industrial melanism in England and in some localities on the continent of Europe. Dark variants, due to single dominant mutant genes, appeared in several species of moths approximately one century ago. Now these variants have become frequent in populations of localities in which the vegetation is polluted by industrial fumes. This has been brought about by the action of natural selection, since the dark variants appear to be protectively colored on polluted, and the light ones on unpolluted, vegetation (Kettlewell, 1956). The spread of the melanic variants in moths is thus caused by human intereference (industrial pollution) with the habitats of certain free-living species. The cause which has brought about the rise of PP chromosomes in the California *Drosophila pseudoobscura* is, unfortunately, unknown. There is, however, some circumstantial evidence that this cause is not man-made. If this is so, the genetic alterations in these *Drosophila* populations represent the greatest observed effect of natural selection in an animal species not appreciably influenced by man.

MICROEVOLUTION, MESOEVOLUTION, MACROEVOLUTION

It is needless to labor the point that the evolutionary changes described above are small compared to those which led from the eohippus to the modern horse, or from an australopithecine-like animal to man. The former are microevolutionary and the latter macroevolutionary changes. Nevertheless, microevolution and macroevolution are parts of a single continuum, and studies on the former help to elucidate the latter. After all, the knowledge of the atomic fission and fusion reactions gained in laboratories helps in understanding the evolution of stellar systems, although even the biggest hydrogen bombs generate amounts of energy which are puny compared to those produced in the sun or in stars. This argument is not meant to imply that studies on macroevolution may be dispensed with. The evidence of paleontology, while not completely clear and consistent, is in favor of the view that macroevolution is compounded of microevolutionary events. The problem of macroevolution is, then, essentially that of the patterns of microevolutionary events which yield macroevolutionary changes of different kinds.

This problem is beyond the confines of the present discussion: macro-evolution cannot be observed at work; only the end-products of its action on our time level can be studied. However, we have recently succeeded in producing in experiments some genetic changes which seem to transcend the limits of microevolution, and for which I have suggested a tentative label of "mesoevolution" (1954).

Reference has already been made to natural selection in experimental populations of *Drosophila*. A mixture of flies with chromosomes of different types, but derived from a natural population of the same geographic locality, is introduced into a population cage; the proportions of these chromosomal types may change from generation to generation, until equilibrium frequencies are attained. The position of the equilibrium depends upon the environment in which the population is kept. The changes observed are microevolutionary ones; the experiments have been repeated many times, and, if reasonable precautions are taken, the results of the selectional changes are predictable and repeatable.

EVOLUTION AS A CREATIVE PROCESS

Now, something else is observed if what may appear to be a minor variation is introduced into the experimental procedure. An experimental population is made up in which the different types of chromosomes are derived from natural populations of different geographic regions; for example, one kind of chromosome may come from California and the other from Texas or from Mexico. In many populations of such geographically mixed origins, natural selection produces alterations in the proportions of the different chromosome types. However, the course which the selection takes in geographically mixed populations is remarkably erratic. Replicate experiments, with the same genetic materials and conducted in similar environments, often give significantly divergent re-

sults. In some populations the changes may be rapid and in others slug-
gish; in some, balanced equilibria may be established and in others, one
of the chromosomal types may be lost (Dobzhansky, 1954).

This may seem to be a strange and even disconcerting situation. Is it
not the criterion of validity of a scientific experiment that its results
should be reproducible? Yet in these experiments we face a real biological
indeterminacy, and this fact is fraught with implications. Evolutionists,
particularly those who work with fossils, long ago pointed out that the
evolutionary transformations which occur in a group of organisms are
unrepeatable and irreversible. The macroevolutionary changes represent
unique and nonrecurrent evolutionary histories. Notwithstanding many
instances of parallel or convergent evolution, we have no reason to think
that any form of life has arisen two or more times independently.

The experiments on *Drosophila* populations of geographically mixed
origin throw some light on this situation. The key to the problem lies in
the prodigious, and indeed prodigal, efficiency of sexual reproduction in
the creation of novel genetic endowments. It is easy to show that with n
genes each represented by m variants (alleles), the number of potentially
possible gene combinations is m^n. An estimate of 1000 for the number of
genes (n) and of 10 for the number of alleles per gene (m) would be
very conservative, at least for higher organisms. But the number 10^{1000} is
so great that only a negligible fraction of the potentially possible gene
combinations can ever be realized.

These apparently fanciful calculations bear directly on the experimental findings. Although we do not know just how many genes segregate
and recombine in the populations of geographically mixed origins, the
numbers must be fairly large. Some of the many possible different gene
patterns that confer high fitness upon their bearers in the experimental
environments arise in different populations; whichever of these patterns
happens to arise first is picked out by natural selection and serves as the
starting point of subsequent evolutionary changes. The replicate populations, though originally alike genetically and exposed to like environments, follow different evolutionary paths. Perhaps no two experimental
populations of this sort will have identical histories, any more than two
evolutionary lineages in nature will have.

Evolution is not striving to achieve some foreordained goal; it is not
the unfolding of predetermined episodes and situations. Macroevolutionary, and to some extent also mesoevolutionary, changes are unique, nonrecurrent, and creative. It is necessary to make quite clear what is meant
by creativity of biological evolution. This is a creative phenomenon because evolution brings about novel and harmonious genetic equipments
which enable their carriers to survive in some environments. These

genetic equipments are mostly new combinations of genes. But the process of formation of new gene combinations is not of the kind to which one can apply the French saying that "the more it changes the more it remains the same thing." Organic development is not gradual accretion of traits produced by the genes independently of each other; the adaptive value of a genetic equipment is a function of all the genes which in the organism are acting in concert.

MAN AS A PRODUCT OF EVOLUTION

Man was not programmed in biological evolution, because evolution has no program. In one sense, man, *Drosophila*, and all other forms of life are evolutionary accidents. If slightly different environmental opportunities had been offered to their far and near ancestors, quite different creatures might have arisen as a result of evolutionary transformations. Even with similar opportunities, the formation at critical times of gene combinations different from those which actually were formed also could have turned the evolutionary changes to different paths.

But, in another sense, man is not a product of a chance concatenation of lucky throws of the genetic dice. The old analogies purporting to describe the fortuitous nature of evolution are wrong. The genetic equipment of the human species is not like a watch which arose by the accidental coming together of disjointed parts of the mechanism, nor is it like a poem accidentally typed out by a monkey pounding the keys of a typewriter. Such analogies overlook the fact that natural selection introduces an antichance quality in evolution. The bodies of our animal ancestors were going concerns and not merely human bodies under construction; these animals were as fit to live in their environments as we are in ours.

Evolution is a response of living matter to the challenges of environmental opportunity through the process of natural selection. The response of the human species, or rather of the species ancestral to man, was a unique one—it developed the genetic basis for the accumulation of, and for the extragenic transmission of, a body of learned tradition called culture. The relations between culture and its genetic basis are all too often misunderstood. This topic is too complex and important to be dealt with lightly, but the basic facts are simple enough. Genes determine the possibility of culture but not its content, just as they determine the possibility of human speech but not what is spoken. The cultural evolution of mankind is superimposed on its biological evolution; the causes of the former are nonbiological without being contrary to biology, just as biological phenomena differ from those of inanimate nature but are not isolated from them (Dobzhansky, 1956).

HUMAN EVOLUTION AT WORK

The genetic equipment of our species was molded by natural selection; it conferred upon our ancestors the capacity to develop language and culture. This capacity was decisive in the biological success of man as a species; it enabled man to acquire unprecedented powers to change and control his environment at will. The very success of culture as a nonbiological adaptive instrument means, however, that man has crossed the Rubicon—he has become specialized to live in man-made environments.

Some strange conclusions are sometimes drawn from the above facts. One is that human biological evolution has ended and has been replaced by evolution of culture. Another is that all men are uniform in their genetic equipment, at least insofar as the latter conditions the capacity to undergo socialization and acculturation. Another is that man's "intrinsic" intelligence (whatever that may mean) has not changed since the times of the Cro-Magnon, or even of the Java man. Still another is that natural selection no longer operates in modern mankind, since men live in such hopelessly unnatural environments.

All these notions overlook the simple fact that it is precisely because the capacity to create, absorb, and transmit culture is so decisive in the success of man as a species that natural selection works not only to preserve but also to augment this capacity. Human biological and cultural evolutions are not separated in watertight compartments. They are interacting processes. All men are equal in rights, but they are most certainly not biologically uniform. Our genetic diversity does influence our tastes and aptitudes for different occupations and professions. But this does not make some of us superior and others inferior; no human being should ever be used as a means to an end.

All human societies, the civilized even more than the primitive ones, have numerous vocations to be filled. Natural selection has made all healthy human beings trainable for the performance of diverse duties. This is, then, a biological adaptation which makes people multiform, not uniform as is sometimes supposed. Educability, the ability to be trained, is consistently fostered in man by natural selection. And yet, the carriers of certain specialized genetic equipments, such as musicians or poets, may excel in the performance of some specialized functions.

Natural selection is active in all human societies, including the most advanced ones (Dobzhansky and Allen, 1956). It must be understood that there is nothing esoteric about the "naturalness" of natural selection. All that "selection" means is that the carriers of different genetic equipments contribute unequally to the gene pool of the succeeding generations. If the relative contributions are decided by human choice, the selection is artificial. If not, it is natural. Natural selection usually maintains or enhances the Darwinian "fitness" or "adaptedness." But "the fittest" is nothing more spectacular than the parent or grandparent of the greatest number of surviving descendants.

It is erroneous to equate Darwinian fitness with excellence in human estimation. Reproductive success may favor genetic equipments which we may hold to be undesirable on other grounds. Selection does not even guarantee that the species will endure; most biological species of the past have become extinct, without issue, and yet their evolution was controlled by natural selection. This is because selection promotes what is immediately useful, even if the change may be fatal in the long run.

The biological evolution of our species continues to be at work. Perhaps no other problem of science is more challenging than the understanding of the biological and cultural evolutions of mankind in their interactions. As pointed out above, evolution in general has no program, and the evolution of man is no exception. No biological law can be relied upon to insure that our species will continue to prosper, or indeed that it will continue to exist. However, man is the sole product of evolution who knows that he has evolved and who has continued to evolve. It is up to man to supply the program for his evolutionary developments which nature has failed to provide. He has gained some knowledge which is a basis of hope that the problem is not impossible of solution.

This is an inspiring task but also a crushing responsibility. Albert Schweitzer once wrote that "our age has discovered how to divorce knowledge from thought, with the result that we have, indeed, a science which is free, but hardly any science left which reflects" (1947). I hope that these angry words do not accurately describe the situation. We need and we have at least some science which is free and which reflects. It is our primary responsibility as scientists to see to it that such science prospers and bears fruit. Moreover, such science ought not to be a monopoly of some kind of technological elite. People at large, and particularly men of action who make the decisions which control so much in our lives, need not be as woefully ignorant of even the simplest principles of science as they are. At least some of the ideas which guide our work as scientists are not beyond the understanding of people of average intelligence who are not scientists professionally. The idea of evolution is one of them. As expounded by Darwin, it is one hundred years old, but we have barely begun to understand its full consequences.[1]

[1] I wish to thank my colleagues Drs. J. A. Beardmore, L. C. Dunn, and J. A. Moore for critical readings of the manuscript of this article.

The Physical Distinctions of Man

Adolph H. Schultz   1950

Our knowledge of the physical distinctions of man, which is basic for all work on the ever challenging problems of human evolution, requires constant revision and re-evaluation as more research material becomes available, new facts are discovered, and modern points of view are being developed. Generally speaking, the list of man's physical distinctions has been lengthened, whereas the significance of the single specific characters has diminished with advance in our understanding of man's true nature. Today there can be no longer any serious doubt that, in spite of all his many distinctions, man can and must be assigned a definite place within the order of primates among the Old World, or catarrhine, forms, he being most nearly related through one common ancestry to the anthropoid apes. From the latter man became distinguished chiefly in connection with his three outstanding specializations: the early and undoubtedly rapid acquisition of the erect posture, the later, gradual and ultimately great increase in relative brain-size, and the comparatively very recent prolongation of his main periods of life.

Most investigators of man's physical distinctions have dealt with conditions as found in adults and frequently as represented by averages of only Europeans. This common and arbitrary limitation has resulted in various untenable claims in the enormous, old and new literature concerned with human peculiarities and has retarded the full appreciation of many of man's evolutionary innovations.

FROM Proceedings of the American Philosophical Society, 1950, vol. 94, pp. 428–449; reprinted by permission of the author and of the Society. This is a well known and important paper by a principal student of morphological variation in primates and man (and a gifted illustrator as well). The author has published another, more recent review of the same general subject (see Schultz, 1957b, in bibliography), but the editor has selected this one for general reading. For long Associate Professor of Physical Anthropology at Johns Hopkins University, Dr. Schultz in 1951 became Professor of Anthropology, and Director of the Anthropological Institute, at the University of Zurich.

With the gradual accumulation of large series of monkeys and apes it has become possible to compare man with other primates on the basis of statistically adequate observations and at all stages of growth. Only in this way can it be decided whether a particular character is really distinctive in all cases within a representative, normal range of variations, or differs merely in regard to the frequency of its occurrence, thus being of lesser significance. With the realization that any evolutionary change, apparent in the adult, is the result of some primary alteration in the processes of growth and development, it seems highly desirable to discover the conditions in which human growth differs from the growth of nonhuman primates. By finding the ontogenetic distinctions of man his distinctions at the completion of growth will become better understood. A large variety of the innumerable specializations in human ontogeny has already been reviewed in another publication by the writer (1949). The present paper is an attempt to demonstrate by means of some random examples how necessary it is to consider fully variability and ontogeny in the investigation of man's evolution and present distinctions. As such this study represents chiefly a compilation and interpretation of some of the writer's old and new observations on primate morphology. A certain unevenness was unavoidable because some of the facts, made use of, have already been recorded elsewhere and hence can here be mentioned quite briefly, whereas other, new data have to be presented in more detail. Most of the new observations have been obtained by the author with the aid of a grant from the Viking Fund, which is gratefully acknowledged here.

OLD VIEWS ON MAN'S DISTINCTIONS

Linnaeus (1758) was the first to assign man a place within the mammalian order of *Primates* which he defined in part as being composed of animals with hands on the anterior extremities. Schreber (1775), however, placed man in a separate "Erstes Geschlecht," restricted to creatures with two hands, and monkeys and lemurs (= "Makis") in his "Zweytes" and "Drittes Geschlecht," respectively, for animals with four hands. In later editions of his great "Naturgeschichte" Blumenbach (1791) followed essentially the same idea by creating a separate order for man, which he termed *Bimana*, and one for all other then known primates, called *Quadrumana*, thus indicating that he regarded man's possession of only two hands as his chief, or at least most evident, physical distinction. This radical separation of the primates into the one two-handed and the many four-handed forms was also accepted by Cuvier (1805) and followed with minor variations by numerous other, later taxonomists until the end of the last century (e.g., Trouessart, 1897).

The differences in form and function between the hands and the feet of adult man are very striking in contrast to the similarities between the hands and feet of most adult nonhuman primates in which the feet are hand-like owing to the frequent opposability of the first toe and the great relative length of the other toes. This distinction, which appeared very impressive to early taxonomists with their limited material and knowledge,[1] has greatly lost in significance with a full consideration of the many variations in foot construction among all primates and in the light of more recent studies on the development of the feet of man and apes.

Figure 1 must suffice here to show that at early stages of growth, just after the digits have become separated from the primary foot-plate, there is as yet comparatively little difference between the foot of man and that of a typical monkey. In both the first toe is short, abduced and not rotated even in the monkey, the free portion of the first toe begins at the base of the second digit, the middle toe is the longest, and touch pads are well formed. It is only through subsequent, widely differing growth changes that the striking dissimilarities develop rapidly in the feet of monkey and man, giving the former a thumb-like first toe and long, finger-like, lateral toes, whereas the latter a great toe which retains the embryonic lack of opposability and lateral toes which have become proportionately even shorter than in early fetal life (for detailed data see Schultz, 1949).

Figure 1 shows also that among the "Quadrumana" there is at least one form with feet which are at best very poor "hands." In the gorilla and, particularly, in the Eastern or Mountain gorilla one can frequently find adult specimens with great toes which are very inefficient for true opposability owing to the facts that they show but little rotation and branch from the sole far distally (for further details see Schultz, 1934b). Surely the differences between the feet of adult man and of the adult Mountain gorilla, shown in Figure 1, are no greater than the differences between the latter foot and that of the adult macaque in the same figure. This same conclusion had already been reached by Huxley (1863), who had stated it more broadly and extremely as follows: "Be the difference between the hand and foot of Man and those of the Gorilla what they may—the

---

[1] For instance, Blumenbach (1808) states: "Les singes et les animaux que l'on nomme ordinairement anthropomorphes, commes les Guénons et les Loris, ne sont réellement ni bipèdes ni quadrupèdes, mais quadrumanes. Ils ont aux mains de derrière un véritable pouce. . . . Je dirai plus, les mains de derrière des quadrumanes méritent mieux le nom de main que celles de devant; elles sont en effet plus propres à l'appréhension." Similarly, Schinz (1827), who also used the separate orders of Bimana and Quadrumana and to whom also the gorilla was unknown, states categoriquement: "Die Affen haben wirklich vier vollkommene Hände, denn ihre Hinterfüsse dienen eben so gut als Hände, als die Vorderfüsse. An allen vier Füssen also hat der Affe vier Finger oder Zehen, nebst einem abstehenden Daum. Dieser Daum aber bezeichnet die Bestimmung des Gliedes zur vollkommenen Hand, oder zum Greifen."

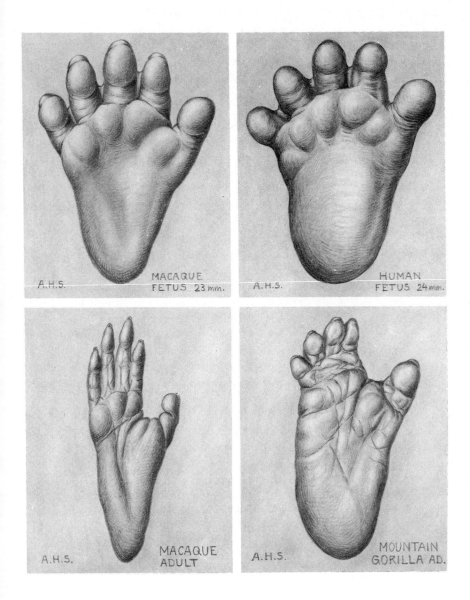

FIGURE 1. Exact drawings of right feet of a Rhesus monkey fetus (sitting height =
23 mm.), a human fetus (sitting height = 24 mm.), an adult male Rhesus monkey,
and an adult male Mountain gorilla, all reduced to same total foot length.

differences between those of the Gorilla and those of the lower Apes are much greater." This remains a perfectly justifiable conclusion (even though Huxley referred to the Lowland, Western gorilla) in consideration of such facts as the vestigial nature of the first toes in many orangutans, the loss of the thumb in Spider monkeys and Guerezas, and the lack of true opposability of the thumb in New World monkeys.

It is astonishing to find that in the most recent work on the physical distinctions of man the author, Professor Wood Jones (1948), still stresses some conditions in the human foot which he lists among what he calls: "Definitive human specific specialisations." Thus he claims that: "In Man the preaxial digit (= great toe) is incorporated into the general mass of the foot to about the mid point of its basal phalanx. In Apes it is free of the general mass of the foot almost as far as its metatarso-tarsal joint." The carefully prepared Figure 2 serves to show here that, actually, a great toe, free of the general mass of the foot to near the base of this digit, is found among the apes *only* in the Hylobatidae (= gibbons and siamang) in which this condition represents a unique specialization. In the great apes merely a small part, or none, of the first metatarsal bone can be regarded as belonging to the free portion of the first toe. In the orang-utan the terminal phalanx of the at best much reduced great toe is congenitally lacking in over half of all cases (Schultz, 1941a). In the series of variations in foot construction among the higher primates the orang-utan represents a more isolated extreme on one side than man on the opposite side. Jones (1948) also claims that the joint at the base of the great toe is an absolutely flat surface in man, whereas "a complicated concavo-convex surface" in apes. This is another incorrect generalization, since this supposedly great human distinction loses its significance, if studied by means of precise measurements on series of higher primates, as had been done by the writer (1930) for an earlier publication. This particular joint on the cuneiform I bone, shown in Figure 2, varies considerably in man between being practically flat and very nearly as convex as in some gorillas.[2] In this respect, therefore, the *average* gap between man and the apes is still bridged by individual variations.

Not all of the earlier writers on mammalian classification have placed main emphasis on the form of the foot when confronted with the problem

[2] The degree of curvature of this joint surface on the cuneiform bone, expressed as greatest height of the joint in percentage of the width of the joint in the same plane, varies among 10 adult negroes between 8.6 and 18.2 and amounts to even 20.8 in an adult Australian aboriginal, whose foot had been kindly sent to the writer by Professor A. L. Burkitt. The corresponding percentages for three adult Mountain gorillas vary between 21.4 and 30.8 and those for ten adult chimpanzees between 39.6 and 51.2. These data on a total of 24 specimens include 7 of the writer's previously (1930) recorded percentages.

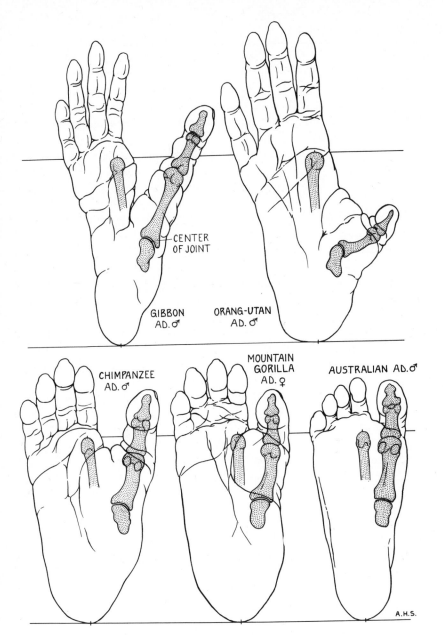

CENTER OF JOINT

GIBBON AD. ♂ ORANG-UTAN AD. ♂

CHIMPANZEE AD. ♂ MOUNTAIN GORILLA AD. ♀ AUSTRALIAN AD. ♂

A.H.S.

FIGURE 2. Exact drawings of right feet of adult higher primates, showing some skeletal structures in their relation to the outer form, all reduced to same distance from heel to distal end of second metatarsal bone. The drawings were made with the dioptrograph, first from plaster casts of the outer feet, then from the ligamentous foot skeletons of the same specimens. The contour of the first tarsometatarsal joint was obtained with the diagraph at the center of this joint.

of assigning a place to man. Thus, Illiger (1811) had put man in a separate order, which he called *Erecta,* in the belief that the erect posture constitutes man's main physical distinction. There can be no doubt that the acquisition of the erect posture is one of man's foremost peculiarities and that it has been both the consequence and cause of many other human specializations. However, a tendency for the assumption of the upright posture and for bipedal locomotion is by no means limited to man. Among the prosimians various forms, notably the Sifakas, can progress on their hindlegs alone when on level ground. Among New World monkeys the writer has seen adult Spider monkeys and Woolly monkeys *run* on a smooth floor with great ease on their two feet and without touching the ground with either their hands or their tails. Among Old World monkeys most species can and do rear up and *stand* erect for considerable time, but cannot *walk* in that position, at least not without special training. The anthropoid apes all can stand fully erect at will and even without the support of their hands, though the orang-utan does this but rarely. Upright and exclusively bipedal walk is possible for and frequently seen in gibbons, siamangs, and the African apes. As a rule this erect "walk" represents rather a clumsy run of short duration, with knees bent and arms ready for support or for balance. Occasionally, however, one encounters individuals which, without having been trained by man, will *walk* upright on the ground slowly and deliberately, and with the knees hardly more bent than in some men. This manner of walk could be observed repeatedly by the writer in a splendid, fully grown siamang at the National Zoölogical Park in Washington (Figure 3) and was seen by the author in its most accomplished form in an adult gorilla at the Central Park Zoo of New York (Figure 4). The latter was sketched in action by the distinguished animal painter, Mr. C. R. Knight, who very kindly sent this sketch to the author. Of the four living, adult chimpanzees, which had been under the writer's care for years, two could stand and walk erect with legs held nearly straight, but the other two would walk on their feet alone only with bent hips and knees. In conclusion it can be stated that erect posture and even bipedal locomotion are, strictly speaking, not distinctions of man, but only the morphological and physiological adaptations and perfections which are closely associated with man's permanent erect posture.

VARIABILITY AND MAN'S DISTINCTIONS

It has frequently been asserted that all men at the completion of growth possess longer legs and shorter arms than at least any of the man-like apes. This is correct only if the length of the limbs is referred to stature, but that is a very misleading procedure, since stature is most unsuitable

FIGURE 3. Adult male Siamang, walking upright, drawn by the writer from life and with the aid of photographs.

FIGURE 4. Adult female gorilla, walking upright, sketched from life by Mr. C. R. Knight and reproduced with the permission of the artist.

TABLE 1

THE RANGES OF VARIATION IN THE RELATIVE
LENGTHS OF THE LIMBS IN SOME SERIES
OF ADULT MALE PRIMATES

Total Length of Lower Limb in Percentage of Trunk Height:

Series	Specimens	Author	Range
Spider monkey (*Ateles geoffroyi*)	25	Schultz	122–143
Gibbon (*Hylobates lar*)	43	Schultz, 1944	132–166
Chimpanzee	11	Schultz, 1940 + new specimens	117–149
Man (several races)	20	Schultz	141–197
Man (Ituri pygmies)	510	Gusinde, 1948	149–209

Total Length of Upper Limb in Percentage of Trunk Height:

Series	Specimens	Author	Range
Chimpanzee	11	Schultz, 1940 + new specimens	158–200
Mountain gorilla	2	Schultz, 1933b	148–160
Man (several races)	20	Schultz	119–174
Man (Whites)	100	Mollison, 1911	137–175
Man (Forest Negroes)	147	Gusinde, 1948	130–188
Man (Twa pygmies)	101	Gusinde, 1949	134–181

for such comparisons, being so largely dependent on leg length itself. The best morphological unit with which to compare the lengths of the limbs in comparative investigations is undoubtedly the length of the trunk which is anthropometrically called *trunk height* and defined as straight distance between suprasternal notch and upper edge of pubic symphysis. If the total lengths of the upper and of the lower limbs[3] are expressed in percentage of the trunk height, it is found that man is not distinct among higher primates in regard to the adult development of his extremities. As shown by the examples in Table 1, the ranges of variations in the relative length of the lower limb overlap in man and several species of simian primates. In other words, some chimpanzees, gibbons, and Spider monkeys have proportionately longer lower limbs than have some human beings, even though an excessive leg length is commonly regarded as one of the most evident human specializations. Among prosimian primates there are various forms in which this relative lower limb length

[3] Total upper limb length = lengths of upper arm + forearm + hand (to tip of longest finger); total lower limb length = length of thigh (from great trochanter) + distance from knee joint to sole below ankle with foot at right angle to leg, measured on the outer body.

compares favorably with that of man. For instance, among eight adult Tarsiers of the writer's collection this proportion, measured in exactly the same manner as in man, varies between 169 and 189, in an adult Indris it equals 147 and in an adult Sifaka 146.

The relative length of the upper extremity varies among Old World monkeys generally between about 105 and 135. In the most expert brachiators, the gibbons, this proportion always lies above 200 in adults and varies to as much as 274 (Schultz, 1944). This extreme lengthening of the upper limbs in gibbons represents a much more far-reaching evolutionary specialization than does the lengthening of the lower limbs in man. Even among the higher primates alone man is not distinguished by the relative length of his upper limbs, but clearly has shared their general tendency to lengthen the upper extremities beyond their proportionate size prevailing among the lower catarrhines. This is demonstrated by the data in Table 1, according to which the arms can be as short as 148 per cent of the trunk height in some gorillas, or 158 per cent in some chimpanzees, whereas they can attain a length of more than 174 per cent of the trunk height in some human beings.

If the length of the upper extremity is compared with that of the lower one, it is found that in this proportion man differs from all other catarrhine primates at least during the later stages of growth. This so-called intermembral index (composed of the total lengths of the limbs and expressing the length of the upper in percentage of the length of the lower limb) falls always below 100 in adult man, whereas above 100 in adult anthropoid apes and Old World monkeys, indicating that in man alone among the catarrhines are the upper limbs shorter than the lower ones. This human distinction, however, is not valid, if the entire order of primates is taken into consideration and, hence, its significance has been frequently over-rated. Thus, Montagu (1945) gives a list of "The principal anatomical features distinguishing man from the non-human primates" which starts with: "1. Fully erect posture, 2. Bipedal locomotion, 3. Legs much longer than arms." Jones (1948) has recently gone even farther by claiming that "Hind limbs longer than fore limbs" is among the characters which distinguish man "absolutely from any other mammal." As shown by the data in Table 2, the lower extremities surpass the upper ones in length in numerous fully-grown prosimian primates and even in some New World monkeys. All of these perfectly normal, wild, freshly dead or preserved specimens had been measured by the author with exactly the same precise methods as he used for measuring the fresh cadavers of the 25 adult human beings,[4] listed in Table 2. The inter-

----

[4] This series is composed of 10 ♂ and 5 ♀ Negroes, 6 ♂ Whites, 1 ♂ Chinese, 1 ♂ American Indian, 1 ♂ Filipino, and 1 ♂ Hawaiian.

TABLE 2

THE LOWEST RANGES OF VARIATION IN THE INTERMEMBRAL
INDEX (TOTAL LENGTH OF UPPER LIMB IN PERCENTAGE
OF TOTAL LENGTH OF LOWER LIMB) AMONG ADULT
PRIMATES OF BOTH SEXES, MEASURED BY THE
AUTHOR WITH THE EXCEPTIONS NOTED BELOW

Species	Specimens	Range
Lemur (*Lemur variegatus*)	1	99.6
Indris (*Indris indris*)*	1	87.7
Avahi (*Lichanotus laniger*)*	1	78.1
Sifaka (*Propithecus verreauxi*)*	1	80.9
Bushbaby (*Galago*, several species)	5	77.9–93.0
Tarsier (*Tarsius*, several species)	8	76.9–84.4
True Marmoset (*Callithrix penicillata*)	1	94.0
Marmoset (*Oedipomidas geoffroyi*)	15	97.6–102.7 (8 below 100)
Night monkey (*Aotus zonalis*)	10	96.7–103.3 (6 below 100)
Man (several races)	25	83.7–90.7
Man (Forest Negroes)**	246	70.0–89.9
Man (Ituri pygmies)**	892	74.5–91.7

* = These rare, wild-shot, embalmed specimens were measured by the writer with the kind permission of their owner, Professor H. Bluntschli in Berne; all other nonhuman primates are from the author's collection.

** = According to Gusinde, 1948.

membral index varies in the small human series to above 90, but ranges to below 80 among nonhuman primates. It is merely mentioned in this connection that in prenatal life man's intermembral index lies above 100, averaging 133 at the beginning of the third month, when it still equals this index in fetuses of many catarrhine monkeys (Schultz, 1926).

Among the reasons which Jones (1948) has given for his proposed, radical separation between man and the anthropoid apes are certain relations between the ethmoid bone and its neighboring cranial elements in the higher primates. If these particular relations are studied on the basis of their variability, which Jones had failed to consider adequately, it can be readily shown that these relations do not represent human distinctions. To provide statistical data on the topographical variations in the relations between the ethmoid and its adjoining bones the author has collected the pertinent information in the literature, has examined his own material of primate skulls, and has made use of the splendid collection of anthropoid crania in the U.S. National Museum, Division of Mammals, and of the fine series of human skulls at Howard University, Department of Anatomy. The writer is greatly indebted to Dr. D. H. Johnson for his kind permission to work at the former institution and to Dr. W. M. Cobb for the hospitality and efficient help at the latter place.

In addition the author has drawn on his records of observations on chimpanzee skulls from certain other collections, which will be referred to fully in another, as yet unfinished report. Finally, Mr. F. C. Howell of the Department of Anthropology of the University of Chicago has very generously contributed his careful, pertinent observations on the cranial series of Guenons and Mangabeys which had recently been collected by Dr. S. L. Washburn of the same department.

Figure 5 serves to illustrate the chief variations in the cranial features to be discussed below. As a general rule the ethmoid bone meets the lacrimal bone on the medial wall of the human orbit, forming a suture at the place of contact, as in A of Figure 5. On the other hand, the frontal and maxillary bones meet and form a suture on the medial orbital wall, separating the lacrimal and ethmoid bones, as in D of Figure 5, according to Jones (1948) in the majority of gorillas and chimpanzees and in some gibbons. Jones admits that the latter relation "has been recorded in Man, but only as a very rare anomaly." The gap between these two different conditions is bridged by occasional variations in which the ethmoid, lacrimal, frontal, and maxillary bones all meet in one point, as in B and C of Figure 5. Table 3 shows the distribution of these different types of formations on the medial walls of the orbits among a total of 1,150 monkeys, apes, and men. These data include those recorded by Thomson (1890), Bianchi (1895, quoted by Le Double), Regnault (1902), Duckworth (1904), and Le Double (1906) for a total of 217 Old World monkeys and apes and the new data on 93 African monkeys, put at the writer's disposal by Mr. F. C. Howell. All other data are based on the author's own, unpublished observations, including those on 136 anthropoid skulls at the National Museum and on 85 human skulls at Howard University. The figures in Table 3 are based on the numbers of orbits, rather than those of skulls examined, on account of the occurrence of asymmetrical conditions in the right and left orbits of the same skulls. Such asymmetries were found in 11 chimpanzees, 2 gorillas, and 4 human beings, and include even cases in which there exist a lacrimo-ethmoid suture in one orbit and a frontomaxillary suture in the other orbit. As shown by Table 3, the lacrimal and ethmoid bones meet and form a suture in all of the great many monkeys, gibbons, and orang-utans which have been examined so far, whereas in only 50 per cent of chimpanzees, 43 per cent of gorillas, and 93 per cent of men. In the remaining African apes and men the frontal and maxillary bones either meet in a point or else form a suture through broader contact. The latter condition is admittedly rare in man, but has been found in 3 per cent of the 161 perfectly normal human skulls, examined by the writer, and a total of 13 other cases have been recorded by Turner (1886), Thomson (1890), Regnault

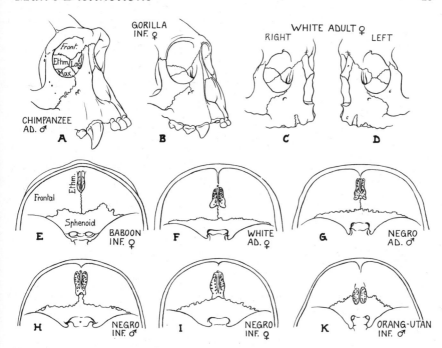

FIGURE 5. *A* to *D* show variations in the relations between the ethmoid, lacrimal, frontal, and maxillary bones on the medial wall of the orbit. *E* to *K* show variations in the relations between the ethmoid, frontal, and sphenoid bones on the floor of the brain case; *E* to *G* show the frontobasilar suture. All figures are author's sketches from specimens in his collection.

(1894), Le Double (1903), and Wolff (1906). It is difficult to understand how Jones (1948) can claim that in the precise formation of the medial orbital wall man is distinct from the anthropoid apes, if as a matter of fact, this lack of contact between the ethmoid and lacrimal bones occurs in the entire suborder of simian primates exclusively in the African anthropoids *and* in man. That this condition exists generally in from 40 to 50 per cent of these apes, whereas in only 3 per cent of men, loses its significance through the fact that among the rare chimpanzees from the left bank of the Congo river the corresponding percentage amounts to only 10, i.e., it is nearer to that of man than to that of chimpanzees from the countries to the north of the Congo. These findings are most readily explained on the basis of the assumption of a common origin for man and the anthropoids from which they all acquired the potentiality for changing the relations between the bones forming the medial orbital wall. These changes happen to have progressed farther, by having affected a larger proportion of the population, in the African apes than

TABLE 3

PERCENTAGE FREQUENCIES OF ORBITS WITH: 1. LACRIMO-ETHMOID SUTURE
(AS A, FIGURE 5), 2. ALL FOUR BONES MEETING IN ONE POINT
(AS B AND C, FIGURE 5) AND 3. FRONTOMAXILLARY SUTURE
(AS D, FIGURE 5)

Series of primates	Totals of orbits examined	Condition		
		1	2	3
New World monkeys	200	100	0	0
Old World monkeys	770	100	0	0
Gibbons and Siamang	126	100	0	0
Orangutan	302	100	0	0
Chimpanzee	326	50	10	40
(Pygmy chimpanzee only)	20	80	10	10
Gorilla	254	43	7	50
Man	322	93	4	3

in man; they are characteristically variable, ranging from the original broad contact between ethmoid and lacrimal, via contact in a mere point, to the new lack of contact, including even frequent asymmetries.

Another supposed "Hallmark of Mankind," stressed by Jones (1948) without adequate regard for its variability, concerns the relations between the ethmoid bone and the sphenoid and frontal bones on the anterior floor of the cranial cavity. According to Jones the frontals meet in the midline behind the ethmoid, separating the latter from the sphenoid, in "typical" Old World monkeys and anthropoid apes (except the orang-utan), whereas in man the ethmoid articulates with the sphenoid and only "partial meeting of the frontals between the ethmoid and sphenoid has been recorded in a few cases in Man."

There exists a considerable literature, dealing with this problem, which was only in part accessible to the writer. He has consulted the publications by the following authors: Sperino and Bovero (1896), Le Double (1903), Gregory (1927b), and Montagu (1943), of which the first was particularly useful since it carefully describes and illustrates no less than 16 cases with the, in man, supposedly rare *sutura metopica basilare* (or frontobasilar suture), 13 of which exist in perfectly normal human skulls.[5] The reports just mentioned furnish pertinent observations on a total of 79 anthropoid skulls[6] and 639 human skulls. To these the author has

[5] The three cases of Sperino and Bovero from microcephalics and cretins have not been included in Table 4 of this paper.

[6] The 24 skulls of great apes from the U.S. National Museum, listed by Montagu (1943), have been omitted in Table 4 to prevent any duplication, because the writer has examined a larger number of such skulls at the same museum.

been able to add the data kindly supplied by Mr. F. C. Howell for 88 Guenons and Mangabeys and his own observations on altogether 611 primate skulls, including 88 anthropoid crania at the National Museum and 89 human crania at Howard University, the remainder of the material being from the collections in the writer's laboratory. It must be mentioned here that the author can contribute this extensive series of endocranial observations only because a great many of his monkey skulls had been opened in various ways for different purposes and, in the case of larger, unopened primate skulls, he used successfully a dental mirror and spotlight, inserted through the foramen magnum.

The results of these combined findings can be briefly listed as given in Table 4, which contains the data on a total of 1,393 primate skulls. In spite of the fact that Jones (1948) refers to the frontobasilar suture (shown by the examples E to G in Figure 5) as a "catarrhine specialisation," this suture was found to exist in about three fourths of platyrrhine monkeys of the family Cebidae. The same suture is present in all but one of 336 Old World monkeys. The rare exception was found in a perfectly normal, adult baboon which has a slender sphenoidal process extending to the ethmoid bone, similar to the condition in H of Figure 5. A frontobasilar suture of varying length exists in all gibbons and siamangs, seen so far, but has been found (by Le Double, 1903) in only one out of ninety orang-utans in which the sphenoid usually articulates with the ethmoid more extensively than in any other primates, not excepting man (see K, Figure 5). In chimpanzees a frontobasilar suture is present in only a minority of the cases and in gorillas in about half of all specimens. In man, finally, this suture has been found in at least 25 cases, forming 3.3 per cent of the total material examined. If negroes are considered separately, this percentage rises to 9, a value which stands nearer to the

TABLE 4

PERCENTAGE FREQUENCIES OF SKULLS WITH: 1. FRONTOBASILAR SUTURE
(AS *E, F* AND *G,* FIGURE 5) OR 2. SPHENO-ETHMOID SUTURE
(AS *H, I,* AND *K,* FIGURE 5)

Series of primates	Total of skulls examined	Fronto-basilar suture	Spheno-ethmoid suture
New World monkeys	42	76	24
Old World monkeys	336	99.7	0.3
Gibbons and Siamang	27	100	0
Orangutan	90	1	99
Chimpanzee	86	23	77
Gorilla	48	52	48
Man (majority Whites)	764	3	97
(Negroes only)	129	9	91

corresponding percentages for chimpanzees and orang-utans than the values of the latter to that of gorillas. Among the eight human skulls (7 adult, 1 infant), in which the writer has found frontobasilar sutures, this interfrontal articulation measures anywhere between 2 and 11 mm., the maximum being equal to the longest frontobasilar suture in any of the chimpanzees seen by the author. A spheno-ethmoid articulation which Jones (1948) claims for a "hallmark" of man, is formed most commonly by only a slender sphenoidal process, reaching the ethmoid on a very narrow front (as in H, Figure 5). Spheno-ethmoidal sutures exist in 91 per cent of negroes, 99 per cent of orang-utans, 77 per cent of chimpanzees, and 48 per cent of gorillas, whereas in only 0 to 0.3 per cent of gibbons, siamangs, and all catarrhine monkeys. These simple statistical data do not conflict with, but effectively support, the well-founded assumption of the genetic relationship between man and great apes. In regard to these topographical relations of the ethmoid bone man is distinct at most and only by the frequency distribution of the variations in these relations.

Through the study of individual variations in a large and representative material of primates one can detect many general evolutionary trends and the comparative stages of progress along these common trends which have been attained by man and the apes. This often reveals unsuspected and not insignificant human distinctions of a quantitative nature. For instance, it is a well known fact that all higher primates have in common the complete lack of an outer tail and a far-reaching reduction in the number of vertebrae in the caudal portion of their spinal columns. This profound evolutionary change has left the tail vertebrae in a highly variable state. As shown by Table 5, the number of segments in the degenerated tail region of the spine varies among higher primates between 0 and 6. Four, 5, and 6 coccygeal vertebrae are far more frequently encountered in man than in the apes, whereas only 1, 2, or 3 of these ver-

TABLE 5

THE NUMBERS OF COCCYGEAL VERTEBRAE IN HIGHER PRIMATES ACCORDING TO SCHULTZ AND STRAUS (1945) AND MANY NEW RECORDS OF THE AUTHOR. THE MAJORITY OF THE DATA FOR MAN HAS BEEN COLLECTED FROM THE LITERATURE

Primate	Specimens	Number of vertebrae in per cent of cases							Average
		0	1	2	3	4	5	6	
Gibbon	311	1	5	37	38	15	3	1	2.7
Siamang	18	—	6	55	33	6	—	—	2.4
Orangutan	112	—	5	38	47	9	1	—	2.6
Chimpanzee	128	—	—	16	50	25	9	—	3.3
Gorilla	105	—	—	21	41	34	4	—	3.2
Man	818	—	—	0.1	11	60	27	2	4.2

tebrae are much more common among the latter than in the former. In consequence it is found that man is distinct among higher primates by possessing the largest *average* number of coccygeal vertebrae, i.e., by having been so far affected least by the evolutionary trend to reduce the tail, a process which man has shared with the apes.

In a very similar manner it can be demonstrated that, on average, man has not progressed as far as have the great apes along their parallel phylogenetic tendencies to decrease the number of lumbar vertebrae and to increase the number of sacral vertebrae. Figure 6 serves to illustrate the following discussion which uses data on vertebral variations which have mostly been recorded in detail by Schultz and Straus (1945). The lower catarrhine primates usually possess 7 lumbar vertebrae and only 6 are found in a small minority of the cases. Among the higher primates the number of segments in the lumbar region has decreased to only 5 in the majority of gibbons, siamangs, and men, and even to only 4 in the majority of all great apes. An occasional orangutan and roughly one third.of chimpanzees and gorillas have already only 3 lumbar vertebrae. The average number of lumbar vertebrae, which equals anywhere between 6.5 and 7.0 in Old World monkeys, has dropped to 4.0 in orangutan, 3.6 in chimpanzee, 3.7 in gorilla, but not that far in man, namely to only 5.0.

The number of sacral vertebrae varies among all Old World monkeys between 2 and 4, being commonly 3. In all higher primates a larger number of vertebrae have become fused to form the sacrum, 5 being the most frequent number in gibbons, siamangs, orang-utans, and men, whereas 6 in chimpanzees and gorillas. In the latter the sacrum can be composed of even 8 vertebrae. On an average man has fewer sacral vertebrae than have the great apes. Man, therefore, has been more conservative than the great apes in regard to these evolutionary changes in the lumbar and sacral portions of the spine.

The above discussed quantitative differences between man and the man-like apes are to a large extent connected with a phylogenetic specialization in the pelvis which is peculiar to the anthropoids. As shown by Figure 6, the pelvis of the chimpanzee and particularly its iliac portions are strikingly higher than those of man. In gorilla and orang-utan the pelvis also extends to nearly the last pair of ribs, whereas in man there is a wide gap between his thorax and the very low iliac blades. From the data in Table 6 it is apparent that among all catarrhine primates only the anthropoids, and especially the great apes, have acquired extremely lengthened iliac bones. In man this relative ilium length has remained fully as short (in relation to trunk height) as in the Old World monkeys. The unique extension of the anthropoid ilia, accompanied by their long contact with the spinal column, has been followed by a gradual

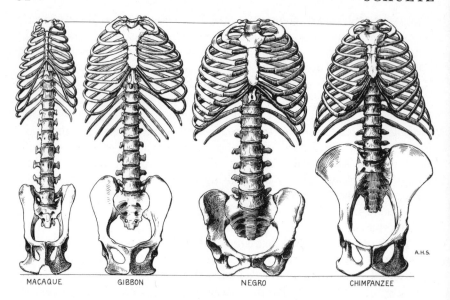

MACAQUE   GIBBON   NEGRO   CHIMPANZEE

FIGURE 6. Dioptrographic drawings of ligamentous trunk skeletons of adult female Macaque (*Macaca mulatta*), Gibbon (*Hylobates lar*), Negro, and Chimpanzee, reduced to the same distance between first thoracic vertebra and caudal end of pelvis. Shrinkage in the spinal columns was held to a negligible minimum by fastening metal rods to the columns before and during drying.

transformation of last lumbar into first sacral vertebrae, still seen by the surprisingly frequent stages of transition, including asymmetrical ones, at the lumbosacral border (for details see Schultz, 1940, 1941a, 1944).

AGE CHANGES AND MAN'S DISTINCTIONS

In early embryonic life all primates are morphologically alike and differences between the various groups and the many species of primates, including the manifold distinctions of man, appear only gradually during growth. For this reason comparative studies on age changes in primates are essential in the search for and the understanding of all human characteristics.

To begin with, the duration of the period of growth shows among primates a clear trend to become lengthened with evolutionary specialization. In the lowly prosimians growth is practically completed at the end of the third year of life, in Old World monkeys this period has increased to 7 years, in the great apes to 11 years, and in man to 20 years. The maximum period of postnatal growth, distinctive of man, appears merely as the extreme advance in the same process which has affected also the man-like apes, though to a lesser degree.

Differences in developmental changes between man and other primates do not necessarily lead to differences at the completion of growth. A good example of this consists in the sequence of eruption of the permanent teeth which, even though it is very different in many groups of modern man than in the other catarrhines, leaves all Old World primates with the same number, types and essential arrangements of teeth in their finished dentitions. The diagram in Figure 7 illustrates the gradual shift in the order of dental eruption and the specialization of man in this respect (for further details and the relevant literature see Schultz, 1935a and 1949). In the tree shrews, which have been assigned to the order of primates by several modern taxonomists, no teeth of the first dentition are shed and replaced before the eruption of all permanent molars which thus form an early addition to the masticatory apparatus in these rapidly maturing, primitive animals. In the majority of the prosimians and a few monkeys the deciduous incisors are replaced by permanent ones before the last of the molar series are added to the dental row. The great majority of the monkeys and all the anthropoid apes have acquired a further acceleration in the appearance of permanent incisors and a corresponding delay in the addition of even the second molars while the eruption of the last molars has become postponed until the milk molars have given way to permanent premolars. This formula of dental eruption has been retained practically unchanged by fossil man and some few groups of recent man, according to reports in the literature. In most races of modern man there has occurred the most extreme and, undoubtedly, rapid and recent

TABLE 6

THE LENGTH OF THE ILIUM BONE IN PERCENTAGE OF THE TRUNK HEIGHT
(MEASURED ON THE OUTER BODY BEFORE PREPARATION OF SKELETON)
IN SERIES OF ADULT CATARRHINE PRIMATES

Primate	Speci-mens	Average	Range of variations
Macaque	10	26.9	24.4–29.2
Baboon	5	27.7	26.1–30.2
Guenon	10	23.6	20.5–26.7
Mangabey	5	24.3	23.3–25.8
Langur	5	23.4	21.9–25.2
Proboscis monkey	10	24.2	22.6–25.8
Gibbon	10	32.8	31.1–37.3
Orangutan	6	35.8	31.6–37.7
Chimpanzee	10	38.0	35.5–42.1
Gorilla	5	38.2	33.7–40.9
Man	10	24.1	22.9–25.5

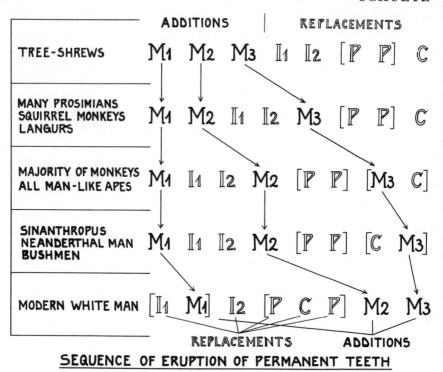

SEQUENCE OF ERUPTION OF PERMANENT TEETH

FIGURE 7. Diagrammatic representation of the sequence of eruption of the permanent teeth in primates. M = molar, I = incisor, P = premolar, and C = canine; parentheses indicate that the particular teeth enclosed erupt in somewhat variable order.

evolutionary alteration in this ontogenetic process, inasmuch as the replacement of the first dentition has largely acquired precedence over the addition of permanent molars. It is tempting to speculate that this human distinction is the result of some natural selection, directly connected with the extreme prolongation of the period of growth in man. The deciduous teeth of man are not more durable than those of other primates, yet they have to serve in the former for much longer periods than in the latter. Hence this newly acquired precedence for the replacement of milk teeth over the addition of molars is undoubtedly beneficial, if not necessary, for man.

Adult man possesses numerous, detailed, morphological characteristics which are entirely due to minor phylogenetic changes in the *rate* of growth and development in the corresponding bodily parts, and are not caused by any deviation from the general *direction* of developmental differentiation common to at least all higher primates. For instance, in the young of man, apes, and monkeys the sternum is composed of a series of separate bones, the so-called sternebrae. In Old World monkeys these sternebrae remain separate throughout life, as shown in Figure 8. Only in rare specimens of an advanced age do the lowest segments become fused. In the anthropoids the bones at the caudal end of the sternum have usually become united when adulthood has been attained, but at least the uppermost two segments of the corpus sterni are still separate at that age, as shown by the examples in Figure 8. With approaching senility the corpus sterni can change into one single bone through complete, but late, fusion of all sternebrae in gibbons as well as the great apes, though this has been found to be highly variable in all anthropoids (Schultz, 1930,

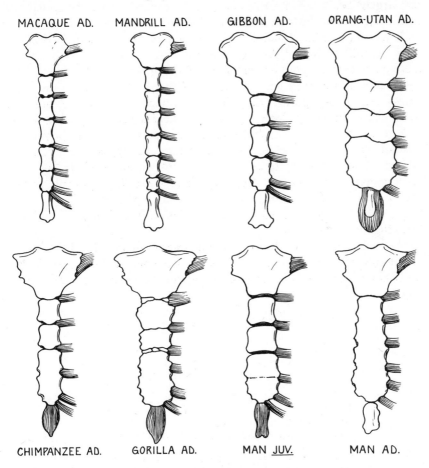

MACAQUE AD.   MANDRILL AD.   GIBBON AD.   ORANG-UTAN AD.

CHIMPANZEE AD.   GORILLA AD.   MAN JUV.   MAN AD.

FIGURE 8. The sternum and left cartilaginous sternal ribs in catarrhine primates with completed, but not worn, dentition and in a juvenile man.

1940, 1941a, and 1944). In man, finally, the segments of the corpus sterni begin to fuse at the lower end during childhood and become solidly united before the dentition is completed in the overwhelming majority of the cases. Thus the adult sternum of man has become distinct from the average sterna of adult (but not old) apes in consequence of an acceleration in a developmental trend which shows the same direction, but slower rate in the other higher primates.

For and with the acquisition of the erect posture in man there had to take place various mechanical changes and perfections which still appear only gradually during growth. One of these adaptations concerns the position of the spinal column within the chest. As shown by Figure 9, in the largely quadrupedal monkeys, such as the macaque, the spinal column projects very little into the cavity of the thorax which is suspended underneath the spine. In adult man, on the other hand, the vertebral column has shifted toward the center of the chest cavity, which is a much more advantageous position for the efficient support of the weight of the upper parts of the erect body. In adults of the great apes, as in the chimpanzee shown in Figure 9, the relative position of the spine approaches that in adult man very closely, showing in this respect a surprising degree of "preparedness" for erect posture. In early stages of development this position of the spine, relative to the thoracic cavity, is in all primates very much as it remains to adult life in monkeys, and even as late as at birth is man in this respect still more monkey-like than typically human (see Figure 9). The distinction of adult man represents merely the extreme of an ontogenetic innovation which as such is clearly recognizable in all higher primates.

The same general conclusion is applicable to another condition in the spinal column which is illustrated by the examples in Figure 10. It is a well-known fact that in adult man the sacrum forms the roof, rather than

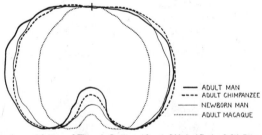

Superimposed Outlines of Thoracic Cavities at Level of Ventral Ends of 6th Ribs

FIGURE 9. Superimposed outlines of thoracic cavities at level of ventral ends of sixth ribs. Tracings of horizontal sections through plaster casts of freshly eviscerated chest cavities of a newborn and an adult man, an adult Chimpanzee, and an adult Macaque, all reduced to same maximum sagittal diameter of section. The centers of the sterna are superimposed at the short perpendicular line on top.

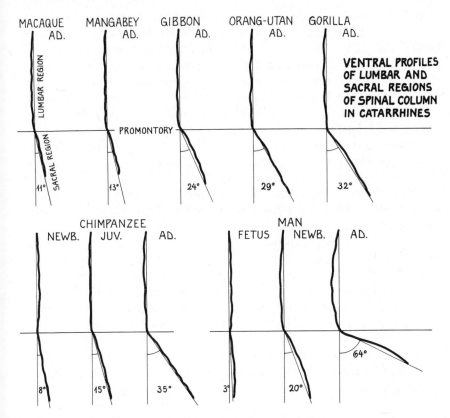

FIGURE 10. Tracings of midsagittal sections of plaster casts of eviscerated abdominal cavities, showing the exact ventral profiles of the lumbar and sacral regions of the vertebral column in some catarrhine primates. The lumbosacral border or promontory is indicated by the horizontal lines.

the posterior wall, of the pelvic cavity and that only the presacral part of the spinal column is held erect. This causes an abrupt change in the direction of the lumbar and sacral portions of the spine and the formation of a striking promontory at the lumbosacral border, as shown by the last curve in Figure 10. No such promontory exists at early developmental stages in any primate. The author has never found an indication of a true promontory in the great many newborn and infantile monkeys which he has eviscerated, but toward the completion of growth there appears in most catarrhine monkeys a slight tilting of the sacrum so that its ventral surface forms an angle with the general direction of the ventral profile of the lumbar spine. This angle, measured in freshly eviscerated animals, can amount to 13° in some adult monkeys. According to the author's determinations this angle measures between 18° and 24° in (10) adult gibbons, between 23° and 30° in (4) adult orang-utans, and over 30° in all (7) adults of the African great apes. At birth this angle equals only 8° in an ape, but already 20° in man, as shown by the examples in Figure 10. It is seen that the tendency for the formation of a promontory through a change in the direction of the sacrum away from the general axis of the spine appears only late in juvenile life and remains very feeble in catarrhine monkeys, it becomes evident at earlier stages of growth and progresses much farther in the anthropoid apes, especially the African ones, and it begins to operate already during prenatal growth and rapidly attains its extreme result in man. This human distinction represents, properly speaking, merely an intensification and acceleration in the same ontogenetic process which has been acquired by all higher primates. In all probability this process has become perfected in man together with the acquisition of the erect posture.

Among all primates man possesses the largest brain at the completion of growth. The cranial cavity, which contains the brain, has a volume of roughly 1,500 cc. in an average fully grown man, or far more than in any recent nonhuman primates, among which this cranial capacity ranges only up to 685 cc., a value found by Randall (1943–1944) in one huge gorilla. Naturally, the absolute size of the brain has much less significance for comparisons than has this size in its relation to the size of the entire body. Since reliable measurements of the volumes of the brain and of the whole body are difficult to obtain for wild-shot primates in the field, the cranial capacity is substituted as a closely corresponding and accurately determined representation of brain volume, and body weight for body volume on the justifiable assumption that the specific gravity of all primates equals roughly 1.0. The author has collected many data on cranial capacity and body weight in normal primates and has expressed the former (in cc.) in percentage of the latter (in g.), obtaining thereby strictly comparable indices, representing the *relative* size of the brain. Only a few examples of these relative capacities can here be quoted: at the completion of growth these percentages average 2.02 in man (26 males and females of several races), 1.94 in gibbons (82 *Hylobates lar*), and 2.97 in Squirrel monkeys (14 *Saimiri örstedii*), but the body weights average in the human series 69.6 kg., in the gibbon series 5.5 kg., and in the last series only 0.86 kg. Adult man, therefore, has a relative brain size which is nearly equalled or even surpassed by the relative brain size of some other adult primates, but all of the latter are very much smaller animals. In primates with body weights similar to those of man the relative brain size is very much smaller. For instance, it averages only 0.76 in 18 adult orang-utans with a mean body weight of 54.9 kg., only 0.92 in 18 adult chimpanzees with a mean body weight of 41.7 kg., and even only 0.40 in 9 adult gorillas with a mean body weight of 154.6 kg. From these data it becomes evident that adult man has the proportionately largest brain among adult primates of similar body size. This is shown also by Figure 11 which gives the growth curves for the relative cranial capacity in different groups of catarrhines.[7] In all primates the brain grows very rapidly during prenatal life when the human distinction in relative brain size among types of corresponding general size has not yet appeared. For instance, in a human fetus, weighing 550 g., the relative cranial capacity amounts to 12.5, or exactly the same as in a newborn Spider monkey, weighing 510 g., and somewhat less than in a chimpanzee fetus of 570 g. with a relative capacity of 14.4 or in a newborn macaque of 400 g. with a corresponding percentage of 13.0. During the later stages of prenatal and all of postnatal life the body weight increases more intensively than the size of the brain, causing the relative cranial capacity to drop continuously, but this difference in growth rates differs markedly in the various major groups of primates, as is demonstrated in Figure 11 by the divergence of the curves. In man the brain continues to grow for a relatively longer part of the period of increase in general body size than in monkeys and apes, in which the brain attains practically its final size at an early age. These data, together with Figure 11, must suffice here to show that adult man's distinction in regard to relative brain size is primarily due to his ontogenetic specialization, consisting in the continuation and intensification of brain growth beyond the degree of such specialization reached by the great apes. The same sort of ontogenetic specialization has shifted the growth curve for the relative brain size of great apes away from the curve for the lower catarrhines and toward the curve for man.

It has long and often been claimed that the extreme increase in the size of the human brain became possible only after the acquisition of the erectly held spine on which the heavy head could rest in ideal balance. Knauer (1916), e.g., had discussed this at length and had concluded (in free translation):

Such an enormous brain development as man has experienced—the most important result of erect posture—could be reached only through the perfected position of equilibrium of the head, because this huge brain represents a luxury-organ. Alone in this way did weight acquire an entirely subordinate role, since it acts in a position of rest only as pressure on the supporting structure and the muscle apparatus is needed very little to maintain this position.

There is no denying the facts that among adults the fulcrum of the head lies much nearer to (but still far from) the center of gravity of the head in man than in any other primate and that this relative position of

---

[7] It is of special interest to find that the author's data for all three types of great apes fit very closely in a single growth curve and that, likewise, those for the many genera of Old World monkeys form only one curve, except the baboons, as shown in Figure 11 (for further details see Schultz, 1941b).

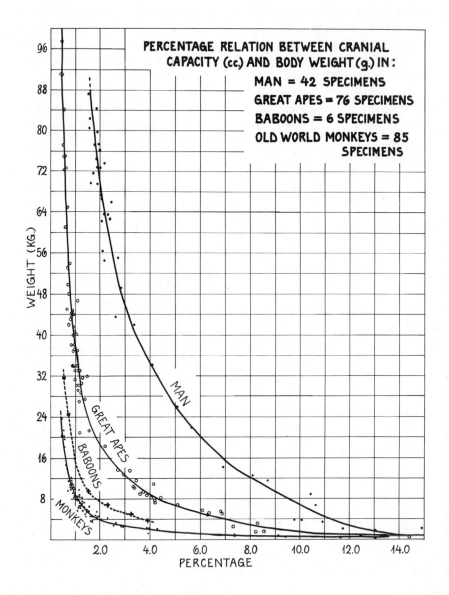

FIGURE 11. Growth curves for the relative cranial capacities of catarrhine primates, based on the old (1941) and new data of the author.

the fulcrum of the head, which is distinctive of man, is advantageous for the erect posture. Naturally, however, it is the weight of the entire head and not that of the brain alone, which is the essential factor in this connection. While the brain has increased in size during human evolution, the face, particularly the dental apparatus, has decreased so that the relative weight of the *entire* head has become actually smaller in modern man than in many apes and monkeys. This is shown by the following data, recorded by the author (1942a) in a special study on head balance: the weight of the entire head in percentage of the weight of the whole body averages in eight adult human beings 5.4, whereas in three adult chimpanzees 5.8, in an adult orang-utan it equals also 5.8, and in two adult gibbons 7.2 and 7.3, respectively. Among adult monkeys this percentage can rise to even higher values, such as 8.9 in a mandrill and 10.5 in a macaque. In all these apes and monkeys the proportionately heavy head is hinged more in front of than above the spine and hence requires a strong musculature for being maintained in that position. It is seen that an increase in brain weight alone cannot be the answer to the question why the comparatively light human head had not retained a position relative to the spine similar to that in all nonhuman primates. The profound phylogenetic change in this relation between head and spine in man can be understood only as an ontogenetic specialization, as will be discussed briefly below.

The occipital condyles, which determine the position of the fulcrum of the head, lie relatively far forward on the skull base in fetuses of all primates and even in early infantile life. There exists as yet little difference in this respect between man, apes, and monkeys, as shown by the few examples in Figure 12 (more examples have been published by Schultz, 1949). During postnatal growth the relative position of the atlanto-occipital joint undergoes practically no change from its fetal and infantile condition in man, but in the other primates it shifts backward in varying and always marked degrees. At the same time the face grows forward and downward much more in nearly all nonhuman primates than in man in whom the size and direction of the facial profile change postnatally less than in all apes and most monkeys. Adult man is distinct among adult primates by possessing occipital condyles situated far forward on the cranial base and by having the face well behind a line perpendicular to the base of the skull at its anterior end. These human distinctions represent primarily ontogenetic specializations, namely in this case the suppression of those growth changes common to monkeys and apes, which produce the ontogenetically late positions of the condyles and the face, characteristic of all nonhuman primates. That man has become able to reach adulthood while retaining essentially infantile conditions in these

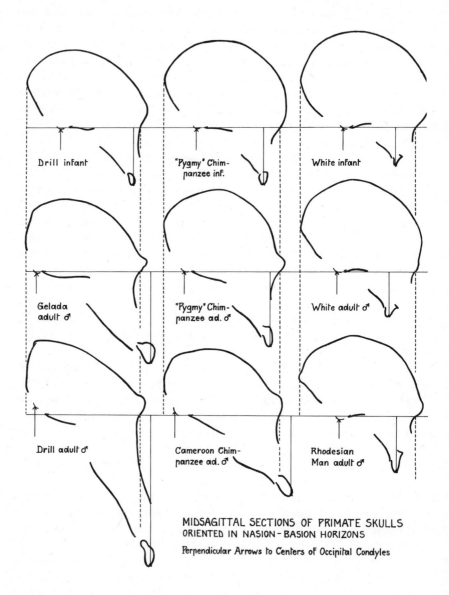

Drill infant

"Pygmy" Chim-
panzee inf.

White infant

Gelada
adult ♂

"Pygmy" Chim-
panzee ad. ♂

White adult ♂

Drill adult ♂

Cameroon Chim-
panzee ad. ♂

Rhodesian
Man adult ♂

MIDSAGITTAL SECTIONS OF PRIMATE SKULLS
ORIENTED IN NASION – BASION HORIZONS

Perpendicular Arrows to Centers of Occipital Condyles

FIGURE 12. Tracings of midsagittal sections of skulls of infantile and adult Baboons, Chimpanzees, and men, all reduced to same length of brain case. The left occipital condyles are projected on the midsagittal plane and their centers are indicated by perpendicular arrows.

features of the head appears as a less profound innovation through the finding that the amount of ontogenetic change in these respects varies greatly among apes and monkeys. For instance, in the so-called pygmy chimpanzee the position of the occipital condyles and that of the face change as a rule appreciably less during growth than they do in other chimpanzees and among the usually long-snouted baboons the Gelada retains the infantile size and position of the face much more closely than do other members of that group of monkeys, as is shown by the examples in Figure 12.

As a final example of the significance of variability and of ontogeny for the evaluation of the distinctions of adult man the conditions of the mastoid process are briefly mentioned here. This large bony process behind the external opening of the ear in adult man is commonly regarded as a human peculiarity. For instance, Weber (1927–1928) states in his great textbook of mammalian anatomy (in free translation): "In man alone does the Mastoid attain the size of his *Processus mastoideus,* most likely in consequence of the importance of the sterno-cleido-mastoid muscle, which inserts on it, for the maintenance and rotation of the head in the erect position." The writer has never seen what could properly be called a mastoid process in any Old World monkey, but among the extensive series of adult anthropoid ape skulls, examined by him, it was found that the mastoid region is extraordinary variable, as he has described and illustrated in another paper (1950a). In chimpanzees and, especially, in gorillas there can appear late in growth true mastoid processes which are fully comparable in size and shape with those of man. In the latter, however, these processes develop in all cases, whereas in the apes they remain small, except in a minority of the specimens. In man the mastoid processes begin to form early in postnatal life, but in apes they never become noticeable before the approach of adulthood and then only in occasional specimens. The largest mastoid processes have been encountered by the writer in old gorillas and chimpanzees. From this can be concluded that the formation of mastoid processes is the result of an ontogenetic innovation which has led to the late development of these structures in only a part of the population of apes and to their comparatively early and constant development in man. Only in this restricted sense can the mastoid process be regarded as a distinction of man.

Summary

Man's exact place among the primates has to be determined on the basis of the characters which are peculiar to man. Such peculiarities can represent absolute, constant distinctions, deeply rooted in the genetic endowment of all individuals, or they can consist of conditions which differ between man and one or another group of nonhuman primates only quantitatively. In the latter case it may be merely the percentage frequency of occurrence of a condition which has become peculiar to man, or a given human feature may have changed primarily only in regard to the age of its appearance, disappearance, rate of differentiation, etc., thereby producing an alteration in the end-result of the respective growth process. The important evaluation of all qualitative and quantitative human characteristics depends upon whether they constitute radically new specializations or manifestations of general evolutionary trends, common to man and at least some other primates, which have merely affected man to a distinctive, but not necessarily to the highest, degree. By stressing these generalizations this paper reviews critically some of the physical distinctions, which have been claimed for man, and attempts to analyze and interpret these and other distinctions on the basis of their variability and ontogeny and through comparisons with corresponding conditions in nonhuman primates. The following main topics have been discussed in varying detail:

The great emphasis of older (and some recent) writers on the profound distinctiveness of man's feet and his posture is no longer justified in the light of our present knowledge of primates.

The important role of variability in the study of human distinctions is illustrated by a series of examples. Thus, it is shown that man does not possess the relatively longest lower extremities of all primates, as is commonly claimed, since individual variations in this respect do share part of their ranges in man and some other primates. The detailed relations between certain bones of the skull, particularly those between the ethmoid and surrounding elements, differ in their general averages between man and the African apes. With the support of large series of new data it is shown that these relations vary extensively in some of the higher primates and do not conflict with, but strongly indicate a close relationship between man and the great apes, man being distinct only regarding the frequency of certain variations in these conditions. Such distinctions in the frequency distribution of variations are shown to exist also in the numbers of segments in some spinal regions. Thus, man is distinct among higher primates by having retained the largest average number of tail vertebrae, but the ranges of individual variations in this number overlap extensively with the corresponding ranges in the anthropoid apes. The variations in the numbers of lumbar and of sacral vertebrae are markedly influenced by the specialized lengthening of the iliac portions of the pelvis in the apes, a lengthening lacking in man, who is distinguished among the higher primates by possessing the proportionately shortest iliac bones and, partly on that account, one of the highest average numbers of lumbar vertebrae.

The gradual emergence of human distinctions in the course of growth in consequence of specializations in developmental processes is demonstrated by a variety of examples. Some of these deal with accelerations, others with retardations in ontogenetic conditions which, as such, are not limited to man. Among the higher primates there has prevailed a general trend to lengthen the period of postnatal growth. This change has reached its extreme in man and has been accompanied by numerous modifications in the sequence and rate of developmental processes. For instance, the bony parts of the sternum, which remain separate throughout life in Old World monkeys, tend to fuse at the lower sternal end with or after the attainment of adulthood in the man-like apes, among which all parts become united only in old specimens. In man all the initially separate bones of the corpus sterni become fused late in juvenile life, this fusion starting also at the lower end, and undivided corpora sterni are typical of adult man.

The position of the spinal column within the chest cavity has shifted toward the center of the thorax in all higher primates and most of all in erect, adult man. This relative position does not change with age in monkeys, but shifts forward during growth in the higher primates as an ontogenetic innovation which is alike in direction, but differs in degree, in man and the apes. The formation of a promontory at the lumbosacral border appears at a late stage of growth and remains very feeble in all monkeys. In the apes this promontory develops earlier and reaches greater perfection than in monkeys. In man this bending of the spinal column begins before birth and progresses to an extreme degree postnatally, producing one of man's purely quantitative distinctions.

Adult man possesses the proportionately largest brain among primates of similar body size at the completion of their growth, but this distinction does not yet exist at early stages of development. The growth curve for relative brain size has become shifted in the apes in the same direction, but not as far, as in man away from the corresponding curve for lower catarrhines. Adult man is unique by having the head resting on the spine nearly in a state of equilibrium through the extreme forward position of the occipital condyles. This position of the condyles is typical for early fetal life in all primates, but becomes rapidly changed in monkeys and apes in which the condyles move with growth from near the center of gravity toward the back of the head. This ontogenetic process has become lost in man whose occipital condyles remain throughout life in the characteristically fetal position.

These random examples, naturally, do not pretend to include all of the many human distinctions. The conditions discussed here have been chosen merely to demonstrate the help which can be expected from the study of variability and of growth changes in human characteristics for the investigation of man's evolutionary history. Generally speaking, the chief and universal human distinction consists in his peculiar combination of characters which, singly, are distinct only with the limitations resulting from the factors of variability and age.

The Riddle of Man's Ancestry

William L. Straus, Jr.   1949

The investigation of man's origin and evolution has necessarily been based largely upon the indirect evidence provided by comparative studies of living forms, for the more direct evidence of paleontology is still relatively slight, fragmentary, and too often ambiguous. Recent years have witnessed the discovery of a considerable number of fossil hominids, many of them obviously more primitive than modern man, and of numerous fossils of other primates. But these, instead of simplifying the phylogenetic story, have merely served to demonstrate its complexity, so that the apparent course of man's evolution is actually more obscure than it was a few decades past. It is noteworthy, moreover, that forms intermediate between the human and any of the other primate groups, forms popularly termed "missing links," are as conspicuous by their absence as they were in Darwin's day, unless the recently unearthed fossil Australopithecinae of South Africa should eventually prove to represent a truly transitional stage connecting the other Old World primates with man. More detailed and more critical work is needed, however, before the precise zoological affinities of the Australopithecinae can be determined (see Straus, 1948a, b).

Ever since 1758, it has been generally accepted that man is a member of that subdivision or order of the mammals known as the Primates. In that year Linnaeus published the tenth edition of his *Systema Naturae*, in which he placed man in the order Primates together with the apes, monkeys, lemurs, bats, and colugos or "flying lemurs." Later studies removed the bats and colugos to orders of their own, but otherwise the

FROM *the* Quarterly Review of Biology, *1949, vol. 24, pp. 200–223, reprinted by permission of the author and of the Quarterly Review. Dr. Straus has long advocated keeping an open mind on the closeness of man's special relationship to the anthropoid apes, and has contributed a sense of perspective by his studies of the monkeys. He has been both Professor of Anatomy and Professor of Physical Anthropology at Johns Hopkins University.*

order Primates as created by Linnaeus still remains the foundation for primate taxonomy.

One of the outstanding features of the order Primates is that its members cannot be defined by any single or peculiar character, but rather only by a combination of characters, any of which can be found in members of certain other mammalian orders. The following definition of a primate was given by St. George Mivart over 75 years ago (1873b) and is still largely valid: Primates are "unguiculate claviculate placental mammals, with orbits encircled by bone; three kinds of teeth, at least at one time of life; brain always with a posterior lobe and calcarine fissure; the innermost digits of at least one pair of extremities opposable hallux with a flat nail or none; a well-developed caecum; penis pendulous; testes scrotal; always two pectoral mammae." As Zuckerman (1933) has noted, "These morphological characters are generally believed to represent a primitive mammalian condition, so that it may be truly said that the Primate, except for its general tendency to cerebral development, is relatively a non-specialized mammal." Indeed, it should be stressed that the single feature at all peculiar to the order Primates is the inclination toward expansion and development of the brain, the rest of the body tending to remain relatively generalized or unspecialized. It is this general lack of structural specialization—which is also evidenced by man—that makes the study of primate phylogeny so difficult.

A classification of the living members of the order Primates is given in Figure 1. The suborder Lemuroidea contains those primates commonly known collectively as "lemurs"; together with the suborder Tarsioidea they are frequently termed, although not entirely happily, "prosimians." This is by way of contrast to the "simians" (monkeys and apes), who with man constitute the suborder Pithecoidea, the rest of the order. The pithecoid primates form two natural groups, those of the New World (infraorder Platyrrhinae) and those of the Old World (infraorder Catarrhinae). The Platyrrhinae comprise two families of monkeys (Hapalidae, Cebidae); the Catarrhinae, on the other hand, are a more varied and differentiated group, embracing the Old World monkeys (family Cercopithecidae); the anthropoid apes (families Hylobatidae and Pongidae) and man (family Hominidae).

The tree shrews or tupaiids, commonly regarded as aberrant members of the order Insectivora, are sometimes included within the order Primates (as by Simpson, 1945, who placed them in the infraorder Lemuriformes). In my present opinion, however, they are best relegated to a separate order of their own, the Tupaioidea.

In this paper, the term *hominid* refers to members of the family Hominidae both living and fossil, the term *anthropoid* to the anthropoid apes (families Hylobatidae and Pongidae), the term *great ape* to the Pongidae alone, and the term *monkey* to the monkeys both catarrhine (family Cercopithecidae) and platyrrhine (families Hapalidae and Cebidae). The term *cercopithecid* applies to all of the catarrhine monkeys (and not to the genus *Cercopithecus* or the

ORDER PRIMATES

SUBORDER	INFRAORDER	FAMILY	SUBFAMILY	GENUS	ENGLISH NAME
LEMUROIDEA	LEMURIFORMES	LEMURIDAE	LEMURINAE	LEMUR	Common lemur
				HAPALEMUR	Gentle lemur
				LEPILEMUR	Sportive lemur
			CHEIROGALEINAE	CHEIROGALEUS	Mouse lemur
				MICROCEBUS	Dwarf lemur
		INDRIDAE		INDRI	Indris
				LICHANOTUS	Avahi
				PROPITHECUS	Sifaka
		DAUBENTONIIDAE		DAUBENTONIA	Aye-aye
	LORISIFORMES	LORISIDAE	LORISINAE	LORIS	Slender loris
				NYCTICEBUS	Slow loris
				ARCTOCEBUS	Angwantibo
				PERODICTICUS	Potto
			GALAGINAE	GALAGO	Bush baby
TARSIOIDEA		TARSIIDAE		TARSIUS	Tarsier
PITHECOIDEA		HAPALIDAE		HAPALE	Common marmoset
				OEDIPOMIDAS	Marmoset
				LEONTOCEBUS	Tamarin
	PLATYRRHINAE	CEBIDAE	CALLIMICONINAE	CALLIMICO	Callimico
			AOTINAE	AOTUS	Douroucouli
				CALLICEBUS	Titi
			PITHECIINAE	PITHECIA	Saki
				CHIROPOTES	Saki
				CACAJAO	Uakari
			ALOUATTINAE	ALOUATTA	Howler
			CEBINAE	CEBUS	Capuchin
				SAIMIRI	Squirrel monkey
			ATELINAE	ATELES	Spider monkey
				BRACHYTELES	Woolly spider monkey
				LAGOTHRIX	Woolly monkey
	CATARRHINAE	CERCOPITHECIDAE	CERCOPITHECINAE	MACACA	Macaque
				CYNOPITHECUS	Black ape
				CERCOCEBUS	Mangabey
				PAPIO	Baboon
				THEROPITHECUS	Gelada
				CERCOPITHECUS	Guenon
				ERYTHROCEBUS	Patas monkey
			SEMNOPITHECINAE	SEMNOPITHECUS	Langur
				RHINOPITHECUS	Snub-nosed langur
				NASALIS	Proboscis monkey
				COLOBUS	Guereza
		HYLOBATIDAE		HYLOBATES	Gibbon
				SYMPHALANGUS	Siamang
		PONGIDAE		PONGO	Orang-utan
				PAN	Chimpanzee
				GORILLA	Gorilla
		HOMINIDAE		HOMO	Man

FIGURE 1. A classification of the living genera of the order Primates.

subfamily Cercopithecinae alone), the term *hylobatid* to the entire family Hylobatidae (and not to the genus *Hylobates* alone), and the term *pongid* to all of the great apes or Pongidae (and not to the genus *Pongo* alone).

THE ANTHROPOID-APE THEORY OF HUMAN ORIGIN

The Origin of Species appeared in 1859. Four years later, Thomas Henry Huxley published his now famous group of essays, *Evidence as to Man's Place in Nature*. In this, he stated that "whatever system of organs be studied, the comparison of their modifications in the ape series leads to one and the same result—that the structural differences which separate Man from the Gorilla and the Chimpanzee are not so great as those which separate the Gorilla from the lower apes [i.e., monkeys]." In essence, this assertion was frequently repeated by Huxley. But he admitted that "the structural differences between Man and the Manlike [i.e., anthropoid] apes certainly justify our regarding him as constituting a family apart from them," although "there can be no justification for placing him in a distinct order." Huxley's clear recognition of a separate family status for man has sometimes been forgotten by those enthusiasts who regard his word as gospel.

Huxley obviously regarded man as having arisen from some sort of actual anthropoid ape. Although he was never explicit about this matter, the implication is nevertheless quite definite. Furthermore, as Wood Jones (1929b) has noted, there was the implication of something closely akin to uniserial evolution within the order of Primates, which in turn entails a belief in "missing links" between the existing members of the order. For, of the Primates, Huxley stated that "Perhaps no order of mammals presents us with so extraordinary a series of gradations as this —leading us insensibly from the crown and summit of the animal creation down to creatures, from which there is but a step, as it seems, to the lowest, smallest, and least intelligent of the placental Mammalia."

It is necessary, however, to examine Huxley's writings with the proper historical perspective. Perhaps he thought that the facts then available justified such definite conclusions. On the other hand, he may not have intended to convey the impression of finality respecting the phylogenetic relations of man and the other primates. He was fighting a tremendous battle for the recognition of not only the principle of organic evolution but also of the animal nature of man. Under the circumstances, it is not surprising that some of his statements now appear to be dogmatic or premature.

In any instance, the impact of his analysis of man's place in nature has carried through the years. He was the godfather, if not the father, of the anthropoid-ape theory of man's origin. Actually, this theory did not originate with him, having been vaguely perceived by certain eighteenth-century philosophers, such as Buffon; but Huxley seems to have been the first to express it in modern, scientific fashion. He was, of course, a highly competent comparative anatomist and a master of English prose, and his statements carried, and in most quarters still carry, a tremendous weight. Indeed, his concept of man's relationship to the other primates today remains the orthodox one, differing only in details imposed by the advance of knowledge.

Darwin, in *The Descent of Man* (1871), threw the weight of his great influence behind Huxley when he stated that "we may infer that some ancient member of the anthropomorphous [i.e., anthropoid-ape] sub-group gave birth to man."

Ernst Haeckel (1874 et seq.) accepted Huxley's analysis with enthusiasm and became its vociferous and popular exponent. It was Haeckel, more than anyone else, who developed the concept of an ascending scale of the living primates culminating in man; and it was he who popularized, if he did not originate, the use of the genealogical or family tree to express organic relationships.

During the latter part of the nineteenth century, and especially during the present century, the Huxleyan concept of man's zoological affinities was extended and developed by a number of workers. In its present orthodox form, this theory assumes that man has evolved from an animal that would be classified as an anthropoid ape. In fact, in one form or another, this anthropoid-ape theory has been so often and so continuously exposited and propagandized that it has become almost a fundamental tenet of biological and more particularly anthropological belief, a sort of canon or article of faith. Time has not altered the implications. Thus, Huxley in 1863 called the anthropoid apes "blurred copies" of man, and Gregory in 1934 emphasized the "pervasive likeness" between man and anthropoid "that constantly recurs in spite of differences in detail, is instantly recognized by almost every one, and has been established as a cumulative fact by the most prolonged and intensive investigations."

It is not necessary to go into the detailed evidence and arguments upon which the anthropoid-ape theory of human ancestry is based. They have become incorporated into so many textbooks and popular treatises that they are well-known; and they have been ably summarized in English by both Sir Arthur Keith and Professor William K. Gregory in numerous publications and by many other competent authors in other languages.

It was Keith, an anatomist, who produced a plausible mechanistic explanation of how an arm-swinging or "brachiating" anthropoid ape could have evolved into an orthograde or upright, bipedal man. In a series of publications, beginning in 1891 (see particularly, Keith, 1923), he developed the thesis that an arboreal apprenticeship of brachiating erectness —such as is exhibited by all of the living anthropoid apes, both great and small, who, in contrast to the catarrhine monkeys, habitually hang and progress by means of the arms, with trunk essentially upright—was a necessary evolutionary prelude to the bipedal, terrestrial erectness of man. Keith recognized three stages in the evolution of man's posture: first, a "hylobatian" or small-bodied brachiating stage, exemplified by the living gibbon and siamang; second, a "troglodytian" or large-bodied brachiating stage, as seen in the living great apes; and third, a "plantigrade" or truly bipedal stage. Thus, of physiological necessity, man needs must have descended from a long-armed, large-bodied, brachiating anthropoid ape. This theory was ingeniously conceived and, at least to many students, extremely convincing. But it ignored or ineffectually explained away certain important and logical objections, so that in recent years it has lost some of its erstwhile canonical flavor, and has even been abandoned by Keith himself (1940); although he has persisted in his belief that man originated, after the separation of the Hylobatidae, from the "great bodied" anthropoid stock together with the three living great apes (1948). For recent studies indicate that adaptation to a brachiating mode of life is inevitably accompanied by striking and extensive specializations—conditions or trends that can scarcely be regarded as truly reversible by even those who do not rigidly adhere to a concept of evolutionary irreversibility—especially in those parts of the body wherein man can only be regarded as essentially primitive or unspecialized. As a notable example there may be mentioned the hand (see Straus, 1940, 1942b).

But perhaps the majority of anthropologists and comparative anatomists still adhere, implicitly or even openly, to something closely akin to Keith's original version of the anthropoid-into-man theory, and so believe that man has evolved from a true anthropoid ape at a relatively late geological date. The Dryopithecinae, a wide-spread and heterogeneous group of Miocene and Pliocene primates—generally regarded as constituting a subfamily of the Pongidae, but as yet known only from their jaws and teeth, which parts are certainly anthropoid in nature—are usually supposed to represent the common ancestors of the extant great apes and man (Gregory, 1916 et seq.; Abel, 1931). Gregory, who has contributed so much to the development of this theory and to its popularity, has affirmed that "man constitutes one of the latest branches of the catarrhine series," being "an offshoot of a primitive anthropoid stock," "a made-over brachiator adapted to life on the ground," and that "with regard to the locomotor skeleton, man is a made-over ape and that his ape-cousins are still living to bear witness to 'man's place among the anthropoids'" (1934b).

Weidenreich (1943b), however, regarded the Dryopithecinae as a specialized side branch, and would derive the hominids and the three living great apes from a common pre-dryopithecine stem no later than the Early Miocene. Notwithstanding, Weidenreich at the same time pronounced that "the result of the analysis of man's zoological character, first undertaken by Thomas Huxley . . . still stands firm: the organization of the human body, whether studied as a whole or in detail, is that of an anthropoid. No fact has become known which has the power to shake this statement." This is going Huxley one better. It implies, with Gregory, that man, although somewhat refashioned, is yet in reality an anthropoid ape.

Three years later, Weidenreich (1946) bluntly proclaimed that Huxley "settled, once and for all, the question of the special place of man in the zoological system" and that "if the human form has gradually evolved from a simian one, the type from which it originated must have had the general appearance of an anthropoid and shown a corresponding organization of body and skeleton." For all that, he denied in the same breath "the idea that the older the morphological age of the human form is, the more it must approach the living anthropoids"—a clear realization that all of the latter are highly specialized. In fact, he was at pains to point out that there is much to suggest "that the tooth pattern of the original common stock may have been retained in man, while the living anthropoid branch has produced special differentiations," and "that the original simian type from which man and the three anthropoids branched off showed more of the human organization than that of orangutan, gorilla, or even chimpanzee of today." This latter concept is somewhat reminiscent of the earlier ideas of Klaatsch (1910, 1923). The statement concerning tooth pattern is of great importance, for teeth, being more readily preserved than other parts of the body, constitute the major portion of the available fossil evidence, and furthermore form the chief evidence of recent students, notably paleontologists such as Gregory and Abel, who have argued for the origin of man from a dryopithecine type of anthropoid ape.

It is of interest briefly to consider which of the living anthropoid apes has been regarded as most closely related to man. On this, there has been no lack of disagreement. Most writers, when they speak of an anthropoid-ape ancestor of man, are obviously thinking of an animal that would be definitely recognized as closely akin to the living anthropoids, more particularly to one of the three great apes. Probably the majority of recent students have regarded the human line of descent as having separated from the pongid or great-ape stock just before or at about the time that the latter split into its modern forms, after the separation of the Hylobatidae, in either the Late Oligocene (Keith, 1934) or the Miocene (Gregory, 1927a) (Figure 8A, line M^2). Gregory (1934b), nevertheless, has definitely indicated his belief that man evolved from a chimpanzee-like form, perhaps in the Late Miocene; and in the same year Keith flatly predicted the future discovery of a common ancestor for man, gorilla, and chimpanzee (Figure 8A, line M^3). Huxley possibly had something of this sort in mind, for although he appears never to have made a categorical declaration, he plainly intimated that man is most closely akin to the two African anthropoids—the gorilla and chimpanzee—a view adopted in recent times by many writers. Other workers have shown a still narrower preference. Thus Elliot Smith (1924) favored the gorilla as man's nearest ally. At the extreme are found Schwalbe (1923) and Weinert (1932), who thought that man and chimpanzee were the last of the so-called "higher primates" to separate phylogenetically, this having occurred, according to Weinert's belief, as recently as the end of the Pliocene period. Haeckel (1896a), however, thought man closest to the Asiatic anthropoids—the orang-utan and Hylobatidae—and postulated two separate lines of anthropoid evolution, one giving rise to the two African apes and the other to man and the Asiatic ones (vol. II, p. 189, table XXV). On the other hand, a few students, notably Winge (1895), Pilgrim (1915), and Werth (1928), have denied the near relationship of man and the great apes, believing, although their ideas were not identical, that man is very closely allied to the Hylobatidae. Certain others, notably Schultz (1927, 1930, 1936) and Le Gros Clark (1934), are in a sense intermediate between the extremes noted above, in that they have envisaged man's ancestral line as having gained independence from a common anthropoid-hominid stem between the points of differentiation of the hylobatids and the pongids, but in close or immediate proximity to the former (Figure 8A, line M^1).

Nonanthropoid Theories of Human Origin

The orthodox theory of human origin, that claims a peculiarly close relationship of man to the anthropoids, with the inevitable corollary that he was derived from an animal that could only be classified as an anthropoid ape, has not lacked critics among serious and sober workers in comparative anatomy. Exactly ten years after the appearance of *Evidence as to Man's Place in Nature*, and two years after the publication of *The Descent of Man*, the zoologist St. George Mivart published a little book, *Man and Apes* (1873a), in which he stressed that man has no special or exclusive morphological affinities with any one kind of primate, the resemblances being rather equally shared with different species, including not only anthropoid apes but also monkeys and lemurs. Actually, he was trying to point out the basically generalized nature of the human body, whereas to the adherents of the orthodox concept, from Huxley onwards, the entire human structure is the culmination of a long period of intensive primate evolution and is, in totality, the most specialized and "highest" among the Primates. The proponents of the latter view confuse the brain with the rest of the body. Mivart, however, had no such illusions. For he noted that "it is manifest that man, the apes, and Half-apes cannot be arranged in a single ascending series of which man is the term and culmination." He went on to say, "The human structural characters are shared by so many and such diverse forms, that it is impossible to arrange even groups of genera in a single ascending series . . . if all the structural resemblances are taken into account. On any conceivable hypothesis there are many similar structures, each of which must be deemed to have been independently evolved in more than one instance." In this last statement, as well as in certain others, Mivart was anticipating the now important concept of "parallel evolution."

The paleontologist Boule published a detailed study of the rich fossil remains of Neanderthal man (1911–13) and subsequently considered the general problem of human evolution in a book (1921). It had long been recognized that in a considerable number of characters, Neanderthal man, who lived during the last glacial period, was somewhat more simian than is modern man. It had also been assumed that in these characters he most closely approached the anthropoid apes. Boule, however, found that this assumption was not in accord with the results of his study. He accused most anthropologists of comparing man with only the anthropoids and of regarding the latter, a priori, as those primates closest to man. In discussing the extremities—parts of the body in which modern man differs strikingly from all of the anthropoids—he emphasized that in those features wherein Neanderthal man differed from modern man he approximated the monkeys rather than the anthropoids. These characters thus unite the Hominidae not to the anthropoids but, rather, to a more generalized simian, at the same time a quadruped and a grasper. Boule believed that the human branch of evolution was independent of neighboring branches, notably of that leading to the anthropoids. He recognized, however, our ignorance of its point of attachment; but he thought that one could reasonably conceive it to be attached to that of the catarrhine primates at a level prior to the departure of the anthropoid-ape branch, or even at the level of the common platyrrhine-catarrhine stem. At the same time, he thought it possible that there had been more than one evolutionary trunk for the catarrhines.

The name of the anatomist, Wood Jones, is inevitably associated with what has been termed the "tarsian hypothesis" of man's descent. This, which vigorously denies to man kinship with both the anthropoids and the monkeys, claims that the line of human phylogeny stems directly from a primitive tarsioid; thus man's only living near relative would be *Tarsius* (Wood Jones, 1918). This concept is succinctly summed up by Wood Jones in a lecture of 1923. Referring to his views of 1918, he stated that "the thesis then put forward was that the general notion that Man had evolved along the line of the Linnean Classification was wrong. Far from the Lemurs, the Monkeys, and the Anthropoid Apes being landmarks upon the line of human progress, it was contended that the human stock arose from a Tarsioid form, that the Lemurs were not ancestors of the Tarsioids and that the Monkeys and Apes were more specialized away from the Tarsioids than was Man himself, and, therefore, were not his ancestors, but rather his collateral descendants from a former assemblage of animals, of which we have only one direct descendant, in the form of *Tarsius spectrum*." Later, more detailed expositions of his views (1929b, 1948) did not fundamentally alter his original hypothesis. If his concept be accepted, then the line of man's descent can be viewed as having become independent very near the base of the mammalian stock, for fossil tarsioids have been recovered from deposits of the Paleocene period, at the very beginning of the Age of Mammals.

Wood Jones believed that anatomical characters are of two sorts—those of "heritage," the result of ancestral inheritance, and those of "habitus," the result of environmental adaptation, and that only the former are of value in assessing genetic relationships. He regarded the resemblances of man to monkeys and anthropoids as chiefly ones of habitus, but those of man to *Tarsius* as chiefly those of heritage. This method might be valid were we able, with any degree of conviction, to separate characters into such distinct categories. The difficulties of such a distinction were long ago appreciated by Mivart (1873b). Furthermore, it is exceedingly doubtful whether such a separation is justifiable, if for no other reason than that it remains to be proven for any character that it is not in some way adaptive. Even assuming that there is such a truly fundamental distinction, there is every reason to believe that gene complexes underlie both such kinds of characters. Subsequent work, moreover, has demonstrated that many of Wood Jones' comparative-anatomical claims are unjustifiable, and his tarsian hypothesis is clearly untenable. Yet, whatever one may think of his detailed views, one should not lose sight of the very important fact that what he was really stressing is the essentially unspecialized structural nature of man. In this, he has been an invaluable counterirritant to the uncritical acceptance of the orthodox theory that derives man from an anthropoid ape.

The tarsian hypothesis of Wood Jones clearly derives from the earlier views of the embryologist, Hubrecht (1897), which in turn are related to those of the paleontologist, Cope (1885, 1896). Since Cope's views respecting human ancestry have at times been misunderstood, it is worthwhile paying them some attention. He has been accused of deriving man directly from the lemurs. Actually, he derived not only man but also the anthropoids from an extinct group represented by the fossil tarsioid *Anaptomorphus homunculus* (identified as *Tetonius homunculus* by Gregory, 1922) of the Early Eocene. It is true that Cope regarded his *Anaptomorphus* as a lemur, but at that time no distinction had been made between the Lemuroidea and the Tarsioidea, so that both the living *Tarsius* and fossil forms now classified as tarsioids were regarded as merely varieties of lemurs. Notwithstanding, Cope (1885) had a clear recognition of the true status of *Anaptomorphus,* for he noted that it bore a great resemblance to *Tarsius,* "perhaps its nearest ally among the lemurs." He concluded that "there is no doubt but that the genus Anaptomorphus is the most simian lemur yet discovered, and probably represents the family from which the anthropoid monkeys and man were derived." Later (1896), he clearly stated his position: "I have advanced the . . . hypothesis that the Anthropomorpha (which include man and the anthropoid apes) have been derived directly from the lemurs, without passing through the monkeys proper. I have expressed, and now maintain as a working hypothesis, that all the Anthropomorpha were descended from the Eocene lemuroids. In my system the Anthropomorpha includes the two families Hominidae and Simiidae . . . It is then highly probable that Homo is descended from some form of the Anthropomorpha now extinct, and probably unknown at present. . . ."

Hubrecht (1897), giving especial although by no means exclusive consideration to embryological data, built upon Cope's idea. To begin with, he recognized that *Anaptomorphus* and *Tarsius* are not only closely related, but that they are not lemurs at all; and he thought them more nearly allied to the monkeys, anthropoids, and man, being intermediate between the latter animals and "an unknown type of Insectivore." As for the lemurs, he banished them from the order Primates—a thesis later elaborated by Wood Jones (1929b, 1948). Next, like Cope, Hubrecht thought it probable that man and the anthropoids are only distantly allied to the Old World monkeys, being more directly related to *Anaptomorphus*. His conclusions respecting man may be summarized as follows: ". . . I would not feel justified in contradicting a hypothetic view . . . according to which a direct ancestor of the anthropoids and man . . . must have sprung directly from a Mesozoic insectivorous ancestor, small in size, but already more or less erect in posture, provided with a spacious brain cavity, with a decidua reflexa, and with a discoid placenta of the Erinacean type of development . . . As to the erect posture . . . we are in no way obliged to follow the general belief that this has been a comparatively late acquirement of our ancestors! Nor that they must needs first have passed through a stage similar to the actual stage of one of our living anthropoid apes." One can recognize this general theme in the core of Wood Jones' more highly elaborated hypothesis.

The paleontologist, Osborn, was originally an adherent to the orthodox, anthropoid-ape version of human origin. Starting in 1927, however, he published a series of papers in which he attacked that theory as "greatly weakened by recent evidence" and advocated "an independent line of Dawn Man ancestors, springing from an Oligocene neutral stock, which also gave rise independently to the anthropoid apes." While agreeing that the line of man's descent passed through an arboreal stage, he believed that the latter did not approach that of the anthropoids, and he predicted the discovery of Oligocene "pro-men" with pro-human rather than pro-anthropoid limbs.

The paleontologist Broom, who has so greatly enriched paleoanthropology by his discoveries of South African primates, has recently stated: "The view supported in the present work is that the line which led to Man and the Australopithecines arose in Lower Oligocene or possibly Upper Eocene from a pre-Anthropoid. This view is essentially similar to that of Osborn and probably near to that of Wood Jones" (Broom and Schepers, 1946). His accompanying genealogical chart definitely assigns not only the inadequately studied Australopithecinae but also the ambiguous *Gigantopithecus* to the human line of phylogeny. As to the more immediate ancestry of man, Broom declared "that we may regard it as almost certain that man arose from a Pliocene member of the Australopithecines probably very near to Australopithecus itself; and that the resemblances between the higher anthropoids and some types of man are merely due to parallel developments and do not indicate any close affinity." It is worth noting that he had previously derived the human line, like Gregory and Abel, from a Miocene dryopithecine.

The Generalized Characters of Man and Their Phylogenetic Significance

It is thus seen that there has been and still is no lack of disagreement respecting the probable course of man's ancestry. Probably the most salient weakness of the orthodox, anthropoid-ape theory is that it concentrates almost exclusively upon the resemblances between man and the anthropoids, the pongids or great apes in particular, at the same time minimizing or ignoring the many differences which exist between them. Most of its proponents ignore the fact that in a considerable number of important characters man can only be regarded as essentially generalized or unspecialized, in the light of current comparative-anatomical philosophy. In these characters man finds his counterparts not in the anthropoid apes but in animals that are clearly to be regarded on both paleontological and comparative-anatomical grounds as more primitive, namely, such primates as the monkeys and prosimians, and even mammals of other orders. In other words, in many characters, and particularly in those that define an anthropoid ape, the anthropoids (and the great ones especially) can only be considered as far more specialized than man. In view of this, and even allowing for the possibility of extensive reversal of evolution—which most present-day students of evolution regard as possible but extremely improbable (see J. Huxley, 1942)—it has been exceedingly difficult for some investigators—to note only Hubrecht, Boule, Wood Jones, Osborn, and Broom—to believe that the hominid line of descent could have developed from an animal that would be classified as an anthropoid ape.

A considerable part of the disagreement is undoubtedly one of semantics. For there is no general agreement as to the lines of zoological demarcation between a monkey, an anthropoid, and a hominid. When would an animal cease to be a monkey and become an anthropoid or a hominid, or when would an anthropoid become a hominid? There probably are no true, natural lines of demarcation, if we are correct in regarding evolution as a continuous, gradual process. Some, like the paleontologists, would stake their diagnoses upon the teeth—a dangerous procedure, if for no other reason than that teeth alone do not make the animal; nor do they, in the primates at least, foretell such things as limb structure, as witness the Early Miocene forms recently discovered in Kenya (see Le Gros Clark, 1948a, b). If we make absolute size of brain the distinctive criterion, as Keith (1948) has done, then man *must* have passed through an anthropoid-ape stage in his evolution, whatever were the other anatomical and the physiological attributes of his immediate precursors. The only manner in which he might have avoided such a stage would have been through evolution by extreme jumps or saltations, an interpretation not in accord with the current views of most geneticists. In any event, such a measure of zoological status is meaningless and does not help in solving the present problem. For one thing, if carried to its logical conclusion, it would debar the Hylobatidae from the anthropoids, and it would otherwise merely serve to confuse the issue. It is the ensemble of bodily characters with which we have to deal, and not the brain alone. Moreover, as noted earlier, it is characteristic of the order Primates as a whole and not of the anthropoids and man alone that the brain exhibits a tendency toward enlargement, both absolute and relative. It may be that the brain has made man what he is, but, zoologically, the brain alone does not make an animal a man.

To me, an anthropoid ape, extinct or living, primitive or otherwise, would possess an ensemble of characters (of skull, dentition, trunk, and limbs, and of soft parts as well as hard ones), that would definitely allocate him to the group of living anthropoids, although in many details of his constitution he would not necessarily bear complete resemblance to any of the present-day forms. The same criteria would apply in the definitions of monkey and hominid. Nor do I believe that the more exuberant protagonists of the anthropoid-ape theory, such as Gregory, Keith, and Weinert, would be in any real disagreement on this point. When they think of their anthropoid ancestors they are thinking of creatures that would be definitely recognized as closely akin to the living anthropoids, more specifically to the great apes, and certainly Gregory (and Keith as well, at least until recent years) also thinks of them as brachiators. The above concepts of monkey, anthropoid, and hominid may not find universal acceptance, but they will at least facilitate discussion. Too often writers have used these terms loosely, without making clear their meanings, or they have used them inconsistently, with resultant misunderstanding and confusion.

The anatomist, Le Gros Clark, wrote in 1934 that "palaeontological evidence leads inevitably to the conclusion that the progenitors of the Hominidae, even if they avoided the specializations distinctive of the modern large apes . . . must have possessed features of the skull and jaws, teeth, brain, and limbs by which they would be quite consistently referred to the category of the anthropomorphous apes. That Man has been derived from a form which—without imposing any strain on commonly recognized definitions—can be properly called an 'anthropoid ape' is a statement which no longer admits of doubt." At first blush this pronouncement appears to agree with those uttered by Gregory in the same year. But a perusal of Le Gros Clark's writings will make it clear that his anthropoid ancestor of man is a very different sort of animal than that envisaged by Gregory. It is what some would term a "generalized" anthropoid ape, one lacking among other things those adaptive specializations concomitant with brachiation. I must confess that it is difficult for me to classify such an animal, and to decide whether it should properly be termed a monkey or an anthropoid ape. To me, it is an animal in taxonomic purgatory. It must be stated, however, that Le Gros Clark would probably be the first to admit that his idea of what constitutes an anthropoid ape may well be open to question, for in an earlier passage he took due note of the semantic difficulties involved in the use of this and similar terms in evolutionary discussion. The same sort of difficulties arise in evaluating Weidenreich's concept of an "anthropoid."

Le Gros Clark (1934) has claimed that "a too rigid conception of zoological classification has evidently been a fruitful source of misinterpretation in the past." This may well be true. But it might also be said, and with equal justice, that a too fluid conception of taxonomy has been and still is a fertile source of misinterpretation. In fact, it would seem desirable, in any event at the present state of our knowledge, to restrict the application of such terms as "hominid," "anthropoid," and "monkey," to those actual fossils (and conceptual ancestors) that really meet the chief criteria needed for admission to any of these living groups—although I admit the difficulty of gaining universal acceptance of such criteria. All fossils that are clearly transitional or ambiguous in character would automatically be denied the use of such terms; and they could well be given new ones, even though these might be only temporary. Here I have in mind such forms, at the moment of uncertain status, as *Parapithecus, Propliopithecus, Gigantopithecus,* the Australopithecinae, and the Early Miocene primates of East Africa. I make this suggestion in no spirit of frivolity, and I do so at the risk of being labelled an unmitigated "splitter" by taxonomists. But in view of our current semantic difficulties, it is obvious that some common ground of definition must be sought.

Returning to the main question, it is my own belief that a nonanthropoid concept of hominid ancestry—using the term "anthropoid" as I have defined it above—is in closer agreement with known facts than is the orthodox theory and that it has been greatly strengthened by data accumulated in recent years. In other words, I believe that the theory which derives the hominid line of descent, at a reasonably early date, from some sort of generalized catarrhine primate, rather than from an anthropoid ape of any sort, is the most reasonable theory in the light of available knowledge. Thus, in a general way, my views have more in common with those of Boule and Osborn than with those of Abel, Gregory, Keith, and Weinert. Nor do I believe that they actually differ fundamentally from those of Schultz and Le Gros Clark. I have arrived at the above conclusion not only upon comparative-anatomical grounds but also from consideration of paleontological evidence. I am particularly impressed by the many points wherein man—both living and fossil—differs from the anthropoids. More precisely, I am impressed by the numerous characters in which man appears clearly to be more primitive or more generalized than the anthropoids, especially the great apes. Space does not permit other than their incomplete listing and precludes a complete discussion even of those; this must be done elsewhere.

Some of these more important generalized or primitive characters of man follow:

1. *The sequence of eruption of the deciduous teeth, involving more particularly the early eruption of the canines* (Schultz, 1944). In man, gibbon, and catarrhine monkeys, the milk canine erupts before the second milk molar, whereas in the great apes it is the last milk tooth to appear. Schultz thought it most probable that the sequence in man, gibbon, and monkeys represents the "original condition."

2. *The tendency toward late obliteration of the cranial sutures* (Bolk, 1913). Bolk has shown that late obliteration should be regarded as a primitive condition. In this tendency, man agrees essentially with the platyrrhines and certain cercopithecid monkeys, whereas early closure occurs in the anthropoid apes.

3. *The anterior convergence of the mandibular rami.* Marked convergence, as seen in the fossil Early Oligocene catarrhine, *Parapithecus* (cf. Werth, 1918), and in extant prosimians, is undoubtedly the generalized condition (Figure 2, A). From this there probably developed, on the one hand, the more curved, less sharply convergent form of mandibular arcade—foreshadowed in such platyrrhines as the Hapalidae (Figure 2, B) and culminating in man (Figure 2, E)—and, on the other hand, the more extremely specialized arrangement with parallel tooth rows—as seen in the anthropoid apes and most of the Cercopithecidae (Figure 2, C, D).

4. *The absence of a backward-projecting "basal plate" or "simian shelf" uniting the two halves of the mandible at the symphysial region.* In being totally exempt from this specialization, man—both living and fossil—resembles the Hylobatidae and the platyrrhine monkeys, in which a

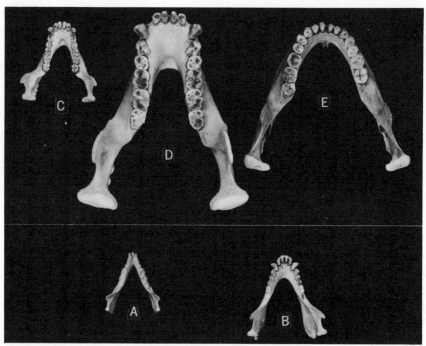

FIGURE 2. Mandibles of various primates, seen from above, to show the angle
between the horizontal rami and the shape of the tooth rows. A, tarsier (*Tarsius*);
B, marmoset (*Oedipomidas*); C, langur (*Semnopithecus*); D, gorilla; E, man
(Negro). C, D, and E are reduced to the same scale; A and B are relatively twice
as large.

simian shelf is entirely absent or at best incipient (Figure 3, A, C, F, G);
and such a structure also is regularly lacking in *Tarsius* and in lemurs
other than the Indridae. Moreover, a simian shelf is not present in the
Early Oligocene catarrhines, *Parapithecus* and *Propliopithecus,* or in the
australopithecine *Plesianthropus* (Broom and Robinson, 1949), or in the
recently discovered East African Early Miocene forms (MacInnes, 1943;
Le Gros Clark, 1948b). This buttress is present, however, in the three
great apes, the cercopithecid monkeys, and the highly specialized lemurine family Indridae (Figure 3, B, D, H); yet it can be relatively quite
small in some cercopithecids, notably in the Semnopithecinae (Figure 3,
E). It is well-developed in most of the Dryopithecinae.

  5. *The comparatively great distance between thorax and pelvis.* Of
this, Schultz (1936) has said, "This large space between thorax and pelvis
in man (even larger in all lower catarrhines) facilitates lateral flexibility
of the trunk. In this respect man retains the condition in the gibbon,
whereas the great apes are most extremely specialized."

  6. *The quadrupedal posture of the hand in which the palm, with ex-*

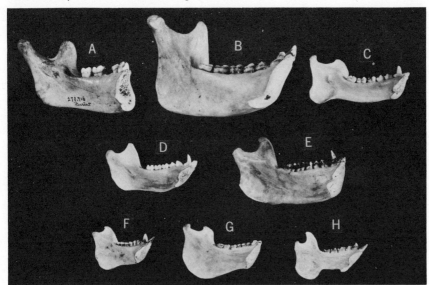

FIGURE 3. Lingual (medial) view of the left half of the mandible in various primates, to show the form of the symphysial region. A, man (Buriat); B, orangutan; C, siamang (*Symphalangus*); D, guenon (*Cercopithecus*); E, proboscis monkey (*Nasalis*); F, uakari (*Cacajao*); G, woolly monkey (*Lagothrix*); H, sifaka (*Propithecus*). The specimens are all oriented according to their main alveolar horizons and the midsagittal plane. All are reduced to the same scale.

tended fingers, is placed against the ground (Straus, 1940, 1941a). This primitive, palmigrade type of quadrupedal posture is common to man, the Old World monkeys, and (on occasion) gibbons, and, with certain modifications, the New World monkeys (Figure 4). The three great apes, however, exhibit a highly specialized type of posture when on all fours, with hand but slightly dorsoflexed and with fingers flexed, so that the body rests upon the middle phalanges (Figure 4).

7. *The comparatively generalized proportions of the hand, particularly relating to the thumb.* The human thumb (metacarpal + phalanges) is comparatively long relative to the other digital rays (metacarpal + phalanges, e.g., of III), its proportional length being closely similar to those found in the more generalized platyrrhines (e.g., Hapalidae, Aotinae, *Cebus*). All of the anthropoids, however, have relatively short thumbs. The Old World monkeys of the subfamily Cercopithecinae are intermediate between man and the platyrrhines on the one side and the anthropoids on the other side, whereas those of the subfamily Semnopithecinae more closely resemble the anthropoids. Length ratios involving, separately, the metacarpals and the phalanges, lead to the same general conclusions (see also Schultz, 1930). Studies on the external hand, comparing total thumb length with total hand length, have produced essen-

MACAQUE

HUMAN INFANT

A.H.S.   CHIMPANZEE

Figure 4. Adult macaque (Macaca), human infant, and adult chimpanzee, in the quadrupedal posture. (Human infant after Hrdlička, 1928). (After Schultz, 1936).

tially similar results (Schultz, 1924, 1926, 1933b, 1936; Midlo, 1943); here, the thumbs of some catarrhine monkeys, notably baboons, are relatively as long as that of man.

There can be no reasonable doubt that a long thumb (relative to the other fingers) is a generalized pithecoid character, or that its marked relative reduction in such animals as the anthropoids, some of the Semnopithecinae, and certain platyrrhines, is an extreme specialization correlated with addiction to brachiation (Straus, 1942b). Ontogenetic studies (Schultz, 1924, 1926, 1933b) also support the conclusion that a relatively long thumb is a generalized pithecoid feature. In this connection, it may be noted that Le Gros Clark (1934) has pointed out that "in many of the Old World monkeys . . . the proportions of the digits approximate closely to those of the human hand (which is indeed a generalized mammalian feature)."

8. *Essentially generalized features in the hand musculature, especially that of the thumb* (Straus, 1942a, b, 1946). (1) A morphologically complete and functional long flexor tendon to the thumb is a basal mammalian as well as primate character. It is constant in prosimians, platyrrhines (except the highly specialized spider monkey, *Ateles*), the Old World monkey subfamily Cercopithecinae, the Hylobatidae, and man (Figure 5, A, D, I, J). It is normally deficient in *Ateles* (apparently always) (Figure 5, B, C), some of the Old World subfamily Semnopithecinae (regularly in *Colobus*) (Figure 5, E), and the three great apes (deficient in over half of the chimpanzees, nearly three-fourths of the gorillas, and over nine-tenths of the orang utans, studied) (Figure 5, F, G, H).

(2) The short, intrinsic, volar muscles of the thumb are regularly well-developed in man, the Hylobatidae, the Old World monkeys (except *Colobus*), the New World monkeys (except *Ateles*), and the prosimians. In the Hylobatidae, however, they tend toward a high degree of peculiar specialization. These muscles, save the adductor pollicis, are inclined to be weakly developed or even lacking in the three great apes, *Colobus*, and *Ateles*.

There is no doubt that the reduction of the thumb musculature in these genera is correlated with the abbreviation of the bony thumb, and that they are in turn associated with brachiation. The fact that the Hylobatidae have avoided these regressive specializations of the pollex can probably be explained by the fact that they have become adapted to brachiation in a manner somewhat different from that of the great apes; notwithstanding, the hylobatid thumb exhibits its own peculiar specializations (Straus, 1940, 1941b, 1942b).

9. *The generalized architecture of the ischial region, including the*

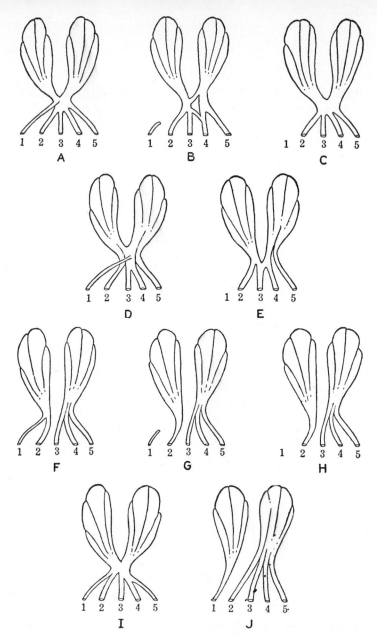

FIGURE 5. Diagrams of the deep, long flexor muscle of the fingers (flexor digitorum profundus + pollicis longus) in various pithecoid primates. A, capuchin (*Cebus*); B and C, spider monkey (*Ateles*), different specimens; D, macaque (*Macaca*); E, guereza (*Colobus*); from data by Polak, 1908); F–H, great anthropoid apes (orangutan, chimpanzee, gorilla), showing three types of arrangement common to all three genera; I, gibbon (*Hylobates*); J, man. This illustration is especially designed to show the enfeebled state or functional deficiency or even complete absence of the tendon to the thumb in *Ateles, Colobus,* and the three great apes. The radial head of the muscle is to the left in each diagram, the ulnar head to the right. The humeral heads of origin are not shown. (After Straus, 1942b).

absence of callosities. Callosities overlying the ischial tuberosities are a catarrhine specialization. Highly developed callosities are found in all Old World monkeys and Hylobatidae, and less developed ones occur in many chimpanzees and in occasional orang utans and gorillas (Schultz, 1936). They are never found in prosimians, platyrrhines, or man. Miller (1945), who studied these structures and the surrounding region in great detail, concluded: "The preceding study of the ischial region suggests that the typical callosity found in the Old World monkeys and gibbons represents a specialized adaptation acquired after these primates had begun their separate evolutionary trend. From the present investigations it is not possible to determine whether the structure found in the great apes represents a typical callosity in the process of evolutionary disappearance or whether it is a parallel development which does not imply genetic relationship with the lower catarrhines. The lack of callosities gives the ischial region of man a superficial resemblance to the generalized arrangement found in the New World monkeys. There is no evidence in this work to suggest that an ischial callosity of any sort was present in the ancestral human stock."

10. *A relatively long midtarsal segment in the foot* (Morton, 1924). Of this, Morton stated: "The pattern of the human mid-tarsal bone[s] resembles more closely that of the gibbon or of the lower primates than of the gorilla or chimpanzee. It does not show the anteroposterior shortening that characterizes this area in the latter animals. . . The mid-tarsal pattern of the gibbon resembles that of the monkeys; in the great apes it is decidedly shortened, while man appears with the more primitive pattern . . . Apparently man could have avoided this shortening only by having separated from the great ape stock before it had occurred."

11. *Essentially generalized features in the leg and foot musculature* (Straus, 1946). (1) The plantaris is a basal mammalian muscle. Among primates, it is usually present in prosimians, platyrrhines, catarrhine monkeys, and man. In the anthropoid apes, however, it exhibits a distinct trend toward complete disappearance (absent, according to Loth, 1931, in 57 per cent of 56 chimpanzees, 96.3 per cent of 27 orang utans, 100 per cent of 25 gorillas, and 100 per cent of 20 gibbons). In man (although it lacks its primitive connection with the plantar aponeurosis), the muscle displays a presence of about 90 per cent. Thus man is in marked contrast with the anthropoids, showing a more generalized condition that agrees essentially with that in monkeys and prosimians.

(2) In the primitive mammalian condition, the tendons of the two long flexor muscles of the toes—the m. flexor digitorum fibularis (flexor hallucis longus) and m. flexor digitorum tibialis (flexor digitorum longus) —are fused and evenly distributed to the five digits; so that a separa-

tion of the two muscles is secondary and a specialization (Glaesmer, 1910). The generalized arrangement is found in prosimians, in which each long flexor typically supplies all five toes (Figure 6, A). The muscles typically are still intimately united and broadly distributed in platyrrhines, especially in the Cebidae (Figure 6, B)—whereas the process of dissociation is more advanced in the Hapalidae. In the Cercopithecidae, the fibularis is characteristically reduced to toes I, III, and IV and the tibialis to I, II, and V (although a tibial component to IV is very frequent) (Figure 6, C). Among the Hylobatidae, the fibularis still shows a broad primitive distribution (typically to all toes except V), whereas the tibialis is usually limited to I, II, and V (Figure 6, D). In all three of the great anthropoids one encounters a very advanced degree of specialization, for the two muscles are commonly quite separate, the fibularis serving only toes I, III, and IV and the tibialis only II and V in both the chimpanzee and gorilla (Figure 6, E); conditions are similar in the orang utan, but in addition the tendon for the great toe is nearly always absent (Straus, 1930, 1942b). Man, however, shows a much more primitive type of arrangement, for the long flexor tendons are always closely united, the fibularis typically supplying toes I, II, and III, and the tibialis all except the hallux (Figure 6, F). Thus man exhibits a considerable resemblance to the Hylobatidae, the monkeys (particularly the Cebidae), and the prosimians, but none at all to the great apes.

(3) The quadratus plantae muscle is an archaic structure, being the mammalian equivalent of the tarsal head of the long digital flexor of urodeles and reptiles. Although it has disappeared in some mammals, it has a broad distribution, being present in monotremes, some marsupials, some edentates, most carnivores, most rodents, a few bats, and some insectivores. It is well-developed in Tupaioidea. Among the primates, it is almost always present in man and the two groups of monkeys (Figure 7, C, B), whereas it has never been noted in either the Hylobatidae or the Lemuroidea, and only once in *Tarsius*. Among the great apes, it exhibits a distinct trend toward disappearance (Figure 7, A), having been found in about one-third of the gorillas, two-fifths of the orang utans, and slightly more than half of the chimpanzees studied (in some chimpanzees where it is present, moreover, it is quite degenerate, being entirely without function as a digital flexor.) Here again the anthropoids display an important specialization entirely lacking in man.

Apropos of the above facts, it may be noted that Wells (1931a) concluded that "in respect of the muscular system of the foot, the ancestors of man were more closely similar to the existing baboons than to the existing anthropoid apes," and I have already made a somewhat similar statement (in Schultz, 1936, p. 441). (The statements relating to the long

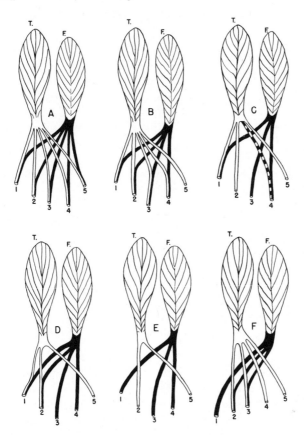

FIGURE 6. Diagrams to show the various types of distributions of the tendons of the long flexor muscles of the toes (flexor digitorum tibialis, T.; flexor digitorum fibularis, F.) in primates. A, prosimians, typical; B, platyrrhine monkeys (Cebidae), typical; C, catarrhine monkeys (Cercopithecidae), typical; D, gibbons and siamangs (Hylobatidae), typical; E, great apes (Pongidae), typical (in the orang utan, the tendon to the great toe is regularly absent); F, man, typical.

flexors of the toes and to the quadratus plantae muscle of man and other primates are based upon my own dissections, plus data taken from the literature.)

12. *Absence of excessive forelimb development.* In the primates, excepting only all of the anthropoid apes and a few highly specialized platyrrhine monkeys, the forelimbs (as expressed by the intermembral index, i.e., length of humerus + radius in percentage of length of femur + tibia) are shorter than the hindlimbs (see Mollison, 1910; Schultz, 1930, 1937). A relatively short forelimb is the primitive lemurine condition (Straus and Wislocki, 1932), and it is reasonable to assume that it

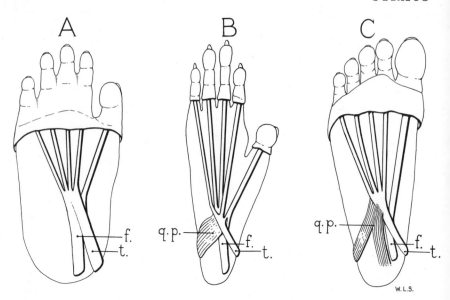

FIGURE 7.   The quadratus plantae muscle in the feet of catarrhine primates. A, gorilla (normally absent); B, Old World monkeys (normally present) q.p., quadratus plantae; f., tendon of flexor digitorum fibularis; t., tendon of flexor digitorum tibialis. (After Straus, 1930.)

was the primitive pithecoid condition as well. In the anthropoid apes, the arms are so long that the intermembral index always surpasses 100, being smallest in the chimpanzee and highest in the orang utan and siamang (Schultz, 1937) (See Figure 4). Man (various races), with an average index of only about 70 (Schultz, 1937), displays close similarity to certain catarrhine monkeys of the subfamily Semnopithecinae (cf. Mollison, 1910; Schultz, 1930; Washburn, 1942a), as well as to some platyrrhines and lemuriform lemurs (cf. Mollison, 1910; Schultz, 1930; Straus and Wislocki, 1932); but the factors involved in producing these similar ratios undoubtedly are not identical in the different primates. In any event, man has avoided the specialization of excessive lengthening of the forelimbs common to all of the anthropoid apes. The intermembral index of Neanderthal man, moreover, was similar to that of modern man (Boule, 1911–13).

The absence of excessive forelimb development in man as contrasted with the anthropoids is further attested by a comparison of the transverse diameters of the heads of the humerus and femur. In this ratio man bears a greater resemblance to the Old World monkeys than to any of the anthropoid apes (see Schultz, 1936).

13. *A primitive sequence of epiphysial union.* Washburn (1946) has

shown that when the sequence of epiphysial union is analysed by regions, man is identical with the lemur and closely resembles the hedgehog and Old World monkeys; contrariwise, he is quite different from the gorilla. In other words, man exhibits, with some relatively slight modifications, the generalized mammalian pattern of union. Schultz (1944), moreover, has pointed out that in sequence of union there is a basic agreement between the Old World monkeys, gibbons, and man, and that the three great apes differ from these especially by evidencing a tendency towards early closure of the proximal epiphysis of the humerus. I venture to suggest the possibility that this early closure at the shoulder may be a specialization correlated with brachiation in heavy-bodied animals.

14. *A comparatively primitive plan of dermatoglyphics.* Midlo and Cummins (1942), after an extensive and detailed study of the palmar and plantar dermatoglyphics of primates, concluded: "Old World monkeys, with the exception of langur, exhibit least specialization of dermatoglyphics; in respect to expanse and character of patterns they have even exaggerated signs of primitiveness . . . The New World monkeys are diverse . . . Gibbon is the most specialized simian. The three great apes and man present specializations which follow different directions. While these divergent specializations render comparison difficult, the order of increasing specialization indicated by the pooled evidence is orang utan, gorilla or chimpanzee, man. Especially in adherence to the basic plan of configurations, man is even more primitive than the orang; inasmuch as that plan is so fundamental a characteristic, it is concluded that man stemmed from an ancestral stock more primitive than any recent ape, having dermatoglyphic traits more closely allied to those of the monkeys." (Also see Cummins, 1946.)

15. *Absence of a sexual skin in the female.* A female sexual skin, correlated with changes in the reproductive cycle, is a peculiar specialization found only among the catarrhines. Nothing comparable to it has ever been noted in either the platyrrhines or the prosimians (see Asdell, 1946). It occurs in all three of the great anthropoid apes (found in the gorilla by Noback, 1936, and Raven, 1936b; in the orang utan by Schultz, 1938; for the chimpanzee, see Zuckerman, 1933, and Asdell, 1946). It has a curious distribution in the Old World monkeys. According to Zuckerman (1933), it is present in some members of the subfamily Cercopithecinae and not in others, a few genera (*Macaca, Cercopithecus*) even exhibiting specific differences; and it apparently does not occur at all in the subfamily Semnopithecinae. The Hylobatidae are usually regarded as lacking a female sexual skin, but their present status is uncertain; for it remains to be determined whether the labial changes noted by Carpenter (1941) during the menstrual cycle of *Hylobates lar* actually constitute evidence

of a sexual skin. As Zuckerman (1933) has pointed out, the fact that there is no trace of a sexual skin in the human female indicates that the genus *Homo* was derived from animals lacking such a structure.

Other, similarly significant, generalized human characters may be briefly noted: The comparatively small permanent canine teeth; the "open" orbit, with usually large orbital fissures; a sphenoparietal junction at the pterion (see Ashley Montagu, 1933); certain features in the internal architecture of the mandible (particularly the high degree of curvature of the "neutral zone" between the upper and lower trajectorial systems of compact bone and of the alveolar canal) (Woollard and Harpman, 1938); the retention of a superficial rectus abdominis ("pyramidalis") muscle; certain relatively generalized characters of the pelvis, more particularly of the ilium (such as the comparatively large size of the sacral surface and of the anteacetabular spine) (cf. Straus, 1929); and the absence of laryngeal pouches or air sacs. Numerous additional points could be added, and perhaps even more if we knew as much about the detailed anatomy of the so-called "lower" primates as we do about that of man and the anthropoids.

Most of these essentially generalized or primitive characters of man are shared, in various degrees, with the monkeys, not only with those of the Old World but also to be a very considerable extent with those of the New World. These characters therefore are in essence monkey-like and not anthropoid. Yet it must be noted that many of them also occur in the gibbon and siamang, which points up the plainly evident fact that the Hylobatidae are far more primitive than the great apes and consequently possess a much larger share of basal, ancestral Old World or protocatarrhine characters. Despite their inclusion within the term "anthropoid apes" they are properly placed in a family apart from that of the great apes or Pongidae; for there is much to justify the statement of Keith (1934) that "the gibbon is a primitive Old World monkey whose body at an early date became transformed to serve the needs of the orthograde arboreal posture."

Of 42 significant human characters that can be reasonably regarded, at the present state of our knowledge, as more generalized or more primitive than their counterparts in the great apes, 29 are shared with the Old World monkeys, 24 with the New World monkeys, 19 with the Hylobatidae, 17 with the lemurs, and 16 with *Tarsius*.

That man shares so many generalized characters with the New World monkeys or platyrrhines has a bearing upon the probable nature of the ancestral Old World primates or proto-catarrhines. Some authorities (e.g., Le Gros Clark, 1934) have thought it probable that the two pithecoid infraorders had a common origin and that the catarrhines passed through a platyrrhine stage but diverged early from the stock that gave rise to the modern New World forms. Others have argued for a diphyletic origin of the two pithecoid groups (e.g., Gregory, 1922). Whatever the precise phylogenetic relationship of platyrrhines and catarrhines, it seems not unlikely that the ancestral catarrhines possessed many primitive features still present in modern platyrrhines, particularly the more generalized ones—possibly a common inheritance from primitive more tarsioid ancestors. Such a reasonable assumption would explain the platyrrhine resemblances of man with respect to generalized features without at all denying the probability of parallel evolution where specialized characters are concerned (e.g., the striking similarity in the basal fissuration pattern of the cerebral cortex, and the common possession of a caput breve m. bicipitis femoris).

Some generalized hominid characters, as Wood Jones has repeatedly emphasized, reach back to the basal primate stock. They link the human line with such forms as the tarsioids, lemuroids, tupaioids, and even other orders of mammals. Certain of these characters have been noted above.

The extent to which "fetalization" or "paedomorphosis," as postulated by Bolk (1926) and others (most recently by Dart, 1948a), has played a role in the evolution of man cannot as yet be stated. As was long since pointed out by Cope (1896), some of man's generalized features can be interpreted as resulting from ontogenetic retardation, but this hypothesis will most assuredly not explain more than a fraction of them (also see Schultz, 1927).

That man is a member of the catarrhine group of primates admits of no reasonable doubt. But that the hominids are descended from animals that could be classified as anthropoid apes, on the other hand, has in no wise been established, the categorical assertions of some writers notwithstanding. Indeed, the large number of basal primate characters which man possesses, and which are absent in the anthropoids, challenges the rationality of such a conclusion. Rather, they strongly suggest that the phylogenetic line leading to man had become independent of the primitive catarrhine stock before there were actual anthropoid apes—not only at a pre-dryopithecine stage, but even before the differentiation of the Hylobatidae. And the fact that in many of the characters, or rather evolutionary trends, shared with the anthropoid apes man is clearly less specialized than one or more, or even all of them, including the Hylobatidae (see, e.g., Schultz, 1936), adds force to such a suggestion.

It may be permissible to speculate briefly upon the nature of those primitive catarrhines from which the line leading to man was derived. For various reasons, one can conceive them as having been, in total structure, much more like monkeys than like anthropoid apes, although of course not at all identical with any existing form. But in view of the semantic rules that I have already suggested, it may be improper to label them "monkeys." They can be imagined, however, as resembling Old World monkeys in general structure (although lacking the specializations of living cercopithecids), but with certain likenesses to modern platyrrhines (as in some characters of skull, hand, foot, and pelvis). Indeed, although one might be loath to regard them as true monkeys, they might be thought of as primitive monkey-like animals that in some respects were not too far above the status of generalized tarsioids. This view would be quite in harmony with the characters of the mandible of *Parapithecus*, perhaps the oldest of known catarrhines, from the Early Oligocene of Fayum.

These presumed earliest representatives of the hominid line of ancestry may consequently be visualized as essentially unspecialized quadrupeds, capable of both terrestrial and arboreal life, and possessed of expanding brains, short tails, and generalized extremities. In their evolution they avoided brachiating specializations and early became terrestrial bipeds, capitalizing upon the tendency toward part-time erectness of the trunk that is characteristic of all primates. Thus they never passed through an actual anthropoid-ape stage, but avoided the distinctive anthropoid specializations of skull, teeth, trunk, and limbs. The inevitable specializations of a brachiating mode of life, moreover, are the fundamental hallmarks of all anthropoid apes. Indeed, the crucial point in the present matter is whether the creatures that gave rise to the hominid line of phylogeny were or were not brachiators. It is quite probable that they indulged in some swinging by the arms and in that sense might be regarded as primitive brachiators, for many catarrhine monkeys indulge in occasional brachiation (Wells, 1931a), and some of the Semnopithecinae, notably *Colobus*, have committed themselves so far that they show adaptive, degenerative specialization of the hand—although they are not so addicted to this mode of locomotion as to have evolved the other specializations, such as the extreme lengthening of the forelimbs, common to all habitual brachiators. Apparently the hand is the first major structure to become adapted to brachiation. Even the Hylobatidae, which seemingly have become adapted differently than other brachiators, exhibit striking manual specializations. That outright, habitual brachiation was a necessary prelude to the terrestrial bipedalism of man, as Keith once believed and as others still imagine, appears to be an illusion. The adult gorilla, with its peculiar quadrupedal posture, is a perfect example of a brachiator come to earth. Its undoubted brachiating ancestry has offered no evolutionary inducement to bipedal erectness. I have repeatedly pointed out elsewhere that not only is there no evidence of a brachiating stage in man's ancestry but that available evidence clearly points to the absence of such a stage (Straus, 1940, 1941b, 1942b, also see Le Gros Clark, 1947a).

We have no idea, of course, of the precise road taken in the evolution of man. *Pithecanthropus, Sinanthropus,* and perhaps *Meganthropus,* already were true men (indeed, probably assignable to the genus *Homo* as well), but all that went before them remains a void. It is quite possible that the Australopithecinae represent a morphological if not a genetic stage in hominid evolution, but one must await a dispassionate assessment of their status. And the Early Miocene primates of Kenya may also be a part of the story. It is significant that neither of these fossil groups suggests that there was a true anthropoid-ape, brachiating stage, with its distinctive specializations, in the course of human evolution.

The cardinal points wherein man and the anthropoids show special affinities are the relatively large brain, the broadened thorax, the segmentally shortened trunk, the complete absence of an external bony tail, and various dental features. But the first four of these are certainly not decisive indications of close relationship, and I question the decisive nature of the dental features alone. The tendency towards evolutionary enlargement of the brain is a common primate character; thus its comparatively excessive size may well be a parallel development in anthropoids and man (as witness the remarkable parallelism in cortical fissuration of catarrhines and platyrrhines). A broad thorax is apparently a postural adaptation of wide mammalian distribution lacking phylogenetic significance (Winge, 1895). Some tendency towards numerical reduction of the thoracolumbar column is exhibited by all groups of primates save the Lorisidae and Tarsioidea, and a drastically abbreviated bony tail is no exclusive property of man and the anthropoids, not even among the catarrhines (Schultz and Straus, 1945). Parallelisms are often developed in animal dentitions (Gregory, 1922); furthermore, there is a growing feeling that the human tooth pattern may be more primitive than that of the anthropoids, instead of vice versa (thus see Weidenreich, 1946, and Le Gros Clark, 1947a).

Nevertheless, if one tentatively accepts the hypothesis of a pre-anthropoid origin of the line leading to the Hominidae—and it matters little whether such pre-anthropoids be visualized as essentially proto-cercopithecids or proto-hylobatids, for the early, ancestral catarrhines may well have been so protean in their genetic constitution that they were incipiently both—it becomes necessary to explain the *special* resemblances between man and the great anthropoid apes. This, I believe, can be done on the basis of *parallelism,* or parallel evolution, through inheritance of detailed characters or genes from a common pool, the generalized, ancestral, pre-anthropoid catarrhine stock. Many of the distinctive characters of man and the great apes are foreshadowed or even paralleled among existing Old World monkeys, which, despite the dictum of Wood Jones to the contrary, are undoubtedly in general the most primitive of living catarrhines; it therefore seems reasonable to suppose that these characters were already present in, or had their definite genetic bases in, the generalized proto-catarrhine stock.

It is not usually recognized that the Cercopithecidae, despite their superficial uniformity of structure, are highly diversified with respect to various features. Some of these features are peculiar to certain monkeys alone, but others resemble features—specialized or otherwise—often regarded as peculiar to man or to the great apes or to both man and great apes. The frequency of such characters may be very high, so that they are typical of a species or genus, or, more commonly, it may be low and hence atypical. In this connection, it is sufficient here to quote Washburn (1942a), who, after a study of two groups of langurs, stated: "At least it is clear that many characters which have been described as occurring only in the higher catarrhines are present in the lower also."

Thus at least many of the characters common to man and the pongids need not be new characters *per se*, but only *in toto*, in combination, and in frequency. The resemblances between man and the great apes therefore do not necessarily indicate close relationship but can be logically explained on the assumption of parallel independent combinations of genes already existing, or potentially existing, in remote common ancestors. We would actually be dealing with differences in gene frequency and gene combinations. Of course, some of the likenesses probably result from parallel mutations acquired independently after both the hominid and great-ape evolutionary lines had parted company with the parent Old World stock. In the proto-catarrhines, many genes now well established in extant groups, such as the Pongidae and the Hominidae, may have existed in low frequency, or they may have been lethal in their genic environment or gene complex. Some of them might well have been recessive (being later affected by dominance modifiers), or have been in different positions, or even in different chromosomes (with later crossing over). Indeed, we are not yet in a position to know whether the special resemblances between the various catarrhines, such as those between man and the great apes, are due to homologous or nonhomologous genes. Thus, assuming that they are the result of parallel evolution, is such parallelism homologous or superficial? Are the likenesses genotypically similar, or are merely the phenotypes similar but based on different genotypes? Probably we are dealing with characters of both sorts.

In any event, it may be reasonably assumed that parallel selection must have played an important role in the evolution of the Hominidae and the Pongidae. It is not at all difficult to see how such characters as a relatively large brain, a broad thorax, a shortened trunk, and certain dental features—to cite only a few examples—could have adaptive values both for a bipedal, terrestrial mode of life and for a brachiating, arboreal one; although different selection factors would be involved in bringing about these mutual adaptations in the two groups of animals. Hence their independent, parallel origin in the hominids and in the pongids appears to be anything but improbable.

The role of parallelism in primate evolution often is not fully appreciated, although some recent authors, notably Zuckerman (1933), Le Gros Clark (1934), Schultz (1936), Broom (1946), and Gates (1948), have stressed its importance. Darwin (1871) was aware of the possibility of the independent origins of man and anthropoids by "analogous variation" but rejected this as improbable. Mivart (1873a), however, as noted above, found the idea of evolutionary parallelism to be quite acceptable and even necessary. Zuckerman seriously considered the possibility that the common ancestors of all the existing Old World primates transmitted certain evolutionary possibilities that were realized at different times by types which had no closer relationship to each other than descent from a common ancestor—a view quite similar to my own. He concluded that the evidence on hand cannot even deny the possibility of man's independent evolution from a time as early as the Oligocene. Nor is the evidence of parallel evolution at all peculiar to the primates. It is well known, for example, that it has played an important role in the phylogeny of the horses. Even more striking is the recent study of Olson (1944), which strongly suggests that mammals have independently evolved at least four times by parallel development from different types of therapsid reptiles.

It may be objected that if the peculiar likenesses between man and the great anthropoids are to be regarded as the results of parallelism, those between man and other primates—such as the monkeys—some of which I have discussed, should be similarly interpreted. Possibly this is so, but these resemblances are of different grades. Those between man and the great apes chiefly involve highly advanced or specialized characters, whereas those between man and the monkeys for the most part relate to primitive or generalized characters. The hominid-hylobatid resemblances are distributed fairly evenly between both categories. It is not to be denied, however, that some resemblances between man and cercopithecids (such as the normal occurrence of only 12 pairs of ribs: Schultz and Straus, 1945; and the development of a true styloid process, normally in man and exceptionally in the monkeys) may be due to parallelism and be no more indicative of particularly close genetic relationship than are similar special resemblances between man and the hylobatids (such as the normal occurrence of 5 lumbar vertebrae: Schultz and Straus, 1945; and the presence of a chin, in man and *Symphalangus* but not in *Hylo-*

bates) and between the cercopithecids and great apes (such as the presence of a simian shelf; and the absence of an anteacetabular spine: Straus, 1929). Such characters serve to indicate the dangers inherent in an uncritical lumping of resemblances when assessing phylogenetic relationships.

CONCLUSIONS

On the basis of available evidence, it might be concluded that the evolutionary lines leading to each of the four existing major groups or families of catarrhine primates (the Cercopithecidae, the Hominidae, the Hylobatidae, the Pongidae) underwent very early separation from the primitive ancestral proto-catarrhine stock and pursued their independent courses of evolution, so that none of them bears any special close genetic relationship to any other (Figure 8, C). Such an interpretation, which bears a certain but by no means complete resemblance to the concepts of Wood Jones and Broom, cannot be excluded on the basis of existing knowledge. But, as Colbert (1949) has pointed out, the concept of such long, independent evolutionary lines discounts the evolutionary phenomenon of adaptive radiation.

A reasonable compromise would diverge the hominid line somewhere between the points of departure of the cercopithecid and the hylobatid lines from the evolving catarrhine stock (Figure 8, B); although any such diagram is probably an oversimplification. Nor can it take into account evolutionary radiations now extinct. Notwithstanding, this is the concept that I regard as the most reasonable at the present time. Among other things, it has the virtue of best explaining the numerous generalized characters shared by man with the cercopithecids and hylobatids but not with the pongids. In other words, man and the anthropoids appear to be the living products of adaptive radiation accompanied by considerable parallel evolution, of a pre-anthropoid, essentially monkey-like stock. In any instance, the orthodox "family tree" that derives man from a joint anthropoid-hominid line of descent at some point *after* the departure of the hylobatids (Figure 8, A) appears to me to be no longer acceptable. It would involve greater difficulties than the one that I have proposed. For one would have to assume that the common stock from which, of living primates, *only* man and the great apes arose, had made but little progress from a proto-catarrhine or monkey-like stage; and that the anthropoid resemblances of the Hylobatidae and the Pongidae, including those of brachiation, have resulted entirely from parallel mutations with channelled selection. This possibility cannot of course be ruled out, but on the principle of parsimony it seems to me the less acceptable at the present moment.

In conclusion, therefore, I believe that from available evidence it is

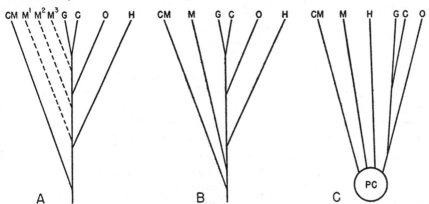

FIGURE 8. Diagrams of "family trees" of the catarrhine primates. CM, catarrhine monkeys or Cercopithecidae; H, Hylobatidae; C, chimpanzee; G, gorilla; O, orang utan; M, man; PC, proto-catarrhines. In diagram A, the three dashed lines (M^1, M^2, and M^3) represent three common variants of the orthodox concept of man's ancestry.

logical to theorize that the phylogenetic line leading to man became independent at a relatively early date, probably no later than the end of the Oligocene, and that the stock from which it arose was far more monkey-like than anthropoid-like. Furthermore, it never passed through an actual anthropoid-ape stage in its evolution. The monkey-like nature of the common ancestral stock of the apes and man is further suggested by the recently unearthed East African Early Miocene forms, which present an intriguing mixture of anthropoid and cercopithecid characters (see Le Gros Clark, 1948a, b, c). It may also be noted that if the Australopithecinae should eventually be proved to be on the road to man, or even upon a closely related bypath, additional support would be afforded not only for this view but also for the view that the Hominidae are more immediately descended from forms that were more monkey-like than anthropoid-like, for some of the known limb bones attributed to the australopithecines are strongly suggestive of cercopithecid rather than anthropoid affinities (thus see Straus, 1948a, and Kern and Straus, 1949). The above is in contradistinction to the view of Cope (1896) and Gregory (1916 et seq.) that the joint anthropoid-hominid line evolved directly from tarsioids without the intervention of a true monkey-like stage.

I wish to emphasize that I am under no illusion that the theory of human ancestry, which I favor at the present time, can in any way be regarded as proven. It is at best merely a working hypothesis whose final evaluation must be left to the future. What I am trying to point out is that, from what we now know, this interpretation appears to be distinctly more valid than the orthodox, anthropoid-ape theory. The ultimate verdict, if there can be a final verdict in such a matter, will rest upon pale-ontological evidence at present lacking; for, with due respect to the Australopithecinae, the gap in the fossil record between man and the other primates remains very great indeed.

What I wish especially to stress is that the problem of man's ancestry is still a decidedly open one, in truth, a riddle. Hence it ill behooves us to accept any premature verdict as final and so to prejudice analysis and interpretation of whatever paleontological material may come to light, as the orthodox theory has so often done and is still doing. One cannot assume that man is a made-over anthropoid ape of any sort, for much of the available evidence is strongly against that assumption.

This publication, which is of the nature of a preliminary report, is a modified version of papers presented at the Sixteenth Annual Meeting of the American Association of Physical Anthropologists, Chicago, Ill., on December 28, 1946 (see Straus, 1947), and at The Viking Fund Second Summer Seminar in Physical Anthropology, New York City, July 8, 1947. Work in progress, briefly reported herein, is being supported in part by a grant from The Viking Fund.

I wish to express my great indebtedness to my colleague, Dr. Bentley Glass, for our many helpful discussions and especially for those relating to my arguments based upon genetics. It is impossible for me adequately to acknowledge his generous aid. It must be emphasized, however, that I am alone responsible for the views expressed in this paper.

Summary

(1) The theory of human origin that derives the hominid line of ancestry from some sort of anthropoid ape had its modern inception with Huxley (1863). Since that time it has been extended and developed, notably by Keith and Gregory; so that it has come to be generally accepted that man has evolved from a true anthropoid ape at a relatively late geological date.

(2) Notwithstanding, the orthodox, anthropoid-ape theory has had its critics and opponents ever since Mivart first exposed some of its weak points in 1873. Among these, Boule, Wood Jones, Osborn, and Broom are especially to be noted.

(3) Probably the greatest weakness of the anthropoid-ape theory is that it ignores the considerable number of human characters that can only be regarded as essentially generalized and which find their counterparts not in the anthropoid apes but in such primates as the monkeys and prosimians. In other words, in many characters, and particularly in those that define an anthropoid ape, the anthropoids (and the great ones especially) can only be regarded as far more specialized than man. Some of these characters are discussed.

Making due allowance for the fact that a considerable part of the disagreement between the various theories of human ancestry is undoubtedly one of semantics, it is suggested that a nonanthropoid concept of man's ancestry is in closer agreement with known facts than is the orthodox theory. The presumed earliest representatives of the hominid line would consequently be visualized as essentially unspecialized, monkey-like quadrupeds who, in their evolution, avoided the brachiating (arm-swinging) and other peculiar specializations characteristic of the anthropoid apes, and therefore never passed through an actual anthropoid-ape stage.

In line with this, it is suggested that the special resemblances between man and the great anthropoid apes do not necessarily indicate close relationship but can be logically explained as the results of parallel evolution.

(4) On the basis of available evidence it might be concluded that the evolutionary lines leading to the four existing major groups of Old World primates underwent very early separation, so that none of them bears any special close genetic relationship to any other. A reasonable compromise, however, would diverge the hominid line somewhere between the points of departure of the Old World monkeys and the Hylobatidae (gibbon and siamang) from the evolving catarrhine stock. In any instance, the orthodox "family tree" that derives man from a joint anthropoid-hominid line of descent at some point after the departure of the Hylobatidae appears to the writer to be no longer acceptable.

It is concluded that available evidence indicates that the line leading to man became independent at a relatively early date, probably no later than the end of the Oligocene period, and that the stock from which it arose was essentially monkey-like rather than anthropoid-like. This concept, however, is naturally no more than a working hypothesis the final evaluation of which must be left to the future. For the problem of man's ancestry is still a decidedly open one, a riddle.[1]

---

[1] Dr. Straus has made the following observations as to his present views on certain matters in his 1949 article (Ed.):

(1) I see no reason to retract the major conclusions; in my opinion they are as valid as in 1949. Additional discoveries and further analyses of both the australopithecines and the *Proconsul* group appear to me to lend additional support to my thesis.

(2) Perhaps, however, I overemphasized the "nonanthropoid" nature of hominid ancestry. It seems more evident than ever that this chiefly involves a matter of semantics: whether one thinks of such primitive animals as having been "anthropoids" or "monkeys," or whatever else you care to call them, depends on how such terms are defined, and on the criteria selected as decisive. The really crucial point, as I then stated and as I still see it, is "whether the creatures that gave rise to the hominid line of phylogeny were or were not brachiators," i.e., whether they had already developed the specializations which are the inevitable hallmarks of outright brachiators. (I underscore the last two words, for all primates frequently assume an upright

posture as far as the trunk is concerned and use their arms on occasion as other than quadrupedal props, and hence are potential or unspecialized proto-brachiators of sorts. Indeed, it seems likely that this is a basic primate character which served as a preadaptation in the acquisition of an erect, bipedal posture.) My answer would still have to be the same as in 1949—they had *not*.

Exponents of a brachiating ancestry for man may cite *Oreopithecus* in support, since this creature exhibits brachiating specializations in its limb proportions. However, this is not a truly valid argument for wherever one places *Oreopithecus* (whether in its own, separate hominoid family or within the family Hominidae) it is nevertheless a highly specialized form with a dentition in part *sui generis*. Thus, even if one regards it as an actual hominid, it must be regarded as an aberrant one, which certainly could not have been directly ancestral to man. It can thus have no immediate bearing on the argument presented in my 1949 paper. It is now evident that brachiating specializations (notably the long arms) developed independently, and at different times, in various members of the different groups of simian primates.

(3) I do not feel as convinced as I did in 1949 that the hominid line of evolution must have branched off and become independent *before* the departure of the hylobatid line. For instance, the *Limnopithecus* finds do not accord well with this hypothesis. I am now inclined to think that line M^1 in my Figure 8A probably agrees better with current knowledge.

(4) I now regard the dental formula of *Parapithecus* as $\overline{1.1.3.3}$ (rather than as $\overline{2.1.2.3}$); this mandible is either that of a specialized tarsioid or of a nonprimate (in such case probably that of a condylarth). In either event, it apparently would have no place in catarrhine phylogeny.

The Bearing of the Australopithecinae Upon the Problem of Man's Place in Nature

William K. Gregory   1949

In the history of anthropology the year 1925 A.D. deserves to be underscored, for it marks the publication of Professor Raymond A. Dart's article in *Nature*, wherein he described the fossil skull which he named *Australopithecus africanus*. His outstanding contribution to the problem of human origin may well be viewed against a mainly historic background, with special reference to the basic assumptions implicit in various theories of the ways in which the human stock has evolved from earlier stages.

TELEOLOGISTS VERSUS EPIGENESISTS

To the teleologists of the past and present the plan of creation has always preceded the thing created. This doctrine has been and is still deeply entrenched in multitudes of human crania. To the epigenesists on the contrary the plan itself originated and developed in time, as new factors came into the ever changing histories of living beings. But did the "plan" grow altogether by "Chance," that is by the accidental coincidence or intersection in time and space of all its causal factors? Or did necessity or "Law" continually limit and control the growth of the plan? A long-

Reprinted by permission of The Wistar Institute Press from the American Journal of Physical Anthropology, *n.s. 7:485–512 (1949). This paper was originally presented at the Viking Fund Conference on the Australopithecinae, August 30, 1949. A survey on man's position among the primates, and further consideration of problems of brachiation and dental relationships noted in preceding papers. Before his retirement, Dr. Gregory was Curator of Comparative Anatomy and of Ichthyology at the American Museum of Natural History in New York, and Da Costa Professor of Vertebrate Paleontology at Columbia University.*

standing interest in the relations of Chance and Law has led me to infer: (1) that the phenomena called Chance are reflected not only in events falling within the normal curve of probability but also in the new or emergent events of evolution; (2) that Chance should not be contrasted or logically opposed to Law, but that both are merely different aspects of one continuous reality; (3) that "Law" connotes recurrent or relatively fixed limiting factors; but (4) the interaction of new and old factors may, by Chance, change the limits and create completely new combinations. As applied to the case of the skull of *Australopithecus africanus*, Chance, that is, the concurrence of many unique events, culminated in its fossilization, preservation, and discovery; but Law, that is, the recurrent factors, also led to the repeated search for others, to their coming into Professor Dart's competent hands and to his evolving knowledge of their significance.

The teleologists have accepted the dogma that Adam was created in accordance with a perfect, preordained plan. To the epigenesists on the contrary the human plan still shows many imperfections, partly the result of inherent liabilities incurred with the adoption of the upright gait. The dualists, believing in man's divine origin and contrasting matter with "mind" or "spirit," classify living things into two major groups: (1) man and (2) all other living things; no intergrades are recognized or admitted. However it might now be pertinent to ask: to which of these two categories is *Australopithecus africanus*, with his sub-human brain, to be referred?

The more far-seeing of the natural philosophers however gradually came to realize that there is a basic similarity in plan even between such different looking creatures as bipedal man and quadrupedal pig. Thus we find Descartes in his famous "Discours de la Méthode" (1637) recommending that if any of his readers wished to learn about the plan of construction of the human heart he should get a surgeon (meaning a barber-surgeon) to dissect before him the heart of a pig.

The more or less intermediate appearance of monkeys between man and animals must have been realized by the European people who applied the name Capuchin to one of the South American monkeys. By 1693 monkeys were classed by John Ray, developing Aristotle's ideas, among the "Animalia Vivipara, quadrupeda pilosa" and were referred to one of the main divisions called "Platyonycha ac Anthropomorphae." Linnaeus (1759) developed this theme much further by inventing the word Mammalia (*mamma*, breast) as the name of the class and arranging its main divisions into successive orders, the order Primates being the highest. Carrying the old idea of an "échelle des êtres" to its logical conclusion, Linnaeus reverently placed the name of Jehovah at the apex of his Systema naturae. Below Jehovah were the archangels and angels. Man, in accord with the word of psalmist was ranked as a little lower than the angels. No objection to this allocation was then recorded.

Pithecophobiacs

The order Primates of Linnaeus was however occupied not only by man but also by Simia, Lemur, and Vespertilio. This was too much for some of Linnaeus' successors and we find Thomas Pennant, for instance, in his "History of Quadrupeds" (1781) uttering the following complaint: "There are faults in his [Linnaeus's] arrangement of the mammalia, that is of animals which have paps and suckle their young, in which class are comprehended not only all the genuine quadrupeds but even the Cetaceous tribe, that oblige me to separate myself in this one instance from his crowd of votaries . . . I reject his first division which he calls Primates or chiefs of Creation; because my vanity will not suffer me to rank mankind with Apes, Monkeys, Macaucos and Bats, the companions Linnaeus has allotted us even in his last System."

This strikingly frank passage reveals the deep cleavage between what we may call the pithecophobiacs who are allergic to their poor relations and the pithecophilians, who may even profess to be proud of their tailless simian ancestors. The pithecophobiacs do not welcome such brutes as *Paranthropus robustus*, as that poor monster was recently sketched by Dr. Broom, and they are not at all cordial to *Plesianthropus africanus*, even when portrayed as an ape-man child of pre-Freudian innocence.

Blumenbach, the reputed father of anthropology, followed Linnaeus in referring man to the Class Mammalia, but he sought a middle course by assigning man to a separate order, which he at first named Inermis, but later changed to Bimana or more correctly Bimanus. Cuvier likewise isolated man under the order "Bimanes" and Illiger did the same, but called the order Erecta.

The isolation of mankind was more reassuringly taught by Richard Owen (1868), who assigned to man the rank of a subclass Archencephala, on account of the marked superiority of the human brain. But what, we may enquire, would Owen have done with Dr. Broom's *Plesianthropus*, whose brain capacity barely exceeded that of a large male gorilla?

To the pithecophobiacs the deeper the cleft between man and the "brutal apes" the better, and it was a grave tactical mistake on their part to leave man anywhere within the class Mammalia. The pithecophobiacs, outside of Clerical and Fundamentalist circles, have included: (1) certain anthropologists, trained to recognize and measure human racial differences, but distrusting all results relating to the evolution of man from lower primates; (2) certain anatomists, skilled in describing the most complex anatomical facts in static terms, but disregarding morphologic and palaeontologic evidence of evolution by transformation; (3) certain zoologists, keen in the search for diagnostic differences between man and apes, but resolute in classing resemblances between man and apes as mere "parallelisms" or "convergences."

Even more obdurate than the pithecophobiacs are the confirmed statisticians, who ban all nonmetrical data and deny both orthodoxy and respectability to those who prefer visual comparison of morphological patterns.

PITHECOPHILIANS

Among the greatest pioneer pithecophilians were Lamarck, Darwin, Haeckel, Huxley, and Keith.

But it is seldom easy to classify independent, free investigators under any single label. Dr. Broom for example may be classed as a pithecophilian in so far as he regards the Australopithecinae as ape-men; but he sounds rather like a pithecophobiac when he rises to refute those who have concluded that the Australopithecinae represent an extreme southern derivative of the *Proconsul-Dryopithecus* group, or that man is not too distantly related to the chimpanzee and gorilla.

IRREVERSIBILITARIANS

The pithecophobiacs have often emphasized the divergent "specializations" of the great apes and the allegedly "primitive features" of man. But in many cases what a man calls specialized and primitive will depend more or less upon his often unspoken assumptions and postulates. To irreversibilitarians, for example, when a "specialization" is once acquired it can never be got rid of. To the epigenesists, on the contrary, the essence of the transformation consists (1) not only in progressive emphasis in some old features but (2) also of the reduction and perhaps elimination of others, together with (3) the appearance of many wholly new features, not to be looked for below the given habitus level. Of course many former specializations have proved to be irreversible, such as the basic vertebrate and basic mammalian construction plans. But some specializations that were once new had to be sacrificed at every stage of advance. This is exemplified by the progressive reduction of the dental formula (of adults) from $\frac{3.1.4.3}{3.1.4.3}$ in primitive placental mammals, to $\frac{2.1.4.3}{2.1.4.3}$ in Eocene lemurs (*Notharctus*), $\frac{2.1.3.3}{2.1.3.3}$ in New World monkeys, $\frac{2.1.2.3}{2.1.2.3}$ in Old World monkeys, anthropoid apes, Australopithecinae and primitive man, $\frac{2.1.2.2}{2.1.2.2}$ in many modern men. Dahlberg's researches suggest that in some future time the typical formula may be reduced to $\frac{1.1.1.2}{1.1.1.2}$.

VECTORIANS VERSUS CLADOGENISTS

A still greater emphasis on the separateness in geologic time of supposedly related lines is expressed by Professor Leo S. Berg, who in his book "Nomogenesis" as well as in his classification of fishes likens the situation to the relation of the leaves to the back of a book. Those who subscribe to this and related theories might therefore be called phyllogenists (phyllon, leaf) or vectorians, in opposition to the cladogenists who visualize evolution as a branching process (clados) after the manner of Darwin. Some palaeontologists are essentially vectorians, because many of the branches in invertebrate palaeontology are far longer than those in mammalogy, including primatology.

HOMUNCULISTS

The idea that *Tarsius*, or rather, some of its distant Eocene forerunners may be nearer to the ancestry of man than are the great apes, stems in part from the paleontologist Cope, who in 1881 described a certain very small fossil lemuroid Primate skull from the Eocene of Wyoming, which he named *Anaptomorphus homunculus*. After noting several features in common with man he suggested that this genus is nearer to the hypothetical lemuroid ancestor of man than any other yet discovered. Another contribution to what may be called the Homunculus theory of the origin of man was made by Hubrecht (1902) who noted that certain features of the placentation and embryology of *Tarsius* are remarkably man-like. Boule (1911–1913) in his memoir on the Chapelle-aux-Saints Neanderthal remains suggested that the name *Eoanthropus*, as invented by Smith Woodward for a large-sized human skull of Pleistocene age, was an unfortunate misnomer and that the true *Eoanthropus* would be found to be a very small erectly walking creature of Eocene age, with large eyes, expanded brain, and small jaws. Ameghino seems to have had a similar idea for he gave the name *Homunculus* to a small fossil South American monkey with large orbits, which he regarded as a remote ancestor of man; but this "homunculus" was shown by Bluntschli (1913) and later writers to be a true South American monkey, related to the douroucouli (*Aotus*). Thus it seems fair enough to class Cope, Hubrecht, Boule, and Wood Jones as homunculists, in so far as they all regarded such large-eyed, large-brained erect "little men" as a suitable starting point for *Homo*.

In *Tarsius* the great development of the eyes and the reduction of the olfactory parts contribute to its elfin appearance, while the animal's amazing power of leaping about among the branches implies an advanced development in muscular coordination and balancing and in the motor areas of the neopallium. It is not surprising therefore that Elliot Smith found in the brain of *Tarsius* a convenient structural intermediate between the less complex brains of typical lemurs and the still more complex brains of monkeys, apes, and man. On the other hand Woolard (1925) in his report on the anatomy of *Tarsius* found it to be a "lemur of lemurs."

From a palaeontological viewpoint the known Eocene tarsioids and *Tarsius* itself are specialized side branches from a lemuroid base and are far more widely separated phylogenetically from the Australopithecinae and Hominidae than are the existing anthropoid apes.

PROTOPITHECOPHILIANS, ANTIBRACHIATIONISTS, ORTHOGENISTS

Those who regard man as a derivative or very early side branch of the Old World or catarrhine stem are neither pithecophilians nor pithecophobiacs. They may therefore be called protopithecophilians. They oppose the idea that the remote ancestors of man were accomplished brachiators like the gibbons, which they regard as far too specialized to have given rise to man. Thus at least most of the protopithecophilians are also antibrachiationists in opposition to the brachiationists who regard the loss of the tail, the strengthening of the sacrum, and the bipedal habit of running on the ground as having probably all been initiated by early brachiators, related on one hand to the ancestral gibbons and on the other to the typical Dryopithecinae. Professors Schultz and Straus have amassed and analyzed a vast amount of accurate anatomical observations and measurements, which, they infer, indicates the extremely early separation of the human from the ape stem.

Somewhat similar conclusions have been reached by Professor Le Gros Clark, partly on the basis of his studies of the wide-ranging East African Lower Miocene primates, which were first discovered and described by Hopwood, Leakey, MacInnes and now, much more fully, by Le Gros Clark. The latter is inclined to the opinion that the remote ancestors of man may eventually be connected with some pronograde, nonarboreal ape, possibly not unlike one of the Lower Miocene East African fauna, which includes *Proconsul* and other genera. The same authority also expresses his acceptance of the principle of orthogenesis and therefore may be classed with the orthogenists in opposition to those who still believe in branching evolution.

In general, pithecophobiacs, irreversibilitarians, vectorians and homunculists prefer to set aside all the known fossils as possible ancestors of man, and they usually disregard the fact that the different members of any widely varying order such as the primates always seem to preserve successive grades of growth or emphasis of any given part. After throwing out the known fossils and all the existing forms the pithecophobiacs proceed to conjure up an entirely unknown series of hypothetical animals of which every one had successfully avoided all "specializations." Thus their favorite fallacy is the *ignotum per ignotius*.

THE AUSTRALOPITHECINAE AND THE EVOLUTION OF THE HUMAN FOOT

Both comparative and paleontological evidence indicate that, in the more primitive Lower Eocene and Paleocene representatives of the Carnivora, Condylarthra, Edentata, and other early Placental orders, the extremities were 5-rayed with short spreading metatarsals and moderately divergent first metatarsals and digits. Among the earliest known primates, including primitive lemuroids (Notharctids), tarsioids (*Washakius, Necrolemur*), the metatarsus of the hallux was strongly divergent, ending proximally in a large olecranon-like process. When this strongly grasping foot is fully extended it is seen to consist of a large inner branch, the hallux, and a still larger lateral branch, comprising the second to 5th metatarsals and digits. I have named this the biramous type of foot. It is fully preserved in its primitive state in all the diverse modern lemurs of Madagascar, as well as in their upper Eocene ancestors, the European Adapidae. This type is approached but not fully developed in the modern tree shrews which are regarded as very primitive survivors of the basal lemuroids. In *Tarsius* also the hallux is divergent and the grasping ability is enhanced by the disc-like expansion of the distal ends of the digits.

The biramous grasping foot is preserved with minor modifications in all the ceboid monkeys; in the marmosets we find it in a somewhat weakened state. In the catarrhine monkeys, the olecranon-like process of the first metatarsal is somewhat less prominent and the hallux can be moved more freely from side to side, whereas in the primitive lemurs the extended proximal process fits into a deep depression in the middle of the tarsus and its lateral mobility is sharply restricted. The anthropoid apes have lost the olecranon-like process but they retain the essentials of the biramous character of the hind foot. This gives them thumb-like great toes and the right to be called Quadrumana, although the deep structure of this hand-like foot is of course radically different from that of their hands.

In view of the wide-spread distribution of this biramous, grasping type of foot, from the primitive Eocene lemuroids to all the modern lemuroids, *Tarsius,* ceboids, catarrhine monkeys, and anthropoid apes, I inferred (1916–1920) that it is one of the most ancient "basic patents" so to speak, of the entire Primate Order and that its apparent absence in man is due to the remodelling of the foot in the course of adaptation to the upright posture and gait. Quite independently Weidenreich (1921) had concluded that the transformation of an ape-like grasping foot into the human stage could be clearly visualized as part of the adaptation for walking erect, that is, in the period when the legs were straightened, the lumbar curve emphasized, and the skull drawn backward above the fulcra of support (acetabula).

Elftman and Manter (1935a, b) very clearly analyzed the movements of the component parts of the foot around certain axes and showed that, when the ape foot is turned partly inward as in climbing, its parts assume positions which would seem to be favorable starting points for the various new specializations of the human foot. In brief their work suggests that, in the ape-like ancestors of man, neither the longitudinal nor the transverse arch of the foot were allowed to flatten down against the ground as they do now in the gorilla, but that, as these arches were held by muscles and tendons in the curved grasping position, the great toe was drawn toward the others and twisted so as to face downward rather than inward; thus the running power of the foot was greatly improved.

Another source of morphological evidence for the reality of the transformation of an ape-foot into a human foot was developed in the beautiful series of comparative dissections (Figures 1 and 2) of the feet of apes and man prepared by the late Henry C. Raven. Under his supervision was also prepared an exhibit of carefully labelled casts, showing the bones, muscles, tendons, and ligaments of the foot of gorilla, chimpanzee, and man.

A comparison of the bones of the foot of gorilla and man indicates that in order to convert the basic anthropoid into the human type it would be necessary to make a series of closely correlated changes, two of which may now be noted: (1) the facet on the entocuneiform against which the hallux abuts would have to be flattened; (2) the long axis of the hallux would be turned and twisted so as to be directed forward and downward.

Now it has been shown by Professor Schultz that in foetal and adult gorillas and men there are considerable ranges of variation in both the curvature of the entocuneiform-metatarsal facet and in the direction of the long axis of the metatarsal; so that the differences which distinguish

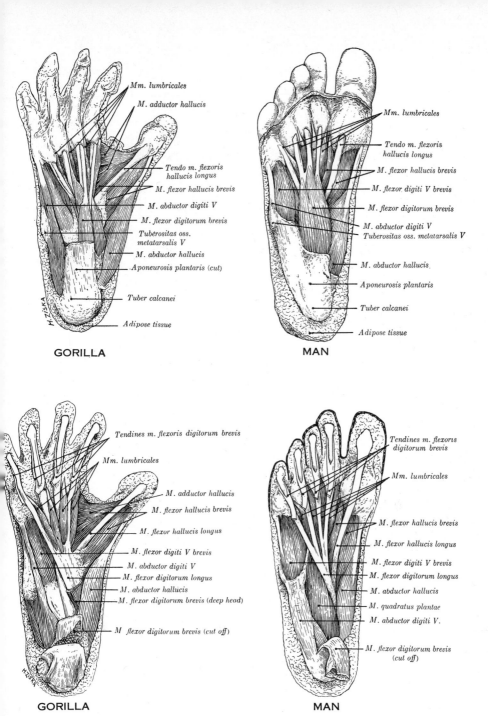

Figure 1. Dissections of plantar musculature. First and second layers. After H. C. Raven. (Courtesy of the American Museum of Natural History)

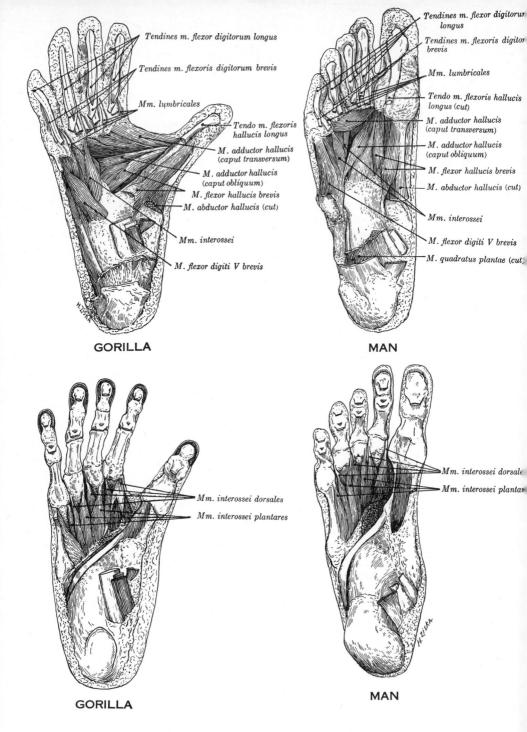

FIGURE 2. Dissections of plantar musculature. Third and fourth layers. After H. C. Raven. (Courtesy of the American Museum of Natural History)

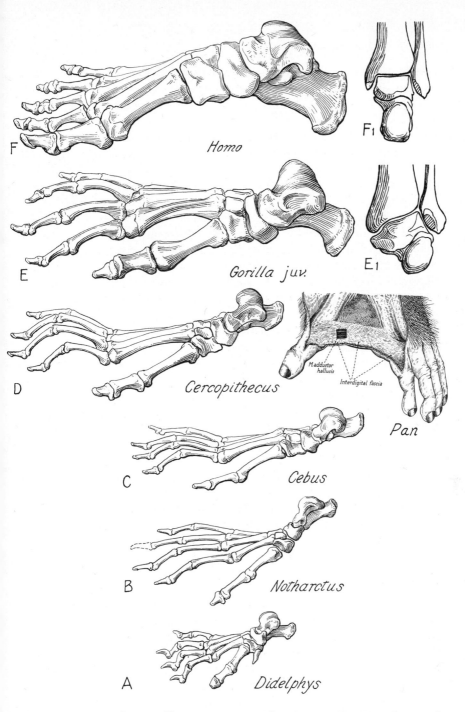

Homo

F₁

Gorilla juv.

E₁

Cercopithecus

M adductor
hallucis

Interdigital fascia

Pan

Cebus

Notharctus

Didelphys

FIGURE 3.   A–F, right pes, oblique inner view. After Gregory. E1, F1, right pes of gorilla and man, rear view. From M. Weber after Topinard. Left pes of chimpanzee (Pan), to show interdigital fascia. After H. C. Raven. (Courtesy of the American Museum of Natural History)

gorilla and man in these features may be regarded as quantitative rather than qualitative. Secondly the first metatarsal of man is closely tied to those of the second and other digits by the transverse metatarsal ligament, a unique feature in man. But Raven showed that in the chimpanzee and gorilla there is a mass of collagenous inelastic connective tissue lying in the thick web between the first metatarsal and the other digits. He suggested that as the gap between the hallux and the second digit was closed the connective tissue gave rise to the transverse ligament between the hallux and the second metatarsal. Such a transformation would imply a marked change in the direction of evolution and it would therefore probably be unacceptable to the irreversabilitarians; but it seems no more remarkable than other rather well documented major transformations, such as the transformation of reptilian forearms into avian wings. Such profound changes of function usually imply equally radical changes in proportions, often with creation of new ligaments and trochleae for restricting motion within certain limits.

Although the construction of the foot of the Australopithecinae is not yet satisfactorily known, their evident adjustment to upright gait in the forward position of the occipital condyle may conceivably have been correlated with an equally human construction of the foot as a whole. Indeed the talus of *Paranthropus*, as described by Broom (1946), is on the whole definitely nearer to the Bushman than to the gorilla type, but the much greater transverse arc of the facet for the navicular as seen in the top view suggests a greater flexibility of the foot itself.

In short, comparative studies of the bones of the extremities in monkeys and apes appear to support the inference that the orang is a heavy bodied arboreal brachiator, the chimpanzee and gorilla partly secondary ground apes, and the Australopithecinae and man bipedal striders of the open plains.

THE OLDEST KNOWN APE (PROPLIOPITHECUS) AND THE AUSTRALOPITHECINAE

The primitive catarrhine stock, which probably included only pronograde monkeys, evidently lies far below the near-human horizon of the Australopithecinae, with no known intermediates. On the other hand the oldest known anthropoid ape stage, *Propliopithecus* from the Lower Oligocene of Egypt, although represented only by a small, incomplete lower jaw, has very well preserved and primitive cheek teeth. It was seen by Schlosser and his successors that the lower teeth of *Propliopithecus*, while contrasting sharply with those of monkeys, appear to supply a structurally ideal ancestral stage: (1) for those of the Lower Miocene

African *Proconsul* group, (2) for the European Miocene *Pliopithecus* and the gibbons, (3) for the diversified European and Asiatic Dryopithecinae. The body of the small mandible of *Propliopithecus* is relatively short and deep and the strength of the masticatory muscles must have been great in proportion to the size of the cranium, a characteristic ape-feature. Thus *Propliopithecus,* as far as it goes, tends to indicate that the Australopithecinae and the Hominidae belong in the anthropoid division, the earlier (Oligocene) members of which were not very remotely related to the gibbons and were presumably arboreal and not yet ground-living apes.

DENTAL ARCHES AND TEETH

The dental arches and deciduous teeth of *Australopithecus africanus,* as Professor Dart originally noted, present striking evidence of close relationship with man; nevertheless the lower molars also have retained the basic *Dryopithecus* pattern of three outer cusps and two inner ones, separated at their bases by a special and characteristic system of grooves. The permanent molars of *Australopithecus prometheus* are very massive. In the great thickness and size of the body of the mandible the Australopithecinae resemble the recent and fossil great apes. In the latter the huge jaws and great muscles are used in breaking off, piercing, and cutting large fruits with tough rinds, as in the orang, or chewing sugar cane as in the gorilla; the latter also strips the surface of certain stems by pulling them transversely through his mouth across his canines to get at the chlorophyll. The mountain gorilla carries huge loads of vegetation in his digestive tract and is essentially a herbivore; but the two captive gorillas in the New York Zoological Park have been conditioned to like meat. In view of the food habits of Australian aborigines and African pygmies it would hardly be surprising if the Australopithecinae, in addition to killing baboons and cracking open their skulls to get at the brains, were also general feeders or even in part carrion feeders, alert to snatch away from the vultures the remains left by lions and hyaenas. The lack of a simian shelf is a point of contrast between the Australopithecinae and the modern anthropoids. But there is no simian shelf in *Dryopithecus, Sivapithecus,* or *Proconsul* or allied forms, and this feature is poorly developed in the jaw of certain female gorillas.

Adloff rules the anthropoids out as ancestors of man, because the males have large tusks. But Gregory and Hellman (1938) have shown that in a presumably female *Sivapithecus* the upper canine crown is remarkably short, and that it seems to be approaching the premolars in the possession of an anterior vertical groove and a slight basal lingual swelling. Weidenreich (1937) also showed that the lower canine of the

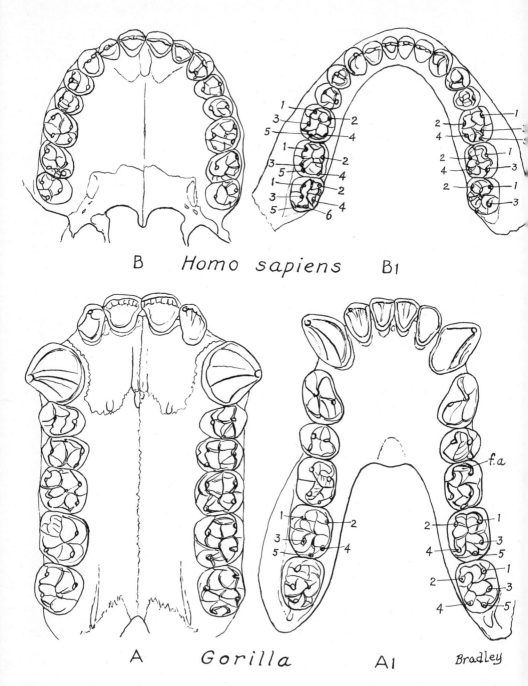

FIGURE 4. Extremes in dentition, palatal and mandibular arches. From Gregory after Röse. *1*, protoconid; *3*, hypoconid; *5*, hypoconulid; *2*, metaconid; *4*, entoconid; *6*, cusp 6; *f.a.*, fovea anterior. (Courtesy of the American Museum of Natural History)

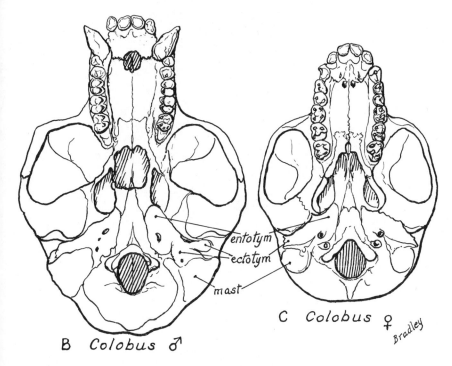

FIGURE 5. Contrasts in dental arches: male with large canines, large diastemata, spreading arch, and wide bizygomatic spread; female with smaller canines, no diastemata, narrow arch, and narrower bizygomatic spread. After Gregory. (Courtesy of the American Museum of Natural History)

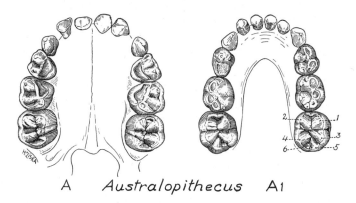

FIGURE 6. Palatal and mandibular arches, with deciduous teeth and first permanent molars of *Australopithecus africanus*. From Gregory, after photographs and casts supplied by Professor R. A. Dart. (Courtesy of the American Museum of Natural History)

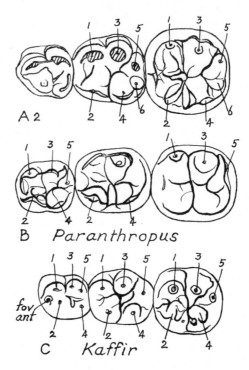

FIGURE 7. Deciduous teeth and lower of: B, *Paranthropus robustus;* C, modern Kaffir. After Broom. (Courtesy of the American Museum of Natural History)

female *Sivapithecus* although very small was morphologically allied in crown-pattern to the lower canine of a certain female orang. The upper canines of Broom's type of *Paranthropus* are quite small in comparison with the molars. Thus indications are not lacking that as the upright posture was attained the dental arches were shortened and the canines reduced.

The high pointed crown of the first lower premolar of the existing anthropoids contrasts with the low bicuspid human form of this crown in the Australopithecinae, *Sinanthropus* and *Homo*. Accordingly the irreversibilitarians hold that the bicuspid could not have been derived from the compressed conical crown and hence that man could not have been derived from any of the Dryopithecinae; but, as pointed out by Hellman and Gregory (1938) a comparative series of first lower premolar crowns indicates that the bicuspid crown of this tooth in man has apparently been derived partly by reducing the height of the protoconid and by a reduction of the transverse diameter across the post cuspidal fossa, although some of the originally oblique asymmetry of the crown

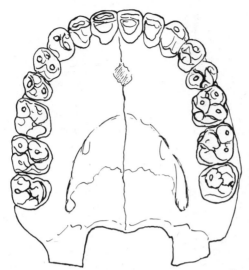

C   Homo (Heidelberg restored)

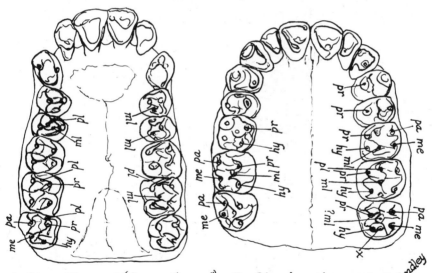

A Sivapithecus ♀ ("Dryopithecus")   B Plesianthropus ♀ Bradley

FIGURE 8.   Restorations of palatal arches. After Gregory and Hellman (A, B); McGregor (C). *pa*, paracone; *me*, metacone; *pr*, protocone; *hy*, hypocone; *pl*, protoconule; *ml*, metaconule. (Courtesy of the American Museum of Natural History)

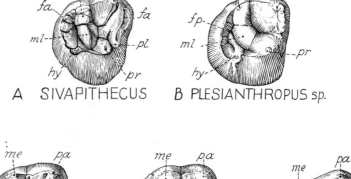

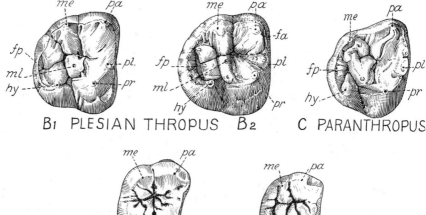

FIGURE 9. Right upper third molars. A–C from specimens and casts; D, D1 after Weidenreich. (Courtesy of the American Museum of Natural History)

is retained in *Sinanthropus* and even in *Homo*. This case exemplifies what I regard as the anachronism of demanding that the remote ancestors of any line must already possess all the habitus features of its distant descendants.

CONCLUSIONS

The balance of present evidence suggests that evolution emerging seems long ago to have overcome most of the objections now posed for her by the irreversibilitarians. She seems indeed to be rather a pragmatist, with her eye on the motto: *solvitur ambulando;* nor does she hesi-

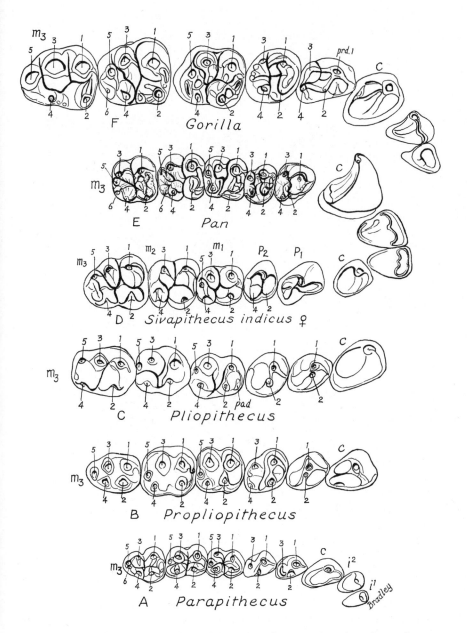

FIGURE 10. Left lower teeth of fossil (A–C) and recent (E–F) anthropoid apes, showing location of principal cusps and grooves. After Gregory. Data from photographs (A–C), casts (A–C), and specimens (D–F). The typical *"Dryopithecus"* pattern is attained in D and somewhat modified in E, F. (Courtesy of the American Museum of Natural History)

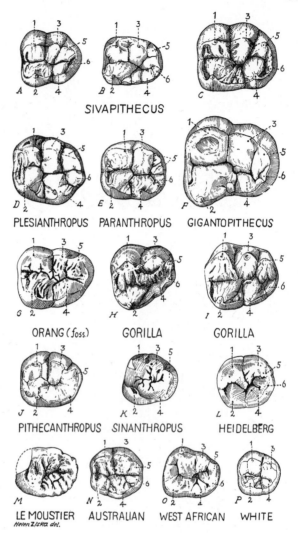

FIGURE 11. Right lower third molars showing *"Dryopithecus"* pattern. From Gregory and Hellman. Based on specimens, casts, and photographs. G–M after Weidenreich. (Courtesy of the American Museum of Natural History)

tate to cast aside, erase, or alter parts of her earlier plans, increasing this part or diminishing that; but always within the limits imposed by the varying incidence of hereditary factors and by changing selective pressures of successive environments.

The Australopithecinae, whether they were direct ancestors of man

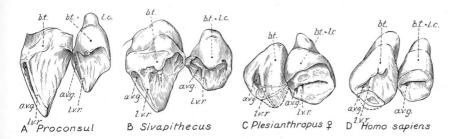

FIGURE 12. Right upper canine and first premolar. Inner view. After Gregory and Hellman. A from cast, B–D from specimens. *a.v.g.*, anterior vertical groove; *b.t.*, basal tubercle; *l.c.*, lingual cingulum; *l.v.r.*, lingual vertical ridge. (Courtesy of the American Museum of Natural History)

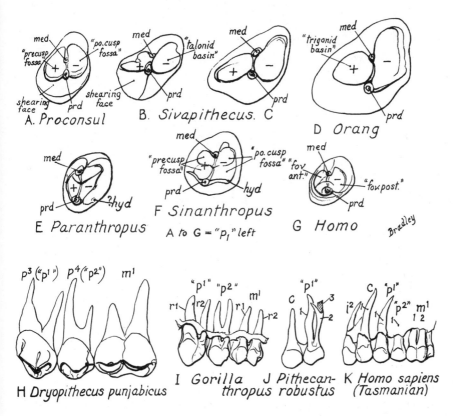

FIGURE 13. Comparative morphology of the anterior lower premolar crowns and of the upper premolar roots. (Courtesy of the American Museum of Natural History)

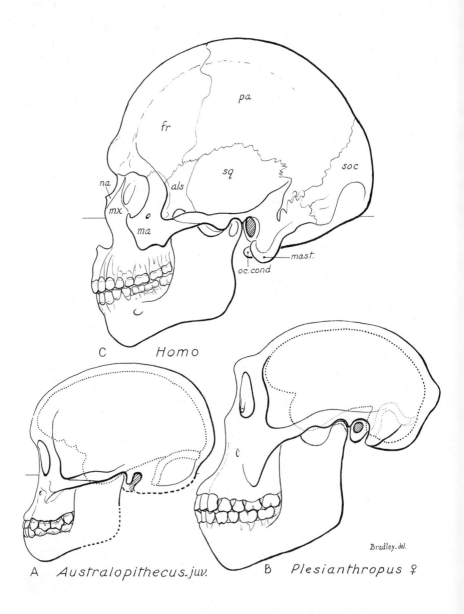

FIGURE 14. A, outline of *Australopithecus* skull. After Dart. B, tentative restoration of *Plesianthropus* skull with inscribed brain cast. Data from Broom and Schepers. C, sketch of Tasmanian skull, with lower jaw adapted from other specimens. Dept. of Anthropology, Amer. Mus. Nat. Hist. (Courtesy of the American Museum of Natural History)

or merely one of his great great uncles, have already contributed materially to this far-reaching definitive result: that man can now be securely linked with the anthropoid stock, not only by cumulative comparative morphological evidence, but also by good fossil evidence. Perhaps their greatest contribution is the fact that although standing on the very threshold of mankind, their brains were distinctly lower than those of *Homo sapiens,* who in turn was once regarded as being only a "little lower than the angels."

On the Relationships of Early Primates

Fredrik Barth   1950

In this paper, early primate evolution is approached in terms of two concepts of paleontology: adaptive radiation and adaptive zone (Simpson, 1944). The adaptive zone of Paleocene and Eocene primates is arrived at by using criteria of structure and of faunal relationship. It seems to have been very generalized and wide, covering what might be called a *primate-rodent* ecologic niche.

The evolution of early primates is however a small part of general mammalian evolution, and must be viewed as part of the general evolutionary sequence. The concept of a *radiation pattern* may be used for this purpose. In terms of it, faunal evolution is seen as a series of cycles, each cycle consisting of: (1) A period of major radiation, in which a large number of forms differentiate quickly and enter the main adaptive zones. (2) A period of reshuffling, with development and extinction of lines within zones. (3) Once established within a single adaptive zone, the evolution of a group appears in the main to follow the "orthogenetic" pattern of phyletic evolution. (4) This will continue until a new cycle starts with wholesale extinction of older forms and radiation of new groups into the main adaptive zones (Simpson, 1944).

As a working hypothesis, placental evolution may be seen to consist of three such major radiations (Olson, 1943). The first, which started at

Reprinted by permission of The Wistar Institute Press from the American Journal of Physical Anthropology, *n.s. 8:139–149 (1950). A general interpretation of the many fossils of prosimian primates of the early Tertiary. Although the various extinct forms and their names may mean little to most readers, and although the specific lines of relationship suggested, and figured on the chart, may be viewed as highly speculative (very few such relationships are accepted at the moment by most paleontologists), this is a clear and simple statement of the evolutionary status of early primates, and the kind of adaptation and radiation they exhibited. Dr. Barth is now Research Associate at the University of Oslo.*

the close of the Age of Reptiles, consisted primarily of insectivore groups and close derivatives. Before this radiation had filled the major adaptive zones, the second radiation of placentals started, and the archaic ungulates and carnivores successfully invaded the main adaptive zones, in part, probably, in competition with the earlier insectivores. The forms representing the first radiation then became restricted to certain secondary "refuge areas" in the ecology, where they in part survive to this day.

The primates are such an early, insectivore-derived stock (Olson, 1943). In what follows, the order will be discussed primarily in terms of the problem: What was the early primate adaptive zone, and in what respects was it restricted through competition with later forms? On the basis of answers to this, inferences may be drawn as to the nature and mode of the evolution which took place, and the evolutionary relationships of the group.

The only materials available for the solution of this problem are paleontological, consisting of the fossil primate material from the Paleocene and Eocene, interpreted in the light of general knowledge of the associated faunas. Primates are poorly represented in the fossil record, mostly by very fragmentary material. Even so, some 55 genera from the Paleocene and Eocene have been defined, many of which can be related in phyletic lines. The present paper will not attempt to discuss the classification of all these forms: Simpson (1940, 1945) is followed. A summary chart of generic names and relationships is appended (Figure 1).

An apparent taxonomic difficulty is inherent in this approach: early primates are considered as a unit, in spite of the common practice of subdividing them into lemuroids (Adapidae) and tarsioids (Anaptomorphidae). The general diffuseness of this distinction is however suggested in Simpson's classification by the great number of unplaceable genera, often anatomically comparatively well known; Adapidae, *incert. sedis* three genera; Anaptomorphidae, *incert. sedis* three genera; Prosimii, uncertain family, 9 genera. Furthermore, the definitions and boundaries of the groups are not agreed upon by leading authorities (Simpson, 1945).

In the Anaptomorphidae (tarsioids) are united some 28 genera for reasons in large part negative (Simpson, 1940). They are enough alike in known parts to be related, but there is little or no evidence showing that this affinity is real. One has, more or less, a continuum from anaptomorphid tarsioids to lemuroids: *Tarsius* is closely similar to *Pseudoloris*, which is related to *Necrolemur* and *Tetonius*. These are linked through dental similarities with *Omomys* and *Hemiacodon*, which in turn have many dental features in common with lemurs, e.g., *Pronycticebus*. The inclusiveness of one or the other family is thus arbitrarily determined by where one draws the line.

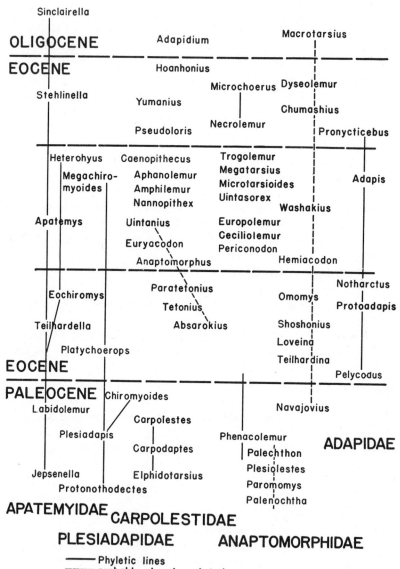

FIGURE 1.

Geographical or temporal grouping of forms does not make the picture any clearer. This suggests that the strict separation of lemuroids vs. tarsioids was not present in Eocene times, and that all these forms may be grouped together. In this scheme, *Tarsius* would be regarded as an aberrant survivor of a specialized lemuroid stock, possibly descended from *Pseudoloris* or *Necrolemur* (Simpson, 1940). In view of the general vagueness of subfamily and family distinctions, this seems the only reasonable conclusion, and the orthodox insistence upon the distinction is more a reflection of the bias that results from comparisons of the modern descendants.

Nature of the Early Primate Adaptive Zone

A determination of the early primate adaptive zone may then be based on the following types of evidence:

1. Structure—progressive specializations of structure occurring in a phyletic line, of probable adaptive value in a specific habitat.
2. Coexistence—the presence of several genera of primates in the same area over a considerable length of time, demonstrating ecologic differentiation.
3. Composition of fauna—the nature of the adaptive zones probably inhabited by other forms in the fauna, indicating what ecologic niches might be left for primates to inhabit.
4. Frequency—the percentage frequency of identified primate individuals in a fauna, showing size and nature of the primate zone.
5. Temporal distribution—the sequence of main deployment of primate families in relation to potentially competing forms.

1. Structure. The families Adapidae and Anaptomorphidae show many typical lemuroid and tarsioid specializations. They seem in great part to have been arboreal, frugivorous or semi-omnivorous small animals, adapted to the same ecologic niches as modern lemurs and tarsiers. A typical form is *Notharctus* of North America. Hopping adaptations were developed in *Hemiacodon*, with tarsal elongation similar to that of *Tarsius*, but anatomically on a different pattern (Simpson, 1940). The Adapidae thus seem to be related to modern lemurs, and to represent essentially the Eocene stock from which modern lemurs may have arisen.

Certain groups within these families show strongly divergent structural adaptations. In the subfamily Paromomyinae two large anterior teeth are developed. The subfamily Necrolemurinae shows similar adaptations, in this case only one enlarged incisor on each side. Occasional other genera of the family show rodent-like enlargement of the anterior teeth. In the phyletic series *Necrolemur-Microchoerus* there is furthermore a progressive trend of molar specialization in which a number of cusps are elongated to form anterior-posterior, almost loph-like ridges. From general parallels, one would expect this to be an herbivorous, probably browsing adaptation.

Rodent-like specializations are carried much further in other primate families. The Apatemyidae have a geologic range from Middle Paleocene to Lower Oligocene, and show a progressive development of rodent-like characters. Already in the earliest form, *Jepsenella,* the lower incisor root extends below the second molar; and in the last member of the family, *Sinclairella,* the skull shows consistent pseudo-rodent adaptations (Jepsen, 1934).

A similar divergent family is the Plesiadapidae, ranging from Middle Paleocene to Middle Eocene. Late genera show extreme specializations, to the extent that the genus *Megachiromyoides,* for example, has been placed variously among primates, insectivores, and rodents. It undoubtedly represents the last of a very aberrant lemuroid phylum (Simpson, 1940). The type genus, *Plesiadapis,* is well known from descriptions by Simpson (1935). Parallelism with rodents is shown in the prominent incisors and in the development of the angular process, which is hook-like and projects backwards and slightly downwards.

A third highly aberrant family is the Carpolestidae of Middle and Late Paleocene. In these forms the premolars have been developed into a long, sharp-edged pair of shears, and in this, as well as in a number of other dental characteristics, the group shows striking similarity to the modern kangaroo rat (Abel, 1931). This form is adapted to a diet of grass and roots for which it burrows. The deduction that *Carpolestes* represents a burrowing, root- and grass-eating, terrestrial primate does not seem unreasonable. The family is characterized by Simpson (1940) as "another sterile offshoot of a poorly differentiated, proto-lemuroid stock."

On morphological grounds it might therefore be deduced that primates in Early Tertiary times successfully inhabited a great variety of ecologic niches, as demonstrated by the existence of insectivorous (*Tetonius*), frugivorous (Adapidae, most Anaptomorphidae), and herbivorous (*Microchoerus*) arboreal forms, as well as arboreal, terrestrial, and burrowing rodent-like forms (Apatemyidae, Carpolestidae, etc.). So wide an adaptive zone would tend to produce a large number of genera and a frequent development of divergent and convergent phyletic lines, all of which is confusingly true in the fossil record.

2. Coexistence. According to this one would further expect a number of primate genera to coexist in one area over long periods of time, filling different ecologic niches and not entering into direct competition with one another. In most Paleocene and Eocene faunas this is the case. Any discussion of Paleocene faunas is, however, made difficult by the nature of the record: most primates occur in small, isolated pockets and quarries, possibly carnivore dens, and general collecting does not turn up the same abundance and richness of forms. The following suggestions must therefore be regarded as very tentative. In the Late Paleocene Tiffany fauna (Mesa Pocket) of North America, 6 genera (more species) of primates are found together with two carnivore genera, one condylarth, etc. (Simpson, 1935). In the Late Paleocene faunas of Bear Creek and Scarett Quarry, 3 genera are found; in Silver Coulee and Clark Fork, 2 genera. General collecting from the Tiffany surface, Plateau Valley, and Paskapoo has as yet only turned up one genus, namely *Plesiadapis*. This is however found in great abundance. Of the total number of genera present in these Upper Paleocene faunas of the Rocky Mountain area, primates constitute more than 10%, which can hardly be paralleled in any modern fauna.[1] A very wide adaptive zone is thus indicated for the order.

3. *Composition of fauna.* The other members of these early faunas might by their adaptations suggest by elimination what ecologic niches were open for primates to inhabit. In the above Tiffany fauna of Mesa Pocket, carnivores, condylarths, amblypods, multituberculates, marsupials, insectivores, and a possible bat are represented (Simpson, 1935). Rodents are not found in this fauna, and are completely unknown in Early and Middle Paleocene. This leaves an adaptive zone open in which multituberculates, primates, and possibly insectivores could compete. Primates are thus in no way excluded by more highly specialized forms from the wide adaptive zone deduced on morphological grounds.

4. *Frequency.* Inhabiting this broad adaptive zone, primates should be a dominating group in the local faunas of the Paleocene, not only in number of genera, but also in the total number of individuals present. In spite of the adverse fossilization conditions for the arboreal representatives of the order, this is quite frequently the case. Of the total number of identified individuals in collections from the Ft. Union, Middle Paleocene, of Montana (although not in the New Mexico facies), primates constitute 20%. Other groups are: multituberculates, 25%; insectivores, 15%; carnivores, 15%; condylarths, 25%. This count is furthermore biased towards a greater number of multituberculates, since all such were identified (Simpson, 1937). As mentioned above, the form *Plesiadapis* is quite common, to the extent of being the type fossil of the level. It is clear from this that the primates must have played an in-

---

[1] This discussion of Paleocene faunas is primarily based on private communication with Bryan Patterson.

comparably greater role in Paleocene faunas than in any modern fauna, and the explanation must be sought in a difference in ecologic habitat.

5. *Temporal distribution.* As the last type of evidence, the time of appearance, deployment, and extinction of early primates indicates the competitive relations of the group. Rodents appear first in the Late Paleocene, after which time no new group of primates evolved clear rodent-like adaptations (the Middle Eocene genera *Trogolemur* and *Uintasorex,* with strong incisor development are questionable exceptions, since their ancestry is not established). All primate families with rodent-like adaptations were thus established by Middle Paleocene, before the appearance of true rodents. The main spread of rodents came in the Eocene, and coincided with the decline and extinction of primitive primates in North America and Europe.

Multituberculates constitute another possible competing group in part of the primate-rodent adaptive zone. Numerous adaptations towards an herbivorous and frugivorous diet are evident (Simpson, 1926), many of them superficially rodent-like. Although probably quite specialized in their adaptations, they exploited the same food source as many early primates, who were thus forced to compete for this food. However, the main flowering of the order Multituberculata was before the primate radiation, and the main deployment of primates is correlated with the decline and extinction of multituberculates, of which the last family lingered on until Early Eocene.

The radical reduction in number of genera of primates in Late Eocene times, and their complete disappearance from Europe and North America by Middle Oligocene, was probably due to a number of factors. Through rodent competition the primate adaptive zone was seriously limited, and the order as a whole driven into an arboreal "refuge area." The progressively colder climates through Eocene and Oligocene may then have driven the jungle, and thus the arboreal primates, out of the more temperate areas where most of the collecting of the fossils has been done. On the other hand, even modern lemurs, which have gone considerably farther in brain evolution than had their Eocene predecessors, today flourish only in geographically isolated refuge areas like Madagascar and the East Indies. Thus even these forms are not able to compete in a fauna with full representation of modern mammals, where they presumably are replaced mainly by monkeys. More progressive groups of monkeys were thus probably a decisive factor in the extinction of lemuroids over large areas in Early Tertiary times. That the group, if left alone, retained capacities for highly divergent evolution is strikingly shown in the Pliocene-Pleistocene lemuroid radiation on Madagascar, where large, ungulate-like herbivores were developed.

Conclusions

It thus seems that primates took prominent part in the first placental radiation, invading a broad *primate-rodent* adaptive zone, and developing a large number of genera and phyletic lines. In ecologic habitat, many of these early primates may be thought of as the rats of the Paleocene. With the later appearance of true rodents, the primate habitat was however markedly restricted, and the order became, as did most orders of the early placental radiation, in part extinct and in part limited to an ecologic refuge area—arboreal habitat. In this restricted niche, competition led to the extinction of more conservative forms, and new adaptations were developed in the more progressive lines. Only in the isolated areas of Madagascar and the East Indies do the less modified descendants of the arboreal early primates persist today in the form of various lemuroid groups and *Tarsius*.

This modification of our picture of the early primates adaptive zone has also certain wider implications, since it invalidates the naive technique which uses gross morphological resemblance as an index of relationship between early and later primates. In invading their early, wide adaptive zone, the primates were taking part in the first placental radiation. They were thus in a different phase of evolution from the later primates (which were evolving within a zone), and were for the most part adapting to a radically different adaptive zone from that inhabited by modern monkeys. A major shift in adaptive zone separates the two groups.

Early primates, by virtue of participating in a major radiation, show a great deal of variation in all preserved features, and within and between families abundant examples of parallelism and convergence can be demonstrated. From this pool of variability later primates were undoubtedly drawn. But because of the limited overlap in adaptive zone one would expect reversals of trend in phyletic lines and delusive patterns of parallel evolution. Morphological features, whether "adaptive" or "nonadaptive," thus cannot be used by themselves as a measure of relationship between early and later primates. They are only meaningful in the context of phyletic lines, where the adaptive shift can be demonstrated and traced.

Summary

Early primate evolution can be approached through the paleontological concepts of adaptive radiation and adaptive zone. The problem— the adaptive zone of Paleocene and Eocene primates—is discussed on the basis of various criteria of structural and faunal relationships. In numerous lines of early primates, chisel-shaped incisors, large diastemata, and grinding molars were developed independently (Apatemyidae, Plesiadapidae, various Anaptomorphidae). Other groups show root-eating (Carpolestidae) and browsing (*Microchoerus*) adaptation. In Early Tertiary faunas primates furthermore play an important role, constituting more than 10% of all late Paleocene mammalian genera from the Rocky Mountain area, and 20% of the total of identified individuals from the Mesa Pocket, Ft. Union fauna of Montana. The conclusion is that early primates inhabited a very broad *primate-rodent* adaptive zone, many of them constituting the "rats of the Paleocene." As a consequence of limited overlap in the adaptive zone, gross morphological resemblance between early and later primates cannot be used as an index of relationship, which constitutes an important limitation upon the comparative method.

The Geologic History of Non-Hominid Primates in the Old World

Bryan Patterson   1954

Disagreements among students of the primates are many and profound —a statement that hardly possesses the charm of novelty. Since these disagreements extend to what should and what should not be included in the order both at the bottom and, in the family Hominidae, at the top, it becomes necessary at the outset to define the term "non-hominid primate." In this discussion, it will include the tupaioids and exclude the *Australopithecus* group. As thus limited, the topic is a very large one, requiring for thorough treatment far more space than can be allotted here. In an attempt to cover as much ground as possible, the setting in which Old World primate history unfolded will be touched upon, the nature of the fossil record reviewed, some points in it singled out for mention, and, in conclusion, a brief discussion given of certain theoretical interpretations that seem reasonable in the light of the knowledge now available.

The Setting

The evolution of the primates in the Old World took place over the greater part of Eurasia and Africa. We may confidently infer that this

FROM Human Biology, 1954, vol. 26, pp. 191–209 (this issue was also published separately by the Wayne University Press under the title The Non-Human Primates and Hominid Evolution). Reprinted by permission of the author and of the Wayne State University Press. The paper was originally presented at a symposium at meetings of the American Association for the Advancement of Science, held on December 27, 1953, in Boston, and organized and edited by James A. Gavan. It is an authoritative review of events, primarily of the later Tertiary, following Barth's consideration of the early Tertiary. It is interesting to note, in connection with the author's comments on the literature on Oreopithecus, how much more has been written on that form in the few years since this paper appeared. The author is Alexander Agassiz Professor of Vertebrate Paleontology at Harvard University.

immense area has always been diverse climatically and topographically, although not as much so, as regards climate at least, in the earlier Tertiary as during the latest Tertiary, Pleistocene, and Recent periods. It was, however, much more cut up at various times in the past than it is now. A great negative belt in the earth's crust extended across it from the Atlantic to the Pacific. This was the site of the Tethys Sea, of which the Mediterranean is a remnant, a major barrier during much of the Tertiary to free faunal interchange between Europe and Northern Asia, on the one side, and Africa and Southern Asia, on the other. This barrier, of course, was neither complete nor continuous; the constant inflow of sediment combined with temporary cessation or slowing of subsidence here and there would have resulted in temporary land connections or insular stepping stones at various places along its enormous length. There were other negative belts, small only in comparison with the Tethys, that played their parts in the fragmentation process; to name only one, I may mention the Uralian trough, which occupied roughly the present site of the Ural mountains and served for some time as a partial barrier to east-west faunal movements in the northern mass. In addition to the long continuing, although not continuous, barriers presented by the negative belts, parts of the land areas were at times flooded by shallow epicontinental seas that must effectively have isolated areas of higher ground. Western Europe, for example, must have been an archipelago several times in its history. Concurrently with these ever-changing relations between land and sea, climatic fluctuations certainly took place, together with concomitant changes in the distribution of forest and savannah, steppe and arid region. Under such conditions, ranges would be shifted, contracted, or expanded; contiguous regions would be sundered, perhaps fragmented, to remain separated for longer or shorter periods of time and then to be reunited. This would seem to be true especially for the earlier part of the Tertiary. As time went on, the area became progressively more unified. Conditions, in short, were excellent for evolutionary diversification. With Old World primate evolution occurring in a setting such as this, it is difficult to take seriously the pronouncements so frequent in the literature that this or that group of primates arose in this or that region—certainly not in the present very sketchy state of our knowledge.

The Nature of the Record

Just how sketchy this knowledge is, a glance at the map (Figure 1) reveals. The various symbols show, very roughly, the distribution of fossil primate finds in space and time. They designate regions rather than specific localities and it was unfortunately not possible on this

FIGURE 1. Occurrences of non-hominid fossil primates in the Old World.

scale to indicate what part of an epoch the symbols represent. A jibe frequently leveled at distribution maps is that what they really show is the distribution of collectors, not that of organisms. The charge must be fully admitted in this instance. Only in Western Europe, the region longest and most intensively worked, do we have anything that even remotely approaches a continuous record. The scarcity of records from the other, much larger, regions stands out in striking contrast. Europe contains the only Paleocene locality that has yielded primates, and there also is found the only Eocene sequence. Extra-European Eocene localities number but two, both Late: one in northern China and one in Burma. All we know about primate life in the Oligocene is derived from a few finds in Egypt and Central Asia. Were it not for the East African Miocene, our records for this epoch would be meager indeed. The Pliocene is represented by relatively abundant although fragmentary material from India; elsewhere chiefly by various finds in Europe, including one new one of outstanding importance—the new material of *Pliopithecus*. Pleistocene symbols are more numerous than any others on the map, but this is unfortunately no indication that our knowledge of the primates of this epoch is adequate. The fact is that nearly every-where, Western Europe excepted, the surface has barely been scratched.

Going on a consideration of the number of genera known (Table 1), the deficiencies of our knowledge become even more apparent. There

TABLE 1

Geological Record of Non-Hominid Primates in the Old World

Divisions of Cenozoic Time and their estimated durations	Tupaioids: Anagalidae	Tupaioids: Tupaiidae	Lemuroids: Plesiadapidae	Lemuroids: Adapidae	Lemuroids: Lemuridae	Lemuroids: Indriidae	Daubentoniidae	Lorisidae: Lorisinae	Lorisidae: Galaginae	Tarsioids: Microchoeridae	Tarsioids: Anaptomorphidae	Tarsioids: Tarsiidae	Inc. Sed.: Apatemyidae	Inc. Sed.: Prosimii, fam. inc. sed.	Cercopithecidae: Cercopithecinae	Cercopithecidae: Colobinae	Catarrhines Inc. Sed.	Pongidae: Inc. Sed.	Pongidae: Dryopithecinae	Pongidae: Hylobatinae	Pongidae: Ponginae	Genera Known in the Divisions of Cenozoic Time
Recent		5			6	3	1	4	2			1			10	6				2	3	43
Pleistocene L (1 million)					6	6									1	1					1	14
Pleistocene M															2	1			1*	2	1	6
Pleistocene E															8						1	11
Pliocene L (11 million)																1						1
Pliocene M															3				2		1	6
Pliocene E								1								1		1	7	1		11
Miocene L (16 million)																			2	1		3
Miocene M																			2	1		3
Miocene E									1							1				2		6
Oligocene L (10 million)	1*																					1
Oligocene M	1																					0
Oligocene E																	4			1?		6
Eocene L (20 million)				3						2		1	1									11
Eocene M		?	1	4						1	1	1	1	2(1*)			2					13
Eocene E			1	1						1	1		1	5								4
Paleocene L (17 million)			2										2									2
Paleocene M																						0
Paleocene E																						0
Genera Total	2	5	4	4	10	6	1	5	3	3	2	1	2	7	16	8	6	1	9	5	3	103
Genera Living	0	5	0	0	6	3	1	4	2	0	0	1	0	0	10	6	0	0	0	2	3	43
Genera Extinct	2	0	4	4	4	3	0	1	1	3	2	0	2	7	6	2	6	1	9	3	0	60

* Exact horizon doubtful.
? Systematic position uncertain.
N. B. A number of genera extend over more than one division of time.

are 43 genera of living Old World non-hominid primates, give or take a few in either direction, according to taste in lumping or splitting. About 60 extinct genera are known, approximately half again as many as the living. This small total becomes even less impressive when we reflect that the vast majority are known only from fragments of mandibles and maxillaries. The number of forms of which we have a fair knowledge of skull structure and/or some acquaintance with the post-cranial skeleton is far fewer. The roll of these is soon called. Paleocene: *Plesiadapis* (from North American material); Eocene: *Adapis, Pronyc-ticebus, Necrolemur;* Miocene: *Progalago, Limnopithecus, Proconsul;* Pliocene: *Mesopithecus, Libypithecus, Pliopithecus;* Pleistocene: most of the Malagasy lemuroids and the African cercopithecids, the Chinese material of *Rhinopithecus.* For the Tertiary this makes a total of 10. Paleontology can speak with some authority on the taxonomy and phylogeny of certain of the living orders of mammals—for example, in Artiodactyla extinct genera outnumber living by nearly 4 to 1, in Perissodactyla by 25 to 1; it is evident, however, that it cannot yet do so for the Primates.

At this point, perhaps, the reader might reasonably expect the discussion to be concluded for lack of evidence. Things are not quite as bad as that, though. In any survey of a history it is very proper to state what the gaps are and where they occur, but it is equally proper to go on and do as well as possible with what is in hand. Every primate fossil is a precious relic that contributes its bit to the history of the order. True, the evidence thus far contributed is often capable of conflicting interpretations, but sooner or later matters iron out; new discoveries permit new perspectives, and progress, however halting, is made. Paleontology may not as yet be able to speak with authority, but it is now in a position to make suggestions that seem reasonable and worthy of attention. From here on, then, we can begin to look more at the positive, or brighter, side.

DISTRIBUTION

Some interesting data concerning geographical distribution are available. The scanty Pleistocene records show that the orang-utan was in India during the Early Pleistocene, and thus suggest that it was present in southeastern Asia throughout most if not all of the epoch. The few remains of Pleistocene gibbons extend the present range of *Hylobates* into southwestern China. Interglacial climates more favorable than the present permitted *Presbytis* to range westward into Europe and *Macaca* to extend as far north as England. *Papio*, together with *Macaca*, has been reported from the Mid-Pliocene of India, but more complete remains would perhaps make a new generic assignment necessary. It is clear that, during the later Tertiary, the gibbon group ranged widely over the Old World, together with the rather heterogeneous and probably artificial assemblage known as the Dryopithecinae. The very few later Tertiary and the Pleistocene records of prosimians are all within the areas now occupied by their surviving relatives, a fact which supports the inference, reasonable on general grounds, that the Prosimii had by then been displaced by the catarrhine expansion, and relegated to the marginal areas or ecologic niches they now occupy. Our knowledge of earlier Tertiary prosimians is almost wholly limited to Western Europe, but we can be sure that the group was very widespread in the Paleocene and Eocene. In general, as Cenozoic time went on, and Eurasia and Africa became progressively more unified, increasing opportunity for wide dispersal was available to successful groups.

The most important single zoogeographical datum in connection with primate history is this: since the Early Eocene, Old World and New World primate evolution appear to have gone their separate ways. We can state with confidence that some Paleocene primate exchange took place between the hemispheres; witness the common presence of plesiadapids. *Plesiadapis* itself, by the way, is the only genus, other than *Homo*, known to occur in both. The lack of Early Eocene genera common to the two is surprising, because this was the time of greatest faunal interchange between Eurasia and North America, indicating a broadly open migration route (Simpson, 1947). Primates surely participated in this interchange, but perhaps ecological barriers may have prevented their rapid spread westward in the Old World. The Early Eocene primate fauna of eastern Asia, if and when it is made known, may well turn out to be more similar to that of North America. So long as nothing is known east of Europe for this part of the Tertiary, it is of little use to speculate concerning the absence of various American supergeneric groups in Europe. Suffice it to say that the general cast of the primate fauna, the degrees of evolutionary advance, etc., were broadly comparable in the two areas.

Following the Early Eocene connection, Eurasia and North America were apparently separated until the Late Eocene. Neither during this nor any of the later connections is there evidence of any primate migrations until *Homo sapiens* arrives on the scene. Conditions in the vicinity of the bridge, which was very probably in the Bering Strait region, were evidently unfavorable climatically for members of the order in existence at the various times of connection. This very early separation of the basal primate stock has a decided bearing on major taxonomy, as will appear.

SOME ASPECTS OF THE RECORD

Space is lacking for any detailed review of the factual evidence, and since nearly all of it has been so well described by authors whose works are thoroughly familiar, this is not too serious. I shall therefore take up only a few specific points and touch on one or two matters of general interest. The absence of any definite records of the Tupaiidae is puzzling, because, be they primates or only near-primates, they have certainly come down to us from the earliest times. It may perhaps be that we have them and do not know it. The tupaiid dentition is quite characteristic, but it is possible that this might have been acquired in post-Eocene time, with Eocene and Paleocene representatives consequently remaining undetected. The question mark in the Mid Eocene in Table 1 refers to two genera recently referred to the family by Weitzel (1949). Unfortunately, his descriptions are cursory and given in general terms, and he does not figure the tooth crowns. The general body form is quite tupaiid-like, but this by itself is hardly sufficient evidence. These forms may perhaps be related to the Paleocene adapisoricids and these in turn could conceivably be tupaioids, but this is all very conjectural.[1] The tupaioid affinities of the Anagalidae have recently been called in question. Bohlin (1951) has described *Anagalopsis* from a deposit in Central Asia that is not precisely dateable, but which may fall somewhere in the later Oligocene if we may judge from the dentition of this form, which is more advanced than that of *Anagale*. Advanced in a peculiar way, the teeth being subhypsodont and unilaterally so, in the manner of many rodents and some other forms. This is a decidedly odd feature for a primate, although not in itself grounds for excluding the family from the order. Bohlin regards the structure of the bulla, as he interprets it, as the decisive character. Since this has an open U-shaped cleft beneath the porus proper, and no meatus, he concludes that it must be formed by the tympanic, and not by the entotympanic as it is in tupaiids. It seems to me, however, that an entotympanic in the course of phylogeny might assume such a form, and I am therefore not yet prepared to throw overboard Simpson's careful evaluation of the evidence favoring inclusion of the anagalids in the tupaioids.

The whole Early Tertiary prosimian complex bristles with difficulties. Forms and series of forms are shuttled about from one division to another

---

[1] Following Teilhard de Chardin, the adapisoricids have been placed in the insectivore family Leptictidae by most authors. The early Eocene species referred to *Adapisorex* by Teilhard is a leptictid, but the type and other late Paleocene species do not appear to be referable to this family.

and there is disagreement over what should be included and excluded. For example, the microchoerids are placed by Gregory, Le Gros Clark, and Simpson in the Tarsioidea (by the last as a subfamily, Necrolemurinae, of Anaptomorphidae), while Hürzeler (1948), who has recently completed a careful study of them, believes that they are closer to the lemuroids and entitled to rank as a distinct superfamily. For some, the Apatemyidae are primates, for others not, and so on. Such disagreements among highly competent authorities, the conflicting evidence responsible for them, and the number of genera that cannot be definitely assigned, strongly suggest that the distinction between lemuroids and tarsioids was not at that time very profound (Simpson, 1945; Barth, 1950).

The mosaic of characters that makes classification of these forms so difficult may be traceable to conditions prevailing in the area during the early Tertiary. The reader will recall the changing relations between land and sea, the fluctuating climates, and the shifting vegetation zones that the geologic evidence seems to indicate. Note that the Paleocene and Eocene together make up almost exactly half of Tertiary time, if we can trust the present crude estimates of the duration of the epochs. Under such conditions and over such a length of time, small-scale adaptive radiations would tend to arise in various separated regions. Reunion of these regions would lead to intergroup competition and to the reduction or elimination of the less well adapted of those groups that had happened to evolve in similar directions. Renewed separation would start the process anew. The genetic complex of any of these various stocks must have had much in common with those of all the others. Many mutations acting in these substrates would thus tend to have similar effects in distinct stocks, the closer the more nearly parallel the trends under way. As a result, not only would similar details of dental morphology be attained, but independently achieved characters would occur in the skull and postcranial skeleton as well. The net result would be a confusing array of small groups, each one resembling the others in a variety of ways, a situation extremely difficult to deal with on the basis of fragmentary fossil material. A small sample from one region, such as we have from Western Europe or from Western North America, obviously will not permit us to reconstruct very much of the story. In fact, if paleontology succeeds in even partially unravelling the tangle it will be doing very well indeed.

At the end of the Eocene and the beginning of the Oligocene there appears a small array of genera—such as *Amphipithecus, Moeripithecus, Parapithecus, Propliopithecus, "Kansupithecus"*[2]—that was probably of the greatest importance in primate history. It is more likely than not that these forms arose from some anaptomorphid stock, and very possible

[2] This name is technically invalid, Bohlin (1946) having failed to name a species.

that they, or rather the group they represent, were broadly ancestral to the Hominoidea and to the Cercopithecoidea. It is therefore the more unfortunate that our knowledge of them is confined to the lower jaw. One, *Propliopithecus*, has been hailed as an ancestral gibbon; it might about equally well, perhaps, be regarded as standing somewhere in the line of the Hominoidea as a whole (the others occur in the table under Catarrhini *incertae sedis*). It is at this point in history, just when things are getting really exciting, that the curtain descends on the higher primates, to remain down for two full subepochs. When it rises again in the Early Miocene, we are presented, thanks to the magnificent discoveries in East Africa, with an undoubted cercopithecid, generalized pongids, and a primitive gibbon.

Taking up the Cercopithecidae first, what strikes the eye is that the colobines have, in the books at least, a longer recorded history than the cercopithecines. This is based on *Mesopithecus*, known from the Early Pliocene, to which the Early Miocene East African form has been tentatively referred in preliminary notices. There is something a little puzzling here. The living colobines tend to be rather strictly arboreal, and their diet, as is well known, consists largely of leaves, for the digestion of which they have a specialized stomach. *Mesopithecus* is probably the most completely known fossil primate and its remains are quite common in Pontian deposits, skulls having been found in groups (Abel, 1927, p. 133). The associated fauna is that of a steppe region, horses, antelopes, and other open country forms occurring in numbers. If *Mesopithecus* was a colobine with the diet and habitat preferences of its living relatives, why is it so common in a steppe fauna? A form living in trees along watercourses, as *Colobus* does in East Africa today, would hardly leave skulls in groups. A reexamination of the affinities of *Mesopithecus* would seem in order; the field evidence suggests cercopithecine relationships. The remaining cercopithecids call for no comment in a review of this brevity.

The case of *Oreopithecus*, frequently considered to be a cercopithecid, deserves passing mention, if only as a horrible example of what should not happen. Originally described in the 1870's, a literature of approximately 80 papers has grown up around it. Three views as to affinities have been held: that it was a pongid, an aberrant cercopithecid, or a sort of connecting link between the two. Hürzeler (1949a) has recently made a thorough restudy of the genus and has concluded that it is a pongid ("anthropomorph") of uncertain affinities, and has nothing to do with the Cercopithecidae. It is shown in the table in the Early Pliocene under Pongidae *incertae sedis*. Now comes the depressing part of the story. Hürzeler believes that only 11 of the many papers describing or referring to the animal were written by authors who had seen original material.

The others were based on the previous literature, on the published figures, or on some casts that appear to have been widely distributed. The figures were inaccurate and the casts were misleading. Schwalbe, author of the longest and most quoted paper, apparently worked from the casts. Gregory, also working from the casts and laboring under the misapprehension that the age was Early Miocene, thought he detected a resemblance between *Oreopithecus* and the problematical *Apidium,* and from this stems the view that *Apidium* might have had something to do with the ancestry of the cercopithecids. Students of the fossil hominids must all be familiar with situations of this sort, expenditures of time and energy that resulted only in confusing the issue. This and similar cases should inspire us to take steps to insure that such does not occur again. Of this more anon.

On dental evidence, the gibbons can be traced back to the Early Miocene, certainly, and perhaps on back to *Propliopithecus.* Of the Ponginae, neither *Pan* nor *Gorilla* has a fossil record. *Pongo* is recorded from teeth throughout the Pleistocene, and Hooijer (1951) has recently discussed a Mid Pliocene P_3 from the Siwaliks, which he finds indistinguishable from that of the living species. The bulk of the pongid records is of course formed by the Dryopithecinae. The relatively numerous Late Miocene and Pliocene finds are unfortunately not very helpful in tracing lines of descent, but they do show that a fairly rich variety of hominoids was then in existence. The magnificent finds of *Proconsul* are so familiar that there is no need to go into any detail here. It is enough to say they reveal that an Early Miocene pongid had a brain of generalized catarrhine type, a jaw that had relatively narrow incisors and lacked a simian shelf, and limb bones that were not specialized for brachiation. Presumably it progressed to a considerable extent on all fours. The contemporary gibbon *Limnopithecus,* the Pliocene gibbon *Pliopithecus* (Zapfe, 1952), and such few skeletal fragments of later dryopithecines as we have, combine to suggest that a similar body form, at least, was characteristic of Miocene and earlier Pliocene pongids generally.

SOME POSSIBLE INTERPRETATIONS

So much for this very brief and necessarily incomplete survey of the available facts. A body of data requires organization if it is to have meaning, and paleontological data are perhaps most succinctly expressed in the form of phylogenetic diagrams. The fact that such diagrams are notorious for the wide difference of opinion they usually display does not detract from their usefulness as shorthand expressions of different viewpoints. The scheme shown in Figure 2 was published recently by Adolph H. Schultz (1953), one of the great students of Recent primates. It

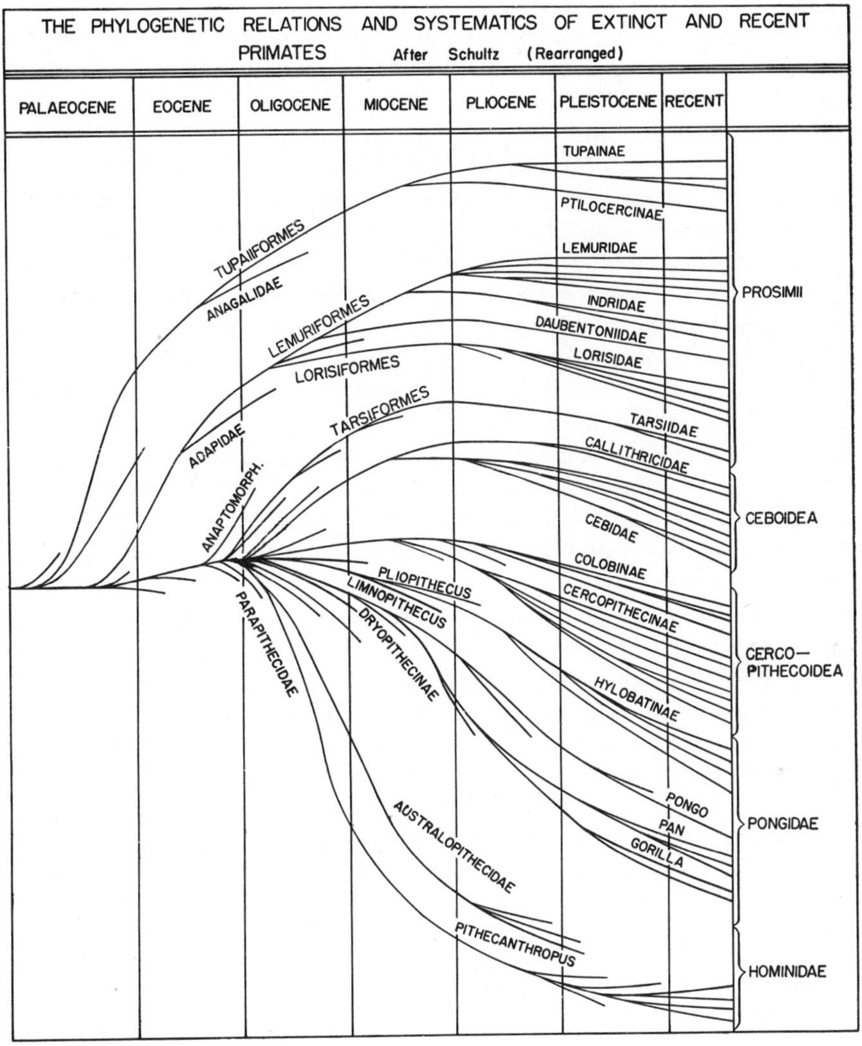
THE PHYLOGENETIC RELATIONS AND SYSTEMATICS OF EXTINCT AND RECENT PRIMATES After Schultz (Rearranged)
PALAEOCENE
EOCENE
OLIGOCENE
MIOCENE
PLIOCENE
PLEISTOCENE
RECENT
TUPAINAE
PTILOCERCINAE
LEMURIDAE
INDRIDAE
DAUBENTONIIDAE
LORISIDAE
TARSIIDAE
CALLITHRICIDAE
CEBIDAE
COLOBINAE
CERCOPITHECINAE
HYLOBATINAE
PONGO
PAN
GORILLA
TUPAIIFORMES
ANAGALIDAE
LEMURIFORMES
LORISIFORMES
TARSIFORMES
ADAPIDAE
ANAPTOMORPH.
PARAPITHECIDAE
PLIOPITHECUS
LIMNOPITHECUS
DRYOPITHECINAE
AUSTRALOPITHECIDAE
PITHECANTHROPUS
PROSIMII
CEBOIDEA
CERCO—PITHECOIDEA
PONGIDAE
HOMINIDAE

FIGURE 2. One view of primate phylogeny.

contains some questionable features. To begin with, some of the lines appear to be split unnecessarily far back. I find it incredible that the Hominidae should have originated at the beginning of the Oligocene, or that the *Australopithecus* group should have parted company with them shortly thereafter. The *Pan* and *Gorilla* lines surely were not separate in the Early Pliocene, and it is perhaps doubtful if the *Pan-Gorilla* and *Pongo* phyla go back as far as the Mid Miocene. On the other hand, the break-up of the Cebidae certainly took place long before the Pliocene. Going on to more general topics, it is misleading to represent all extinct groups as so many minor twigs from main branches that extend without deviation or interruption from the distant past to the present, and the depiction of a main trunk running from Paleocene almost to Oligocene is somewhat of an oversimplification. Schultz's diagram has not been singled out merely for the sake of captious criticism, but because I suspect that it is a rather representative example of how primate evolution may appear to those who look into time from the vantage point of the Recent.[2a]

Figure 3 is submitted as an example of how the picture appears to one who tends to look into time from the opposite direction.[3] Viewed in this light, primate history has the appearance of a succession of radiations of varying scope.

The dashed lines at the base of the figure are not there for purely decorative purposes. As Professor Jepsen remarked in the course of the Symposium, only three living orders, one of them nonplacental, have a longer recorded history than the primates. A character fundamental to the evolution of the Theria was the acquisition of the so-called tribosphenic molar, from which the primate and all other types have been derived. It is now known that this molar type had come into existence by the middle of the Cretaceous Period. During that part of the Age of Reptiles represented by the Late Cretaceous—a long stretch of time, probably longer than the Eocene, for example—mammals must have un-

[2a] Note by the editor: Dr. Patterson and Dr. Schultz wish me to point out that the rearrangement shown here, of Schultz's original, was done for purposes of making comparison with Figure 3 simpler, and that it may convey impressions not intended by the original as to emphasis on time periods and distinctness of phylogenetic lines; also, that the original was published in preliminary form, specifically to invite criticism, and has been carefully reworked and republished since then (e.g., Schultz, 1957b, and in *Primatologia*, vol. I, 1956). This does not affect Dr. Patterson's point in discussion.

[3] Those familiar with the scheme presented by Simpson in his *The Meaning of Evolution* (1949, Figure 17, p. 91) will note a considerable degree of resemblance. The two are actually independent. The explanation for this lies in the fact that Simpson's book exists in two editions. In one, which I read, presentation and discussion of factual evidence are abbreviated, and the figure in question is not included. I did not see it in the first edition until after Figure 3 had been drafted. The agreement between the two is encouraging.

dergone a considerable amount of diversification. At present, we know next to nothing about this earliest therian radiation, but we can infer that it took place—the diversified mammals of the Early Paleocene certainly did not come into existence overnight. "Proto-primates" and "para-primates" surely formed part of it. Tupaioids, macroscelidids, perhaps apatemyids may have appeared at about this time, together with such poorly known groups as the adapisoricids and metacodontids.[4]

Out of this radiation, possibly even a part of it, came the prosimian complex of the Paleocene and Eocene. If the dentition is any guide, these forms were a highly diversified lot, and it is possible, as Barth has suggested, that they were not all arboreal but may have filled a number of ecologic niches open to small mammals, particularly in Paleocene and earlier Eocene time. This prosimian radiation seems to have largely ended with the Eocene, at least in regions from which we have reasonably good fossil records. The rise of modern types of rodents and of carnivores, which occurred about this time, may have been a contributing factor, but more important, probably, was the rise of the catarrhines. Tupaiids, lorisids, and tarsiids have managed to survive the catarrhine inundation, but only by adaptation to ecologic niches in which they have escaped from competition. The only later Cenozoic prosimian expansion, that of the lemuroids, is the result of an accident. African prosimians, perhaps adapines, reached Madagascar (a region to which no non-hominid catarrhine, and indeed few mammals of any sort, ever penetrated), possibly in Oligocene time and certainly by overseas transport, and there gave rise to the profusion of Recent and Late Pleistocene forms for which the island is so justly famous.

A point to be made here is that the Paleocene and Eocene forms, not the terminal twigs that survive today, were the "real" Prosimii. As noted, the early forms have much in common structurally, and constitute a reasonably compact group. As regards taxonomy, I would heartily agree with Simpson that it is preferable to include all, both early and late, in one suborder.

If I may be pardoned a digression into the New World, the platyrrhine radiation, like the lemuroid, was also the result of an accident of dispersal, this time from North America. The South American fossil record permits the assumption that the date was in the first half of the Oligocene. As Gregory has suggested, the ancestral forms may possibly have been notharctines, but this is very uncertain. A peculiar fact concerning the platyrrhines is that we have no good evidence that they ever evolved predominantly ground living types, despite the fact that the general

---

[4] The last, a North American group, may be represented in the European Eocene by *"Adapisorex" anglicus* Forster Cooper.

situation, absence of placental carnivores, etc., would seem to have been more favorable in South America than in the Old World. This appears to be one more instance showing that the existence of an evolutionary opportunity does not insure that it will be seized. In Figure 3, the lines of descent of the various ceboid subgroups are projected very nearly to the presumed date of ingress. Theory and an excellent example from another order may be cited in support. As Wright (1949a, p. 387) has remarked: "When . . . unoccupied territory is reached, a very extensive and rapid adaptive radiation should follow under the divergent selection pressures toward exploitation of the various special ecological niches, opened up by . . . the mere absence of competition . . ." The caviomorph rodents, whose ancestors reached South America by accidental means at about the same time as those of the platyrrhines, illustrate this perfectly, their major subdivisions becoming established almost from the start.

The fact that South American primates had an ancestry distinct from that of the catarrhines since at least the Early Eocene, taken together with their morphological peculiarities, entitles them, I believe, to subordinal rank. Retention of the time-honored terms Platyrrhini and Catarrhini would appear to be justified.

The catarrhine radiation, the most important from our point of view, began before the end of the Eocene. Beyond this important fact we know almost nothing, due to the fragmentary nature of the few known Late Eocene and Early Oligocene specimens and the lack of any records from the Middle and Late Oligocene. The cercopithecoid-hominoid dichotomy occurred before the Miocene but just when we do not know. Very successful in their own sphere, cercopithecoids clearly had nothing to do with the ancestry of any other catarrhine group, and need no further consideration here.

In reading the descriptions and discussions of the Miocene hominoids, it is possible to detect here and there a note of surprise concerning the evidence that they seem to have possessed a quadrupedal gait. The catarrhine radiation was a fairly late one, geologically speaking; the ancestral forms were certainly quadrupedal, and it is therefore not too remarkable that the earlier hominoids should also have been to an extent quadrupedal or that some, at least, remained so into Pliocene time. The new discoveries in fact deal a death blow to some old arguments concerning the origin of man, arguments which appear to have stemmed from typological thinking. Gibbons have rather distinctive molars, and because of this it is possible to trace a phyletic thread back from the present that does not get lost in the dryopithecine tangle. The Early Oligocene *Propliopithecus* could on this evidence be an ancestral gibbon, and has often

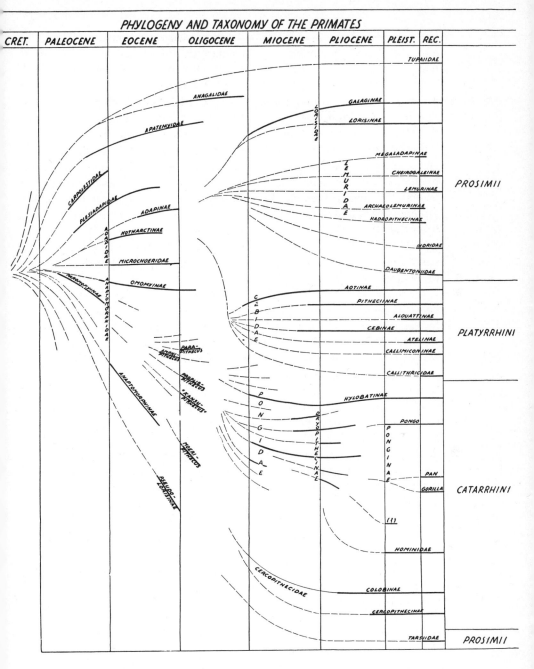

FIGURE 3. Another view of primate phylogeny. Known ranges are shown in solid lines, starting with the earliest forms that can be referred with assurance to a particular group.

been so regarded. As a result, a train of reasoning something like this appears to have prevailed in some quarters: living gibbons are brachiators par excellence; *Propliopithecus* was a gibbon, ergo it was an excellent brachiator; the ancestral pongines must have been too; man does not brachiate, ergo his ancestors must have branched off before this adaptation became established; *Propliopithecus* is Early Oligocene in age, ergo the Hominidae arose in the Eocene; Q. E. D. The new evidence, which rather strongly suggests that extreme specializations in locomotion occurred quite late in hominoid history, does away with this old objection to close affinity between hominids and pongids. Proponents of this affinity no longer have to combat the contention that a radical change in the direction of adaptation would be necessary in order to derive the one from the other. The concept responsible, basically, for the old arguments against such derivation was the notion, once rather prevalent, that all parts of animals evolved at about the same rates, a view repeatedly shown to be erroneous.

The generalized locomotor apparatus of later Tertiary hominoids has been hailed as showing that man's ancestry did not pass through a brachiating stage, hailed almost with relief, as though brachiating were some deadly sin. I submit that this is going too far and that there is no real evidence for it. The objections to such a stage perhaps stem in part from old views and may also be in part semantic—the word brachiation being associated with the extreme conditions in living pongids. There would seem to be nothing in the known structure of the earlier pongids to indicate that they did not brachiate to some extent, and, as Gregory has long insisted, a moderate amount of brachiation seems to be the best explanation of how the hominid line got up on its hind legs. Our ancestors, however, unlike those of the living pongids, were able to take their brachiation or leave it alone. The extreme degree of this adaptation shown by hylobatines and pongines today may be as recent an event in primate history as acquisition of the upright gait.

Some recent authors who favor an origin of the human stock from the pongid, branch us off in the Early Miocene, if not earlier, again perhaps in an effort to avoid the demon brachiation. In Figure 3, this event is postulated to have occurred considerably later. In view of the rapid evolutionary progress made by the hominid line during the Pleistocene, there seems to be no compelling reason for assuming that the earlier stages should have required longer than the 10 million years or so allotted to the Pliocene. Man is the result of an adaptive shift in the direction of evolution, and such events are rapid, geologically speaking. But man is a non-non-hominid primate and I must not discuss him further.

These are the ideas of one paleontologist concerning the reasonable suggestions that paleontology can make about primate history (novelty for any of them is, of course, disclaimed). They are as tentative as our story is incomplete, but the history of primate discovery holds forth the promise of a far better base on which to build. Vertebrate paleontology is roughly 150 years old. By the end of the first third of this period, say up to 1859, only 7 extinct genera of primates had been described. Between 1860 and 1900, 21 more were added (these figures are for the world); between 1901 and 1925, 33 and since 1926, 46. If this can be kept up, we should be well off some day, but in the meantime we are not getting the most out of what we have. Professor Straus recently remarked that it would be nice if good casts of the australopithecines were generally available. I should like to go further and say that casts or photographs of all important fossil primate specimens should be prepared and made widely available for exchange or purchase. With existing media, especially latex, magnificent casts can be made. Stereoscopic photomicrographs from various aspects would serve for small and delicate specimens. This sounds like an ambitious program, but it seems a good way to avoid more *Oreopithecus* incidents. If, then, we can continue the rate of discovery and provide for wide use of the materials we have and hope to get, our grandchildren will perhaps have the beginnings of a workable outline of primate phylogeny, and on this properly qualified note of optimism this brief presentation may be closed.

The Analysis of Primate Evolution with Particular Reference to the Origin of Man

S. L. Washburn 1951

There are three reasons why this is an appropriate time to discuss the origin of man. The first is the finding of abundant fossils of a new kind of missing link in South Africa. The man-like apes indicate an unanticipated stage in human evolution which radically alters all current theories of human origins. The second reason is that, through the work of numerous geneticists, zoologists, and paleontologists, a theoretical framework is now available which is far superior to any previous evolutionary theories. The third is the fact that evolutionary speculations can be experimentally checked to a far greater extent than has been realized in the past. It is the combination of new facts, new theories, and new hopes of proof which makes this an auspicious moment to reconsider the problems of human origins.

Why the matter needs reconsideration after all the mass of work done on it deserves a word of comment, which may be divided again under the headings of facts, theories, and proof. The facts bearing on human origins were largely collected in the nineteenth century, or according to principles developed at that time, and there has been no "New Comparative Anatomy" comparable to the "New Systematics" or any "Modern Synthesis" as in evolution. The result is that the vast quantity of materials of very unequal value (Zuckerman, 1933; Simpson, 1945) is difficult

FROM Cold Spring Harbor Symposia on Quantitative Biology, vol. 15, 1951, pp. 67–78, reprinted by permission of the author and of the Long Island Biological Association. Originally presented at the symposium on "The Origin and Evolution of Man," held at Cold Spring Harbor, June 9–17, 1950. The author, as reference to the bibliography of this volume indicates, has long emphasized that only comprehension of function will permit understanding of the relative taxonomic importance of different morphological features of fossils. This well known article is probably his best illustration of the point. Dr. Washburn is Professor of Anthropology at the University of California at Berkeley.

to use. Each author tends to use only a small part of the easily available information, and the basis for selection is by no means clear. If the papers by Schultz (1936) and Straus (1949) on human origins were examined, it would be hard to tell that the same animals were under discussion, for few facts are mentioned in both papers and their evaluation is totally different. The mere collection of more facts will not advance the understanding of human evolution. Before progress can be made, methods must be outlined for deciding which facts are important.

The evaluation of differences in fossil bones and living primates leads to the question of theory. Certainly the ideas of orthogenesis, irreversibility, and the supreme value of nonadaptive characters have thoroughly blocked the development of effective thinking about human evolution. They have been used to rule every known kind of primate out of the line of human evolution. Actually, scholars who specialized in human evolution (and it should be stressed that this includes many human anatomists and others besides physical anthropologists) are in an extremely poor position to develop evolutionary theory. Since they are interested in the origin and classification of a single group of animals, and in actual practice almost entirely with man, there are not enough examples to develop and prove theories. Those interested in human evolution must borrow their general theories and principles from others who have access to wider data and more manageable subjects. The task of the anthropologist is to fit knowledge of the primates into the framework of modern evolutionary theory, as described by numerous authors in *Genetics, Paleontology, and Evolution* (Jepsen, Simpson, Mayr, 1949) and as developed in *The Meaning of Evolution* (Simpson, 1949).

The importance of experiment arises from the nature of the anthropologist's task. If he would demonstrate that one theory is better than another, he must have a method beyond personal opinion of deciding which facts are important. Facts and good theories are important, but people feel strongly on the subject of their own origin and there will be wide disagreement until a modern, experimental comparative anatomy can take its place among the tools of the student of evolution. At the moment, whether man is regarded as derived from an ape in the late Pliocene (Weinert, 1932) or an unknown, unspecialized, tarsioid of Eocene age (Jones, 1948) depends on personal evaluation of the same basic facts.

The origin of man has been studied by so many people, so many different ideas have been expressed, and the nomenclature is in such a complete state of confusion that it will clarify matters if I briefly outline my ideas first, then defend them in some detail and consider a series of problems of general zoological interest.

The earliest primates were distinguished from other primitive mammals by the use of the hands and feet for grasping. This is anatomically a complex adaptation, involving elongation of the digits, flattening of the terminal phalanges and thinning of the nails (Le Gros Clark, 1936). This basic adaptation has been the foundation of the whole history of the primates, which has been in other ways remarkably diverse. There is no single trend with regard to way of locomotion (which included slow clingers and fast hoppers), or dentition (there are forms with huge incisors, aye aye; or none, Lepilemur; canines may be huge, mandrill; or small, many female Old World forms and hominids), or diet (many primates eat a mixed diet, but one group of lemurs, Indrisidae, and one group of monkeys, Colobidae, have specialized in leaf eating and have developed specialized viscera). It is this great diversity in secondary characters and ways of life which makes primate classification so difficult. Particularly in fossils the hands and feet are usually not preserved, and the main pattern is not reflected in the jaws and teeth. I believe that this accounts for the difficulty in placing many of the Eocene genera (Simpson, 1940).

The early primates took to the trees with the special senses of the primitive mammal. There were tactile hairs, movable ears, and a sense of smell which was predominant. The changes which produced the forms we call monkeys were either present in the advanced lemurs (or tarsiers, I doubt that this is a fundamental distinction) or developed by parallel evolution. For in both New and Old World monkeys active, arboreal forms developed, with reduced external ears and ear muscles, reduced sense of smell, and with stereoscopic, color vision. These arboreal quadrupeds replaced the lemurs, except where the latter remained protected (Madagascar) or by being strictly nocturnal (as the tarsiers, lorises and galagos). The brain greatly increased in size, and Elliot Smith (1924) was the first to appreciate the multitude of differences which came from converting a primitive smell-brain into a sight-brain. Changes at this stage are clearly reflected in the skull by the reduction in parts associated with the olfactory mechanism (reduction in the turbinal bones, interorbital region, and cribriform plate with correlated changes in the anterior fossa).

The origin of the primates was primarily a locomotor adaptation. The first radiation lasted approximately a third of the age of the mammals, perhaps twenty million years. The second was a reorganization of the special senses, making the monkeys successful in the Old World tropical forests by day. The third radiation of Old World primates depended again on a locomotor adaptation. In the apes, a series of modifications in

the arms and trunk leads to locomotion of a sort not found in the quadrupedal monkeys. (Spider monkeys brachiate; this is another example
of the extensive parallelism in the New and Old Worlds. But spider
monkeys also move in typical quadrupedal fashion and have prehensile
tails. The combination of brachiation and quadrupedal locomotion is not
found in the Old World and shows how the ape type of locomotion may
have arisen). Brachiation involves changes in the motion of the arms
and the abandoning of the use of the back in the typical quadrupedal
manner. The anatomical changes are in the wrist, elbow, shoulder, and
thoracic region. None of these are duplicated in any of the monkeys,
and brachiation is an elaborate behavioral and anatomical complex, every
essential detail of which is shared by man and the living apes.

Some idea of the profound changes in anatomy which accompany
brachiation, as practiced by the apes, is given by the changes in the
muscles of the trunk and arm. The scalenes migrate upward; psoas
major, rectus abdominis, and the origin of sacrospinalis migrate down;
serratus anterior increases in size, as does the deltoid; pectoralis major
migrates up, pectoralis minor changes its insertion to the coracoid process; origin and insertion of arm extensors are reduced and the flexors are
increased. These are correlated with the changes in the joints previously
mentioned. (Loth, 1931, is the best general source of information on the
muscles of primates.)

The discovery of the pelves of the South African man-like apes, or
small-brained men, has made it possible to outline the basic adaptation
which is the foundation of the human radiation. These forms have brains
which are in the range of the living apes, and their teeth show both
human and ape characters, but the ilia are practically modern-human.
Men were bipeds first, and later large-brained, small-faced bipeds. Just
as the differences between monkey and ape are in the upper extremity
and trunk, so those between ape and man are in the pelvis and foot. To
mention but a few differences: in apes gluteus maximus is not maximus,
gracilis is not gracile, biceps femoris has one head, and semitendinosus
and membranosus are not as the names imply. The bone-muscle-func-
tional complex of the leg distinguishes man from the apes as sharply as
the comparable complex of the arms shows their similarity and distinguishes both from the monkeys.

The above outline differs from prevailing theories in several ways. The
gibbons are regarded as typical apes and placed in the same family with
the living apes and with numerous extinct forms. The South African
forms are regarded as in the same family as man, part of the same radiation. However, the arrangement is in the main similar to many others

(Hooton, 1946; Simpson, 1949; Zuckerman, 1933). Lemurs, monkeys, apes, and men represent a series of radiations. Each is later in time and each is less variable than the one which preceded it.

Among the lemurs there are radically different locomotor, dietary, and dental patterns. At the other extreme man is represented by a single form, being far less variable (even if all fossil forms and the South African man-apes are added) than lorises, galagos, or indris-like lemurs.

Finally, anatomically speaking, man is highly specialized. He represents an extreme and odd form in his way of locomotion. In no other animal can the anatomy of pelvis and foot be matched. His trunk and thorax are very peculiar, their structure being shared only with the great apes. Obviously the brain is a recent and extreme adaptation. This modern, ground-living ape would amount to little without tools. The fact that we number more than a few thousand, ecologically unimportant bipeds living in the Old World tropics is due to the development of tools. And it is important to remember that tools are surely older than Java man. The appearance of all modern forms of men is long after tool-using. The origin of the human radiation may be treated just as that of any other mammalian group, but the use of tools brings in a set of factors which progressively modifies the evolutionary picture. It is particularly the task of the anthropologist to assess the way the development of culture affected physical evolution.

In defining the major groups of primates the effort has been made to use the most important characters, that is, to use the ones which made the evolutionary radiations possible. In general, characters may be divided into three categories: (1) Primary characters which are responsible for the radiations; (2) secondary characters which are a necessary consequence of the new selection, based on the acquisition of the primary ones; and (3) incidental characters which happen to be selected along with the primary ones. For example, if the group of apes which gave origin to man had a particular type of dentition, this would automatically become part of the original heritage of the hominids. Other features might be due to genetic drift in small groups of early men.

If modern man be examined, he is found to be a mixture of basic primate features, the primary characters of the first or lemuroid radiation. (The hands show a remarkable amount of the primitive grasping adaptation with long digits, nails, etc. It should be remembered that the most perfectly opposable and relatively largest thumbs among all the primates are found in the lorises, and not in man, as often stated. Human feet are a recent modification of the same pattern, fundamentally differing only in a single ligament and the length of the toes.) The next complex is that of the head, brain and special senses which is achieved, except for changes in proportions, in the monkey radiation. Then the arms and trunk become essentially modern. Perhaps then, many millions of years later, the bipedal complex was developed. Finally, the secondary features of the human radiation became general, the small face and the large brain.

Evolution proceeded at different rates in various parts of the body. This is not to suggest that at any time the animals were not functioning wholes adapted to a way of life, but it does mean that there may be a considerable degree of independence of a given part. The eye of monkey, ape, and man are remarkably similar despite major changes in other parts of the body. In spite of a variety of ways of life the same sort of visual mechanism was advantageous and was maintained by selection.

There are three implications of this scheme of evolution for the study of human origins: *First,* different characters are of very unequal taxonomic value at various stages in human evolution. If similarity in trunk and arm show the community of man and ape and if the difference lies primarily in pelvis and legs, a long list of characters in which both features of arm and leg are included may be misleading. Especially is it misleading to say that of so many characters man shares this percent with one form and that percent with another. Similarities in arms, legs, and skull have different meanings. The *second* implication is that there are real changes between ancestors and their descendants. To say that all apes have longer arms or canine teeth than man (Jones, 1948; Weidenreich, 1946) in no way bars them from human ancestry. The ancestors were parts of different radiations and were specialized accordingly. The search for the unspecialized common ancestor becomes either a denial of evolution or a hunt for an illusory, philosophical archetype. The *third* is that there will be many incidental differences at each level which are of no major importance. Even if every ape had one form of pterion and every human another, it would be of no importance. Actually the form varies in both groups and experimental alteration of suture patterns shows that this type of difference does not change the functional pattern of the cranial vault.

It is clear that adaptation to life on the ground is the basis of the human radiation. Many groups of Old World primates have come to the ground at different times and places, but no group of New World monkeys has taken up life on the ground. Two, perhaps three, different groups of baboons, patas monkeys, vervets, and macaques have become ground-livers. On the other hand not a single group of the leaf-eating monkeys (Colobidae) have taken up life on the ground. The restriction here is clearly diet. The soft leaves and fruits of the tropical forests are not available in plains country, and monkeys adapted to this diet have not become ground-livers, although there seems no reason as far as the locomotor system is concerned why they could not. If the ground-living and tree-living Old World monkeys are contrasted, a series of differences appears which are of the greatest importance for the understanding of human evolution. The ground-living forms have far greater ranges and are divided into less distinct varieties than the tree-livers. For example, the vervets, which are only partially ground-livers, still are very similar from Uganda to the Cape, whereas in the *nictitans* group of cercopiths there are several perfectly distinct varieties in Uganda alone. Or, to take an Asiatic example, macaques of the irus group (long-tail, long face, small size), are distributed throughout Southeast Asia, while the arboreal leaf-monkeys of the same area are divided into four major groups, three of which are subdivided into numerous species. As far as monkeys are concerned, the sort of difference which Dobzhansky (1950) has shown between the tropical and temperate forms exists in the tropics between the strictly arboreal forms and those well-adapted to the ground. The great number of forms are in the rain forests. The implication for classi-fication is that the ones well-adapted to life on the ground will not divide up neatly into the sort of localized varieties which the tree-livers do. The attempt has been made repeatedly to divide the baboons into sharply defined groups. The chaos which has resulted is the result of expecting that plains forms, which have vast reaches of similar habitat open to them, will subdivide as the tree-restricted monkeys do.

The implication for human evolution is clear. Once man's ancestors were efficient plains-livers, they probably occupied large ranges with anatomical variation but without separation into distinct forms. In the case of early man-like forms, more difference should be demonstrated before taxonomic groups are set up than in the case of fossil anthropoids believed to have been tree-livers.

Turning from the general implications of efficient ground-living to the anatomy involved, I think that we have every reason to believe that this was fully achieved by the South African man-apes. The pelvis of these forms (known by three specimens, described by Broom, 1950a and b, and Dart, 1949a) is so human in form that some have argued that it must belong to an early hominid which became mixed in the man-ape deposits. Although the ilium is short and broad and of essentially human form (although differing in detail, especially in the shape of the iliac crest) the ischium is ape-like. The muscular attachment area of the ischium is separated from the glenoid cavity by a greater distance than is the case in modern man (Broom, 1950b). The differences are not great but are sufficient to preclude the possibility of the pelves belonging to other animals than the man-apes. The pelvis of a large baboon found in the same deposits is utterly unlike that of the man-apes, being typically baboon. According to all investigators (Broom, 1950b; Dart, 1949b;

Camp, 1949; Barbour, 1949b) there has been no great change in the climate of South Africa since these forms lived. They are associated with the bones of baboons and numerous antelope, the typical fauna of the African plains, and forest forms are lacking. The man-apes were bipedal, plains-living forms, derived from the forest-living apes. Morphologically they are ideal representatives of a stage in our evolution and chronologically they may be actual ancestors or the first cousins of the same (Le Gros Clark, 1949b). That is, these forms may be representative of populations which were directly ancestral to such humans as Java man.

The derivation of this type from an ape is best regarded as a case of rapid or quantum evolution (Simpson, 1944). It may soon turn out to be one of the best-documented cases. Since the South African materials are abundant and more are being found, and since there is an impressive number of well-preserved human fossils, the main features of the transition should soon be fully known.

Since this is the beginning of the human type of locomotion, the principal problem is to understand the locomotor changes. If an ape stands erect, it can walk, and the gibbon can get along fairly rapidly, but it cannot complete powerful extension of the leg. It should be stressed that it is not the extent of the motion which is different but the ability to finish with a real drive. When walking on a flat surface, the ape goes with a bent-knee gait (Hooton, 1946). In modern man the muscle which finishes swinging back the thigh is gluteus maximus. This is an exceedingly massive and powerful muscle, arising from the posterior part of the ilium and the sacrum. In modern man, if gluteus maximus is paralyzed, the trunk is said to jack-knife. That is, the extreme extension of the thigh necessary for normal human walking is not possible, but a flexed gait, comparable to that of the apes, is perfectly easy. The paralysis of this single muscle makes the human type of very-extended bipedal locomotion impossible. It shows that the form and function of this particular muscle is critical in the evolution of man's posture and gait.

In the apes gluteus maximus is a small muscle. In monkeys it is about one-half the size of gluteus medius! Since the ilium of the living apes is long, gluteus maximus lies primarily lateral to the greater trochanter and is an abductor of the thigh. (The relation to the hip joint, and so its function, varies with the position of the leg. A study based on action current is needed to tell when the muscle is really in action.) The primary effect of bending back the ilium is to bring gluteus maximus behind the hip joint, thus making it an extensor. Gluteus medius now lies lateral to the joint and becomes an abductor, taking over the old function of the maximus. Since selection is for function, it is clear that bending the ilium will change the selection on the gluteal muscles. It is my belief that this single change is the thing which initiates human evolution.

Before continuing to an examination of the circumstances under which such a change might occur, it should be pointed out that the statements above are susceptible to experimental verification. The function of these muscles in a man and ape can be checked. This should be done. Further, I believe that it is impossible to reconstruct a gluteus maximus on the pelvis of a man-ape which is anything but an extensor. The importance of gluteus maximus in human locomotion, the effect of bending the ilium on the function of gluteus maximus, and the position of gluteus maximus in the man-apes can all be determined independently by as many people as want to take the trouble. In this sense there can be an experimental and ultimately quantitative study of the critical events in human evolution.

The pelvis has several different functions. It serves to connect the hind limb and the trunk, gives origin to many muscles, and serves as a bony birth canal. If the ilium becomes shorter, it must have a greater angle with the ischium in order to keep the same diameter of the canal. This is illustrated in the accompanying figure (Figure 1). The figures for apes are from Weidenreich (1913). Many monkeys would be much the same, but in the leaf-monkey (*Presbytis rubicunda*) with a very short ilium the angulation of the ilium, relative to the ischium, is greater. Man and the man-apes are characterized by exceedingly short ilia, far shorter than apes of equivalent size. Without fossils it is impossible to tell whether shortening or bending came first, but a considerable shortening of the ilium (of the sort actually seen in other primates) would of necessity result in bending it, which would give the necessary pre-condition to the change in function of gluteus maximus. It should be noted that the difference between the langur and the "hypothetical" form is no greater than that between the hypothetical and the known human extremes. In the Bush race the sciatic notch is extremely wide (Orford, 1934; Washburn, 1949). Comparing an extreme human type to an extreme monkey type gives a totally different idea of the gap than comparing male European to living ape. It should be noted that continued bending, although an advantage from the locomotor point of view, is disadvantageous in females because·it narrows the outlet of the birth canal. This accounts for the fact that the bending has been carried further in human males than in females. There is a notable sex difference in the sciatic notch which is directly related to locomotor and postural differences between men and women.

The argument runs as follows: among apes who were living at the edge of the forests and coming to the ground, were some who had

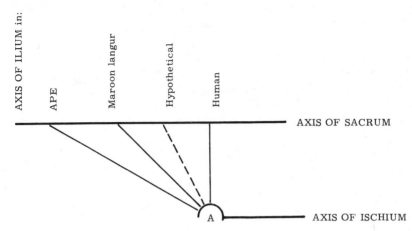

FIGURE 1. The effect of shortening the ilium on the angle between the ischium and the ilium. A = the acetabulum.

shorter ilia. These ilia had to be more bent back for obstetrical reasons and in some this carried gluteus maximus far enough so that it became effective in finishing extension. This started a new selection which favored bigger gluteus muscles and ilia still further bent. The beginning is, of course, supposition, but the functional results can be experimentally checked and the initial shortening and bending is not much beyond the range of known forms.

Characters closely associated with the primary changes in the pelvis are those in the feet and in the muscles of the legs. The feet of the mountain gorilla have approached the human condition in many ways (Schultz, 1934b). Changes from a foot of such a sort to the human would not involve any major evolutionary changes. After all, the joining of the first metatarsal to the second by a ligament may well account for a great many of the features which differentiate the feet of apes and men.

Changes in the muscles are extensive but follow a pattern already seen in the monkeys. When a man walks, he straightens the leg primarily with the muscles on the front of the thigh (Q. ex. femoris). This is the same action which an ape or monkey uses in climbing. In running, the apes and monkeys use primarily the muscles in the back of the thigh. If the mass (weight) of the muscles on the front of the thigh is compared to that of those on the back (quadriceps to the hamstrings), it is found that the relation is 2/1 in man, 1.2/1 in mangabeys, 1/1 in arboreal cercopiths (nictitans), and 1/1.2 in mixed ground-livers (vervets), and 1/2 in baboons. The first and last figures are from Haxton (1947), the others from monkeys obtained in Uganda. Even by such a crude method it is

clear that the proportions of the major muscle masses closely follow the
habit of the animal. Climbing is pre-adaptive for human walking. Quadrupedal running tends to build a different pattern of muscles. Aside from
mass, there are a number of differences in the leg muscles of man and
ape, which can best be described as the attenuation of the muscles other
than quadriceps, and the migration of the insertions closer to the knee.
These changes are of degree only, and the functions are the same. There
is no radical alteration of form and function as in the case of gluteus
maximus. Once the major change in the pelvis had taken place, these
other changes may well have followed rapidly.

It is difficult to determine to what extent these changes had already
taken place in the man-apes. There are only fragments of limb bones.
However, the ape-like character of the ischium suggests that the hamstrings may not yet have achieved modern human form. The lack of an
iliac tuberosity suggests some differences, but many changes in the leg
muscles are little, if at all, reflected in the skeleton. The differences between mangabeys and baboons, for example, which are functionally important, make no discernible difference in the femur. However, in the
man-ape, the distal end of the femur is very large. This is the critical
point. If these forms were walking erect, the femur must have borne the
weight and given origin and insertion to the enlarged muscles concerned
with locomotion. I believe that the argument between Le Gros Clark
(1947b) and Kern and Straus (1949) over the details of morphology of
the femur is irrelevant. Any different group of animals may have somewhat different features of a particular bone. There is no reason why the
femora of the man-apes should be identical with man, ape, or monkey.
The morphology is of a general primate type and the size is in accord
with the idea that these forms were bipeds. Granted a reasonable conformity of shape, the important thing functionally is size.

Considering the arms of the man-apes, the distal end of the humerus
has been discovered, and Le Gros Clark (1947b) has claimed that it is
of the human type and Straus (1948a) that it is catarrhine. However, according to the plan suggested here, one would not expect any fundamental difference in the end of the humerus. The basic ape features, still
preserved entirely in modern man, are the great size of the trochlea and
conforming width of the proximal ulna and the rounded capitellum. The
meaning of these features is that the stability of the elbow joint is determined by the fit between the trochlea and ulna, the radius being freed
from stability and support is better adapted for rotation. Naturally, the
precise detail of this pattern varies from group to group. These little
variations are not of evolutionary significance. The major features and
their importance can be easily determined. Cut the annular ligament

(which holds the head of the radius in place) in a monkey, and the elbow joint loses its stability. Do the same in man, chimpanzee, or gibbon, and the hinge part of the joint functions nearly normally. The distal fragment of the humerus of the man-apes shows that they were typical members of the ape-human stock. The proximal humerus, clavicle, and scapula tell the same story, although detailed study will surely reveal some minor differences from other known forms.

Several authorities have claimed that forms such as the great apes could not be ancestral to man. The reasons given are that the ape's arms are too long and thumbs too small (with the thumb muscles reduced) and that changes in these proportions would break the law of irreversibility of evolution. First, it should be stressed that no one thinks that man is descended from one of the living apes (see Simpson, 1949, for discussion on this point). The question is: could man be descended from a form which had relatively longer arms and smaller thumbs than modern men? Precise differences from living forms are not the issue, but the relations of two kinds of organization. First for the facts: Schultz (1936) has shown that man's arms are, in fact, very long by general primate standards. There is far less difference in length between man and gorilla than between gorilla and orang. The same is true relative to the proportions of the hand. With regard to the thumb muscles, the long flexor is present in all gibbons, over half of chimpanzees, and lesser percentages of gorillas and orangs (Straus, 1949). Once our ancestors had become bipeds, the selection on the arms, hands, and associated muscles would have been different from that of tree-living apes. Selection must be quite different for the living gorilla and orang. The issue is, then, could a trend toward long arms and small thumbs in apes be reversed in their descendants when selection pressures were radically changed? That such reversals can and do take place has been recently emphasized by Colbert (1949), Gregory (1949), and Simpson (1949). The idea that such reversals cannot take place seems to be based on the idea that the trends are due to orthogenesis, rather than to continued selection of the same sort over a long period. The fact that orthogenesis is not necessary to explain the facts of evolution seems well established and was dealt with at length by several authors in the volume *Genetics, Paleontology, and Evolution,* also by Simpson's *Tempo and Mode in Evolution,* and more recently by Jepsen (1949). In spite of all this one reads in *Races,* published in 1950 (Coon, Garn, and Birdsell), that, "Evolution, we are told, is irreversible." Wright (1934) has shown that the missing digits of the foot of the guinea pig may be brought back by mutation. These digits are normally not there at all. It seems that this is precisely the sort of situation in which the cooperation of geneticists, paleontologists, and anthropologists is needed. Great knowledge of the proportions and variations of the primate arm and hand is rendered useless by outmoded concepts and by the failure to realize that reversals, far greater than changing the hand of the living chimpanzee into a human-proportioned hand, have actually been produced in the laboratory.

Turning to the skull, the teeth have been most extensively studied and the evidence has been carefully reviewed by Le Gros Clark (1949b). There is nothing in the dentition which would militate against the idea that these forms are direct ancestors of late Pliocene age. The molars of ape, man-ape, fossil man, and modern man form as nearly perfect a morphological record as one could hope to find (Gregory, 1949). There is no gap in the record at all, and, on the basis of molar teeth, one would have an exceedingly difficult time in deciding where apes left off and man began. This gradation is in marked contrast to the pelvis. It supports the idea that there was no sudden moment when selection on the dentition changed, rapidly producing a new type. These molar characters would then be regarded as incidental, useful in sorting, but not fundamental. It should be remembered that some arboreal monkeys have dentitions identical with plains-living ones. There seems to be no reason why the dentition should be different and, in fact, it is not.

The size of the molar teeth is of interest. As Broom (1946) has indicated, the best match for the teeth and jaws of the man-apes outside of Africa is the form named *"Meganthropus"* (Weidenreich, 1945). But the limb bones associated with the African forms are not large, the best match being with a small female Bushman, about the lower limit of size of living humans. This shows that large molars do not necessarily mean giant bodies. After all, a small monkey may have larger molars than a modern man. The correlation of body-size and tooth-size among primates is not high. Of course, if nonprimates were considered too, the correlation would be far lower. Think if human standards were used to reconstruct body-size from a wart hog's molar! It is particularly dangerous to reconstruct body-size from the teeth of an unknown form.

The canine teeth offer points of interest. Von Koenigswald (1948) has shown that some at least are not as small as has been claimed. However, they are small compared to those of male apes. Of course, in female apes the canines may be exceedingly small, wearing like incisors and narrower than the first premolar (gorilla). In male monkeys the ground-living forms tend to have larger canines than the tree-livers. The extremes in canine size are all in male ground-livers (baboons, mandrills, some macaques). (See measurements published in Washburn and Avis, 1958. Editor.) The function of these teeth is in the organization and protection of the group. The males dominate in the social organization (Zuckerman, 1932), and no female has a chance in fighting against the great canine teeth of the males. The big males likewise act as sentries and guards. From the evidence of other primates one would expect a male plains-living ape to have at least as large canines as the forest-forms. The fact that they are much smaller in the man-ape suggests that the teeth were less important in protection and fighting than among the living apes. This supports Dart's (1949a) hypothesis that the man-apes were already using tools. However, this cannot be definitely proved at the present time. Differences in the size of the canine teeth should not be overemphasized because there is a complete series in size and form linking man and ape.

At least some of the problems of the dentition can be dealt with experimentally. It would be useful to know to what extent size and pattern of the teeth are independently inherited. The simpler pattern of the molars of some of the small modern domestic pigs suggests that reduction of cusps may be only one aspect of size reduction. Weidenreich (1941) indicated the same in small dogs. This could be checked experimentally. Also, it would be possible to prove the importance of the large canines in the social organization of the monkey. With groups such as those on an island off Puerto Rico, the social organization could be studied, the dominant male trapped and his canines removed. A quantitative, experimental approach is possible so that the significance of the changes shown in the evolutionary record could be documented by fact and raised beyond the level of individual opinion. Tree shrews would be ideal experimental animals for this type of problem. They are small, hardy, and can be raised in the laboratory. If anthropologists and geneticists plan to cooperate in the solution of problems of mutual interest, it will be necessary to develop some new laboratory animals, and tree shrews may well prove to be the most suitable. Some experimental analysis of cranial form has been attempted (Washburn, 1947).

The evolution of the brain has always been of particular interest in the primates. Since the brain of modern man is so big and since man likes to think of himself as a rational animal, there has been a tendency to define man in terms of brain size. (Keith, 1948, defined the border of man and apes as 750 cc.) The idea that mammals as a group have triumphed over the reptiles because of better brains received a set-back from the work of Edinger (1948). She showed that the brain tends to follow in evolution, that the earliest mammals did not have brains in advance of reptiles, and that at least several of the orders of mammals had established locomotor and dental adaptations prior to having their characteristic brain form. The hominids follow Edinger's pattern perfectly. The range of variation in cranial capacity is:

chimpanzee and gorilla	325– 650
man-apes	450– 650
Java man	750– 900
Pekin man	900–1,200
Neanderthal	1,100–1,550

The range for Java man is too small, because of the small number of specimens. The figure for the man-apes should perhaps be raised because of a later, partially described find (Broom, 1949). So there is either a complete series or very close to one. There is no doubt that all human fossils described so far have human pelves and limb bones and the man-apes were remarkably human in these features. Therefore, it appears that the differences in the brain between apes and man, just as those in dentition, were attained after full human status had been achieved in the limbs and trunk (Le Gros Clark, 1949b).

If one considers the primates in general, the same pattern seems to hold. The lemurs have bigger brains than the tree shrews, the monkeys than the lemurs, the apes than the monkeys. With each major advance in primate evolution the brain doubled or even tripled its size. If the human brain is viewed from this point of view, the remarkable thing about man is that his ancestors went through three major different locomotor adaptations during the age of mammals and one major reorganization of the special senses. After each of these the brain at least doubled its size. Viewed in this way the remarkable size of the human brain is due to the number of times this organ had to adjust to new ways of life. This is added to the general tendency for mammalian brains to increase in size, and to the fact that at least the last doubling was after the use of tools, which may have greatly increased the selection for large brains.

The final adjustment in brain size seems to have been rapid. If capacities of 800–1000 were common in the early Pleistocene (and they may well have been less in the beginning), and 1200–1400 common in the third interglacial, the same rate of change would make the man-ape capacities expected in direct ancestors of the late Pliocene age. If the change in brain size follows the change in locomotion, it might be expected to continue rapidly until a new plateau is reached. If so, there is some justification in projecting the known rate back for at least a short period of time, and even a short prolongation of the known rate would reduce brain size to that of the apes and man-apes. Brains of this size may have been characteristic of apes for many millions of years. There is almost no direct evidence, but the skull found by Leakey (Le Gros Clark, 1949b) would be in accord with such an idea.

In summary, the critical primary adaptation initially responsible for the origin of man as a distinct group is in the pelvis. Efficient, bipedal locomotion of the human type involves primarily the pelvis and gluteus maximus, but a series of secondary changes in thigh, leg, and foot must have followed soon to complete the adaptive complex. This complex may have been further improved by continued selection, but, as far as can be determined from the skeleton, had reached modern form in the early Pleistocene. Changes in the teeth, brain size, and many other parts of the body took place at a much slower rate and continued on into late Pleistocene times. These changes are the result of the secondary selection patterns which followed after the establishment of the primary human pattern. Finally, there are many little differences between any two forms. These incidental features may be due to a variety of causes and should not be allowed to confuse the major patterns.

It is customary to present the results of phylogenetic speculations in the form of a classification. There has been so much overemphasis on classification and names, especially with regard to the primates, that common names have been used here as far as possible. At the moment they are better guides to the identity of living primates than the supposedly scientific ones. Without wishing to stress names or overemphasize their importance, the views expressed in this paper imply a reduction in the number of names of categories among the primates. If the term "family" is reserved for a group of animals representing a major adaptive radiation (such as the Indridae, Lorisidae, or Galagidae), then the gibbons belong in the same family as the great apes. Bipedal man might be put in a separate family. The reasons for granting bipedal man more taxonomic distinction from apes than the ground-living monkeys from the tree-living monkeys, is that there is a much greater series of anatomical changes in the case of man. Within the human family one genus, *Homo*, might easily include all the Pleistocene large-brained hominids (Java man, Pekin man, etc.). One other genus, *Australopithecus*, might contain the man-apes (*Australopithecus, Plesianthropus, Paranthropus,* and perhaps *Meganthropus* and even *Gigantopithecus*). Obviously, since little is known of the time when these forms lived, the extent of their range and how many local forms there may have been, the significance of this category is uncertain. If such forms were widely spread over the Old World in late Pliocene and early Pleistocene times probably there were quite distinct local groups. It seems convenient to place these small brained men in a single genus, at least until there is more evidence to the contrary. The number of names is a function of the kind of interest of the investigator (Broom, 1950a). If one is primarily interested in classification, in type specimens and priority, then the less there is known about fossil primates the more names there will be. If one is interested in the mechanics of evolution, in the understanding of process, a cumbersome and constantly changing classification is a great liability and the tendency will be to lump, to leave fragmentary bits unnamed, and to create new groups only when absolutely necessary.

In conclusion, it might be repeated that this is an appropriate time to reconsider the problems of the origin of man; for the traditional phylogenies have been upset by the discovery of new fossils; the old theories of orthogenesis, irreversibility, and the supremacy of nonadaptive characters have been proved false; and because experimental procedures offer methods of raising some conclusions beyond the level of individual opinion. Looking to the future, fossils are being found at a rate undreamed of in the past. The cooperation of geneticists and paleontologists has produced a rich evolutionary theory which places the fundamental contribution of Darwin in modern form. Facts are increasing and new theories are challenging, but methods must be developed for proving and checking the importance of particular facts and the fit of any given theory. Such testing requires a knowledge of fossils, of living forms and the application of experimental procedures. All three types of evidence are necessary and a science of human origins can be built only upon this triple foundation.

Without fossils, ancestors can be reconstructed only by what has been called "mental triangulation." With all the vast effort which went into the comparative anatomy of the primates, no one reconstructed an animal with a human ilium and an ape's head. There were attempts in this direction and Weidenreich (1947b) recognized that the evolution of the locomotor system preceded that of the head, but before the discovery of the man-apes, and before Edinger's investigations, it remained equally logical to maintain that the brain was the primary and initial factor in human evolution. The actual course of evolution can be determined only from fossils.

But, fossils, at best, constitute a very limited source of information. Adaptations in the digestive, circulatory, reproductive systems, and special senses affect the skeleton little or not at all. The significance of many changes in the skeleton cannot be determined, unless living forms of comparable structure are available for study. Unfortunately, much of the fossil record of primates is limited to teeth and jaws, and the extent to which these parts can be misleading is well shown by the living lemurs. The skulls of lorises and galagos show not only detailed similarity but comparable trends, yet the whole postcranial skeleton is different and the animals represent opposite extremes in locomotor adaptations. From the point of view of the comparative anatomist the primates have definite advantages, for there are living representatives of all the major primate radiations, and numerous parallel series offer opportunities for the analysis of the causes of anatomical similarity. Of course, the living forms are not ancestors and will not reveal the detailed anatomy of extinct types, but a far fuller understanding of a lemur can be gained by studying fossils and living forms than by the study of either one alone. Obviously, the chimpanzee is not studied to prove that it is *the* human ancestor but to understand the kind of organization which may have been characteristic of the ancestral forms.

After the study of fossils and living animals, when theories take definite form, then experiments should be planned. Particularly the importance of adaptive complexes and the precise nature of adaptation can be advanced far beyond the level of individual opinion. The fact that gluteus maximus functions differently in man and ape is not a matter of opinion but can be precisely determined. Again, the importance of gluteus in walking can be quantitatively investigated and placed beyond the realm of debate. The study of human origins requires an appreciation of the nature of evolutionary change in animals, an understanding of the specific problems of the primates, and a detailed comprehension of form and function of man and ape. Solution of the problems will require the cooperation of many scientists, and it is hoped that this conference may be the beginning of much close cooperation between anthropologists and others interested in the origin and differentiation of the human stock.

On the Earliest Phase of Hominid Evolution

Emil Breitinger   1959

A˙few months will see the hundredth anniversary of an event which stands as a milestone in the history of biology: the publication (in 1859) of Charles Darwin's work *On the Origin of Species By Means of Natural Selection*. With this, Darwin made possible the triumph of the doctrine of the evolution of organisms, of the gradual transformation and multiplication of living creatures out of simple beginnings to their present variety, fifty years after J. B. A. de Lamarck (1809, the year of Darwin's birth), had given the doctrine a clear scientific formulation. Charles Darwin's success rested in the first place on the breadth of his own reliable observations in the field, in comparative morphology, in animal geography and animal husbandry which, in the course of decades of work, he had assembled into a comprehensive body of circumstantial evidence in favor of the phylogenetic relationship of organisms. The decisive reason, however, for the resounding success of his book, which was sold out on the day of its publication, was its manner of making plausible the revolutionary view of the changeability of species through the factors of natural selection. This explanation is based on the fact that every species constantly produces far more descendants than are necessary to its existence, and that the preponderance of these are lost

Originally entitled "Zur frühesten Phase der Hominiden-Evolution," from Beiträge Osterreichs zur Erforschung der Vergangenheit und Kulturegeschichte der Menschheit (*pp. 205–235*), *ed. by E. Breitinger, J. Haeckel, and R. Pittioni, publication of a symposium held at Burg Wartenstein, Austria, September 8– 12, 1958, under the auspices of the Wenner-Gren Foundation for Anthropological Research. Reprinted by permission of the author and of the Wenner-Gren Foundation. In this article, on the timing and the manner of emergence of hominids, principal tenets of the modern synthetic theory of evolution are applied specifically to the case of man, as a guide to the testing of hypotheses. Dr. Breitinger is Professor and Director of the Anthropological Institute, University of Vienna.*

in turn before they successfully reproduce. In addition, Darwin was aware, from his researches on the variability of organisms, that the descendants of a species manifest differences, even in close inbreeding, which are in part determined by heredity. Among these variants some, by possession of certain hereditary characteristics, are better adapted to the prevailing environment and conditions of life than are others, and these individuals will, through their adaptive advantages, on the average survive oftener in the population and give rise to a more numerous progeny. Nature, in other words, constantly chooses the better adapted individuals. So it is that these relationships between the hereditary adaptability on the one hand, and conditions which differ regionally and which change over time on the other, constitute in the broadest sense a mechanism which makes evolution comprehensible without special assumptions or the need of a metaphysical principle.

By Darwinism, as far as this term is still in use, we understand, contrary to general usage, not the idea of evolution itself, but rather the explanatory principle offered by the selection theory. This theory has in the last hundred years freed itself from the deficiencies of the knowledge of Darwin's own time and has further developed through the united labor of morphology, physiology and taxonomy, of ecology and sytematics, with genetics and paleontology, into the modern synthesis of evolution. The basic idea of the mutation-selection theory appears entirely correct in the light of critical appreciation of modern knowledge (W. Ludwig, 1954). It is a testimony of total ignorance when someone still occasionally asserts that "Darwinism" has been finally refuted, as happened again recently in the daily papers on the occasion of the discovery of a skeleton of *Oreopithecus*.

1

No biologist today doubts the reality of evolution, and there are no physical anthropologists who are not persuaded from this that man himself is likewise the outcome of an evolutionary history. They differ among themselves, however, in their views as to the course of this hominid evolution, as much as they agree on the basic fact. Darwin foresaw the prejudices with which the new hypothesis of the modification and transformation of species must take account, including the unavoidable involvement of our own species. He contented himself with the suggestion that through his book, light would be thrown on the origin of man. In his *Descent of Man*, published twelve years later in 1871, Charles Darwin also limited himself to the conclusion that the origin of humanity must be looked for in some ancient representative of the "anthropomorphous subgroup." This might well have taken place as early as the Eocene, since, as the existence of *Dryopithecus* shows, the higher primates had already branched off from the lower forms of the order by the Upper Miocene. The courage and intuition of the young E. Haeckel is the more remarkable, in the light of the meager sources of that time, for having proffered, in 1866, the first family tree giving the geological and systematic relationship of man to the rest of the animal kingdom and especially to the higher primates, in his *"Generelle Morphologie."* In a presentation still acceptable today, he placed the separation of the hominid line and that of the African pongids approximately at the border of the Miocene and Pliocene. Countless such diagrams have appeared since then, as well as still more essays and discussions on primate and hominid evolution, most of which correspond in general to the scheme first put forth by Haeckel, although some depart widely in their general viewpoint.

Differences of view may first of all be traced to their factual foundations, since the sources which should give the key to historical development are not adequate for the opinions based on them, in respect either to their quality or quantity. This holds for both types of source material: for biological data on recent primates as well as for fossil finds.

Biological data, which we know for modern man in a great range of morphological structure, function, and behavior, and which we know for other representatives of the primate order only in outline, do not provide unambiguous historical evidence for the elucidation of biohistoric problems. They do no more than show us the results of a biohistorical development. When we compare the details of this development and wish to arrive at their course in the past, we may make cautious use of of the principle of homologies: that is, in general the number and the grade of expression of homologous characteristics are directly proportional to the grade of the phylogenetic relationship. In other words, the more numerous and more pronounced is the expression of homologous characters in two primate groups, the more recent should their common parental species be assumed to have been. But this kind of triangulation cannot be used exclusively in a scale having such fine steps as is desirable for the higher primates, quite apart from the fact that the criteria for the determination of homologies are not always easy to apply. Accordingly, even careful methods leave considerable latitude in the interpretation of the phylogenetic relationship between hominids and other primates.

Fossil finds, on the other hand, are definitely historical documents, and provide the indispensable time element for phylogenetic studies. If random samples of fossils from historically sequent populations were available, reliable information as to the actual course of hominid evolulution would be possible, starting with the geochronological time period in which the bodily form of the earliest hominid could be recognized, and going through form changes in subsequent ancestral generations. However, this prospect will never be realized, not even very distantly, since one cannot suppose that such random samples of all formerly existing hominid populations still exist as undiscovered fossils. Known finds of fossil hominids up to the present consist largely of individuals in broken or incomplete condition from the last million years of earth history, the Pleistocene; and even these quantitatively and qualitatively unsatisfactory documents are by no means always so safely and comparably dated as would be necessary for an exact historical evaluation.

As a consequence of all these and other deficiencies of the basic data, any biohistoric synthesis is consistent with more than one possible interpretation. This being so, one of the problems of such a synthesis is to assess the relative plausibility of different possible interpretations of the available data.

Evidently anthropology cannot develop the necessary criteria and methods for this task while preoccupied with the family of the hominids alone, any more than it would be able to make out, from the study of the heredity of parents and children, the particulate nature of the genetical material and the rules by which the genes are transmitted from generation to generation. But whereas the basic concepts and research methods of genetics found their way into studies of human heredity soon after the sensational rediscovery of Mendel's Laws, the new knowledge and principles of the modern synthetic theory of evolution, which were only achieved in the last two decades through the cooperation of the traditional and the new genetic disciplines of biology, have not yet come into general use as ordinary tools in the interpretation of the above-mentioned typical sources of hominid phylogeny. There often persists, from the pre-evolutionary era of taxonomy, the concept of an ideal type which is thought to represent the combination of characteristics of a group as an abstraction. According to this idea, for example, a species in the older sense would be represented by a type specimen, and a newly found specimen would be classified following a comparison with known types, or by placement in a species represented by such a type or, not uncommonly, set up as a new species. This typological procedure of individual comparison and diagnosis may well seem appropriate in other areas of science, for instance in the study of material culture, because one may here adopt the point of view that, for example, the form and decoration of a pot follows a certain ideal, according to a definite pattern, a type, so that this type can be reliably represented by a single pot.

In biology the assumptions for the classification of an organism are of a totally different kind. Here we do not deal with types determined in the same way and represented by single examples, but rather with the inherent presence of variation of all organisms in space and in time. The biological unit of classification is accordingly not the individual but rather the population, that is to say a group of more or less similar organisms who live with one another in a breeding community. The population has no individual type representative. Rather, it is recognized as a group through the extent and the nature of its variation. In this group variation an extreme variant is just as important as any other. In the new systematics we would say that we classify an individual not as a specimen, but as a member of a population. We regard an individual find as an indicator of what species the population might be to which it belonged. Naturally a single individual often may yield very little; several individuals may be more productive of information. Only when one may make use of a whole group are closer indications as to variation to be expected, and this knowledge then makes possible answers to the complicated questions of the relationship to other groups.

The basic unit of classification is the species. This consists generally of several such populations, which are actually or—if geographically distant from each other—potentially capable of interbreeding, while they are isolated from the populations of another species through biological limits on reproduction. Such a species can have a world-wide distribution: for example the populations and races of *Homo sapiens*. These may also have a considerable time depth; in the case of *H. sapiens* we may trace them back as far as the Upper Paleolithic. The variation of a species must comprehend all its local populations and geographical races, and in phylogenetic considerations it must be borne in mind that the total variation in the course of long periods may not have remained the same. This multidimensional species is at the same time the evolutionary unit, because its variations are limited to the changes which it alone experiences in the course of time, neither affecting nor being affected genetically by other species. The populations and races within a species, on the other hand, may as time goes on mix and once again break up into new local groups and races. Genetically speaking, each species consists of groups of individuals with more or less similar gene combinations, which provide them with an adaptation to the given environment. Under natural circumstances selection is constantly at work: individuals with adaptive advantages have a greater prospect of asserting themselves and expanding their genotype in the following generations than other individuals with less favorable gene combinations.

For the origin of new species, the primary problem of evolution, experimental and historical biology provide two models for the understanding of both important phenomena, that is to say, the multiplication of species on a time horizon and the transformation of a species in a time sequence.

The first phenomenon, contemporaneous related species, comes about

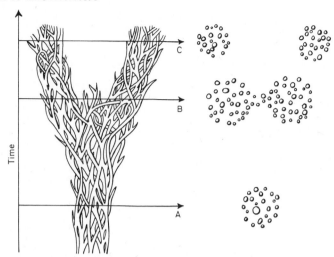

FIGURE 1. Diagram of the splitting of a species (time horizon A) into two species (time horizon C). After Th. Dobzhansky, 1955.

through the step-by-step differentiation, denoted speciation, within the population network of a species as visualized schematically in Figure 1 by Th. Dobzhansky. Such a speciation may, for example, be initiated by the geographic separation of part of the populations of a species; these species fragments, at first divided only spatially, may in new ecological conditions arrive at certain gene combinations and new mutations leading to a definite adaptive advantage, and then in the course of a long succession of generations be favored by selection, resulting eventually in genetic differences relative to other groups, possibly similarly transformed genetically, of the original species. If this genetic difference between the two population groups becomes so great that it is effective as a barrier to interbreeding, then the original species has given rise, by splitting, to two new species, which thenceforth possess independent possibilities of future evolution.

This picture of a division suggests at once that genotypic and phenotypic changes appear among the variations of the new species which may persist over a long period and eventually bring out a definite trend in the transformation of the trait complex of the species in question. Accumulated changes in such an evolving species may be of such an extent that the descendants differ from the ancestral populations in the same degree as that usually encountered between two related species living at the same time. In this case one species has appeared from another through phyletic evolution, and the two taxonomic units following one another in time are known as phyletic species. To distinguish these from contemporaneous species which have come about by splitting, and which are genetically isolated from one another, phyletic species constitute segments from a breeding community spread out in a continuum over geological time.

Finally, G. G. Simpson (1953) discusses, as a third mode of evolution, the relatively rapid transformation of a species as an extreme case of phyletic evolution. Such rapid change is occasionally to be recognized in paleontological material—for example, in equid evolution—when a species arising through splitting encounters totally new ecological conditions, in which it can survive only under the relatively rapid course of interaction between genetically determined adaptations and environmentally determined selection. Simpson calls this quantum evolution.

2

Following this preface we may better understand those systematic concepts and their evolutionary consequences which are necessary in the consideration of problems of the origin and of the earliest phase of hominid evolution.

By "hominids" are to be understood all members of populations of that phyletic line which led to the recent species *H. sapiens* after splitting off from some fossil primate group, whenever this may have taken place. The totality of taxonomic units composing this phyletic line constitutes the systematic category of the family Hominidae. A family, of course, stands in systematic rank over a species and a genus. It has its origin, however, in normal speciation, and therefore is itself a species in the earliest phase of its evolution. Since in the course of division and branching of a species it is always whole populations which are given off by the species group (Figure 1), a normal and significant variability will be exhibited by the ancestral species, in this case, of the hominids. This consideration, to which we will return in discussion of the ancestral species, is important in the evaluation of whether, on the one hand, only a single progressive evolving species was involved at all times in hominid evolution, that is to say a single continuum of phyletically successive species, or whether through further splitting sidelines arose, all of which must have been blind alleys, since at present only the single species *H. sapiens* survives. Phylogenetically the family Hominidae is classified as a systematic category *ex post facto,* from knowledge of that last segment of the phyletic line which, on present data, extends from the present backward to the Plio-Pleistocene boundary, thus comprising about a million years in absolute chronology. Figure 2 is an attempt to visualize how this last segment of hominid evolution may be subdivided, in accordance with the criteria of the new systematics already outlined. A brief review, reflecting both the history of discoveries of fossil hominids

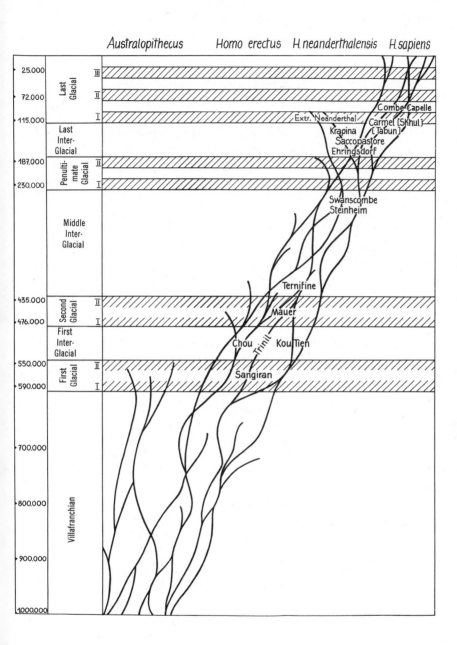

FIGURE 2. Phyletic relationships of Pleistocene hominids.

and the gradual broadening of schemes of hominid relationships, will, so to speak, lead us from the periphery toward the core of present-day problems of the earliest hominids.

The framework of geochronological subdivision of the Pleistocene as far back as the first glacial is drawn up following the dates given by F. E. Zeuner (1952) whom I have also followed in the chronological ordering of the various finds. On every time horizon, the species is symbolized through the genetically open web of population and racial lines. Looking backward from the present the population complex of the species *H. sapiens* may as of now be traced back to the first interstadial of the last glacial. The species *H. neanderthalensis* comprises the geographic races of the extreme Neanderthals in Europe (La Chapelle-aux-Saints, La Ferrassie, La Quina, et cetera), in Africa (Broken Hill, Eyasi, Saldanha) and Asia (Ngandong) and, in time span, all those populations represented by the so-called "generalized" and "Pre-" Neanderthals of which we have knowledge, as far back as the calvarium from Steinheim, toward the end of the middle interglacial. This taxonomic division is nowadays approved of in many quarters, the more readily since the species *H. neanderthalensis* (King, 1864) has long been accepted. As the diagram shows, the idea that *H. sapiens* and *H. neanderthalensis* are segments of a phyletic continuum refers above all to the interglacial populations of *H. neanderthalensis*. I have elsewhere (1955, 1957) discussed this phyletic evolution of *H. sapiens* in greater detail. A parallel development of Neanderthals and so-called presapiens representatives reaching far back into the Pleistocene cannot be based on the available finds, but can only be constructed typologically.

For a long time *H. neanderthalensis*, whose human nature was never denied even in the case of the original find of 1856, ruled as the oldest species of man for which, on the basis of several skeletons, a fairly precise picture could be made out. By contrast, the Trinil find of the so-called Pithecanthropus of 1891/92 was still placed among fossil pongids in the second edition of R. Martin's "Lehrbuch" (1928, p. 14) in spite of the fact that G. Schwalbe had already convincingly established the placing of the find in the hominids through his investigation of the skull cap. This judgment received general recognition only following the discovery of the skull caps, jaw fragments, and teeth of the so-called Sinanthropus from Chou Kou Tien, which was similar in form and age, and substantially better preserved. In this case, the proof of stone tools and remains of fire left no doubt even for nonbiologists that these fossil finds actually represented man in a very primitive form.

With the demarcation of the concept of the hominids outlined above, it is obvious that the name of this family can in no way be used as a synonym for the concept and the name of "man" even though this still happens in present-day writings. It must once more be expressly pointed out here that the taxonomic and systematic concept of the family Hominidae comprises the entire phyletic series beginning with the earliest species yet known to us up to the terminal species, *H. sapiens,* the latter being the image which lay persons ordinarily consider identical with the concept "man" in our vernacular speech. Particularly do we combine in the concept "man" and "human" the idea of those psychical qualities which all healthy members of present-day humanity possess, such as the capacity for communication by language, for making use of elementary culture materials, and so forth; in a word, a certain minimum grade of intelligence. In the case of prehistoric populations we deduce this psychic level from their cultural remains. Accordingly, both the Neanderthals and the hominids from Chou Kou Tien are rightly to be regarded as men, even though their skull forms are decidedly different from that of current humanity. K. P. Oakley's (1950a, 1951) suggestion that all "toolmakers" among fossil hominids should be classified as man has been widely agreed to, since only such an archaeological criterion may be made use of in judging a minimum grade of intelligence retrospectively. This possibility is doubtless of the greatest significance for problems in the area of the synthetic theory of evolution. Indeed, such leading students of evolution as J. S. Huxley (1942), G. G. Simpson (1951a), Th. Dobzhansky (1955), and B. Rensch (1957) have spoken of a cultural and social evolution, new and unique to man. This, as is demonstrable archaeologically by stone tools, was of decisive significance for the dominant position of man in the natural world, because of his ever-expanding medium of tradition and communication making possible the transmission and diffusion of cultural acquisitions, together with continuing factors of organic evolution. It must always be kept in mind, however, that the sense and the extent of the category "man" as defined above does not correspond with the taxonomic category. In German vernacular writing it has long been customary to let the term "Mensch" be coextensive in time with *H. sapiens,* and to refer to the Neanderthals as "Urmenschen," and to finds related in form or in time to those of Chou Kou Tien as "Frühmenschen." Still older hominids have been referred to collectively as "Vormenschen." This division is acceptable as a general frame of reference outside a scientific work. The anthropologist, however, naturally cannot adopt it, since he would be turning his back on basic taxonomic concepts, genetically defined, and needed in international systematics as well as in accommodation to biological evolutionary research. Furthermore, W. E. Le Gros Clark (1955) has correctly pointed out that the terms "man" and "human," since they both possess for us, as human beings, conscious or unconscious emotional force, all too easily lead us into the danger of subjectively influencing our judgments when they are made use of in phylogenetic considerations. In paleoanthropology, therefore, we should avoid the designations "man" and "human" entirely, and try to achieve international understanding through the use of species, genus, and family names, or where these are not practical, the name of the site of discovery. As has been said, this is not to deny the interest for paleoanthropology of cultural evolution, which allows the division of biological hominid evolution into a prehuman phase (Le Gros Clark, 1955) and a human phase. This, however, is something which depends entirely on prehistory, and archaeological criteria must never be confused with biologically defined categories. Interchanging the concepts "Hominidae" and "Man" has all too often led to confusion. If one accepts the archeological correspondence: man = tool-user one may distinguish finds from Chou Kou Tien, Ternifine, and Sidi Abderrahman, as a human phase, from an older prehuman phase. Such a sharp line, naturally, can never be drawn. G. Heberer's (1958b) term "Tier-Mensch-Übergangsfeld" (animal-human-transition zone) emphasizes the gradual transition into the human phase, but pushes too far the antithesis between tool-using men and those older hominids for whom this capacity is not demonstrated. Since this antithesis "animal-human" appears in the title of Heberer's essay, the fact that "subhuman" is used for the "animal" phase will scarcely soften the effect on nonbiologists. Heberer apparently did not wish to use the generally corresponding term "prehuman" phase instead of "subhuman" phase, since this would unavoidably lead to a confusion with his "Praehomininae"—the *Australopithecus* group—which he places in the "Übergangsfeld." This example also demonstrates the kind of complication introduced into paleoanthropology by classification and terminology which departs from zoological systematics.

In Figure 2, the finds of Chou Kou Tien, Trinil, Sangiran, Mauer, and Ternifine are placed in the population network of the species *H. erectus*. This taxonomical assessment is based on the suggestion of E. Mayr (1944, 1951), that the similarities of the skull caps of Chou Kou Tien, Trinil, and Sangiran justify only subspecific rank, and certainly not that of genera. On the other hand, the Trinil and Sangiran skull caps of Java are not sufficiently different from the Upper Pleistocene skull caps of Ngandong, belonging to the species *H. neanderthalensis*, to allow a generic difference. Accordingly, if the genera named Pithecanthropus and Sinanthropus, and Arambourg's (1955b) genus Atlanthropus for Ternifine, cannot be accepted, these various hominids ought to be ranked in the genus *Homo* as a phyletic species *H. erectus*. The length of the Middle Interglacial leaves it entirely possible that the populations of

H. erectus stand in a phyletic relationship to those of *H. neanderthalensis.* Furthermore, this conclusion corresponds far better with the archaeological knowledge that the hominids of Chou Kou Tien, Ternifine, and Sidi Abderrahman were tool-makers and, according to this criterion, must be ranked as men. To emphasize the point again, it is far more conservative to view the species variation in each time horizon as relatively broad than to postulate specific differences, such as could be established only on the basis of a general knowledge of the variation, for the individual finds which are usually available. For example, if one wished to rank the hominids of Trinil and Chou Kou Tien as different species, this would reflect the phylogenetic view that only one of them could have bequeathed the genes and characteristics of *H. neanderthalensis,* while the other must have ended in an extinct side-branch. No one is in a position to decide which of the two should be regarded as an ancestral species and which as a blind side-twig. The tendency of many typologies to explain all fossil hominids as side-twigs can be taken note of as a curiosity. It is a matter of interest for the main point that the long debated question of whether the Trinil femur belonged with the skull cap has been dismissed, since it can be taken as established by the *Australopithecus* finds that the development of upright posture and the concomitant adaptation of the lower extremities for bipedalism took place at a much quicker pace in evolution than the transformation and size increase of the brain and its bony container.

Considering that it was the variation of recent and fossil men, as then known, which was used as the basis of diagnosis of hominids, we may readily appreciate the difficulty which attended the taxonomic placing of the *Australopithecus* finds, especially since no artifacts were present to help in the recognition of these as men, and their family diagnosis as Hominidae had to be arrived at on morphological data alone. The general impression of the cranial vault and facial skeleton, of the first child's skull from Taung, discovered in 1924, is so decidedly pongid that the classification expressed in the genus name *Australopithecus* is readily understandable. The judgment of P. Adloff (1932), based on the teeth, that it was a primitive hominid, remained unique. Strangely enough, Adloff (1939) was equally positive in judging as pongid the teeth of the first finds of Sterkfontein (1936) and Kromdraai (1938), which R. Broom had designated as Plesianthropus and Paranthropus. Broom had the satisfaction of seeing his own opinions sustained by the 1947 find of the nearly complete calvarium Sterkfontein S 5. The present almost unanimous placing of the *Australopithecus* group in the family of the Hominidae, however, is due to the find of hip bones belonging respectively to a small individual of the size of a Bushman, to a very strongly built and apparently large-sized individual, and to a child. These hipbones, and specifically the ilia, are pronouncedly hominid in form: they exhibit the low height and considerable breadth characteristic of hominids as walkers, the development of a tuberculum iliacum, ,and the deep recession of the incisura ischiadica major, which, contrary to the reservations expressed by W. Gieseler (1957) can be interpreted only as the static and functional adaptation of the ilium to upright posture and bipedal progression. In Figure 3, c and d are shown the hipbones of the two adults from Sterkfontein (c) and Swartkrans (d), following R. Broom and J. T. Robinson (1950, 1952), oriented on the plane of the greatest breadth of the ilia. For comparison, I have reproduced in Figure 4, upper row, a male (a, c) and female (b, d) hipbone of Europeans (a, b) and Bushmen (c, d) drawn on the same scale and in the same orientation using .the dioptrograph. Racial variation in form is negligible. On the other hand, the incisura ischiadica is in both races somewhat wider in the female sex than in the male. The expression of this characteristic, which is statically very important, in the two *Australopithecus* ilia lies clearly within the range of variation of *Homo*. The only notable difference is the spina iliaca ventralis, extending further forward in both *Australopithecus* ilia. The spina ischiadica forms as elevated a point in the Sterkfontein hipbone as in *Homo,* while it seems to have been eroded post mortem in the Swartkrans innominate. The fact that, in the latter, the acetabulum is visible to the same extent as in *Homo* is an important indication of a similar sagittal position of the ilium relative to the median plane. In the lower row of Figure 4 the same innominate bones, which in the upper row are shown oriented by the greatest iliac breadth, are shown vertical to the median plane. In this position, the ilium appears relatively shortened, but the acetabulum is shown more in plane view, and the ischial and pubic rami are more markedly profiled. Since classification as a pongine is the only other possible alternative for *Australopithecus,* Figure 3 shows, in addition to the hipbones of Sterkfontein and Swartkrans, the right innominate bone of *Pan,* by the same dioptrographic technique of drawing, and in the same scale, positioned in b in the same way, on the greatest iliac breadth, and in a, identically with those in Figure 4, lower row, on the median plane of the pelvis. Such great and unmistakable differences as those between this pongine hipbone and the fossil pieces from Sterkfontein and Swartkrans make it plain without further research that the *Australopithecus* finds cannot possibly be considered as belonging to pongine primates. Suffice it here only to mention the relation of the iliac breadth to the iliac length which, according to E. Rickenmann (1957) averages 121 in *H. sapiens* with a variation of 103–129; in other primates this proportion lies sub-

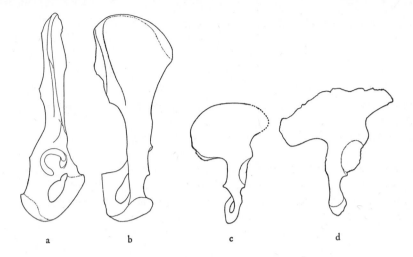

FIGURE 3. Right hipbone of *Pan* (a, b), Sterkfontein (c), and Swartkrans (d). Drawings a, b, original. Drawings c and d after R. Broom and J. T. Robinson, 1950, 1952.

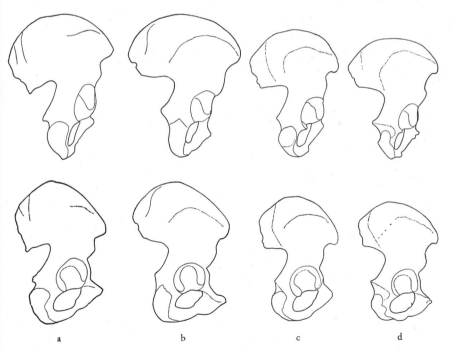

FIGURE 4. Right hipbone of male (a) and female (b) Europeans and male (c) and female (d) Bushmen. Upper row oriented by greatest iliac breadth, lower row by median plane of pelvis.

stantially below 100; in *Pan* it averages 62 (59–67), and in the lowland gorilla, who possesses relatively the broadest ilium of the pongines, it averages 89 (79–94). In the more complete specimen of the innominate bone from Sterkfontein the ilium is obviously broader than it is long; going by measurements taken from the drawing, the index should approximate 110. As we have said, the inescapable similarity of both *Australopithecus* ilia with the special adaptive characteristics of the ilium of *Homo* leads to the only possible diagnosis, that these primates were walkers. Since among all primates only the hominids are walkers, and since the primary and decisive specialization in hominid evolution was in fact the upright posture and bipedal locomotion (Schultz, 1951), these pelvic specimens allow no further doubt that *Australopithecus* is to be placed with the hominids.

Our conception of the hominids was greatly extended through the discovery of the *Australopithecus* fossils. Thorough study of the calvarium Sterkfontein S 5 and the other skull fragments yielded definite indications of the hominid nature of this individual; and the teeth had been adjudged hominid-like even in the case of the child's skull from Taung; nevertheless, none of these finds had led to so positive a judgment as the innominate bone, since their transformation in the direction of the most strongly characteristic traits of *H. sapiens* has obviously progressed less far. E. Mayr (1951) endeavored to reduce the several stages of transformation to figures, by rendering as 0 the grade of expression of a characteristic in the ancestral species from which hominid evolution took its departure, and as 100 the grade in *H. sapiens*, and suggesting the following percentages for the statuses in *Australopithecus:* pelvis, 90; occipital condyles, 80; profile of mandible, 30; premolar teeth, 75; incisors, 55; molars, 40;. form of dental arch, 70; and brain, 35. Though there might be differences of opinion over these figures or their ranking, there can be no arguing the fact that, in the course of hominid evolution, the characteristics of brain, cranial vault, and facial skeleton, of the dentition and of the postcranial skeleton, did not change by synchronous or harmonious degrees, but in different tempos, that is to say, allometrically. While in the case of Neanderthal Man the form and size of the brain case left no doubt that he was a hominid, the Trinil skull cap gave rise to a long-continuing discussion over the systematic placing of the find, and in the case of *Australopithecus* it was finally the ilium that made unequivocally clear the systematic position of the group. We should expect, therefore, that in dealing with still older hominids the skull form and the size of the brain, as well as the dentition, cannot lead to any diagnostically decisive conclusions, and systematic judgments will rest on the pelvis and particularly on the ilium.

In classifying the *Australopithecus* group taxonomically, it should be provided, to distinguish it from the genus *Homo*, at least with the rank of a genus (S. L. Washburn and B. Patterson, 1951). By the international rules of nomenclature, this genus must retain the name of *Australopithecus*, even if the sense of this name expresses an actually different evaluation. Much more important than the sense of the word is the strict rule that a definite designation of a find must endure unaltered, and thus give it unmistakable international recognition. Otherwise every improvement of knowledge would make a constant change of name necessary, and give rise to a hopeless confusion as to which earlier names were synonymous with the current one. A change of nomenclature is possible only when the original taxonomic rank of a find cannot be sustained, as is the case with Pithecanthropus and Sinanthropus. This, however, is basically no change in name, but rather a new assignment of rank, and in this case the genus name *Homo*, to which this phyletic species is to be joined as *H. erectus*, is already established. It is still being debated whether, in the case of *Australopithecus*, the existence of another species should be considered in addition to *A. africanus*, and the question should remain open in the interim. The possibility is indicated in Figure 2. Broom accepted the geological age of *Australopithecus* as Upper Pliocene. Such a dating would allow the genus *Australopithecus* to be regarded as an ancestral group of the genus *Homo* without embarrassment, since structurally it corresponds broadly with the expectation of such an ancestral group. On the basis of special studies, especially of the accompanying fauna in the bone breccia, and following various expressions of opinion, interested students have united on an age for *Australopithecus* which is at the most Lower Pleistocene, corresponding to the Villafranchian. F. E. Zeuner (1952) places the Villafranchian before the First Glacial. If the entire Pleistocene comprises one million years and if, according to the absolute chronology of Milankovitch, the beginning of the First Glacial is to be placed at 600,000 years ago, there is allowed for the Villafranchian the very great span of time of 400,000 years. Since those authors who have themselves done work in the Transvaal, such as K. P. Oakley (1954a) and F. C. Howell (1955), are not in agreement over the relative chronological ordering of the *Australopithecus* individuals from the five sites of Taung, Sterkfontein, Makapan, Swartkrans and Kromdraai, no attempt has been made to put the place names in Figure 2. J. T. Robinson (1954, Figure 7) still accepted the Upper Pliocene as the date, except for Kromdraai. However, even a placing in the Villafranchian leaves the possibility open that *Australopithecus* forms a phyletic ancestral genus for the genus *Homo*.

By consistently applying the principles of the new systematics, the geochronological series of the known hominids of the last million years may be arranged as a model example of phyletic evolution. This conception preserves wide scope for the intraspecific variation of populations of any time horizon, from which, at the best, we have the remains of a few individuals only, and does not forestall decisions as to the phyletic relationships between the subspecific groups which might be based on a more comprehensive later body of evidence. In any case, this interpretation at the present is more conservative than the opposite assumption of contemporary species with the divisions thereby implied. Heberer's (1956) latest representation of "phyletic relationships within the hominids" (Figure 79, page 539) in the form of branchings off of sidelines, as is usual in the case of the splitting of species, is in obvious contradiction to his own expressly stated view, that "Humanity at every time horizon formed only a single—polytypic—species" (1951a, p. 76). A. Remane showed decades ago (1927a) and again more lately (1959a, 1954) that a dichotomous representation in the case of phyletic relations between subspecific groups is false.

3

In the evolution of the hominids there has been only one *a priori* certain case of a complete speciation and splitting, namely that which explains their separation from some Tertiary primate species. This original splitting constitutes the earliest phase of hominid evolution. The crucial significance of this earliest phase for understanding and knowledge of hominid evolution has been characterized by A. Remane (1954) in this sentence: "The problem of the derivation of the hominids in general will have been solved when we know the place of the branching off of the hominids from their nearest relatives, the time of branching off, and the physical structure of this first early form." At the present there are only indirect clues for judging the three aspects of this problem. They are more copious today than a hundred years ago, and modern evolutionary theory has brought closer understanding of the factors and the causal connections in the processes of splitting and phyletic transformation of species. Still the picture, which we can put together for the earliest phase of hominid evolution, remains shadowy and uncertain in comparison to the outlines which historical evidence allows us to draw for the end phase of the development of our own primate family. From three directions the attempt has been made to obtain indications as to the geochronological time and the systematic place of this first division, as well as of a first morphological diagnosis of the earliest hominids, and to make these useful for the synthesis of hominid evolution.

A. Looking back from the better-lighted end phase into the darkness of hominid origins at first permits only the obvious assertion that the splitting off from some other primate species certainly took place in the Tertiary. Within this period of some 74 million years (Simpson, 1949) we need practically to take account, as E. Haeckel long ago concluded, of only the last 27 million years of the later Tertiary, with the two epochs of the Pliocene (11 million years) and the Miocene (16 million years). In looking for a more precise limit for the splitting off, it might seem attractive to date the transformation of the locomotor apparatus for the upright position and bipedal progression, which had already been reached by *Australopithecus*, by judging from the impressive increase and change of the brain, of its bony envelope, and of the facial skeleton in the course of the last million years of hominid evolution. According to paleontological experience (Simpson, 1951a, p. 65) such an extrapolation from the known trend of one phase to an unknown tempo of evolution of another adaptation in an earlier phase is however unreliable, if we must assume that the evolving species has entered a new adaptive zone and in the course of this, has undergone a profound change in the direction of its adaptive type, for example, in locomotion, which was of decisive importance for its future condition. In this case an adaptation which can be recognized retrospectively as a "key character" will, under the influence of a high selection pressure, develop incomparably faster than any later trend which might be discerned in the formation of particular traits. An entirely analogous situation must have existed in the earliest phase of hominid evolution. As already stated, the earliest hominids, in the course of their splitting off from a Tertiary primate species, under pressure of ecological circumstances—the usual slogan is "disappearance of trees"— and conditioned by their genetic possibilities for adaptation, underwent that decisive change in direction of the adaptive nature of their posture and progression, which resulted in the key character of orthograde locomotion and which corresponds with the general concept of the transition to a new adaptive zone. Since the change in ecological circumstances would scarcely have occupied millions of years, there could not be a very great time span for the attainment or failure of orthograde locomotion, the decisive adaptation for the further progress of the new species. Under conditions of parkland or wooded steppe a very small progress in the dominance of bipedal locomotion would have constituted a significant selective advantage for the new species, and so it seems plausible that this dominance of orthograde locomotion would have proceeded in the tempo of a quantum evolution. With this notion of a relatively very rapid development of the bipedal progression of hominids, favorable in the new adaptive zone, we have, however, made little progress toward the evaluation of the geological point of their origin, unless we assume that this quantum evolution of bipedalism was attained just before the phyletic phase of the genus *Australopithecus,* that is to say, in the Upper Pliocene. More possibilities as to this time point are kept open if we suppose that the development of bipedalism was followed by a phase of stabilization which would be difficult to delimit in time, during which the new species could spread and undergo regional differentiation. Thus, in looking at things from the end phase of hominid evolution, narrower time limits for the period of splitting off are not possible.

On the other hand it may now be taken for granted, following the finds of *Australopithecus* with his unequivocal bipedalism, with more confidence than formerly, that this locomotor adaptation arose with the original splitting off, and apparently developed fairly rapidly: in other words, that bipedalism constitutes the "key character" of the hominids. This leads, analogously with the culture-historical equation: man = toolmaker, to the biohistorical equation: hominid = walker = bipedal primate.

B. Comparative biology of recent primates provides inferences as to the systematic position of the parental species from which the splitting off of the hominids took place.

The principle of the traditional method of morphology is the use of the evidence of homologous characteristics in two or more species to make deductions as to homologous structures of the common parental species. Among recent primates there is such a manifold similarity between the species belonging to the family Pongidae and the single representative of the Hominidae, the species *H. sapiens,* in traits of the skeleton, the dentition, the muscular and nervous systems, the inner organs, in metabolic function, serological reactions, length of gestation and so forth, that the creation of a systematically superior superfamily Hominoidea to express the phylogenetically close relationship between hominids and pongids is widely recognized. In using homologies as criteria, there is little disagreement that within the family Pongidae a primary division into the two subfamilies Hylobatinae and Ponginae took place, that later on the Asiatic genus *Pongo* branched off from the pongine line and that from a final division there arose the two African genera, *Pan* and *Gorilla.* In contrast, the junction for the departure of the hominid line is debatable. This departure most likely took place, according to A. Remane (1952b) and many other authors, from the phyletic ancestor of the two African pongines, although A. H. Schultz (1956; 1957b, p. 334) would put it much earlier, following the branching off of the hylobatines. But no matter how different these and similar interpretations of the same body of fact may be, they are opposed to other extreme hypotheses which will not be referred to here, in being based on the same view, namely that the numerous homologous developments of the Hominoidea in both families were not evolved independently from one another, but actually constitute phylogenetic indicators of a fairly long common phase of evolution prior to the division of the hominids from the pongines.

Further clarification of this question is aided by the evidence of general evolutionary studies that speciation, the basis of all division of species, is an adaptive process. In the divisions among the primates, locomotor adaptation has played an important role. This is especially true also for the family of the pongids, who are given the special term brachiators, from the nature of their locomotion in the trees, mainly grasping and swinging by both arms. The locomotor apparatus—trunk and arm—of these brachiators in fact exhibits a complex of adaptive traits which are not present in the same combination in any of the lower, pronograde, Old World primates: the rib cage of brachiators is flattened; in distinction from the proportion of the keel-shaped rib cages of the pronograde primates, their thoracic index amounts to over 100 even in the newborn (A. H. Schultz, 1956); in this increase in the thorax breadth, the sternum also takes part; furthermore, the vertebral column is recessed somewhat into the rib cage by the pronounced curvature of the ribs, and the lumbar region is relatively short. Further recognizable traits are, in the shoulder girdle, the transversely oblique form of the scapula; in the humerus, the size of the form of the joint surfaces, specifically the breadth of the trochlea as well as the degree of torsion of the shaft; in the ulna, the corresponding breadth of the proximal joint and the reduction of the olecranon fossa; in the radius the pronounced capacity for rotation. Hand in hand with these adaptive traits of the skeleton went analogous adaptations in the motor apparatus: in comparison to the relationships in quadrupedal primates, the arm extensors in brachiators are reduced in origin and insertion, whereas the flexors are relatively powerful; the Mm. serratus anterior and deltoides are strongly developed, the area of origin of the M. pectoralis major is limited to the upper ribs, insertion of M. pectoralis minor is displaced to the coracoid process of the scapula; the Mm. scaleni have migrated upward and the Mm. rectus abdominis, psoas major, and the origin of M. sacrospinalis downward. All these related structural adaptations in the pongids connected with brachiation, in the locomotor apparatus of trunk and arm, are characteristic in varying degrees, as common trends in the sense of A. H. Schultz (1950c), for the hominids also. Now since, in the division of hominids from Tertiary primates with the transition to ground living and bipedal progression, it is obvious that a completely new adaptive process, in the locomotor sense, came into play, directing its influence toward the transformation of pelvis and leg, it is not possible to regard the concordant adaptive traits in the arm-shoulder apparatus of hominids and pongids, with methodological consistency, as convergent developments or homoplasias. A. Remane (1956a) drew the conclusion, after a thorough analysis of all facts and inference which can be assembled from knowledge of the locomotor adaptations of recent primates relative to the origin of upright walking in hominids, that the separation of hominids took place from moderate brachiators using occasional bipedal progression on the ground.

This view, often spoken of today as the "brachiator hypothesis," has been generally preferred ever since E. Haeckel's first attempt to draw up a family tree for the hominids. This is, after all, for the very reason that in all probability the transition to upright bipedal progression could have been arrived at only from a half-erect posture of the trunk, such as the pongids generally assume in quadrupedal locomotion on the ground. Since pongids also may be bipedal over short stretches, and since they therefore already possess typically hominid locomotion as a secondary function, it appears so much the more plausible that they possessed the prospective adaptation (Simpson, 1953) for the decisive shift in direction of the locomotor adaptation, which is assumed to have been present in that primate group from which the origin of the hominids took its departure. Misunderstandings arose partly through the ambiguity of the term "brachiator," as well as through too narrow an interpretation of the concept of pongids. Many authors have believed that the brachiator hypothesis demanded, for the Tertiary parent from which the hominids departed, the presence of the whole complex of adaptive characteristics for suspension which we know from the recent pongids. This is by no means the case. Just as the hominids of a million years ago were far from exhibiting the complete set of characteristic traits which we know from the terminal species *H. sapiens,* so we hardly expect to find in the early phases of evolution of the family Pongidae a full expression of the trait complex known from the recent species. A. Remane (1956a) has lately once more expressly emphasized "that the appearance of a new mode of locomotion must not be confused with the typically much later appearance of structural specializations related to it. Furthermore, the fact must not be lost sight of that different structural changes connected with a given way of life may appear at different times. The transformation of the vertebral column with a half erect position may have arrived first, and later the transformation of the grasping mechanism; and only much later the extreme lengthening of the forearm of the hylobatines which to my knowledge no author has been willing to assume as having been present in the brachiation phase of hominids."

On the other hand, spokesmen for the so-called anti-brachiationist hypothesis supposed that the Tertiary pongid from which the hominids arose corresponded in habitus and locomotion broadly with the modern cercopithecids, with fore and hind limbs of approximately equal length, with the capacity for occasional swinging or clambering, but using quadrupedal pronograde progression on the ground (G. Heberer, 1958b). This hypothesis was certainly inspired by a pair of limb bone fragments of Tertiary pongids, but has for the most part been nourished by the old typological concept that a morphological adaptation for brachiating constitutes the kind of specialization, in the sense of a limitation of possibilities for adaptation in other directions, which could not have been present in the pongid ancestors of hominids, who are automatically thought of as unspecialized. It is to be noted that the trait differences of the trunk and arm region between recent pongids and hominids are principally of a quantitative nature, as is often the case in phyletic lines, whereas the derivation of hominids from a source approximating the pronograde Cercopithecids, without an intervening phase of brachiation, would impose quite different demands on the evolutionary potentials of change. In the case of the originally arboreal cercopithecids, when they were obliged to adapt themselves to life on the ground, nature has, so to speak, provided a crucial experiment, for example, in the baboons. Mollison (1933) has made the point precisely: "For such a monkey, when he changes to life on the ground, there is not the least necessity to rise erect and go on the hind legs, any more than for a dog or any other lower mammal. Only in the anthropoid apes accustomed to brachiating would this impulse to erectness, or rather the retention of an upright posture, be suggested."

While, therefore, the same locomotor adaptations in the trunk and the arm-shoulder region of pongids and hominids serve as phyletic indices pointing to a common phase of evolution, the far-reaching differences in the structure of pelvis and foot in the two families make an impressive expression of the opposing trend of adaptation, which was operative in the speciation and splitting off of the hominids upon the transition to bipedal progression on the ground. Locomotor adaptation for upright posture and bipedalism of hominids presumably affected the pelvic girdle first and foremost. The ilium of hominids in particular underwent changes in size, proportions, and form, already reviewed in reference to the pelvic fragments of *Australopithecus*, presented in the same scale in Figures 3 and 4. Supplemental to this, Figure 5 shows the inner aspects of the right innominate bone of three pronograde Old World primates (*Macaca, Papio, Presbytis*), of the hylobatines (*Hylobates, Symphalangus*), of pongines (*Pongo, Pan, Gorilla*) as well as of man, rendered parallel to the planum ilicum, and reduced to the same pelvic height (Rickenmann, 1957). The ilium of hylobatines is only slightly modified relative to the cercopithecids; even in the pongines there is merely a relative increase in

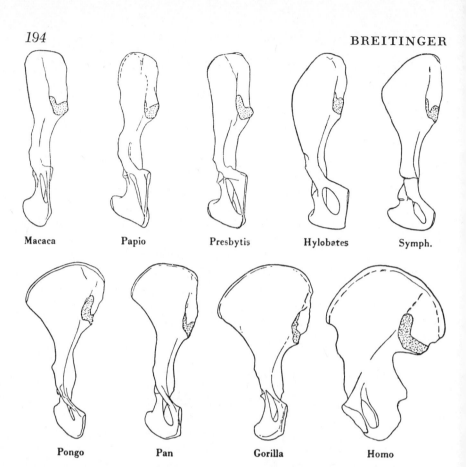

FIGURE 5. Right hipbone, inner aspect, of cercopithecids, pongids, and *Homo*, oriented in the plane of the planum ilicum and drawn to the same height. (From E. Rickenmann, 1957).

the iliac breadth—obviously in relation to their larger body size. In this comparison, the ilium of man is more exceptional in characteristic details of form: the iliac crest seems almost circular, the relatively very wide pars sacralis is bent down posteriorly; the facies auricularis, which transmits the weight of the upper body to the sacrum, has achieved a statically favorable lowering of the distance from the acetabulum and thus from the transverse axis of the hip joints, through the backward bending of the ilium. When pongids rise on two legs, the sacrum is much higher relative to the transverse hip axis because of the absolutely great height of the ilium; and since in relation to stature the trunk is relatively much longer than in the case of man, the center of gravity of their bodies is placed at a decidedly disadvantageous height over the hip axis. It is certainly for this mechanical reason that pongids find it difficult to balance on their

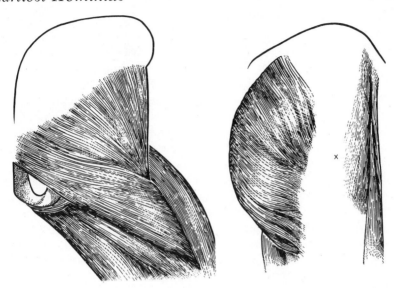

A   B

Figure 6.   M. gluteus maximus. a: *Gorilla* (from H. C. Raven, 1950), b: *Homo* (after Spalteholz). X = position of trochanter major.

hinder extremities. Of special importance for the maintenance of upright posture through muscles and ligaments are the changed topographical relations between pelvis, trunk, and legs due to the re-formation of the ilium. One particular factor, on which S. L. Washburn (1951a) has correctly placed the greatest emphasis, need be singled out here: as a result of the bending back of the ilium the M. gluteus maximus, now placed back of the hip joint to the hinder side of the femur, has achieved a position of pull which makes it possible to be the strongest extensor of the hip. Its large muscle mass forms the characteristic buttock contour of man (Figure 6, b); together with the M. quadriceps femoris it insures an energy-saving extension of hip and knee joint in the upright position, and meets the new problems of motion and bipedalism. In the pongids, and even in the gorilla, who has relatively the broadest ilium of pongids, gluteus maximus, a flat triangle, lies on the outer side of the ilium and runs over the trochanter major deep down on the outer side of the femur (Figure 6 a). In this topographic situation it can normally work only as an abductor. In the pongids it is not the strongest hip muscle, nor by its position and function does it deserve its name, gluteus maximus, or "great buttock muscle," which because of studies on man has been extended into comparative anatomy as well. Even Buffon had correctly recognized: "Buttocks belong only to the human species." Among other statically and dynamically important adaptations of the ilium of man to upright posture and bipedalism we may name only this: the strongly developed spina ischiadica which gives attachment to the ligamentum sacrospinosum important in the binding of the pelvis, as well as the tuberculum ilicum, developed in response to the influence of the strong ligamentum iliofemorale (Bertini), the passive opponent of the gluteus maximus. A secondary deepening of the incisura ischiadica major comes about through the backward bending of the ilium and the pronounced development of the spina ischiadica. This can, in fact, be particularly significant diagnostically in fossil hipbones of the most fragmentary condition, because, lying next to the relatively thick corpus of the ilium, it has a better prospect of surviving and becoming fossilized than, for example, the peripherally placed crista iliaca. In addition to the demands of locomotion, the importance which should be assigned to aspects related to the process of parturition as selection factors of development of the total form of the pelvis of hominids must be passed over here. In any case it seems indubitable that the above-mentioned traits of the ilium of *Homo* constitute convincing and diagnostically useful evidence of the static and dynamic adaptation of the pelvis to upright posture and bipedalism.

From the facts, already reviewed, of the comparative biology of recent primates, and the well-founded idea that the first decisive specialization of hominids was the upright posture and bipedalism, it should be possible to recognize, in Tertiary finds of hominoids, the first definite hominid status, if a pelvic fragment should be obtained, in a condition making it possible to determine the presence of an ilium of low and broad proportions with a correspondingly narrow incisura ischiadica. To find a complete foot, such as might show that the first metatarsal lay alongside the second as in man, would be an extraordinary piece of luck, since even in recent finds of skeletons the foot bones are usually incomplete. Also, it is entirely possible that the transformation of the foot skeleton was considerably later than that of the pelvis. From what has been said above, traits of the arm skeleton would not afford possibilities of reliable distinctions between Tertiary pongids and hominids. This would also seem to be so, judging from the experience of *Australopithecus*, of traits of the skull, at least when represented only by fragments, even teeth. The possibility of finding evidence of the earliest hominids is therefore strongly limited, in that phase following the genetically completed speciation, which—still referring to G. G. Simpson (1953) on the mode of evolution of speciation —might yield morphologically tangible evidence of adaptation of the pelvis, and especially of the ilium, for upright posture and bipedalism. As to how long the previous period of lack of morphological differentiation in the process of genetic speciation may have lasted, there is no hint.

Since selection works on the adaptive capacities of a given genotype under given circumstances, that is to say on functions, and since the morphologically recognizable effect is a subsequent result of this process, which is spread out over generations, it would not be possible to identify the hominid nature of particular finds from populations in the actual stages of speciation; even if the key characteristics of hominids, upright posture and bipedalism, developed relatively very quickly, as a form of quantum evolution.

C. Finds of Tertiary pongines can hardly be expected, after these considerations, to give an immediate answer as to the parental species and the point in time of its establishment in hominid evolution. In order to forestall misunderstanding as to taxonomic and phylogenetic interpretations of the term Ponginae, which nowadays is used in different meanings, let it be expressly emphasized that the subfamily Ponginae is meant to include not only the three recent genera, but also their phyletic line and any extinct side branches as far back as its splitting off from the other pongid subfamily, Hylobatinae.

Also, the attempt to estimate a geochronological point for the splitting of the hominid line from that of the subfamily of Ponginae by indirect means encounters great difficulties both methodologically and factually. For pongine evolution was certainly not marked by any such profound change in direction of type of adaptation of locomotion and of an entire way of life, as was the earliest phase of hominid evolution. Doubtless the adaptation of the pongines toward brachiating has been under way since the earliest part of the later Tertiary, obviously reaching an extreme degree in *Pongo*. But the essentially continuous adaptive trend of the Tertiary primates leaves no clear possibility of distinguishing, even with sufficient fossil material, some phase of their evolution which could be demarcated, and thus used diagnostically, as being definitely already posterior to the separation of the hominids. Add to this the factual difficulty of the small number and the highly incomplete condition of the actual fossil materials. At the present, Tertiary pongines are known mostly from jaw fragments and teeth, fragments of extremities being a great rarity. Under these conditions, the varied assumptions, and chronological estimates for the splitting off of the Hominids, depend largely upon ideas as to the diagnostic importance of traits of the dentition of Miocene and Pliocene pongines.

The dentition of Tertiary pongines in general exhibits characteristics similar to those of recent genera but often less pronounced in degree. These are: conical canines, projecting from the tooth row, along with the functionally related single-cusped sectorial form of the first lower premolar (P_3), as well as a diastema between the upper canines and the lateral upper incisors. An older view, expressed as early as E. Haeckel's first attempt at a primate family tree, and since then adhered to by many authors, regards this heteromorphic canine group as a specialization of the pongines, which could not have been present in an ancestral form of the hominids; from this verdict it follows that the splitting off of the hominids must have occurred before the earliest appearance of this specialization. On present knowledge this would be even before *Proconsul* from Kenya, which is dated, according to the critical synchronization of E. Thenius (1958a), not in the lower Miocene (Burdigalian), but rather in the middle Miocene (Vindobonian). In contrast, A. Remane (1924), W. K. Gregory (most recently 1951) and W. E. Le Gros Clark (1955) have cited reasons for thinking that the canines of early Hominids did not have the brachydont spatulate form known for *H. sapiens,* and also that the two-cusped P_3 of known hominids is to be derived originally from a mainly single-cusped and moderately sectorial form. While the final judgment for such an evolutionary transformation can only be arrived at through accurate paleontological documentation, there is nevertheless to be found in existing indications "no theoretical reason why the hominid type of dentition should not have been derived from the generalized pongid type in some of the Miocene or Pliocene apes, and such indirect evidence as is available certainly supports this proposition." Le Gros Clark particularly draws attention to *Ramapithecus* from the Siwalik deposits in India, in which the nature of the wear of premolars and molars, the small canines, their medial position in the tooth row of the mandible, moderate degree of convergence of the upper dental arcade, the lack of a definite diastema, and the relatively small degree of prognathism are just what might be supposed to exist in a transitional form, in an evolutionary transformation of the hominid dentition from that which was characteristic for most other Pliocene and Miocene pongines. And since the beds containing *Ramapithecus* should be placed, according to Colbert, in the middle Pliocene and the upper part of the lower Pliocene—E. Thenius (1958a) on later information on the Siwalik formations places the find in the upper Pliocene (Astian)—*Ramapithecus* is in any case one of the youngest representatives of the Tertiary pongines, if not the youngest. If one takes the more cautious view that *Ramapithecus* is not a hominid transitional form, but rather the representative of a species of pongine whose teeth exhibit none of that kind of specialization which would rule out a derivation of hominids from the range of variation it represents, then the chronological position of the finds (they may have been placed too far back in their previous evaluation, as with the Pliocene) might provide a geochronological *terminus a quo* for the origin of hominid evolution which seems in agreement with the considerations set out under A. and B. Even the upper Pliocene commands a duration several times that of the Pleistocene. It may be true that older pongines already exhibited irreversible, typically pongine, traits, since in the middle Pliocene the lines of the recent pongines may very well already have split off. For example, A. H. Schultz in his revised family tree (1956, Table 1) has *Pongo* branch off from the line of both African pongines at the border of the middle and upper Miocene, with the latter dividing at the border of the middle and upper Pliocene. There may have been still other lines now extinct reaching up into the Pliocene from a Miocene pongine radiation, as G. G. Simpson suggests in his phyletic scheme (1949, Figure 17, p. 71). On the other hand, of course, the possibility is to be remembered that *Ramapithecus* belonged to a species already differentiated, genetically speaking, as a typical pongid, the variation of whose dental traits, however, included those degrees of development which one must assign to a pongine parental species for hominids. All standard studies of Tertiary primates give an impression of a very wide range of individual variety of form, from which A. Remane (1954) drew the conclusion that in the origin of the hominids a high individual variability of almost all characters is to be looked for from the time of their first branching off. If we discount the possibility of *Ramapithecus* as a pongine parental species for hominids, then we must ask how far back before the middle Pliocene the hominid separation may be placed. At the moment, the middle Miocene would be a very liberal lower boundary to take, since in the Vindobonian we already encounter in *Proconsul* the most primitive of the pongines so far known. In spite of the caution exercised by Le Gros Clark and Leakey (1951) in their original work on the *Proconsul* finds, as to the mode of locomotion, based on fragments of the extremities, the antibrachionists in general jumped to the conclusion that no brachiation was present at all. Hence we must point to the results of the study by J. R. Napier and P. R. Davis on the forearm of *Proconsul africanus* discovered in 1951, reported as follows by Napier (1959)[1] at the session of the Deutsche Gesellschaft für Anthropologie in Kiel, 1958: "Until recently there was no evidence as to the manner by which the specialised brachiators evolved from the unspecialized forms. However, the recent discovery of the fossil forelimb bones of *Proconsul africanus* on Rusinga Island, Lake Victoria, has provided certain clues as to how this might have come about. *P. africanus* shows a remarkable combination of anatomical features indicating on the one hand its essentially generalised quadrupedal

---

[1] In the meantime there has also appeared the detailed monograph of J. R. Napier and P. R. Davis, 1959. See "The Fore-limb Skeleton and Associated Remains of *Proconsul africanus*," *Fossil Mammals of Africa*, Br. Museum (Nat. Hist.), London. (Note added by author.)

arboreal nature and, on the other, the beginnings of a more specialised brachiating mode of life. The fossil limb provides no evidence of terrestrial adaptation and therefore one can find no support for Pocock's assertion that brachiating habit evolved in the Pongidae as an aromorph following a period of terrestrial life." This result supports the validity of the brachiator hypothesis. In any case, judging from the mode of locomotion of this pongine, and the already recognizable morphological features adapting it to arm suspension, there is not the least reason to set the separation of the hominids prior to *Proconsul*. In the same vein, Le Gros Clark (1955) has said: "So far as the evidence at present available can be assessed, the origin of the Hominidae and the Pongidae from a common ancestral stock seems well assured. There is no sound argument for pushing back the origin of the Hominidae to the Oligocene (or, as some would even suggest, to the Eocene). There is, in fact, no reason why it may not have occurred in the early part of the Pliocene."

Only unambiguously interpreted and reliably dated Tertiary hominids can furnish direct evidence for their definitive separation; give a clear answer as to their appearance; and confirm, contradict, or narrow down the systematic position and the time relationships of the parental species before the separation. All of this now rests on indirect clues alone.

Quite recently, taxonomic rank as a Tertiary hominid has been awarded to the primate *Oreopithecus bambolii*, known since 1872 through jaw fragments and teeth from lignites of Grosseto province in Tuscany, and according to the accompanying fauna, placed in the lower Pliocene (Pannonian). J. Hürzeler, to whom we owe a thoroughgoing reconsideration of the materials known up to 1949, and above all, for the arduous recovery of new materials of *Oreopithecus*, in his latest preliminary report (1958, which refers to all other pertinent literature) bases the diagnosis as hominid on six features of the teeth. These are: proportions of mediodistal lengths of the teeth, homomorphy of the mandibular premolars, the lack of a diastema (in 12 jaw fragments only one shows a possible diastema), the small canines, the fovea anterior of the maxillary molars, and the verticality and wear of the incisors. He also refers to three traits of the jaws in general: the relative shortness, the relatively vertical chin profile, and the high position of the mental foramen. These characteristics "sketch a silhouette of unmistakably hominid character." According to Hürzeler, they are already so well developed in *Oreopithecus*, at a period which is at least ten times further back than that of the oldest previously known hominid—according to E. Thenius (1958b) a precise statement over the exact position of the finds within the Pannonian cannot at the moment be made—that hominization would already have been "in full swing." Separation of the hominids accordingly is placed considerably earlier than the Pannonian. Since Hürzeler rates *Proconsul* as "typically pongid" in the sense of a "non-hominid hominoid," he accepts a "pre-Miocene" separation of the Hominids.

While Hürzeler's new taxonomic ranking of *Oreopithecus* has found support in some quarters (J. Kälin, 1955; G. Heberer, 1955; J. Piveteau, 1957), a comprehensive comparison of primate dentitions has led A. Remane (1955) to a decisive rejection, which he summarizes in the following sentences: "1. In the greatly preponderating majority of characters, the teeth of *Oreopithecus* are further from hominids, including the Australopithecus group, than are those of pongids (sic) and virtually all Pongidae including *Proconsul*, in fact further than those of the Hylobatidae and many platyrrhines. 2. There are a few similarities with hominids, for example, the good development of the metaconid on P_3 and the relative size and certain proportions of the canines. The same features, however, are present in primitive platyrrhines. 3. A few particulars coincide with the Cercopithecidae, for example, the possession of a mesial cusplet on I^1, general proportions, a basal cingulum, and some ridges of the molars. 4. Of the special characters of *Oreopithecus*, a few are primitive, for example, the paraconid on M_1, the large trigonid portion on the second deciduous molar, the form of the canine; others, however, are completely individual developments, for example, the form of the central incisors of the maxilla, and the projecting foveae on the mesial border of the molars. On the basis of these findings, a ranking in or near the Hominidae, from the existing material, appears inadmissible. As claimed by Schwalbe in 1915, and by Gregory, a special family Oreopithecidae must be erected for *Oreopithecus*, which stands further from the Hominidae than the Pongidae and the Hylobatidae."

These opposing conclusions of two outstanding experts on primate dentitions show what diagnostic difficulties may appear in the taxonomic evaluation of the teeth of Tertiary primates in assigning them even to a superfamily. On the other hand, skeletal parts recovered from the Grosseto lignites include a proximal fragment of a right ulna with a relatively broad articular surface for the trochlea of the humerus and a very low olecranon process, these being adaptive traits of the Hominoidea which, together with other concordant findings on the arm-shoulder region, serve as evidence for the brachiator phase passed through in common by pongines and hominids. Therefore, this ulna fragment cannot serve, as Heberer (1956, p. 462) believes, to support the diagnosis of "hominid" but rather allows only the conclusion, demonstrated also by Hürzeler (1958), that *Oreopithecus* is a hominoid. Clarification of the question as to whether it is a pongine or a hominid as seen in the light of facts and considerations detailed in section 3, can only be expected from findings which would give reliable indications as to the nature of adaptation and locomotion, so different in the two groups, meaning upright position and bipedalism in hominids. Of primary significance would be information on the pelvis, and particularly on the ilium. The few fragments of the pelvis available to Hürzeler for his preliminary report of 1958 are not sufficient to reveal the essential characteristics. On the other hand the exciting news of the recovery of an *Oreopithecus* skeleton, in the journal *Life*, for September 15, 1958, with the pelvis apparently complete according to the pictures, even though this is supposedly flattened by pressure, leads to the hope that, after preparation, it will be satisfactorily clear whether *Oreopithecus* possessed the capacity for upright posture and bipedalism, in the recognizable and morphologically demonstrable degree of a hominid. E. Thenius (1958b) regards bipedalism in *Oreopithecus* as unlikely, on the basis of the biotype and "the conditions obtaining at the time in question, in the former lignite-forming swamps and woods, which must be regarded as representing a 'damp' stage." "The relative frequency of remains of *Oreopithecus bambolii* in the lignite of Grosseto strongly suggests that the habitat of this species was in the lignite-forming woods and that accordingly it was much more likely to have been a tree dweller than an upright walking form, whose habitat would be sought in the open landscape." Meanwhile, the assignment of the lower Pliocene primate *Oreopithecus* to the hominids is in any case not proven.[2]

[2] A. H. Schultz (1960), on the basis of study of the postcranial skeleton, finds that *Oreopithecus*, "with his broad trunk, shortened lumbar column and short, unmuscular upper thigh," . . . "must have been a relatively slow-moving tree animal of approximately chimpanzee size." (Note added by author.)

The Subhuman Evolutionary History of Man

Gerhard Heberer 1959

1. On the Divisions of Hominid Phylogeny

It may be said today that the fossil history of hominids extends significantly further back in geological time than finds of fossil euhominines (that is, "true" men in the sense of tool producers) would have directly suggested. The oldest euhominines clearly recognizable as such belong to the archanthropine group. These are the Pithecanthropus-like types from Java (*Pithecanthropus modjokertensis* von Koenigswald and *P. erectus* Dubois). This group is already as late as the Middle Pleistocene, perhaps completely so, although the evidence as to the exact limits of its greatest geological age is not definite. Earlier finds, the prehominines (= Australopithecinae), belong in the Villafranchian, and only on Java were prehominine forms—*Paranthropus palaeojavanicus* (von Koenigswald), earlier known as *Meganthropus*—contemporary with archanthropines.

The presence of the clearly hominid prehominines in the Villafranchian, embodying a type of structure (completed bipedalism, typically hominid dentition) which is far removed from the brachiating pongids, urges the view that these oldest hominids known to us must have had a long independent earlier prehistory. The special line of the hominids cannot today be traced, through fossil finds of unquestionable character, back beyond the Plio-Pleistocene boundary. Our ideas, therefore, as to when and with what body form the hominid line became separate from a nonhominid (hominoid) stem are decidedly hypothetical.

Originally entitled "Die subhumane Abstammungsgeschichte des Menschen" from Die Evolution der Organismen, *2nd ed., 1959, ed. by G. Heberer, pp. 1110–1142. Reprinted by permission of the author and of Gustav Fischer Verlag, Stuttgart. This article deals, in more concrete paleontological materials, with the same topic as the preceding one by Breitinger, that is, the timing and manner of the emergence of hominids. Dr. Heberer is Professor of Anthropology at the University of Göttingen.*

It is the purpose of this article to set forth the present situation relative to the above problems. In doing so it is not possible to cite *in extenso* the nonhominid fossil material which must be considered in this connection. For this the reader should turn to recent general reviews (Abel, 1931; Vallois, 1955b; Piveteau, 1957; Remane, 1956b; Heberer, 1956).

Several times—the last time was in 1958—I have suggested a clear, unambiguous division of the independent phylogeny of hominids. We designate the group whose particular phylogeny extends from its first isolation to the appearance of the euhominines as Hominidae, a family within the superfamily Hominoidea. It is clear that to the Homindae there belong forms whose resemblance to the present hominid type decreases as their geological age increases. Finally we arrive—obviously this is theoretical—at the critical stage, in which the first hominid forms are not to be distinguished morphologically from their nonhominid ancestors. This is the point of departure for the special phylogeny of hominids.

We do not know precisely with what kind of morphological forms the hominid phylogeny began. The types one might consider likely in this connection depend on what time point one takes for the separation of the hominid branch. We shall go into this in detail further on. The development of hominids proper led to a second critical phase. We call this phase the "Tier-Mensch," or animal-human, transition zone (for details see Heberer 1958a). The time period preceding the Tier-Mensch transition is the "subhuman phase." Hominids of this phase were psychically animals. In the older parts of this phase their form must have been thoroughly ape-like or monkey-like. Types within the Tier-Mensch transition zone would allow us no decision on morphological grounds as to whether their psychic constitution might already have been viewed as human, in the usual sense. Chronologically, they would appear to belong to the Upper Pliocene.

The period following the Tier-Mensch transition zone in hominid phylogeny, coming down to the present, we call the "human" phase. We have no evidence for its earlier, late Pliocene, portion and must reconstruct this hypothetically. But the later Pleistocene parts have furnished us—though most fragmentarily—with fossils.

We may thus divide the entire special phylogeny of the hominids into three phases:

1. From the original isolation up to the Tier-Mensch transition zone = subhuman phase
2. The critical transition period = Tier-Mensch transition zone
3. From the Tier-Mensch transition zone to the present = human phase[1]

[1] We take the optimistic view that "human" mankind of the present will be able to reach a fourth phase, which we should like to name "humanitarian."

In what follows, the subhuman phase will be dealt with in detail, that is, its beginnings, the problem of isolation, its course, and its arrival at the Tier-Mensch transition zone. Figure 1 (right side of drawing) shows the division suggested.

The phase preceding the subhuman phase of hominid phylogeny is identical with the history of nonhominid primates. The problem which primarily concerns us is the question of the time point at which hominids became isolated, marking the beginning of their special history.

Referring to the diagram, we may briefly outline the most important hypotheses. There obtains in these today a considerable divergence of opinion. Very schematically, modern views can be ranged in three groups, of which the first two can also be brought together as "pongid theories." These assert that the direct ancestors of the subhuman hominids were pongids. There is much to support this general assertion (for the factual material see von Krogh, 1959), but the question remains as to the form to be ascribed to these ancestral pongids. On this point there are, schematically speaking, two views. One sees the hominid ancestors as having the morphology of differentiated brachiators (that is, swinging and hanging tree climbers), a morphology for which the model is furnished by recent pongines, and which is characterized, among other things, by relatively long arms and relatively short legs. The second view does not assume morphologically fully differentiated brachiators, especially forms possessing the typical brachiating limb proportions, but rather forms, essentially still pronograde, which possessed an intermembral index of about 100. If one is a "brachiationist," one must set the beginning of the subhuman phase of our phylogeny in the Pliocene, perhaps in the Middle or even Later Pliocene; if one is an "antibrachiationist,"[2] one allows oneself greater time limits for the dating of the process of isolation, or about from the Upper Miocene to the Upper Oligocene.

The third group of hypotheses places the time of isolation of the hominid branch still further back, so far in fact that the parental form is looked for not in pongids but in prepongid types. This leads, of course, to different conclusions. While some authors would see the ancestors of subhuman hominids in protocatarrhine types, others go back to tarsioid forms (and thus approach the older "tarsian hypothesis" as it was especially put forward by Wood Jones).

It can be seen from this schematic summing-up that opinions as to the timing of the process of isolation vary widely, in fact from a past of 2 or 3 million to 30 million years (see arc in Figure 1)! It is clear, as I have mentioned, that different estimates as to the time of the isolation call for

[2] The designations brachiationist and antibrachiationist are taken from Gregory (cf. Kaplan, 1948).

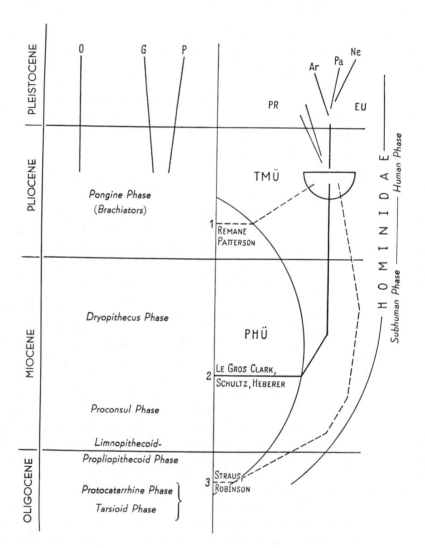

FIGURE 1. Phase divisions of hominid phylogeny and the isolation hypothesis. 1. brachiator hypothesis. 2. early pongid hypothesis. 3. protocatarrhine hypothesis. PHÜ-pongid-hominid transition zone. TMÜ-Tier-Mensch transition zone. PR-prehominines. EU-euhominines. Ar-archanthropines. Pa-palaeanthropines. Ne-neanthropines. O-orang utan. G-gorilla. P-*Pan* (chimpanzee). (After Heberer, 1958b).

accepting quite different morphological base types for hominid phylogeny. We now have the task of weighing these hypotheses against one another.

2. THE SUBHUMAN PHASE OF HOMINID PHYLOGENY

Derivation of the primates from an insectivore stem, by way of forms for which the Tupaiidae may serve as models, is to be taken for granted. The Tupaioidea, whose systematic position was long debated, have been recently recognized as primates—though having structural peculiarities of their own—particularly through an outstanding and thoroughgoing analysis of the skull by Saban (1957). They are most closely related to the Lemuridae, and are "the first branch to become separated from the primate trunk."

Except for the Lemuroidea (which are not to be regarded as ancestral models for the higher primates) and the surviving groups of the Tupaioidea (Tupaiidae) and Tarsioidea (Tarsiidae), the many lines of the very complex prosimian radiation of the Paleocene and Eocene are extinct. Among these the Anaptomorphinae (subfamily of Microchoeridae, Hill, 1957) in particular should apparently be viewed as the primary model for the catarrhine radiation of the Oligocene, and thus as the model for prepongid ancestral forms. The recent Tarsiidae (the spectral tarsiers) are also moderately closely related to them. Figure 2 gives as an example (because it is the best preserved) the skull of *Tetonius homunculus* (Cope)[3] (= *Anaptomorphus homunculus* Cope), of the Upper Paleocene to the Lower Eocene, from the Wasatch formation of the Bighorn Basin of Wyoming. Excepting for specialization of the anterior teeth, there is no great difficulty in deriving the "Dryopithecus pattern" of the crowns, so well known from the work of Gregory and Hellman (1926), from this early tarsioid form, through establishing the trigonid and talonid at the same height, individualizing the cusps, and deepening the double Y-form system of furrows between the cusps. Remane (1956b) regards the Eocene *Anaptomorphus-Washakius* group, so named by him, as possible forerunners of the Pithecoidea.

Accordingly, in the Oligocene and perhaps the Upper Eocene, a "proto-catarrhine" stage had already been reached, although this can as yet hardly be demonstrated paleontologically. The very fragmentary finds which might be placed therein are in part highly problematical.[4] We cannot go into them more fully here. In any case it seems likely that the Cercopithecoidea and Hominoidea as independent lines go back to the

[3] The genus *Tetonius* was created in 1915 by Mathew.
[4] According to Hürzeler, the possibility must now be considered that *Amphipithecus* probably does not belong to the primates.

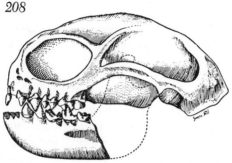

FIGURE 2.. *Tetonius homunculus.*
About 2 times natural size. (From
Hill, 1957, redrawn after Hubrecht)

protocatarrhine level. There is already present in the Lower Miocene of
Kenya the genus *Mesopithecus* which, whether colobine or cercopithecine, exhibits a pronounced bilophodonty. This specialized crown development must certainly have a long history of differentiation behind it.
I have expressed myself on this point several times (Heberer, 1952a
1956).[5] Simpson (1949) and Patterson (1954) trace both groups of catarrhines, the Cercopithecoidea and the Hominoidea, back separately to a
tarsioid basis.

From these brief remarks it may be seen that we can legitimately say
very little of a reliable nature as to the actual phylogenetic roots of the
Hominoidea. If we still place *Parapithecus fraasi* (Figure 3) from the
Lower Oligocene of the Fayum (Egypt) in the Hominoidea, this is
because of the pronounced five-cusped crowns of the lower molars.[6]
Certainly *Parapithecus* exhibits definite specializations in his anterior
dentition, characterizing him as a special line; nonetheless he may be regarded as morphologically the oldest representative of the hominoid
group (*Parapithecidae*). Unfortunately only the mandible is known.

It is interesting that a find exists making a morphological bridge from
Parapithecus to the Tarsioidea. This is *Alsaticopithecus leemanni*, from
the Eocene (Lutecian) of Buchsweiler, described by Hürzeler (1947).
The molars have a true hypocone ("Hypoconifera" in the sense of Hürzeler). The upper molars, still triangular in the Tarsioidea, have become
quadrangular, and the lower molars have no paraconid, but have a well-
marked hypoconid. According to Hürzeler, the dentition of *Alsaticopithecus* exhibits no detail "which would not permit its differentiation in the
direction of the above-named Oligocene genera (*Parapithecus* and
Propliopithecus)." I should like to cite my own opinion of 1956, "Therefore *Alsaticopithecus leemanni* could well be a first find linking an Eocene
tarsioid base and the protocatarrhine forerunners of the Hominoidea."

[5] Cf. also Le Gros Clark (1949b).

[6] This formation has been clearly demonstrated by a recent close investigation of
the original specimen by Kälin (abstract from the Versammlung der Deutschen
Anthropologischen Gesellschaft zu Kiel, August 1958).

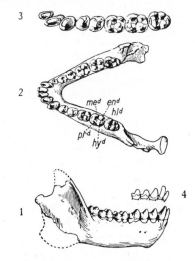

FIGURE 3. *Parapithecus fraasi.* About natural size. (From Abel, 1931)

The attainment of the catarrhine plateau from a tarsioid base is thus at the moment extremely sparsely documented.

We reach somewhat more solid ground with a second find from the Lower Oligocene deposits of the Fayum oasis. This is *Propliopithecus haeckeli*. Once more, however, we have the remains only of the mandible. *Propliopithecus* is a definite hominoid, which is already to be allied with the Hylobatidae. Compared to him, his contemporary *Parapithecus* gives the impression of a relic of Eocene times. *Propliopithecus* is an indication that catarrhine history, with its hominoid branch, must be traced back into the Eocene. It possesses close relationships to the first tangible hylobatids of the Lower to Middle Miocene (Vindobonian), as they have been described under the genus *Limnopithecus* from Kenya (Le Gros Clark and Leakey, 1951). The similarities of the two genera *Propliopithecus* and *Limnopithecus* are such that they may be referred to as the *Propliopithecus-Limnopithecus* group (Heberer, 1956).

Thus, generally speaking, a protocatarrhine phase leads on to a propliopithecus-limnopithecoid phase (cf. Figure 1). From this there ensues on the one hand the further development toward recent hylobatids via the *Pliopithecus* group, and on the other hand it is probable that in a propliopithecus-limnopithecoid level we should also look for the roots of the pongids, whose oldest morphological expression we see in the *Proconsul* group (see below).

From the point of view of the history of science it is interesting that, in setting the *Propliopithecus-Limnopithecus* group as the base of the hominoid branch, the hypothetical *"Prothylobates"* of Haeckel (1896b) is made real.

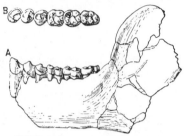

FIGURE 4. *Propliopithecus haec-keli*. Teeth and mandible. About natural size. (After Schlosser, 1911)

With reference to more recent discussions, it is notable that the extremities of the skeleton of *Limnopithecus* are sufficiently known (Le Gros Clark and Thomas, 1951) so that it may safely be said that the *Propliopithecus-Limnopithecus* group did not yet possess the typical specializations for brachiation seen in the recent hylobatids. This is not to say that the group could not indulge in brachiation. Ferembach's (1953) researches lead to the conclusion that this was already the case (see below, for pertinent details in *Proconsul*). We shall not pursue further the phylogeny of the hylobatids. They play no role in the later history of pongids and hominids. It may be noted, however, that even in *Epipliopithecus vindobonensis* (Zapfe, 1951; Zapfe and Hürzeler, 1957) from the Helvetian of Neudorf a. d. March the proportions of the extremities typical of brachiators have still not been attained, although it is the hylobatids which developed the most extreme expression of these proportions within the Hominoidea. This may be taken as a sign that this special adaptation to rain forest came about relatively recently in history—in general, too late to enter into consideration as a preparatory stage for upright progression—quite apart from other considerations which weigh against this.

We now turn to the treatment of fossil pongid material of the greatest significance for the question of the phyletic derivation of the hominids. We already encounter, in the Oligocene hominoids *Parapithecus* (supposedly) and *Propliopithecus*, the crown structure of the lower molars known, following Gregory, as the "*Dryopithecus*" (5-Y) pattern. We believe, contrary to the advocates of a derivation of the hominids from protocatarrhine or even tarsioid forerunners, that the fact of so far-reaching a similarity in the *Dryopithecus* pattern constitutes a decisive indication of the origin of the hominids from a parent in whom this pattern was already fully developed, a parent, therefore, which in this respect must already have corresponded to a *Propliopithecus-Limnopithecus* level.

Figure 5 provides an example of the definite similarity of the *Dryo-*

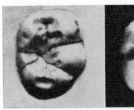 

FIGURE 5. *Dryopithecus* pattern of the lower molars. Left, third lower molar of *Dryopithecus germanicus* Abel, from Melchingen. Right, lower molar of recent man. About 2 times natural size. (After Mollison, 1933)

pithecus pattern between the Dryopithecinae and the Hominidae. A tooth is not an organ of genetically simple determination! It rests on a complex genetic basis, and it is unlikely that such a basis developed several times independently in the course of the phylogeny of the Hominoidea. Tooth structures in the primates have a considerable stability. This is particularly true of the Pongidae.

Perhaps the oldest Pongidae known to us in some measure as fossils (in fact the best known) are the Proconsulinae (subfamily of Pongidae).[7] They are relatively early geologically, originally having been thought to correspond to the Lower Miocene (Burdigalian), though perhaps they must now be put in the Middle Miocene (see Thenius, 1958a, who dates them to the Vindobonian; cf. Table 1) of Kenya (Victoria-Nyanza Basin). As Kälin (1955) has emphasized, they strongly recall protocatarrhine (not cercopithecoid) characteristics. Latest researches lead us to see in them primitive Pongidae, from which evolution to biped hominids was no longer possible but which still convey a picture of structural conditions out of which isolation of the hominid branch might have come about.

Remains of proconsulines have been known since the end of the 1920's, though a large majority of the finds were recovered by the British Kenya Expedition (1947, 1948), remains being particularly copious on Rusinga Island in Kavirondo Gulf of Lake Victoria. The most important specimen is a skull, in somewhat fragmentary condition, of the form designated *Proconsul africanus* (Figure 6). At the moment, several "species" are distinguished for *Proconsul: africanus* Hopwood, *nyanzae* Le Gros Clark and Leakey, and *major* Le Gros Clark and Leakey, these ranging in size from that of a pigmy chimpanzee to that of a gorilla (cf. Figure 7). For the larger forms, a primarily terrestrial life is to be assumed.

Having a typically fundamentally pongid dentition, the skull form of *Proconsul africanus* is surprising in its special structure. Taken altogether, the skull recalls a cercopithecoid rather than a pongid conformation. Surely we see here the preservation of protocatarrhine conditions. There is a pronounced prognathism. The supraorbital torus is totally lacking, though frontal sinuses are developed. The frontal is rounded with a

---

[7] The Proconsulinae have been made by me (1956) a separate subfamily of the Pongidae.

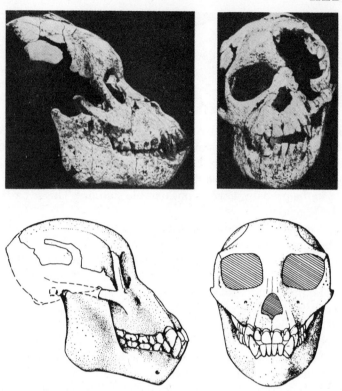

FIGURE 6.   Skull of *Proconsul africanus*. Above, original. Below, reconstruction by Robinson (1952). About 2/5 natural size. (From Heberer, 1949)

relatively flat outline. The presence of a frontal sinus is very important; in the older brachiationist theory ("chimpanzee theory") the presence or absence of sinuses played an essential role. Today the phylogenetic significance of this trait is no longer decisive, with understanding of its phylogeny and of the variability of its ontogenetic development; and proof of sinuses in *Proconsul* has indicated that one should not try to perceive in it any sign of special phylogenetic relations. Within the Hominoidea, frontal sinuses have not been acquired by the "gorilla-chimpanzee-man group" alone, the "Summoprimates" in the sense of Weinert (1925). The orang utan must have lost them sooner or later in the course of his history. We do not know whether or not the dryopithecines had them. As for body posture, the skull form indicates that this was pronograde, though not in the sense that we are dealing with quadrupedal terrestrial animals.

Of primary significance is the dental structure of the proconsulines.

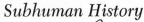

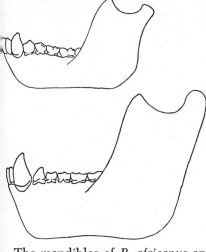

FIGURE 7. Mandibles of *Proconsul africanus,* above; and *P. nyanzae,* below. About 1/2 natural size. (After Le Gros Clark and Leakey, 1951)

The mandibles of *P. africanus* and *P. nyanzae,* represented in Figure 7, clearly show the significant variability in size prevailing in this group, not only in absolute size but also in special form, which is manifest without description. The dentition has the typical heteromorphic development of the canine group, with a sectorial P₃. The large canine is matched by a strongly developed diastema in the upper jaw. If we compare the mandible of a young specimen of *Proconsul* with that of a chimpanzee of the same dental development (Figure 8), differences, particularly in the incisive region, are evident, this region being more emphasized in *Pan.* Furthermore, the simian shelf in the angle of the symphysis is already definitely developed; in the proconsulines it is missing even in the adult condition. Comparison of adult mandibulae of the two forms reveals that the primitive traits were present in the adult *Proconsul* as well (Figure 9). Although definite signs of primitiveness appear in *Proconsul,* nonetheless the dentition is typically pongid even in individual features, although naturally specializations are also present.[8] We agree with Le Gros Clark and Leakey (1951), who see a still primitive set of hominoid relations in the skull and teeth. Assuming secondary differentiation (proscopiny, or visor-like projecting supraorbital tori; broadening of the mandibular symphysis; parallel tooth rows from C to M₃; enlargement of the C; and correlated morphological changes, et cetera), we may envisage the origin, from this, of the skull structure of recent pongines, perhaps as it had already been more or less realized in the Dryopithecinae.

The brachiationist school thinks it possible that the hominid skull and

[8] For details of these structures the reader must refer to Le Gros Clark and Leakey (1951) and Heberer (1952b, 1956).

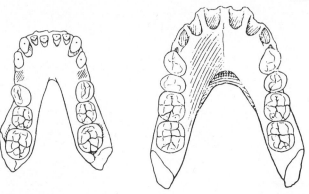

FIGURE 8. Mandibles of *Proconsul nyanzae* (reconstructed), left; and *Pan* (juvenile), right. Same stage of dental development. Approximately 2/3 natural size. (After Le Gros Clark and Leakey, 1951)

teeth ·emerged from a state of differentiation such as the present pongines exhibit and which, as above, had perhaps already been developed in the later Dryopithecinae (see for example Figure 15 on page 225). This hypothesis appears to us improbable, since it demands too complex, genetically correlated, changes in many traits in a relatively short time. Even the stage present in the proconsulines seems already too strongly specialized in the direction of the dryopithecine-pongine group. We prefer here the hypothesis which accepts, as a point of departure for the development of the hominid dentition, a masticatory apparatus possess-

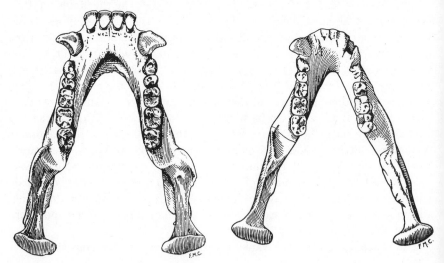

FIGURE 9. Mandibles of *Proconsul nyanzae*, right; and *Pan*, left. 1/2 natural size. (After Le Gros Clark, 1949a)

ing still fewer specializations than are already evident in *Proconsul*. In this category belongs, for example, the strongly developed heteromorphy of the canine group. It must however be clearly borne in mind that this is a matter of opinion, and that a sectorial P$_3$ is also viewed as a possible phyletic forerunner of a bicuspid P$_3$. Note here that at the beginning of dental differentiation the primates obviously possessed a caninized, unicuspid P$_3$. This then gave rise to the differentiated form of the pongines on one side and to the molarized bicuspid form of the hominids on the other. The problem will occupy us again in discussion of *Oreopithecus bambolii*. The general skull form of the proconsulines can, as I have mentioned, serve well as a model for differentiation in both directions: hominid and pongid.

If at this point we conclude that the proconsulines will not serve as basic model for the dental differentiation of the Hominidae, we cannot do the same for the postcranial skeleton, although the material found does not permit definite conclusions. We have available a femur and a humerus. There is no valid objection to ascribing these parts to the *Proconsul* group. Figure 10 shows a fragmentary femur belonging (supposedly) to *Proconsul nyanzae*, compared with the oft-cited and still ambiguous femur of *Paidopithecus eppelsheimensis* Pohlig, and with that of a chimpanzee. There is a general similarity of the *Proconsul* femur

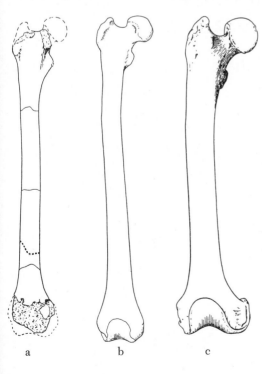

FIGURE 10. Right femur of *Proconsul nyanzae* (a); *Paidopithecus eppelsheimensis* (b); and *Pan* (c). About 2/5 natural size. (After Le Gros Clark, 1949a)

a   b   c

with that of *Paidopithecus,* but the latter, though of almost the same size, is less robustly constructed, and is strongly distinguished in its lesser robusticity from that of the chimpanzee. On this basis we may well deduce a less powerful structure of the skeleton of the extremities of the proconsulines. The humerus (Figure 11) is more indicative. Though about the same length as that of a chimpanzee, the humerus of *Proconsul* is decidedly more slender, and also more lightly constructed than the humerus described in 1856 by Lartet and ascribed to *Dryopithecus fontani.* The shaft of the *Proconsul* humerus is somewhat bowed forward in the middle. This may be viewed as reminiscent of a protocatarrhine condition. There is present a weakly developed supinator crest, to which the M. brachioradialis attaches, whereas this crest may exhibit a very pronounced development in the case of brachiators. Even if the variability of this trait is taken into account, the state of affairs in the *Proconsul* humerus scarcely bespeaks a specialized brachiator, and one does not expect, in the case of a single find, that an extreme variant is more likely to be found than a medium development (which latter is statistically more frequent) particularly since it fits better into the entire constitutional picture. In Figure 12 one may compare different degrees of development of this ridge of insertion in cross sections taken about 2 cm above the border of

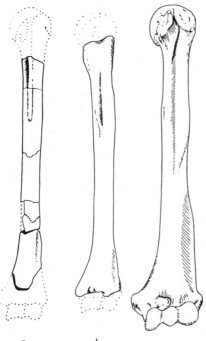

FIGURE 11. Left humerus of *Proconsul nyanzae* (a); *Dryopithecus fontani* (b); and *Pan* (c). 1/2 natural size. (After Le Gros Clark and Leakey, 1951)

a   b   c

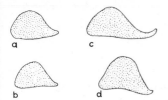

FIGURE 12. Cross sections (2 cm. above the proximal border of the olecranon fossa) of *Dryopithecus fontani* (a); *Proconsul nyanzae* (b); *Pan*, male, (c); and *Homo sapiens* (d). 1/2 natural size. (After Le Gros Clark and Leakey, 1951)

the olecranon fossa. Here the difference between *Proconsul, Dryopithecus,* and *Homo* on one side, and *Pan* on the other, is dramatically shown. Relative to the question of whether the proconsulines were brachiators equivalent to the modern swinging, hanging clamberers, comparison of the extremities thus makes it appear that they were not yet so specialized.

The problem of brachiation, both in general and in particular connections, is warmly argued at the moment. In particular, Remane, to whom we owe recent valuable observations of a methodological nature on the problem of hominid phylogeny (Remane, 1952–1956), has taken the field as an advocate of the brachiationists. Remane sees the following alternatives: 1. Hominid bipedalism is derived from a brachiating group. 2. Hominid bipedalism developed directly from quadrupedalism. However, this opposition does not go to the heart of the modern problem since, naturally, it is the general conviction as Böker (1935) says, "It is to be entirely rejected that four-footed progression on level ground can have been the forerunner of human locomotion." In reference to matters dealt with later, we may mention that this is meant in the morphological-structural sense. The point of departure for human bepedalism was in any case an arboreal form, not a terrestrial one. By "brachiators" the antibrachiationists on the other hand more or less tacitly understand the typical form of *recent* brachiators, with specialized limb proportions (long-armed apes) and structure (hook-like hands). However, it is not claimed that the capacity for brachiating locomotion is the property of these specialized brachiators alone. On the other hand one should constantly emphasize that this hanging progression is possible to branch-clasping climbers as well—as a "related function" in the sense of Remane. However, this capability—and here Remane is quite correct—cannot be discerned directly from structure. I have often explicitly said "that forerunners of later hominids who were still in a climbing stage occupied a position near at the same time to preponderantly quadrupedal grasping climbers and to hanging climbers . . ."; "but our forebears certainly did not possess the limb proportions characteristic of present day brachiators" (Heberer, 1955a). Others besides me specifically mean, by "brachiators," *long-armed* swinging climbers. A second citation, with particular relation to the proconsulines (Heberer, 1955b), "Nothing is opposed to the notion that the proconsulines were to a slight degree capable of swinging progression, but they did not possess the limb proportions of brachiators. There are living monkeys, such as the guerezas, who are good swingers without manifesting brachiating proportions."[9]

Thus it will be observed that there are misunderstandings of semantic origin. When Patterson (1954) equates brachiation with the *extreme* conditions seen in living pongids, he is thereby advocating—and the "brachiationist" Remane would also surely take the view that no *extreme* brachiator is to be found at the base of the hominids—the view already formulated thus by Gustav Schwalbe (1923), "a creature not yet persuaded by an extreme development of the arms to an exclusively arboreal life," and on a similar basis we agree with Remane, when he (1956a, p. 45) likewise expresses the view that "extreme swinging-hanging types are not demanded as hominid ancestors." Nevertheless, he regards it as possible that the "hook-like hand" of extreme brachiators was the structural basis for the human hand. In support, Remane notes that children exercising on the horizontal bars use the hand as a hook hand without a full grasp, and only learn "thumb-around" at the behest of instructors. However, this really demands statistical proof—and if one observes young pongids these hangers (!) will be seen occasionally to place the "thumb around" if it is long enough (for example, Fiedler, 1956; Figure 74). In any case, this kind of argument seems insufficient. It may be remembered that modern pongids, going on the ground, progress with the help of all four extremities, practicing a "knuckle gait," while our own children in the "quadrupedal" stage place palms flat on the surface, like the Cercopithecoidea. In this respect, the hand musculature of hominids essentially corresponds to that of primitive old world monkeys (Straus, 1949). Such a ground-dwelling pongid as the mountain gorilla (*Gorilla g. beringei* Matshie) had indeed attained certain resemblances in his foot structure to the supporting foot of hominids, but this foot can in no wise serve as a model for the true bipedal foot of hominids (Kälin, 1949 and in correspondence).

Morton (1922, 1924), who is often cited approvingly by Remane, and to whom we owe important insights into the process of transformation by which a hominid supporting foot is traceable to a grasping foot, must be quite right in saying that hominid forerunners possessed "arms and legs of equal length or nearly so (!)" and indeed one cannot deny possible brachiating functions to this structure as well. And when Remane then explains that typical "hangers" further developed those structural special-

---

[9] Both of these citations (1955a, 1955b) are taken from publications which appeared one year before Remane's criticism of my position on the brachiation hypothesis. Thus, to a degree, Remane is knocking down straw men.

izations which are determined by a brachiating existence, he is only expressing what the "antibrachiationists" have always held to be the case.

After this digression into contemporary discussion, we return now to *Proconsul.* Investigation of the postcranial skeleton led Le Gros Clark to the view that *Proconsul* "had not developed specialized brachiating habits (such as those of the modern gibbon)"—and the extreme brachiating structure of the Hylobatidae appears, like the same thing in the Ponginae, to be a phyletically independent and a phyletically late acquisition, as we have seen in considering *Epipliopithecus.* Somewhat earlier forms, such as *Limnopithecus,* also did not yet exhibit the relatively long arms of hangers in the structural sense, as may be seen in Figure 13, although, according to the report of Ferembach (1953), allowance should be made for the physiological possibility of brachiation in *Limnopithecus.*

When Patterson (1954) writes, "The extreme degree of this adaptation shown by hylobatines and pongines today may be as recent an event in primate history as acquisition of the upright gait," this agrees exactly with what has been said for years by others and by me, namely that the structural specialization for brachiation in the Pongidae came too late in the course of history to be considered as a possible preceding stage in the bipedalism of hominids. Let us cite here one of the outstanding students of the problem, A. H. Schultz (1957a), who said, "After forty years of research on primates, I have come to the conclusion that the branch representing human evolution must already have been divided from the primate trunk by the beginning of the Miocene. It seems to me that only with such a view it is possible to accommodate all the facts known to the present . . . It seems to me beyond doubt that the hominids must have set out upon their own way *after* the beginning of upright posture, loss of an external tail, existence of a truly opposable thumb, etc., but before the pongids had developed such specializations as extreme changes in regional numbers of vertebrae, the capability of brachiation, the enormous lengthening of the ilium, and the many other special anthropoid features."

Now however there are available for *Proconsul* the results of new research by Napier and Davis. The above lines had been written down long before there came to my attention these new findings in a presentation by Napier at the Sixth Session of the Deutschen Gesellschaft für Anthropologie in Kiel, in 1958. Napier points out that the designation "brachiator" has been the cause of misunderstandings, and he distinguishes between generalized and specialized brachiators. I myself have suggested speaking of nonstructural (functional) brachiators on the one hand and structural (morphological) on the other. The capacity for brachiating locomotion has often been observed not only in *Colobus* (see

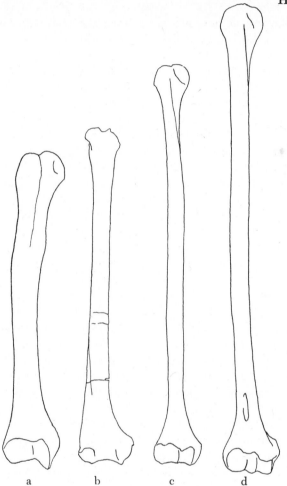

a   b   c   d

FIGURE 13. Right humerus (anterior view) of *Macacus nem-estrinus* (a); *Limnopithecus macinnesi* (b); *Hylobates leuciscus* (c); and *Symphalangus syndactylus* (d). 1/2 natural size. (From Heberer, 1952b, redrawn after Le Gros Clark and Thomas)

above) but also in *Cebus, Brachyteles, Presbytis, Nasalis,* and *Papio* (!).[10] Napier and Davis were able to study the forearm of *Proconsul africanus,* recovered in 1951 on Rusinga Island. The forearm "reveals characteristics of arboreal quadrupeds as well as those of brachiators."[11] In its proximal segment, the humerus is similar to tree-living "quadru-

[10] Information of Napier, who in connection with this paper showed a film on brachiation in *Nasalis.*

[11] Cited from a German-language abstract of the paper.

pedal" monkeys, while the distal joint surfaces are like the chimpanzee. The radius exhibits a mixture of traits of nonstructural and structural brachiators, the morphology inclining somewhat more toward the first group. The brachial index (86) resembles that of *Pan*. The structure of the hand is particularly interesting. The relations of the fingers are cercopithecoid (that is, protocatarrhine), while the main segments of the hand, on the contrary, resemble more the relationships in *Pan*. The thumb, however, is relatively long, longer than in all structural brachiators; at the same time the metacarpals resemble these, while the carpus is relatively primitive. From their finds, Napier and Davis judge *Proconsul* to be a transitional stage in which "an active quadrupedal form was developing the characteristics of a brachiator." With these most interesting conclusions, the possibility is not diminished, but in fact underlined, that the Proconsulinae furnish a general model for the derivation of the Ponginae (adaptation as structural brachiators to the rain forest biotype) and on the other hand for the Hominidae (adaptation as bipedal upright walkers to ground life in the steppe biotype). There appears no reason at the moment to change our judgment as to the derivation of bipedalism.

Remane is indeed a brachiationist, but certainly not an extreme one. We also pay our respects to brachiation, but to a still less extreme form (see above, discussion of hook hand). Both versions of the brachiation hypothesis consider antibrachiationism, in the sense of deriving the hominids from a quadrupedal ground form, as unacceptable. Differences of opinion thus obtain *among* the brachiationists, with particular respect to the structural type (potential or obligatory) of brachiators, from which derivation of hominid bipedalism might be expected. This is also expressed in our diagram (Figure 1). In any case, agreement prevails that the *modern* brachiators cannot be regarded as ancestral types, which would instead be more primitive forms. So it appears that the discussion among the brachiationists, partly due to semantics, is relatively immaterial.

In 1952, in defining the fully differentiated bipedalism of the australopithecines, I wrote the following (p. 602), which Remane has also cited in full, "Since bipedalism was already present in the Pliocene"—this should now be corrected to "Villafranchian," although this does not affect the problem—"then, if the ancestors of hominids were in fact actual brachiators, such an ancestral stage must already have held sway for a very long time. We must surely project this stage back into the Miocene. Here, however, the most recent finds show us (agreeing with older suspicions) that the 'Miocene pongids were not yet specialized brachiators'—or as we would now say, extreme structural arm-hangers! This prompts the supposition that emergence of upright walking for hominids and of brachiating specializations for pongids, as we see them in recent pongids, took place contemporaneously in parallel from undifferentiated beginnings so that the *phylogenetic* separation of the pongid and hominid branches was very early, at the latest in the Lower Miocene. From this viewpoint also we must note the improbability of the pongid theory in its classical form (to which I am opposed) i.e. the brachiator stage for hominids." Here I am in full agreement with Patterson (see above) in the notion that the extreme development of brachiating structure is as young in primate history as its upright walking, and nothing in the above passage suggests that I would derive hominid bipedalism directly from primitive quadrupedalism (Remane, op. cit.; see above, in connection with "semantics").

Today, six years later, I have nothing to alter in the passage cited; indeed, it is even more strongly supported, as we shall presently see.

Such a discussion as the above, between "antibrachiationists" and "brachiationists," emphasizes the unfortunate condition which still prevails in studies of the subhuman phase of hominid evolution, and how precarious the construction of theories is. Actually, we should take note of the wide agreement that structural brachiators are not likely to have been the basic group of hominids; today it is seldom that an author views them as ancestors.

For the hypothesis presented here, of a derivation of the hominid branch no later than the Middle Miocene, from still relatively primitive anthropoid apes, it is not entirely necessary to pursue the further history of this latter group of animals. It deserves, however, a summary view,[12] which will furnish us with a few more aspects of the relationships to one another of the two main branches of the Hominoidea.

First of all, let us use Table 1 to summarize the fossil material, following the stratigraphic presentation of Thenius (1958a). It should be noticed that some of the genera included are not generally recognized as such. The Dryopithecinae form a complex group, the systematics of which must be regarded as decidedly provisional.

It has been suggested that the known dryopithecines should be divided into a western and eastern group (Heberer, 1956). Piveteau (1957) likewise distinguishes a European group, primarily of the genus *Dryopithecus*, and an Asiatic group, primarily of the genus *Sivapithecus*. The former seems to lead in general to *Gorilla-Pan*, the latter to *Pongo* (orang utan). Perhaps the prehistory of the Pongidae ran much of its course in Africa. In any case it is here that we find our models for

[12] For details, refer to the complete presentations of Abel, Vallois, Piveteau, Remane, and Heberer, cited on page 204. The special literature is also cited in these works.

TABLE 1

GENERA OF FOSSIL PONGIDS AND THEIR GEOLOGICAL DATES

	Standard classification[a]	Europe	Africa	Asia
Pliocene	Astian Piazentian	—	—	*Rama-* *Ankara-* *pithecus*
	Pannonian	*Rheno-* *Paido-* *Dryo-* *pithecus* *Siva*(?)-	—	*Sugriva-* *Dryo* (?)- *Siva-* *pithecus* *Brama-* *Indo-*
Miocene	Sarmatian	*Hispano-* *Dryo-* *pithecus*	—	*Sugriva-* *Siva-* *Dryo-* *pithecus* *Brama-*
	Vindobonian	*Siva-* *Austriaco-* *pithecus*	Sivapithecus Proconsul	*Udabnopithecus* (*Kansupithecus*)
	Burdigalian	—	—	(Upper Oligocene ?)

a After Thenius (1958a).

prototypes (*Propliopithecus-Limnopithecus* group, Proconsulinae) as well as the recent *Gorilla-Pan* group. During the Middle Miocene, the dryopithecines attained an adaptive plateau, on which a radiation of forms took place which made possible a broad geographic expansion. Supposedly this took place outward from Africa, in the course of the great Miocene migrations of dryopithecines, leading to their wide distribution from Western Europe to the Far East (China). *Ankarapithecus* (Anatolia) and *Udabnopithecus* (Georgia) make the geographic bridge between western and eastern groups of Dryopithecinae. Dryopithecines disappear from Europe in the Upper Pliocene, for which the progressive deterioration of climate is probably responsible.

Details of this history and the special morphology of types are of little interest here. It is, however, important that the dryopithecines possessed a structure, at least in respect to jaw and tooth form, which does not deviate essentially from that of recent pongids, and further, that among them we can discern nowhere any clear trend toward the hominids. In Figures 14 and 15 are shown examples of the western and eastern groups, respectively. Without lengthy description it can be recognized that typical pongine structures of dentition and jaw are present both in *Dryopithecus fontani* from France (Figure 14) and in *Sivapithecus sivalensis* from the Siwaliks of Northwest India (Figure 15). Differences from recent anthropoid apes appear to be minor.

The dryopithecine dentition is marked by incisors which are still relatively small, although inclined in position. In comparison, the canines

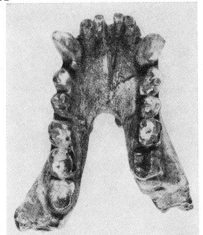

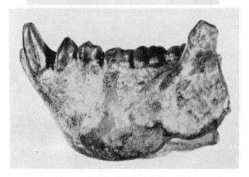

FIGURE 14. Mandible of *Dryopithecus fontani*. 2/3 natural size. (From a cast.)

are large; the upper jaw exhibits a corresponding diastema. P_3 is caninized, possessing an oblique mesiodistal axis, a large protoconid, and a weakly developed metaconid. Thus, a pronounced heteromorphy obtains in the lower canine group. The lower molars have the typical "Dryopithecus pattern," with a strongly developed hypoconulid. The total proportions of the dentition correspond to recent pongines, and like them the tooth rows from C to M_3 run parallel.

Among these Siwalik pongids, the genus *Ramapithecus* for a long time —perhaps still, in the minds of many authors—rested under the suspicion of having special human traits, and thus phyletic relations to the hominids. This was particularly emphasized by Lewis (1934), but was strongly contradicted by Hrdlicka (1935). Figure 16 shows a mandibular fragment assigned to *Ramapithecus*, found in 1935. Its traits are preponderantly those typical of pongines, with a heteromorphic canine group corresponding to a diastema[13] in the upper jaw. While a simian shelf is developed in other dryopithecines (Figures 14 and 15), although rela-

[13] An upper jaw fragment has also been found.

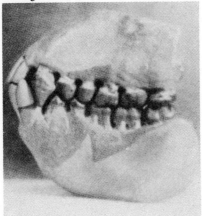

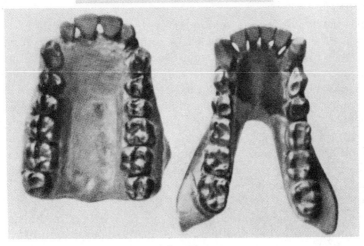

Figure 15. *Sivapithecus sivalensis,* reconstruction of anterior jaw region after Hellman. Above, lateral view. Below, upper and lower jaws, occlusal view. 2/3 natural size. (After Gregory, Hellman, and Lewis, 1937)

tively weakly, this must have been missing in *Ramapithecus.* Unfortunately no casts of the material are available. If the molars of *Ramapithecus* have an appearance more like hominids than is the case in other dryopithecines, this is more an example of parallel evolution than a sign of direct ancestry. This does not involve an entire pattern of traits, and thus cannot be used as a phylogenetic guidepost.

It is therefore manifest that since *Proconsul,* that is to say at least since the Middle Miocene (Vindobonian), the pongid dentition within the Dryopithecinae had only a very minor evolutionary velocity, and in these twenty million years evinced no structural changes of an essential kind.

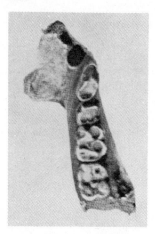

FIGURE 16. Mandibular fragment of cf. *Rama-pithecus brevirostris*. 2/3 natural size. (After Gregory, Hellman, and Lewis, 1937)

It would thus hardly be possible to derive the hominid dentition, demonstrated as far back as the Villafranchian in the Prehomininae (= Australopithecinae), from the typical pongid dental structure. Now, the latter is known since the Middle Miocene. It may therefore be viewed as possible, indeed probable, that the hominids have existed as an independent branch at least since the Middle Miocene, and that the division of the Hominoidea into the two main branches Pongidae and Hominidae is to be dated as no later than this time level. If so complex a structure as the dentition and the chewing mechanism of the anthropoid apes has a stability extending over long geological periods, it is most improbable that this stability should give way relatively quickly to a phase of instability and then rather abruptly attain a new stable phase, once again lasting a long time, as was the case for the hominid dentition. Quantum evolution, in the sense of Simpson, can hardly be cited here, since the point of departure was too strongly differentiated. Robinson (1956) is also of the opinion that the long persisting stability and specific structural adaptation of the pongid dentition does not support a derivation therefrom of the dentition of hominids.

On the above grounds (and there are others) the Dryopithecinae should accordingly be excluded as an ancestral stage for hominids. This view is by no means sympathetic to an overworked "specialization-mindedness" against which Remane has correctly warned students of phylogeny.

As to whether the Dryopithecinae were already structural brachiators (long-armed hangers), this cannot yet be decided. The question was raised early in connection with the fragmentary humerus (Figure 11), which was discovered in 1856 near St. Gaudens by Lartet. This exhibits, as has been mentioned, a relatively feeble marginal crest, from which may be deduced a poorly developed musculus brachioradialis; but it is to be admitted that this humerus may also have belonged to a particularly feeble individual. In any case, it still falls in the range of variation of chimpanzees. In general it is statistically more probable that in a single case one should not find an extreme variant but rather a more average fragment. Dryopithecine dental specialization, which had progressed far in the direction of pongines, necessarily suggests that, in correlation, the postcranial skeleton had also progressed toward pongine relationships, that is to say, in the direction of structural brachiation. On the other hand, it must be said that different body systems may possess completely different rates of evolution. Ehrenberg (1938) has already drawn attention to this in relation to pongid history in his description of *Austriacopithecus*. Briefly, the problem of the structural locomotor type of the Dryopithecinae is unsolved. If future finds reveal that the Dryopithecinae were already structural brachiators, the present hypothesis, which does not view the Dryopithecinae as an ancestral model for the hominids, would be materially supported.

In closing this discussion of the material, insofar as it relates to fossil nonhominid Hominoidea, we show in Figure 17 the geographical distribution which, though not permitting detailed conclusions, demonstrates the extraordinary breadth of the expansion which these primate groups achieved in the course of the Tertiary. In any case, this distribution furnishes no hint as to the eventual locality where the isolation of the hominid branch took place. Any hypothesis hangs almost completely in the air.

This ignorance as to the geographical place of isolation of the hominid stem and the beginning of the process of hominization which then culminated in the achievement of bipedalism naturally does not prevent us from making suggestions as to how this development may be thought of.

Let us assume a pongid (modeled on *Proconsul*), structurally not yet a brachiator, or scarcely so, living in a woodland steppe containing occasional woods. He would be obliged to come to the ground to seek out food and sexual partners. The character of the biotype would then have provided a plausible complex of conditions which makes understandable the progressive development of bipedalism. How would such a pongid first progress on the ground? Doubtless as a "quadruped," since he would be incapable of sustained locomotion as a "biped." We may imagine that this ground was not without vegetation, but had steppe grasses and scrub bush. As a quadruped, this pongid would not have been able to notice enemies, especially predatory cats, quickly enough; as arboreal forms, his ancestors had enlarged the eyes and repositioned

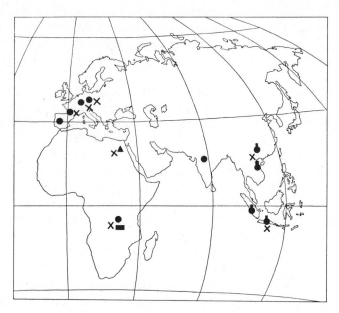

FIGURE 17. Geographical distribution of nonhominid fossil Hominoidea. *Ankarapithecus* (Anatolia), *Udabnopithecus* (Georgia), and *Dryopithecus keiyuanensis* (Yünnan) are not included. ▲ = Parapithecidae, **x** = Hylobatidae, ■ = Proconsulinae, ● = Dryopithecinae, ♦ = Ponginae (*Pongo*). (After Heberer, 1956)

them forward, allowing stereoscopic vision, an extremely important transformation of the facial structure of the skull for life as a climbing animal in the spatially complicated world of trunks and branches. In correlation with the enlargement of the optic sense organs, however, the nasal region diminished. The sense of smell of the Pithecoidea is not imposing, and is certainly not to be compared with that of ground-living game animals, who *smell* an enemy. Such an immediate detection of the presence of enemies through smell is thus not possible to a pongid on the ground, who must compensate by the use of eyes. To do this in vegetation on the ground, however—to "scout"—he must stand erect to obtain a sufficient field of vision.[14] One may now imagine that those mutations were selectively favored which provided a better capacity for the upright scouting position than their forerunners, and which also, through constantly longer maintenance of the upright position allowed their owners to get back to the nearest sheltering trees bipedally. We may suppose that eventually "running" was attained by mutations

[14] A. H. Schultz has lately (1955) plausibly shown that there can be no intermediate phase, a kind of "half-erect" position.

which allowed the covering of long distances completely in fast-running as a biped. The paleontologist Romer has pointed out that crossopterygians became transformed into land-living tetrapods (as the oldest forms, the ichthyostegids, have so dramatically shown) because they "wished" to remain in the water. In an environment becoming progressively more arid, they lived in evaporating water with less and less oxygen. This they had to leave, going overland in search of new water. Le Gros Clark has expressly applied this seeming paradox to those pongids who finally went over to terrestrial bipedalism; they became ground forms because they "wished" to stay in the trees.

That arboreal life was the primary point of departure for hominid bipedalism allows of no doubt. The primates are clearly a group of mammals which, supposedly as early as the Cretaceous, became climbers with hands and feet, by preserving extremities with five digits, thus bringing with them the necessary prerequisites for the grasping function or becoming adapted thereto (opposability of the first digits). An arboreal way of life by grasping and climbing calls for "hands," functionally speaking, on all four extremities. Only in a tree biotype can these arise and *persist*. A primary and persistently ground-living form does not develop fourhandedness. The present forelimb of the hominids is incomprehensible without prior arboreal life. But since this also makes necessary grasping feet, the hominid supporting foot must have arisen from a grasping foot. Thus, in the course of progressive adaptation to ground life, four-handed quadrupeds became two-handed bipeds, that is, the grasping foot became transformed during the subhuman phase of evolution in hominid phylogeny into a standing and running foot.[15] "Running" is a peculiarity of hominids alone; in this, only the toe segment of the foot is placed on the ground. Thus, an extra lever segment is attained and a corresponding acceleration made possible in locomotion. However, we cannot here go into the details of the anatomical changes involved.

The changes in construction necessary to attain hominid bipedalism from a "nonstructural" brachiator are much less fundamental than those which follow if we take typical structural brachiators as models for hominid ancestors. This latter would involve not only transformations of the extremities, the pelvis, et cetera, but also those which must take place in the dentition. The stability of the typical specialized pongid dentition obtaining since the Miocene has already been referred to above.

The preceding is naturally a hypothetical, but plausible hypothesis which is furthermore in no way original. Basically the same view of history is to be found as early as Lamarck's work, *Philosophie Zoologique*

[15] Cf. the witty remarks of H. Dingler (1941) on the "Four-handed animal."

(1809), 150 years ago, and among later authors we may mention Keith (1950 and earlier) and Le Gros Clark.

Now comes this question. Is there any actual fossil material from the subhuman phase of hominid phylogeny, during which the hypothetical changes in body structure took place, and which ended with the attainment of hominid bipedalism? This raises the problem, much debated at the moment, of *Oreopithecus bambolii!*

The group of finds, known as *Oreopithecus* ever since the 1870's, from the Grosseto lignites of the Upper Miocene or Lower Pliocene (Pontian) of Tuscany (Italy) has, after many misunderstandings, only recently been given an adequate examination by Hürzeler, 1949a). He first came to the decision that *Oreopithecus* was not, as had previously been accepted by many, a cercopithecoid form but rather a hominoid, although also possessing certain traits which lately have led many authors to pronounce *Oreopithecus* once more as cercopithecoid or at least standing close to Cercopithecoidea (v Koenigswald 1955b; Remane, 1955; Robinson, 1956). With the progress of his morphological analysis, Hürzeler (1954) has become more precise as to the position of *Oreopithecus*, placing it systematically as a hominid. This judgement has given rise to a widespread discussion, which is still in full sway and which, because of the constant occurrence of new finds, thanks to Hürzeler's intensive excavations, particularly in Baccinello (near Grosseto), has reached an exciting point. Various authors have agreed with Hürzeler's judgement of *Oreopithecus* as hominid, for example, Heberer (1956), who has ranked the form as a subfamily, Oreopithecinae, in the Hominidae.[16] Chronologically, its position naturally lies well down in the subhuman phase. Kälin (1955) has given the form its own family, Oreopithecidae in *his* superfamily Hominoidea. This superfamily does not include the Pongidae, but according to Kälin, is made up of the families Oreopithecidae, Australopithecidae, and Hominidae. If we disregard evaluations of rank, Kälin and Heberer agreee basically as to the placing of *Oreopithecus*. Piveteau also (1957), in his "Traité de Paléontologie" has placed *Oreopithecus* in the Hominidae (without systematic rank[17]) and Kurth likewise (1957, 1958) agrees as to the hominid (subhuman) nature of this find, so important for hominid phylogeny. While the present article was in preparation, Hürzeler (1958) published another note (still termed "preliminary") on the material so far recovered, covering a large amount of new data,[18] and replying to the published views of those (von

---

[16] Thus, the family Hominidae would comprise three subfamilies: 1. Oreopithecinae, 2. Prehomininae = Australopithecinae, 3. Euhomininae (Homininae).

[17] A. H. Schultz has also agreed in correspondence with Hürzeler's evaluation of *Oreopithecus* as hominid.

[18] A complete skeleton of *Oreopithecus* has been recovered at Baccinello.

FIGURE 18. *Oreopithecus bambolii.* Right dental arch of upper jaw (mirror image). 2 times natural size. (After Hürzeler, 1949a)

Koenigswald and Remane) opposed to classifying *Oreopithecus* as a hominid.

Within the limits of the present broad consideration of the subhuman phase of hominid phylogeny, discussion of *Oreopithecus* cannot be gone into *in extenso.* This will be done elsewhere. I may however remark, in connection with my own opinion, that I have had the advantage of full acquaintance with all the original material.[19]

A few traits of *Oreopithecus* will be briefly mentioned, of which any one alone would obviously not justify the judgement of "hominid," but which taken in combination hardly permit any other opinion. Figure 18 shows the upper dental arch. From this it appears that the tooth row is closed and has no diastema. Correspondingly, the canine is relatively small and its point only slightly exceeds the level of the other teeth. With respect to the canine, there is no significant sexual dimorphism. The lack of a diastema is typical for *Oreopithecus.* Out of twelve specimens, one piece, which shows a diastema, is uncertain in this regard. The diastema may be absent in occasional cases in pongids as well, just as, contrariwise, it may very occasionally be present in man. Nonetheless it is typically present in pongids and absent in hominids. Also, the dental arch of *Oreopithecus* lacks the typically pongid straight line from the point of the canine to the third molar, being instead curved in hominid fashion.

Figure 19 shows the lower tooth row from the side. We note here only the fact that P_3 is clearly bicuspid. This is made particularly clear in Figure 20, which compares it with a unicuspid sectorial P_3 of a chimpanzee. If, in the case of *Pan,* the lingual cusp of P_3 may occasionally be so well developed as to approach a bicuspid form, we are merely led to conclude from this unusual relationship that the trend toward molarization of the premolars is indeed present in the Hominoidea, but has led

[19] I am most grateful to my colleague Hürzeler for having made his material available to me on numerous visits to Basel.

to the presence of a *typical* bicuspid only within the Hominidae. While
Remane has remarked, in connection with this homomorphy of P₃ in
Oreopithecus, that examples may be found in the platyrrhines in which
P₃ possesses a protoconid and metaconid of equal'height, it would seem
that this parallelism in a phyletically distant group is methodologically
pointless for the problem under discussion, that is, the position of
Oreopithecus.

Relative to tooth structure, it may further be commented that—in
spite of contrary opinions of the authors cited—the lower molars fundamentally show the *Dryopithecus* pattern. There is no connection with the
bilophodonty of the Cercopithecoidea. *Oreopithecus* gives evidence of
being a hominoid by possessing, on the canine, a mesial furrow only on
the crown. In the Cercopithecoidea, this longitudinal furrow carries
beyond the cingulum without a break to the point of the root. The
further facts that orthodonty is present, that the incisors bit occlusally
in human fashion, that the face is relatively short, that the chin appears
vertical and rounded (without a simian shelf), should not be without
importance in the total trait complex of the masticatory apparatus.

Particularly meaningful, though nevertheless not decisive alone, are
the mesiodistal tooth lengths of the upper and lower teeth of *Oreopithecus*. The values for *Oreopithecus*, represented as a curve, and compared
with the values in Cercopithecoidea, Pongidae, Prehomininae and Euhomininae (Figures 21 and 22), allow it to be clearly seen that the length
proportions of the teeth of *Oreopithecus* belong definitely on the hominid
side.

As to the postcranial skeleton, little can be said at present.[20]

FIGURE 19.   *Oreopithecus bambolii.* Tooth row of mandible, right.
P₃—M₃. 2 times natural size. (After Hürzeler, 1949a)

FIGURE 20.   *Oreopithecus bambolii,* P₃ (left)
compared with P₃ of *Pan* (right). Mesial view.
2 times natural size. (After Hürzeler, 1958)

[20] See footnote 18.

A vertebral fragment comprising three lumbar and two sacral vertebrae make possible the interpretation, because of its relatively heavy construction, that perhaps *Oreopithecus* was already favoring the lower extremities in locomotion. Pelvic fragments so far known allow no statements as to the mode of locomotion. Of interest and significance is the structure of the ulnar joint (Figure 23), which is hominoid in its general conformation. It possessses an unusually weakly developed olecranon. Similarity to hominids is present in the form of the incisura semilunaris. This holds also for the insertion of the triceps muscles and the flexors. The eventual completion of our knowledge of the postcranial skeleton will be very interesting.

Altogether it may be said that, in the morphology of *Oreopithecus*, as far as it is now known, there is an unmistakable trend in the direction of hominid structures. *Oreopithecus* is surely no representative of a group directly parental to the later hominid forms known to us. There must have been numerous branchings in the subhuman hominid branch, which came to an end sooner or later. At successive time horizons, there would supposedly always have been several phyletically independent groups, to one of which, at the Miocene-Pliocene boundary, *Oreopithecus* would have belonged.

Piveteau formulates the phyletic significance of *Oreopithecus* as follows, "We may see in him concrete evidence of the early segregation

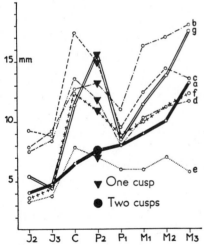

FIGURE 21. Mesiodistal length of mandibular teeth of *Oreopithecus* (a); *Gorilla* (b); *Pongo* (c); *Pan* (d); *Hylobates leuciscus* (e); *Dryopithecus fontani* (f); *Theropithecus* (Cercop.) (g). b to e and g = male, a = sex (?). (After Hürzeler, 1954)

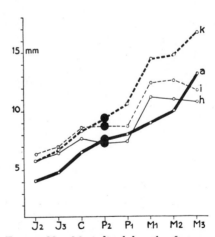

FIGURE 22. Mesiodistal length of mandibular teeth of *Oreopithecus* (a); *Homo sapiens* (h); *Sinanthropus* (i); and *Paranthropus crassidens* (k). After Hürzeler, 1954)

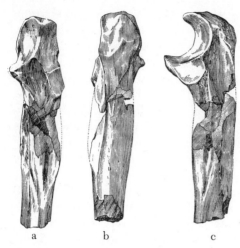

FIGURE 23. *Oreopithecus bambolii*, ulnar joint (mirror image). (a), anterior; (b), posterior; (c), and radial view. 3/4 natural size. (After Hürzeler, 1958)

a   b   c

of the human line," which agrees precisely with our own view expressed since 1956. If we kept the diagnosis of hominid for the Oreopithecinae, this has significant consequence for the nature of our views of the course of hominid phylogeny. "We have, then, with *Oreopithecus* a sign of the presence of hominids (naturally subhuman!) about ten million years ago. This serves, however, mainly as one element in a series of indications already suggesting to us a distant isolation of the hominid branch of the Hominoidea, perhaps reaching back into the Lower Miocene" (Heberer, 1956). As a subhuman hominid, *Oreopithecus* points to the independence of the hominid branch at a time when typical structural brachiators are not yet to be thought of. Grist for the mills of the "antibrachiationists"!

3. OBSERVATIONS ON THE "TIER-MENSCH" TRANSITION ZONE

The subhuman phase of hominid phylogeny ended with the Tier-Mensch transition zone (Heberer, 1958a). This zone must have been reached step by step in the course of the subhuman segment of history. At this point, the process of hominization was basically finished. We may estimate a series on the order of 600,000 to 400,000 generations for the subhuman phase. Such a series would suffice for the changes which took place to be ascribed to the known mechanisms of infraspecific evolution (Heberer, present article and 1958c), the more so since on reaching a new adaptive zone such as the open steppe, we may suppose the operation of quantum evolution in Simpson's sense, which implies a speeding-up of evolutionary rates. It can be assumed that the essential changes which led to the attainment of fundamental bipedalism took place at a relatively high evolutionary velocity.

The final development of bipedalism had as its most important consequence the freeing of arms and hands from locomotion. These could now be put more and more to other activities. The hand of grasping and climbing monkeys is entirely capable, in its functional anatomy, of carrying out the essential manipulations called for in the production of tools. However, those animals lack a differentiation of the corresponding brain centers needed to initiate and control these manipulations. Only in that part of the chain of generations which passed over into bipedal ground life did the needed brain mutations appear (multiplication and growth of centers), which were then favored by selection. The activities of the freed hands consisted in the progressive employment of instruments. Instruments constitute a compensation for increasing physical defenselessness because of retrogression of the pithecoid dental weapons, these correlated trends proceeding inversely. These first instruments were "implements" in the sense that they were not yet fashioned for definite, predetermined ends, but only selected from what nature provided, as more or less suitable for the needs of the moment. The actual capacity to invent and make such implements into artifacts, into "tools" according to abstractly formed mental patterns for a future purpose, was first developed in the Tier-Mensch transition zone.

Even recent pongids, who may be in a limited degree potential toolmakers, as the well known experiments of Koehler, Yerkes, and Hayes have shown, make no tools in the primeval forest. At least, nothing of the sort has been observed. The stimulus and the need are lacking. It was those hominids who were constant toolmakers (Oakley 1950a, 1951, 1956c) who became the "first" human hominids. Pongids who may today be persuaded to make tools under experimental conditions have not thereby reached that stage which is basic to the "human" hominids and which underlies their mental evolution: the stage which betokens the capability, fostered particularly through the prolongation of childhood typical of euhominines, not only to make inventions but also to enculturate them, and to accumulate knowledge in the course of generations. This was achieved with the aid of a corresponding mechanism of communication (speech), which eventually took form within a structure of society, which in any case, being present in monkeys, must also be assumed for the subhuman hominids.[21]

We recognize well enough how difficult it is to render the critical phase of the first tools in terms of material definition. We may recall the "eolith" discussion of fifty years ago and more, which just now is beginning to raise its head again in recent works by Rust (1956). It might be suggested that tools must be accepted as far back as *Oreopithecus*, but there is not the slightest probability for this; the brain of this

[21] On this problem see the article by von Eickstedt (1959); also Kraft (1948) and Narr (1956).

form was too small for such activity, and certainly too little differentiated (quite apart from the persisting uncertainty as to the systematic and phylogenetic position of *Oreopithecus*). On the other hand, its occasional use of *implements* (a phase lasting perhaps even longer) may not be improbable, and in the course of the subhuman phase such use of implements must have slowly increased. On such a base, through many intermediate steps, actual production of tools grew up.

Just as it is extremely difficult, perhaps impossible, to recognize the "first" tools, so it should also be impossible to deduce the capability of toolmaking from the anatomy of subhuman-human transitional forms, for example, from the skull capacity. In the fossil material, we have the prehominines (australopithecines), who fit nicely as anatomical models between the subhuman and human phases. Chronologically, however, they are too recent to be actual representatives of the Tier-Mensch transition zone, belonging stratigraphically to the Villafranchian; the Tier-Mensch transition zone must be placed in the Upper Pliocene. Thus, these prehominines cannot be considered as direct ancestors of the euhominines. But are they still subhuman for all that?

In Figure 24, an attempt is made to reconstruct the living appearance of a prehominine (*Australanthropus = Australopithecus*). The physiognomy in this attempt is naturally pure speculation, but the general constitution strikes the right note. It presents a fundamentally human body form. The question is, therefore, whether this group is to be spoken of as "human" in psychic function. Did the prehominines possess human intelligence?

If, for the subhuman phase, the decisive anatomical process was the attainment of upright walking and the development of the typical hominid dentition, the decisive process for the human phrase was *cerebralization*. In this regard the Tier-Mensch transition zone took on a quantitative aspect, in which a judgement of "still subhuman" or "already human" cannot safely be made. Keith (1950) attempted to set a quantitative "Rubicon" (Tier-Mensch boundary) at 750 to 800 cc. Let us now look at capacities of the Hominoidea shown in Table 2.

TABLE 2

CRANIAL CAPACITY OF THE HOMINOIDEA IN CC
(M = Mean)

Group	M	Range of variation
Homo	1350	950 to 2100
Archanthropines	1000	770 to 1300
Prehominines	600	450 to 800 (1000?)
Pongines	450	290 to 685
Hylobatids	95	80 to 140

FIGURE 24. Reconstruction of appearance in life of a prehominine of the *Australanthropus* group ("*Plesianthropus*"). (After Oakley, from Heberer, 1952b)

The prehominines are in fact intermediate in position between pongids and euhominines, something which obviously is of no special consequence with respect to the phyletic relations among these several groups. Otherwise we would be neglecting the fact that skull or brain capacity is to be evaluated relative to body size. A pigmoid prehominine of a stature between 1.20 and 1.50 meters cannot be directly compared with a large pongid which surpasses it in brain size.

In the scope of this discussion, quantitative capacity is no criterion of functional capacity. Thus, for example, we cannot deny a prehominine the basic capacity for speech simply because his brain corresponds quantitatively to those of chimpanzees and gorillas. On the contrary, we know that sapiens children begin to speak at the age of two years with a capacity of only 650 cc. This is a matter not of quantity but rather of gyrus development, the number of ganglion cells, their specialization, the number and size of centers, and their associational connections, all of which factors obviously cannot be deduced from fossil material.[22] Thus, capacity is no index of the "Rubicon." In critically

[22] The attempts to find homologies of gyri in skull impressions are mostly very uncertain.

evaluating the body constitution of the prehominines (Figure 24), we must certainly ascribe to their brain the fundamental capacity for human functions. Because he lacks specializations for particular biotypes and possesses numerous primitive organic traits, Gehlen (1950) has designated man as a "deficiency creature." Biologically, such a concept is applicable only *cum grano salis*. In any case, he emphasizes that the human hominid is an "open ecotype," exhibiting the ability to exist in the most varied biotypes. To this ability, he owes the great specialization and intellectual potency of his brain, which not only bestows on him the typical abilities of the human phase, but also lies at the base of his extended ecological potential.

The prehominines (australopithecines) clearly present, in their bodily constitution, the open ecotype of the human hominids. By this, we mean that it is justifiable to place the prehominines as already on this side (speaking from the present) of the Tier-Mensch transition zone.

Have we now, in addition to these general reflections, criteria of a more concrete nature for the correctness of these judgements? Such signs can be found only in relics of human *activity*. Such relics are principally 1. use of fire, and 2. tools.

1. Dart, in earlier writings, accepted the use of fire for the prehominines. However, Oakley (1955b, 1956b), in particular, has shown that the use of fire by the australopithecines is not probable, as far as the apparent remains are concerned. These relics of "fire" may be otherwise explained, and are recognized in part as blackening due to manganese dioxide. Other observations also make it probable that "human" mankind since the Tier-Mensch transitional zone, although already in possession of differentiated stone cultures, did not use fire for hundreds of thousands of years. The first sure traces of fire use occur at the site of "*Sinanthropus*," Chou Kou Tien in China, that is, no earlier geologically than the Middle Pleistocene. Thus the "Deed of Prometheus" has nothing to do with the development of man (Heberer, 1958b).

2. The question of tool use by the prehominines is unanswered. At present it appears as though the answer would be negative. In any case, all the finds which have heretofore been considered as indications, including Dart's so-called osteodontokeratic culture of the prehominines (Dart, 1957a) have run into strong critical objections. The bone instruments accepted by Dart and the accompanying collections from the bone breccia of Makapan may also be interpreted as hyena leavings. Furthermore, coprolites of hyenas have recently been found in these breccias (Washburn, 1957).

Now the australopithecine-bearing levels have also yielded indubitable stone tools. These were first found at Makapan, the site of *Australanthropus* (*Australopithecus*) "*prometheus*" (*africanus*). The tools in question are pebble tools of the simplest kind, such as are also present in perhaps even older geological deposits in the Vaal Valley. At Sterkfontein (site of *"Plesianthropus"* = *Australanthropus transvaalensis*), however, there were found hand axes of Oldowan type! This information (Brain, van Riet-Lowe, and Dart, 1955; and Robinson, 1957) by no means leads to the conclusion that the prehominines were in fact the makers of these tools. Particularly, one should not on this basis alone credit the prehominines with the production of hand axes. Robinson is of the opinion that these tools imply the presence of a contemporary but already more highly developed euhominine form. He considers this to be *Telanthropus capensis* from Swartkrans, which is in any case much disputed as to its morphological position.

It is thus probable that the prehominines were not themselves the "hunters" but rather the "hunted" (Washburn, 1957; Straus, 1957), while the bone collections in the australopithecine deposits are, as mentioned, also explicable as due to hyenas.

Undisputed proof of intentional tool production by prehominines is thus as yet not in evidence;—nevertheless, these early human forms must have used instruments to a large degree, whether they were still only "implements" or already, perhaps only in part, "tools." "Deficiency creatures" physically, they had to compensate for the "deficiency" by the capacity for instrument use and by the potential of their brains.

Finally, let us now cast a glance at a phyletic diagram once more, in Figure 25. This shows the radiation of forms in the human phase. With the attainment of this phase, there was reached again a most fateful adaptive level. It made possible the florescence of the open ecotype. On this level were based the phylogenetic events of the human phase. We should assume that a radiation took place from the late Pliocene Tier-Mensch transition zone, from which the prehominines issued. From this radiation, we have the early Pleistocene prehominines (*Australanthropus* group, *Paranthropus* group).[23] Although relatively early, they already constitute a relic of the Pliocene. A branch of this radiation, at the Plio-Pleistocene boundary, attained a new adaptive plateau, and from this there followed a further radiation. These are the euhominines, whose Pleistocene fanning-out has at a few points furnished us with fossils. Very schematically, we may distinguish three groups of euhomines: the Archanthropines (*Pithec-Sinanthropus* group), the Palaeanthropines (Neanderthal group), and the Neanthropines (*sapiens* group). The special phyletic connections of these three groups are still largely concealed from us and constitute one of the most interesting and pressing problems

[23] At present the *Gigantopithecus* group should also be placed herein (cf. Heberer, 1958a).

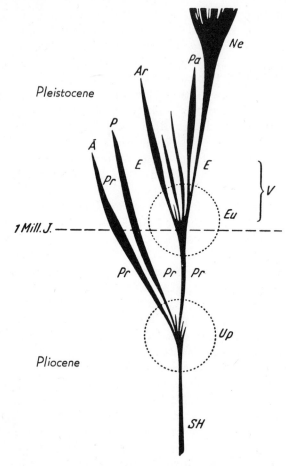

FIGURE 25. Expansion of the euhominines following passage through Tier-Mensch transition zone. SH, sub-human hominids; Up, original prehominines; Pr, pre-hominines; and Eu, euhominines. A, *Australanthropus* group; P, *Paranthropus* group; Ar, archanthropines; Pa, palaeanthropines; Ne, neanthropines; E, euhominines; and V, Villafranchian. (After Heberer, 1956).

of present-day phylogenetic paleoanthropology. At present, only speculative answers are possible. One such is given in Figure 25; however, we must always be ready to modify such a temporary picture, when new finds demand it.

Editor's Note: Professor Heberer wishes to draw attention to considerations resulting from new discoveries and publications:

1. (*Epi*)*Pliopithecus vindobonensis*, of which the extremities have been recently fully studied by Zapfe (1959), although a member of the hylobatid line, was assuredly no fully specialized brachiator in its morphology. Zapfe believes it possible that (*Epi*)*Pliopithecus* was not exclusively arboreal but, like modern cynomorphs, was also a ground-dweller; recovery of skeletal remains from fissure fillings accords with this. A similar possibility arises from the circumstances under which *Oreopithecus* and the new *Dryopithecus* from Carinthia were found. The relatively late achievement of the special adaptation of the hylobatids to the rain forest biotype, by means of development of

the typical swinging-hanging proportions, may be taken as a general sign that brachiation in fact appeared historically rather late. This may also hold for the Ponginae. According to Zapfe, the dryopithecines were also at least potentially terrestrial.

2. *Proconsul africanus* has been described (the 1951 material, especially the arm and hand) in a monograph by Napier and Davis (1959). The material establishes that the Proconsulinae were indeed differentiated for brachiation, but by no means exhibited "hanger" body proportions; the hand is not hooked with a short thumb and lengthened metacarpals. *Proconsul* thus still serves as a model for a prebrachiator.

3. *Oreopithecus* has been the subject of much recent discussion, without agreement as to whether its taxonomic position is pongid, oreopithecid, or hominid. A. H. Schultz's (1960) study shows that the pelvis differs significantly from that of Pongidae and approaches hominid conformation. In Cercopithecidae, it possesses a narrow, short ilium; in Pongidae, a broad and long ilium; and in *Oreopithecus*, a broad and short ilium and a similarity to hominids. Schultz concludes that *Oreopithecus* constituted a deliberate clamberer inhabiting woodland. Taking all the evidence into account, if one were to reconstruct a hominid form of the Mio-Pliocene boundary, this might easily resemble *Oreopithecus*, with all respect to the specializations of the latter, which characterize him at least as a side branch of the hominids, with a long independent history.

4. Opinions on *Australopithecus* expressed in the above article have been both broadly sustained and also modified by new finds published by Dart and by Leakey (see Heberer, 1960, for a review of recent literature). Dart finds proof of the actuality of the osteodontokeratic culture of the Makapan australopithecines in comparing it with the Kalkbank culture (Transvaal), of an age of 15,000 years, and thus the work of *Homo sapiens*. The latter revealed combination bone tools and marked signs of use, and are thus not referable to predators' leavings. There is thus little reason to doubt that the Limeworks Australopithecinae ("*Australopithecus prometheus*") were the producers of the osteodontokeratic tools, which in technique are almost identical to the Kalkbank forms of 15,000 years ago. The "hyena hypothesis" of bone collection by carnivores now no longer seems probable. As to the stone tools, present at Makapan and Sterkfontein, opinion as to their makers is still divided, although Leakey, with his finding of a *Paranthropus*-type skull at Oldoway (named by him "*Zinjanthropus*") shows that it is highly probable that the making of stone tools of pre-Abbevillian type lay within the capacity of the australopithecines, and indeed the whole Oldowan industry as well may be assigned to them. At the same time, Robinson (1961) holds to the euhominid, *Telanthropus capensis*, as the actual toolmaker. The problem of the australopithecines is thus in a most interesting stage. The impression has grown, so as to be almost irresistable, that they were already *human* hominids (in the sense of the above article). Their dating also appears in a new light: Kurtén's recent (1959a) careful faunal analysis has shown that all known finds of the Australopithecinae belong to the Middle Pleistocene, and thus are no longer to be assigned to the Villafranchian.

Taxonomic Categories in Fossil Hominids

Ernst Mayr   1951

It is one of the most fruitful procedures of modern science to bring specialists of various fields together to discuss the problems that concern the zone of overlap of their fields. Not possessing any first-hand knowledge of paleoanthropology, my own contribution to the question of the taxonomic categories of fossil man will be that of a systematist. Significant progress has been made within recent years among biologically thinking taxonomists in the understanding of the categories of subspecies, species, and genus, and it is my hope that this knowledge may help in a better understanding of fossil man.

The whole problem of the origin of man depends, to a considerable extent, on the proper definition and evaluation of taxonomic categories. But there is less agreement on the meaning of the categories species and genus in regard to man and the primates than perhaps in any other group of animals. Some anthropologists, in fact, imply that they use specific and generic names merely as labels for specimens without giving them any biological meaning. The late Weidenreich, for example, stated that in anthropology "it always was and still is the custom to give generic and specific names to each new type without much concern for the kind of relationship to other types formerly known." Broom (1950b) likewise

FROM Cold Spring Harbor Symposia on Quantitative Biology, *vol. 15, 1951, pp. 109–117, reprinted by permission of the author and of the Long Island Biological Association. Originally presented at the symposium on "The Origin and Evolution of Man," held at Cold Spring Harbor, June 9–17, 1950. By a leading systematist, whose primary zoological interest is ornithology but who has been constantly interested in human evolution, this article, applying the perspective of general zoology, has served as a potent corrective to the tendency to divide fossil hominids into many species and genera. It has been widely noted, as other papers in this volume demonstrate, even if his reduction of all known hominids to a single genus, Homo, has not been fully accepted. Dr. Mayr is Alexander Agassiz Professor of Zoology, and Director of the Museum of Comparative Zoology, at Harvard University.*

states, "I think it will be much more convenient to split the different varieties [of South African fossil ape-man] into different genera and species than to lump them." The result of such standards is a simply bewildering diversity of names. In addition to various so-called species of *Homo,* the following names for various hominid remains have been found by me in the literature: *Australopithecus, Plesianthropus, Paranthropus, Eoanthropus, Giganthopithecus, Meganthropus, Pithecanthropus, Sinanthropus, Africanthropus, Javanthropus, Paleoanthropus, Europanthropus,* and several others. No two authors agree either in nomenclature or in interpretation. It seems to me that an effort should be made to give the categories species and genus a new meaning in the field of anthropology, namely, the same one which in recent years has become the standard in other branches of zoology.

A re-evaluation of the terminology of hominid taxonomy is facilitated by the fact that in recent years a magnificent body of new data has been accumulated by anthropologists, partly based on comparative anatomical studies and partly on significant new discoveries of fossil man in southeast Asia and in eastern and southern Africa.

The nomenclatural difficulties of the anthropologists are chiefly due to two facts. The first one is a very intense occupation with only a very small fraction of the animal kingdom which has resulted in the development of standards that differ greatly from those applied in other fields of zoology, and secondly, the attempt to express every difference of morphology, even the slightest one, by a different name and to do this with the limited number of taxonomic categories that are available. This difference in standards becomes very apparent if we, for example, compare the classification of the hominids with that of the *Drosophila* flies. There are now about 600 species of *Drosophila* known, all included in a single genus. If individuals of these species were enlarged to the size of man or of a gorilla, it would be apparent even to a lay person that they are probably more different from each other than are the various primates and certainly more than the species of the suborder Anthropoidea. What in the case of *Drosophila* is a genus has almost the rank of an order or, at least, suborder in the primates. The discrepancy is equally great at lower categories, as we shall presently see. It is not mere formalism to try to harmonize the categories of anthropology with those of the rest of zoology. Rather, the evaluation of human evolution depends to a considerable extent on the proper determination of the categories of fossil man.

There are two recent developments in general systematics that will be particularly helpful in our efforts. The first one is that the biological meaning of the categories species and genus is now better understood than formerly, and second, that, in the attempt to close the gap between the complexity of nature and the simplicity of categories, the number of existing categories has been augmented by intermediate and group categories, such as "local population" or "local races" and "subspecies groups." The adoption of these intermediate categories facilitates classification without encumbering nomenclature.

The Taxonomic Categories

The work in the new systematics has led to a far-reaching agreement among zoologists on the meaning of the categories subspecies, species, genus, and family. In the following an attempt shall be made to see how far the current usage of these categories can be extended to fossil hominids and what such a reclassification means in terms of human evolution.

The genus: The genus is a taxonomic category for a group of related species. It is usually based on a taxonomic group that can be objectively defined. However, the delimitation of these groups against each other, as well as their ranking, is frequently subjective and arbitrary. A conventional definition of the genus would read about as follows: "A genus consists of one species, or a group of species of common ancestry, which differ in a pronounced manner from other groups of species and are separated from them by a decided morphological gap."

Recent studies indicate that the genus is not merely a morphological concept but that it has a very distinct biological meaning. Species that are united in a given genus occupy an ecological situation which is different from that occupied by the species of another genus, or, to use the terminology of Sewall Wright, they occupy a different adaptive plateau. It is part of the task of the taxonomist to determine the adaptive zones occupied by the various genera. The adaptive plateau of the genus is based on a more fundamental difference in ecology than that between the ecological niches of species.

Unfortunately, there is no such thing as a recognized or absolute generic character. This was known already to the earlier taxonomists, in fact, Linnaeus stated, "It is the genus that gives the characters, and not the characters that make the genus." The genus is a group category and it defeats the object of binomial nomenclature to place each species into a separate genus, as has been the tendency among students of primates.

The acceptance of the new concept of biologically defined polytypic species (see below) necessitates the upward revision of all other categories (Mayr, 1942). Often what was formerly a group of allopatric species is now a single polytypic species with numerous subspecies. To leave each of these polytypic species in a separate genus deprives the genus of its significance as a truly collective category. I shall illustrate this need for the combining of genera by an example. Gorilla and chimpanzee are two excellent species which, as Professor Schultz has shown, differ from each other by a wealth of characters. At one time several species of gorillas and of chimpanzees were recognized, but the allopatric forms within the two species are now considered subspecies. Being left with one species of gorilla and one species of chimpanzees, we are confronted by the question whether or not they are sufficiently different to justify placing them in different genera. A specialist of anthropoids impressed by the many differences between these species may want to do so. Other zoologists will conclude that the differences between the two species are not indicative of a generic level of difference when measured in the standards customary in most branches of zoology. To place these two anthropoids into two separate genera defeats the function of generic nomenclature and conceals the close relationship of gorilla and chimpanzee as compared with much more different orang and the gibbons. Recognizing a separate genus for the gorilla would necessitate raising the orang and the gibbon to subfamily or family rank as has indeed been done or suggested. This only worsens the inequality of the higher categories among the primates.

The same is true for the fossil hominids. After due consideration of the many differences between Modern man, Java man, and the South African ape-man, I did not find any morphological characters that would necessitate separating them into several genera. Not even *Australopithecus* has unequivocal claims for separation. This form appears to possess what might be considered the principal generic character of *Homo*, namely, upright posture with its shift to a terrestrial mode of living and the freeing of the anterior extremity for new functions which, in turn, have stimulated brain evolution. Within this type there has been phyletic speciation resulting in *Homo sapiens*.

The claim that the many described genera of hominids and australopithecines have no validity, if the same yardstick is applied that is customary in systematic zoology, is based on two major points. Both of these are admittedly somewhat vulnerable. One is the over-all picture of morphological resemblance with a deliberate minimizing of the brain as a decisive taxonomic character. To this point we shall return presently. The other point is the assumption that all these forms, including *Australopithecus*, are essentially members of a single line of descent. Additional finds might easily disprove this. However, taking all the available evidence together, it seems far more logical and consistent at the present time to unite the hominids into a single genus than to continue the current multiplicity of names.

This re-evaluation of the generic status of the fossil hominids forces us to consider also the categories above the genus. Does *Homo* belong to a separate family Hominidae? The morphological differences between *Pan*, the genus to which the chimpanzee and gorilla belong, and *Homo* are so slight that there seems to be no justification for placing them in separate families. There is even less justification for placing South African man in a separate subfamily, the Australopithecinae. The most primitive known hominids, those of South Africa, combine certain typical hominid characters, such as upright posture, with others that are usually considered simian, such as small size of brain and protruding face. It is noteworthy, however, as pointed out by several investigators, that these hominids, even at this primitive stage, lack certain other simian features that were formerly considered as primitive: powerful canines, large incisors, a sectorial form of the first lower premolar, an exaggerated development of the supra-orbitals, a simian shelf, and powerful brachiating arms. It now appears probable that many of these characters are functional specializations which were acquired by the anthropoid apes after the hominid line had branched off.

The fact that the hominids lack these specializations has been used by some authors as evidence to postulate a very early human origin and a very isolated position of the hominid branch. This is by no means the only possible interpretation. Rather it seems to me that most of these typical characters of the living anthropoids may well be a single character complex evolved in response to a highly arboreal mode of living. It now appears probable that the African anthropoids, the orang, and the gibbons, may have acquired most of these characters independently and are therefore, in a sense, a polyphyletic group. The available evidence seems to indicate to me that man may be more closely related to the gorilla-chimpanzee group than this group is either to the orang or to the gibbons. The degree of similarity in certain morphological traits cannot necessarily be used to measure degree of phylogenetic relationship. The arboreal, brachiating large anthropoids are exposed to a similar type of selection and will therefore evolve in a parallel, if not convergent, manner. When the *Homo*-line acquired upright posture it entered a completely different adaptive zone and became exposed to a severely increased selection pressure. This must have resulted in a sharp acceleration of evolutionary change leading to the well-known differences between man and the living anthropoids. This factor must be taken into consideration when the phylogeny of man and the anthropoids is reconstructed. It would therefore appear to be misleading from the purely morphological-phylogenetic point of view to separate man from the anthropoid apes as a special family. It would be equally misleading to go to the other extreme and to use the evidence of the somewhat independent evolution of man and the various anthropoids as a means to deny their close relationship.

Denying the genus *Homo* family rank is based on purely morphological considerations. It does not take into account man's unique position in nature. Man has undoubtedly found an adaptive plateau that is strikingly different from that of any other animal. There are some who feel that there is only one way by which to emphasize this uniqueness of man, namely, by placing *Homo* into a separate family. The conventional standards of taxonomy are insufficient to decide what is correct in this case.

From the purely biological point of view man is certainly at least as different as a very good genus. We have thus the evolution of a new higher category in the geologically short period of one to two million years. This is another significant illustration for the rapidity by which one major taxonomic entity can be transformed into another one, without any jumps.

The subspecies: Before we can attempt to answer the question how many species of fossil man have existed, we must say a few words on infraspecific categories. The species of the modern systematist is polytypic and multidimensional. It has the geographical dimensions of longitude and latitude and also the time dimension. It is polytypic because it is composed of lower units, such as subspecies and local populations. Customarily in anthropology, distinct local populations have been referred to as races, and a similar custom exists in some branches of zoology as, for example, in ichthyology.

The amount of geographical variation and the degree of difference among the geographical subdivisions of a species are different from case to case. Some species appear quite uniform throughout their entire range; other species have a few or many more or less well defined subspecies. For instance, the two African forest anthropoids, chimpanzee and gorilla, show only a moderate amount of geographical variation, although both have well-defined subspecies, and attempts have been made to split the chimpanzee into several species. Geographical variation is much more pronounced in the orang and even more so in some of the South American monkeys where geographical races are often different enough to be considered full species by conservative authors.

Modern man is comparatively homogeneous because there is much interbreeding between different tribes and races. Still, we find in close neighborhood to each other such strikingly different races as bushmen and Bantus in South Africa, or the Congo pygmies and Watusi in central Africa, or the Wedas and Singhalese in Ceylon. There is much indirect evidence that primitive man was much more broken up into small scattered tribes with little contact with each other, intensely subject to local selective factors.

In addition to this much greater geographical variation of primitive man, there is evidence also of greater individual variation (including sexual dimorphism). The variability of Mt. Carmel man has been commented upon in the literature. It seems possible, if not probable, that the various South African finds, *Australopithecus, Plesianthropus,* and *Paranthropus,* might well be age or sex stages of a few related tribes, notwithstanding Broom's (1950b) assertions to the contrary.

Differences between young and adult and between male and female appear to be greater in the gorilla and orang-utan than they are in modern man. Variability may increase or decrease in the course of evolution. Abundant proof for this statement can be found in the paleontological literature. I interpret the available literature to indicate that primitive man showed more geographical as well as individual variation than modern man.

Why primitive man should have been more variable than modern man is not entirely clear. A study of the family structure of anthropoids might shed some light on this problem. Perhaps there was a greater functional difference between male and female than in modern man. Perhaps the ancestral hominids had a system of polygamy that would favor the selection of secondary sex characters in the male. We don't know. Whatever the reasons, we should not use the variability within populations of modern man as a yardstick by which to judge the probable variability of extinct populations.

This point is important because it bears on the question whether or not more than one species of hominid has ever existed on the earth at any one time. Indeed, all the now available evidence can be interpreted as indicating that, in spite of much geographical variation, never more than one species of man existed on the earth at any one time. We shall come back to this point later.

The species: As described in several publications, the concept of the species has undergone a considerable change during recent years. The morphological and typological species of the early taxonomists has been replaced by a biological species. The species is now defined "as a group of actually or potentially interbreeding natural populations that is reproductively isolated from other such groups." When this concept is applied to man, it is at once obvious that all living populations of man are part of a single species. Not only are they connected everywhere by intermediate populations but even where strikingly distinct human populations have come in contact, such as Europeans and Hottentots, or as Europeans and Australian aborigines, there has been no sign of biological isolating mechanisms, only social ones.

The problem of species delimitation is much more difficult with respect to fossil man. How shall we determine which populations are "actually or potentially interbreeding"? It is evident that we must use all sorts of indirect clues. The first concrete problem is what types of fossil man should be included in the species *Homo sapiens.* Cro-Magnon man is so nearly identical with *Homo sapiens* that its inclusion in that species is not doubted by any serious student.

The problem of Neanderthal man is much more difficult. Should he be included in the same species as modern man or not? When the first finds of Neanderthal man were made there seemed to be no problem. These fossils were characterized by distinct morphological features and were clearly replaced by modern man in Europe on a distinct chronological level. There is no morphological or cultural intermediacy. Additional finds, however, have caused various difficulties. In Palestine the Mt. Carmel finds belong to a population that combines some features of Neanderthal with some of modern man. It is immaterial whether we interpret this as a hybrid population, as an intermediate population, or as a population ancestral to both. The fact remains that Mt. Carmel man makes the delimitation of modern man from Neanderthal exceedingly difficult, if not impossible, as pointed out by Dobzhansky (1944). Weidenreich supported the theory that modern man was a direct descendant of Neanderthal man. Boule and others have raised serious objections to this theory. But how can we reconcile the apparently incompatible views that modern man and Neanderthal are conspecific and that modern man is *not* a descendant of typical European Neanderthal? A possible clue is furnished by the hominids that were widespread in Europe in mid-Pleistocene. The skulls of Steinheim, Swanscombe, and of Fontéchevade combine features of modern man and of Neanderthal man, together with primitive and specialized features of their own. They lived apparently in interglacials and were more closely linked with a warm climate than Neanderthal man.

If I understood the evidence correctly, it is possible to interpret these early European fossils as remains of populations of *Homo* that were ancestral both to *sapiens* and to "classical" Neanderthal and from which these two forms evolved by geographical variation. Tentatively the working hypothesis can be made that Neanderthal in its classical form was a geographical race that occurred in central Europe and was represented in Africa by Rhodesian man and in Java by Njandong man, while a more *sapiens*-like population occurred at the same period as some of these Neanderthaloids either in north Africa or western Asia or in some other area that has not yet yielded remains of fossil man. When *sapiens* began to expand and spread, he eliminated the other contemporary races just as the white man drove out the Australian aborigines and the North American Indians. The process of elimination of the Neanderthal characters in mixed populations was presumably helped by selection preference in favor of the characters of modern man.

It is very probable that additional finds will make the delimitation of *sapiens* against Neanderthal even more difficult. It seems best to follow

Dobzhansky's suggestion and to consider the two forms, as well as the ancestral group that seems to combine their characters, as a single species.

Homo erectus: Java and Peking man are sufficiently distinct from modern man so that they have to be considered a separate species, which must be called *Homo erectus.* This is true regardless of the fact that on Java, at least, Ngandong and Wadjak man may have formed a practically unbroken chain of hominids leading from Java man to modern man. Peking man (*Homo erectus pekinensis*) is, on the whole, so similar to Java man that it should be considered merely subspecifically distinct, as I proposed previously (Mayr, 1944).

In spite of its obvious similarity to *Australopithecus* too little is known of the still earlier Java *Meganthropus* to assure a correct classification. This is even more true of *Giganthopithecus* whom some authors consider hominid and others anthropoid. One thing about *Giganthopithecus* is, however, very probable, namely, that it was not necessarily a giant in spite of its giant teeth. Jaws and teeth of early fossil man were relatively much larger than they are in modern man.

Homo transvaalensis: South African ape-man again is one level further back and is sufficiently far removed from Java man to be considered a full species. Actually, no less than three genera and five species of South African ape-man were described which, in Broom's terminology, have the following names: *Australopithecus africanus* 1925 (Taungs), *A. prometheus* 1947 (Makapan), *Plesianthropus transvaalensis* 1936 (Sterkfontein), *Paranthropus robustus* 1938 (Kromdraai), and *Paranthropus crassidens* 1949 (Swartkrans). Most of these names may not have any validity, according to the Rules of Zoological Nomenclature, Article 25A, as revised in 1930. According to these Rules a name has validity only if the description includes diagnostic characters. Since one of these names was based on a child, another on an adult female, a third on an adult male, an enumeration of diagnostic differences is virtually impossible. The extant skulls are somewhat altered in shape due to crushing, and the fact that the cephalic index in the Taungs child is 62.4 while it is 83.5 in the Sterkfontein male is therefore not as significant as Broom thinks. Nor is the fact that the finds are associated with different faunas. Contemporary modern man can be found associated with akapis or elephants or tigers or kangaroos, or South American edentates or with polar bears. The various finds of South African man are presumably not contemporary, but there is nothing in the evidence that has so far been presented (e.g., Broom, 1950b) that would prove that more than one species is involved.

Until a real taxonomic distinction has been established, it will be safer and more scientific to refer to the different South African fossils by vernacular names. There is no danger of confusion if we speak of the Sterkfontein or Makapan finds, while it implies an obviously erroneous conclusion, namely that of generic distinctness, if we refer to them as *Plesianthropus* and *Australopithecus*. New discoveries are still being made in these cave deposits and many of those that have already been made have not yet been fully worked out. There is good reason to believe that it will be firmly established in the not-too-distant future how many different tribes, temporal subspecies, or even species of South African ape-man once existed. To consider them all as one species is the simplest solution that is consistent with the available evidence.

A more important question is whether South African man is ancestral to modern man or merely a specialized or aberrant sideline. The exact dating of these fossils has not yet been achieved but they are believed to be very early Pleistocene or latest Pliocene, in fact, they presumably ranged over a considerable period of time. There is thus no definite chronological reason why the South African ape-man could not be considered a possible ancestor of modern man. The principal objection that has been raised is that South African man shows a combination of characters that "should not" occur in an early hominid. This argument is based on typological considerations. Adherents of this concept believe that missing links should be about half-way between the forms they connect and that they should be half-way in every respect. This undoubtedly is not the case with *Australopithecus*. It is apparently amazingly like modern man in its upright posture, structure of the pelvis, and other features, while it is very simian in its massive mandibles, large molars, prognathism, and small brain. *Australopithecus* lacks those specializations that stamp gorilla, orang, and gibbon as typical anthropoids.

The peculiar combination of characters that is found in *Australopithecus* is due to the fact that during evolution of man different characters evolved at different rates. If we would set the point where the human line branched off from the other anthropoids as zero and the *Homo sapiens* stage as 100, we might give arbitrarily the following points to the various organs of *Australopithecus:* pelvis, 90; premolars, 75; occipital condyles, 80; incisors, 55; the setting of the brain case, 70; shape of the tooth row, 70; the profile of the jaw, 30; the molar teeth, 40; the brain, 35; etc. It is obvious that one type does not change into another type evenly and harmoniously, but that some features run way ahead of the others.

. . . .

The simplified nomenclature of fossil man: Reducing the bewildering assortment of genera and species of hominids to one genus with three species results not only in simplicity but it also makes certain conclusions obvious that were previously not apparent. Before discussing these conclusions, however, I might point out some of the disadvantages of such a simplified classification.

There have been two trends in human evolution as, indeed, there are in the evolution of all organisms. First of all, there is a continuous evolutionary change in time, the so-called phyletic evolution, starting in the hominids with the most simian forms and ending with modern man. Simultaneously a centrifugal force has been operating, namely, geographical and other local variation, which tries to break up the uniform human species. This geographic variation leads to the formation of races and subspecies, and if this trend would go to completion, to the formation of new separate species. There are all sorts of intermediate stages in both these trends and it is obvious that all the many possible differences and gradations between the various kinds of hominids cannot be expressed completely in the simple nomenclature of species, genus, and subspecies.

For instance, man as he exists today, has pronounced racial groups, such as the Whites, Negroes, and Mongoloids, which might well deserve subspecific recognition. But there are minor racial differences within each of these subspecies. Furthermore, preceding modern man there have been types of *Homo sapiens* that are now extinct, like Cro-Magnon man and his contemporaries. This, no doubt, is a different level of subspecies from those of living man. Neanderthal man is a third level, and the pre-Neanderthal man, who combines certain features of *sapiens* and Neanderthal, is a fourth level. It is unsatisfactory for biological, as well as for practical reasons, to treat each of these levels as a separate species. On the other hand, combining them into a single species conceals the pronounced differences between these levels and reduces the taxonomic difference between Neanderthal and modern man to the level of difference between White Man and Negro. How can this be avoided?

First of all, we must realize that no system of classification and nomenclature can ever hope to express adequately the complicated relationships of natural populations. However, by giving species and genus the well-defined meanings that we have assigned to these categories, we make at least an attempt to standardize taxonomic categories and make them comparable. A possible solution of our particular difficulties may come from a refinement of the levels of infraspecific categories. In addition to the subspecies we may use such infrasubspecific categories as "race" and "local population," as well as the suprasubspecific category of the "subspecies group." Hence, we should be guided by the following practical rules:

1. Not to assign a formal name to any local population or race that does not deserve subspecific rank.

2. To give trinomials to all forms that do not deserve higher than subspecies rank.

3. To group together as subspecies groups all those subspecies within a species that form either geographical or chronological groups.

Such subspecies groups in *Homo sapiens*, for instance, might be:
   (a) modern man
   (b) Neanderthal group
   (c) pre-Neanderthal group

4. Not to give formal generic and specific names to new fossil finds that are not sufficiently known. Vernaculars, such as "Steinheim man" or "Piltdown man," are just as useful and much less misleading. The formal application of generic and specific names simulates a precision that often does not exist. To give the impression of an unjustified precision is as much of a methodological error as to make calculations to the fifth decimal when the accuracy of the original data extends only to the first decimal.

Anthropologists should never lose sight of the fact that taxonomic categories are based on populations, not on individuals. Different names should never be given to individuals that are presumably members of a single variable population.

Conclusions

The arranging of all finds of fossil hominids into a single genus with three species helps to focus attention on the following conclusions.

The question of the "missing link." Ever since there has been an appreciation of man's anthropoid origin there has been a search for the "missing link." Some anthropologists may disclaim this and say that they realize the gradual evolution of mankind but the fact remains that accurate criteria of humanhood are elaborated even in the most recent literature, such as Sir Arthur Keith's criterion of the brain volume of 750 cc.

The analysis of this problem will be facilitated by the realization that it is an oversimplification to use in this case the uninomial alternative "ape" versus "man." Taxonomists know by experience the inadequacy of uninomialism. Classifying man binomially as *Homo sapiens*, it at once becomes apparent that we must look for two missing links, namely that which connects *sapiens* with his ancestor and that which connects *Homo* with his ancestor. Or, to express this differently, the two points of interest are of the one on the phyletic line of man where he reached the *sapiens* level and second the place where the *Homo* line branched off from the other primates.

Let us look more closely at these two problems of the origin of man. The branching off of *Homo* from the other anthropoids was a case of orthodox speciation distinguished only by the fact that the new species simultaneously reached a new adaptive plateau. It is now evident, as has been stated by many authors, that a change in the mode of locomotion and a corresponding alteration of the entire organization of the body, in other words, the assuming of the upright posture, were the essential steps that led to the evolution of *Homo*. This evolutionary trend apparently affected first the pelvis and posterior extremities, followed closely by the anterior extremities. The corresponding re-organization of the skull lagged apparently behind. It is therefore singularly difficult to localize both in time and space this important evolutionary step of the attainment of the upright posture with the help of jaw and tooth fragments, such as constitute most of the primate and anthropoid remains in eastern Africa during Pliocene and Miocene.

To determine the exact point in the phyletic evolution of *Homo* where the *sapiens* level was reached, is quite impossible. It was a very gradual process leading from *erectus* to *sapiens* and no particular form can be singled out as the missing link. However, there is a lower level in the phyletic evolution of *Homo* that is of special evolutionary interest, namely, the level at which the hominids first displayed those intellectual qualities that are considered distinctly human rather than simian.

Attempts have been made to measure the attainment of this *Homo* level in terms of brain size. This method is fraught with difficulty. First of all, brain size is to some extent correlated with body size. If, for instance, a large gorilla should have a brain of 650 cc. this is not at all necessarily equivalent to the brain of a fossil hominid of 650 cc., if that hominid were much smaller than a gorilla. If the brain of the gorilla averages one-fourth larger than that of the chimpanzee, it does not mean that he is on the average 25 per cent more intelligent. The correlation between brain size and intelligence is very loose. There is good evidence that the brain size of late Pleistocene man may have averaged larger than that of modern man. If true, this does not mean necessarily that there has been a deterioration of man's intelligence since the Pleistocene, for intelligence is determined not only by brain size. It is, of course, still unknown what neurological structures affect intelligence but the folding of the cortex and all sorts of specializations within the cortex appear to be as important as size. It is therefore dangerous, in fact, outright misleading, to use size as an absolute criterion and to say that the *Homo* stage was reached when brain size reached a level of 700 or 750 cc.

It has been suggested to measure the attainment of the human level by some cultural achievement, such as the use of fire, rather than by an anatomical standard like brain size. This is unquestionably a superior approach, but has the practical difficulty that the first moment of fire making was not fossilized and can never be dated accurately. However, the first making of fire may have occurred not much after the first use of tools by hominids and some lucky finds may shed light someday on the period when that occurred. South African man was presumably already a user of tools, and the first use of tools may be coincident with the evolution of South African man.

Speciation in man: In the strict sense of the word, speciation means the origin of discontinuities through the origin of reproductive isolating mechanisms. How often has man speciated? The answer is that he has speciated only once if our assumption is correct that never more than one species of man existed on the earth at any one time. This single event of speciation was the branching off of *Homo* from the anthropoid stock. That some fairly distinct hominid remains have been found in approximately contemporary deposits does not prove their specific distinctness. The subdivision of the human species into independent tribes favors diversification. If fossils of Congo pygmies and of Watusi were to be found in the same deposit by a paleontologist, a million years hence, he might well think that they belonged to two different species. As stated previously, the known diversity of fossil man can be interpreted as being the result of geographic variation within a single species of *Homo*. This led to the evolution of such aberrant types as Piltdown man of England, but apparently nowhere to the simultaneous occurrence of several species of *Homo*. What is the cause for this puzzling trait of the hominid stock to stop speciating in spite of its eminent evolutionary success? It seems to me that the reason is man's great ecological diversity. Man has, so to speak, specialized in despecialization. Man occupies more different ecological niches than any known animal. If the single species man occupies successfully all the niches that are open for a *Homo*-like creature, it is obvious that he cannot speciate. This conforms strictly to Gause's rule. Also man is apparently slow in establishing isolating mechanisms. This is indicated by the numerous instances of incomplete speciation in the history of the hominids. In no case was this speciation completed because the segregating populations were either absorbed by intermarriage or exterminated. Man is apparently particularly intolerant of competitors. The wiping out or absorption of primitive populations by culturally more advanced or otherwise more aggressive invaders, which we have witnessed so many times during the eighteenth and nineteenth centuries in Australia, North America, and other places, has presumably happened many times before in the history of the earth. The elimination of Neanderthal man by the invading Cro-Magnon man is merely one example.

There is one striking difference between man and most of the animals. In animals whenever there is competition between two subspecies the one that is better adapted for a specific locality seems to win out. Man, who has reached such a high degree of independence from the environment, is less dependent on local adaptation, and a subspecies of man can quickly spread into many geographically distant areas if it acquires generalized adaptive improvements such as are described by the social anthropologist. Such improvements do not need to and probably often do not have genetic basis. The authors who have claimed that man is unique in his evolutionary pattern are undoubtedly right. Even though the phyletic evolution of man will continue to go on, the structure of the human species at the present time is such that there appears to be very little chance for speciation, that is, for the division of the single human species into several separate species.

SUMMARY

1. There is no conclusive evidence that more than one species of hominids has ever existed at a given time.

2. It is proposed to classify fossil and recent hominids tentatively into a single genus (*Homo*) with three species (*transvaalensis, erectus, sapiens*).

3. The recognition of subspecies groups within the species facilitates classification.

4. The ecological versatility of man and his slowness in acquiring reproductive isolating mechanisms have prevented the breaking up of *Homo* into several species.

Prehominid Dentition and Hominid Evolution

J. T. Robinson   1954

The teeth of an animal are exceedingly important structures: to the animal, because of their use in acquiring and masticating food, self defense, and their influence on the structure of the animal; to the student of animal history, because of the information they give about the animal and its relationships, and the relative ease with which they are preserved.

Since World War II there has been a phenomenal increase in the number of australopithecine fossil remains known and many of these are teeth. The new information thus gained has thrown much light on the relationship of these creatures to man and on hominid evolution in general. In this paper I wish to discuss some evolutionary trends in the australopithecine dentition as a whole and some of the effects thereof. In the first part trends in the evolution of crown size will be considered, then the effect of the dentition on skull architecture, and, finally, what conclusions may be drawn about the ecological requirements of the australopithecines with particular reference to competition and coexistence.

NOMENCLATURE

The taxonomy of the australopithecines has been dealt with elsewhere (Robinson, 1954). It seems clear that they belong, as a group, in a separate subfamily from that including tool-making man. This was suggested,

FROM Evolution, 1954, vol. 8, pp. 324–334, reprinted by permission of the author and of the Society for the Study of Evolution. This and the two following articles express Dr. Robinson's interpretation of morphological differences existing among fossils of the Australopithecinae, and the relations of these to other hominids. The first two papers, published in 1954, have been slightly abridged, mainly to avoid duplication by the most recent article. Dr. Robinson, formerly assistant to Dr. Robert Broom, is Professional Officer in Charge, Department of Physical Anthropology and Vertebrate Palaeontology, in the Transvaal Museum, Pretoria, with a large body of australopithecine material in his care.

among others, by Heberer (1951b), who placed the former in the sub-family Praehomininae and tool-making man in the subfamily Euho-mininae. The subfamily Australopithecinae had, however, previously been erected by Gregory and Hellman (1939) as a subdivision of the Pongidae. As this subfamily contains no true pongids it may simply be transferred to the Hominidae. The latter family then comprises the Aus-tralopithecinae and the Euhomininae—a system which agrees much more closely with accepted nomenclatural principles than does that of Heberer. To avoid constant repetition of the latinized names, "australopithecines" and "prehominids" are used interchangeably for the former group and "euhominids" for the latter.

CROWN SIZE TRENDS IN HOMINIDS

The euhominid material adds greatly to our knowledge of hominid dental evolution. A glance at a complete set of upper or lower teeth of the prehominids suffices to show that the relative proportions of crown size along the tooth row are not the same as in the case of modern euhominids. The most striking difference is the relatively small size of the anterior teeth as compared to the cheek teeth. This feature has been regarded by some workers as a specialization showing that the prehominids as a group could not have been the stock from which euhominids arose. I have previously attempted to show (Robinson, 1952b) that a different construction may be placed on this matter and, with recent additions to the collections, the evidence is now clearer.

In the following discussion crown sizes are compared by using the module

$$\frac{\text{Length} + \text{Breadth}}{2}$$

This module clearly does not give an actual direct measure of the crown volume, but, as the teeth which are compared in this way are homologous, belong to closely related animals, and hence of much the same shape, the results given are accurate enough for the purpose. This module is a com-monly used method of combining the length and breadth of a crown, which are significant measurements, to give a single figure which greatly facilitates comparison. Wherever possible and unless otherwise stated the dimensions used are mean values.

The earliest known euhominids have larger teeth, on the average, and are more prognathous than is the case among modern euhominids. There has, therefore, been a reduction in the degree of projection of the face and in the size of the dentition in the course of euhominid evolution. All of the teeth have, however, not been reduced proportionately. This is

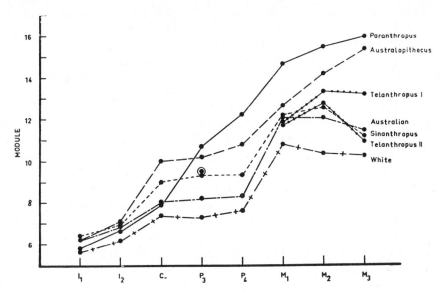

FIGURE 1. Graph showing modules of the mandibular teeth of some prehominids and euhominids. All values are averages except in the case of *Telanthropus*. The encircled, isolated point represents the module of P₃ of *Telanthropus* I.

indicated by the fact that the relative size of the lower molar crowns in modern euhominids is usually $M_1 > M_2 > M_3$ while in the Sangiran mandible of *Pithecanthropus* the situation is just the opposite; $M_1 < M_2 < M_3$.

The modules of the mandibular dental elements of some hominids are plotted in Figure 1. Those for the known teeth of *Telanthropus* are also plotted and these alone are not modules of mean values. The graph for the maxillary dentition is so similar that it is not given here.

From this diagram it is clear that differential reduction of the molars has occurred: M_1 has been affected least and M_3 most. In the prehominids the molar crown size formula is $M_1 < M_2 < M_3$. In only one individual (SK 23), where all three molars are in situ, is there any indication that M_3 is approaching the size of M_2. In *Telanthropus* only one jaw is known with all three molars in situ and in that the formula is $M_1 < M_2 > M_3$ but in the second mandible it is clear that M_3 must have been much reduced (see Robinson, 1953b), and, if that was the case, the formula would be the same for both mandibles. *Telanthropus* is thus more advanced than the prehominids with respect to the reduction of the crown size of the mandibular molars. It would be extremely interesting to know what the condition was in *Pithecanthropus*, but unfortunately only the single mandible from Sangiran is known with all three molars in situ. This has the formula $M_1 < M_2 < M_3$ (Weidenreich, 1945) and therefore agrees with the condition in the prehominids. But the molars of the only upper jaw known are in the following size order: $M^1 < M^2 > M^3$ with M^3 considerably reduced. This agrees well with the situation in the *Telanthropus* lower dentition. Although the maxilla normally leads the mandible in the reduction process, it is reasonable to assume that M_3 must also have been reduced to some extent in some members of a population including such individuals as the above in which M^3 is so much reduced as to be smaller than M^1.

Sinanthropus (Weidenreich, 1937) has M_3 appreciably reduced, on the average, compared to M_2. As in the maxillary dentition of the *Pithecanthropus* palate from Sangiran, M_3 is actually smaller than M_1 as a rule. Here also, for upper and lower dentitions the size sequence is $M_1 < M_2 > M_3$. This sequence also occurs in Neanderthal man. The next stage in the reduction of the molars is that in which M2 is reduced to the same size as M1 or even further. The size sequence then is either M1 = M2 > M3 or M1 > M2 > M3. In the Australian Aboriginal (Campbell, 1925) the lower molars are in the former size order, while the maxillary molars are in the latter sequence. In modern American Whites (Black, 1902) both upper and lower molars are arranged in the sequence M1 > M2 > M3. The South African Bantu (Shaw, 1931) are a little unusual in that the average sizes of the three molars are almost exactly the same. In Neanderthal man there are no average figures based on a fair sized population but the size order of the molars seems to vary from M1 < M2 > M3 to M1 > M2 > M3.

The evolution of molar size can therefore be traced quite clearly from the prehominid stage to that of modern euhominids. Much of this evolution has gone on independently in a number of different lines. Hence the fact that the size sequence is not identical in all the living ethnic groups.

The differential reduction of the third and second molars was probably caused initially by space shortage. The first permanent tooth to come into functional position is usually the first molar. The remaining permanent teeth must, therefore, fit into the remaining space on either side of it. M3 is normally the last tooth to erupt and it is, therefore, conceivable that space shortage would affect it more than the other teeth. This would particularly be the case in the reduction of the jaws from the massive prehominid type to the smaller euhominid type. It has been pointed out from time to time that failure to erupt—or impaction—of M3 is not always a result of space shortage in modern man. This does not invalidate the suggestion that lack of space was the operative factor in the early stages of face reduction. The continued reduction of the third molar may be an example of the phenomenon recently demonstrated by Waddington (1953a and b), the genetic assimilation of an originally environmental effect, the character "crossveinless" in *Drosophila melanogaster*. What was originally a reduction brought about by space shortage may now be genetically assimilated and influenced by selection, which is related not only to space shortage in the jaw but also to other factors.

The evolution of crown size in the teeth anterior to the molars is not nearly so clear-cut but nevertheless is of considerable interest.

Reference to Figure 1 will show that with the exception of *Paranthropus* the curves are very similar anterior to M_1, if one allows for the relatively small amount of reduction of M_1. The incisors of all the forms dealt with are very similar in size. This suggests that reduction of the canines and premolars has been of comparable extent without producing marked differential changes such as those posterior to M_1. There is comparatively great variability in the size of the upper lateral incisor and this tooth also shows considerable individual variability in modern euhominids, in some cases being congenitally absent. It has been assumed that this is a result of rapid reduction of this tooth, but the fact that the Sterkfontein form has lateral upper incisors as small as the average for American Whites indicates that this tooth has probably been small for a very long time in hominid history. Perhaps it never has been a large tooth.

The curve for *Paranthropus* does not follow the others nearly so well, and in both the upper and lower dentitions the curves for the latter cross that of *Australopithecus* between the positions for the canine and first premolar. The reason for this reversal will be inquired into in a later section of this paper.

If it is assumed that the large size of the cheek teeth of *Paranthropus* represents an earlier prehominid condition, then it is possible to interpret the condition in the known prehominids as a result of a reduction process that started at the front of the jaw and passed backward. According to such a supposition, the process has gone further in *Paranthropus* because the incisors and canines have been affected as well as the first premolar to a certain extent. In *Australopithecus* the canines and first premolars have not been affected. As previously mentioned, the incisors have probably never been large teeth and the reduction which they have suffered is probably very slight. It is possible, on the other hand, that the *Paranthropus* curve is of a different nature because the post-canine teeth were enlarging, not reducing in size. This does not seem likely to me, because the general trend in the early stages of hominid evolution is generally toward reduction of the face and there are signs of this in *Paranthropus* in the uniformly shortened face. While it is not impossible that the tendency was reversed in this one phyletic line, strong evidence of it would be necessary before accepting such a change. It is more probable therefore that the *Paranthropus* curve is unusual only because the anterior part of the tooth row was reduced very rapidly or because some factor retarded the reduction further back. This conclusion is supported by the fact that the small-crowned canines are generally very robust-rooted, suggesting that the reduction of the canines was not yet complete. *Australopithecus* has robust canines, crown and root; *Paranthropus* has robust-rooted, small-crowned canines; *Telanthropus* probably had canine crowns of the same size as those of *Paranthropus*, but the root sockets are small.

In view of these facts it seems likely that reduction occurred in two phases: one process starting at the rear end of the tooth row and gradually passing forward, and the other starting from the front end and passing backward toward M1. The dominating position of M1 is probably partly due to the fact that it is normally the first of the permanent teeth to come into functional position.

Instead, therefore, of a series of static types of relative size formulae for the different dentitions, we see a dynamic process of change going on which converted a prehominid type of dentition into a modern euhominid one. *Paranthropus* and *Australopithecus* are not members of one phyletic line (Robinson, 1954) nor does either appear to fall on a line which actually gave rise to euhominids. They nevertheless probably give a good idea of stages through which the actual euhominid ancestor did pass while in the prehominid phase.

DENTITION AND THE FORM OF THE SKULL

The graphs showing comparative tooth sizes along the tooth row are interesting in that they give rise to another line of thought besides the one dealt with above. What is the reason for the prehominid with the smallest incisors and canines having the largest cheek teeth? A possible explanation is suggested below in conjunction with discussion of the resulting changes in the architecture of the skull.

It is clear that the teeth of the prehominids were put to heavy use, especially the molars of *Paranthropus*. The latter are massive, with very thick enamel (as much as 3 mm. on the occlusal surface), and yet, by the time M3 erupts, M1 has already been worn quite flat, with the dentine exposed in places. In older individuals, where the occlusal surface of M3 is moderately flattened, M1 usually no longer has enamel on the occlusal surface. When M3 is strongly worn, the crown of M1 is almost entirely gone. The occlusal surface enamel of a tooth in full use has numerous well marked scratches, which run at right angles to the length of the tooth row, i.e., in a buccolingual direction. Both upper and lower jaws are massive, particularly at the level of the molars. *Australo-*

pithecus also has these characters, but to a less marked degree except for the relative rate of wear of the teeth, which is much the same in both groups. A feature common in the Swartkrans dental material is chipping of enamel from the edge of the occlusal surface. That this chipping occurred in life is clearly shown by the fact that most of the roughened areas left after such flaking are smoothed by subsequent use of the tooth. Chipping is not confined to the anterior teeth.

All these features suggest heavy use of the teeth of the prehominids in general, and particularly in *Paranthropus*. The relatively great disparity in size between the front and the cheek teeth, the rapid flattening of the premolars and molars, and the considerably thickened bone around the molar roots indicate that crushing and grinding was the main function involved. The most suitable sort of diet for such a primate dentition would probably consist predominantly of vegetable materials, including shoots and leaves, berries, tough wild fruits, roots and bulbs. The latter ingredients may have resulted in grit particles being chewed, causing chipping of the enamel. The South African Chacma baboon eats roots and bulbs, among other things, and enamel chipping of just the same sort as that found in *Paranthropus* occurs on the teeth of this form. The relatively small anterior teeth—particularly canines—would be consistent with the diet and would also suggest that *Paranthropus* was not an aggressive, predaceous creature, and had means of defense (and offense if required) other than dental ones. These were probably in the form of any sticks, bones, or stones conveniently to hand, coupled with a certain amount of intelligence and cunning.

Australopithecus, with less disparity in size between anterior and posterior elements of the dentition, with appreciably larger canines and smaller premolars and molars than *Paranthropus*, probably had a more nearly omnivorous diet, which may have included a fair proportion of flesh as indicated by evidence brought forward by Dart (1949b).

These differences in diet may well account for the differences in the pattern of dental reduction processes in the two prehominid lines. The heavy use to which the molars, especially, were put in *Paranthropus* may have resulted in their reduction being retarded as compared to the less important anterior teeth.

As Benninghoff (1925) and others have shown, the face skeleton is highly organized with regard to the forces of mastication. It is interesting to compare the skulls of *Paranthropus* and *Australopithecus* in the light of this work.

Both are stressed forms, with the result that the nasal region has much the same shape and structure; the nasal region does not protrude and the margin of the pyriform aperture is thick. If Washburn's (1953) reading

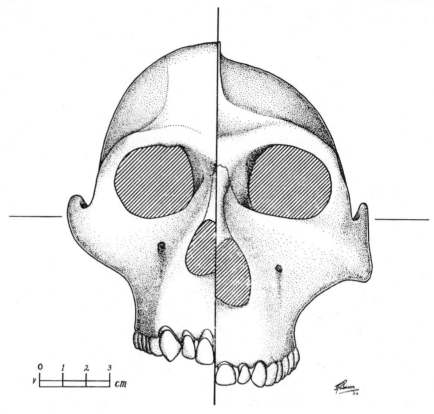

FIGURE 2. The left half of this drawing depicts half of the face of *Australopithecus* from Sterkfontein (Sts 5) and the right half that of *Paranthropus* (SK 48) from Swartkrans. The latter had to be restored in places, but this was done from other specimens from the same site. The dentition of Sts 5 is missing but it has been restored here from Sts 52 which has the dentition complete and only very slightly worn. The incisors of SK 48 are missing and are here restored from SK 55. Both halves are oriented on the Frankfort plane and the vertical register is determined by the latter plane. The *Australopithecus* face is distinctly more prognathous than the other. As far as can be determined both skulls belonged to female individuals.

of the evidence is correct, as seems probable, then one may note in passing that the flattened and rather pongid nasal region of the prehominids is in no way a bar to their being euhominid ancestors—as has been suggested. The flattened shape, in this view, results from this region being stressed. With relaxation of the forces affecting this region, as a result of reduced dental size in descendants, the nasal region would be more protuberant and without the strong buttressing on either side of the pyriform aperture. As one might expect from the larger-canined form, *Australopithecus* usually has relatively more pronounced buttresses on either side of the pyriform aperture, but this is not an absolute distinction.

Farther back along the tooth row, the results of the much greater masticatory stresses in *Paranthropus* become more obvious. The alveolar region, which contains the molars, is much thickened and the malar-zygomatic buttress is very robust. The zygomatic process of the maxilla and the zygomatic bone are much thickened, compared to the condition in *Australopithecus*. The top end of this buttress, the supraorbital torus, is also relatively robust in *Paranthropus*.

The wide and very flat bony face of *Paranthropus* is largely a result of the decreased size of the anterior teeth and the nasofrontal buttress, and the greatly increased robustness of the malar-zygomatic buttress. However, the matter does not stop there. The robust mandible of *Paranthropus* and the strength required for the great masticatory activity have resulted in a well developed temporal muscle. One may note here that, although the masseter muscle was well developed, it may have been relatively poorly developed compared to the other muscles of this region in *Paranthropus*. The angle of the mandible is turned inward to a small extent and has strong rugosities on the medial face for the attachment of the medial pterygoid, whereas the markings on the outer face of this region, for the attachment of the masseter, are poorly developed. The temporal muscle may therefore have been relatively more important in this form than in euhominids, but the evidence is not sufficient for this to be more than a tentative conclusion.

The temporal muscle is so well developed in *Paranthropus* that it frequently reaches the sagittal plane. Perhaps this is the usual adult condition, for it is present in the only three adult specimens known in which the relevant region is preserved. Under such conditions, a bony sagittal crest develops. Washburn (1947) has shown that the presence, size, and position of nuchal and mastoid crests in the rat are determined entirely by mechanical stress due to muscle function. This work confirms and extends conclusions drawn by earlier workers using other mammalian material. The presence of a bony sagittal crest in *Paranthropus* does not, therefore, suggest that there is some close genetic relationship between this form and the pongids, among which crests are common. It merely indicates that the same combination of robust teeth and temporal muscles with a relatively small brain case is to be found in both groups. The sagittal crest is not something intrinsically determined as such.

In *Australopithecus* with its less powerful masticatory apparatus, the temporal lines are, on the available evidence, usually well separated. Of five specimens showing this region only one fragment of skull from Makapan, consisting of the occipital region, clearly had the temporal lines meeting in the region of the vertex.

The condition in the occipital region of the skull is interesting in cases where a sagittal crest is present. The temporal muscles do not meet the nuchal musculature nor do the temporal muscles meet each other in the midline posteriorly. This is very clearly demonstrated in the Makapan occipital fragment and less clearly in SK 48, from Swartkrans. There is no continuous nuchal crest nor does the sagittal crest pass right back to the occiput. It stops short of the position which would have been occupied by a nuchal crest had there been one. This is not in agreement with the views of Zuckerman (1952), who feels that, because in primates and mammalia in general nuchal crests are almost invariably associated with sagittal crests, this should also be the case in the prehominids. He says, "But unless *Paranthropus* provides a single exception to what seems to be a general feature of the architectural dynamics of the Primate skull, our observations about the coexistence of sagittal and nuchal crests in Primates seem to indicate clearly that *Paranthropus crassidens* had a strong nuchal musculature of the kind seen in extant great apes, and that it would have had nuchal crests."

As we have seen, these crests and their position are resultants of mechanical factors which are themselves part of a pattern involving the whole head, at least. In the prehominids, the brain case is relatively long compared to that of pongids, such as the gorilla, and the occiput is much more nearly horizontal in position. The large temporal muscles can meet in the midline in the region of the vertex, for the skull is relatively low and narrow anteriorly, but they do not reach the occiput, which is wide and does not extend so far up the skull. The more nearly horizontal occiput is associated with the bipedal posture of the prehominids, of which there is now considerable evidence. The predominantly vegetable diet of a large animal has resulted in heavy temporal musculature. As the brain case is relatively small anteriorly, these combined result in an incomplete sagittal crest but no nuchal crest. As this particular combination of features is not found in other primates, or mammals in general, it is not surprising that prehominids should provide an exception to the general rule about the association of nuchal and sagittal crests. Modern euhominids do not have either crest. Not only has the brain case expanded considerably but also the dentition has been reduced in size along with the forces of mastication. Consequently, the conditions for producing either crest do not arise. This, however, is no reason whatever for supposing that those conditions did not arise at some earlier stage of euhominid evolution.

Much of the difference in general skull form between the *Paranthropus* and the *Australopithecus* lines is, therefore, due to the differences in nature and amount of use to which the dental battery is put. These in turn affect the evolution of the teeth by modifying the general pattern common to the euhominids as a whole. The retardation of the reduction

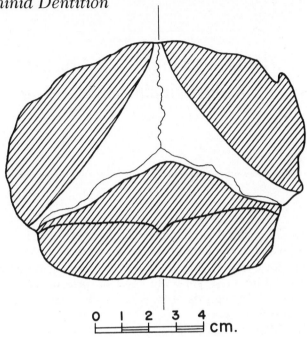

FIGURE 3. Semidiagrammatic drawing (modified after Dart) of the first occipital fragment of *Australopithecus* from Makapan. The hatched areas are those covered by the temporal and nuchal musculature. A sagittal crest must have been present near the vertex but is not present posteriorly, nor is there a nuchal crest.

of the post-canine teeth in *Paranthropus* as compared to *Australopithecus* is probably a result of the relatively greater amount of work required of these teeth in the former case. If an australopithecine was ancestral to the euhominids, as is clearly suggested by the nature of *Telanthropus*, then a continuation of the dental reduction observed would have resulted in a euhominid type of dentition, with consequent effect upon the architecture of the face in particular and of the skull in general. The expanding brain would have helped further to transform the skull into one of euhominid type.

.   .   .   .

The Genera and Species of the Australopithecinae

J. T. Robinson[1]   1954

The taxonomy of the Australopithecinae has been in need of revision for a long time and in the light of the recent advances in our knowledge of this group this task may now be undertaken with some profit.

The nomenclature most generally used at present is that outlined by Broom (1950b), though there is widespread dissatisfaction with this scheme, which is as follows:

Subfamily: (1) Australopithecinae
                     Australopithecus africanus
                     Plesianthropus transvaalensis
              (2) Paranthropinae
                     Paranthropus robustus
                     Paranthropus crassidens
              (3) Archanthropinae
                     (*Australopithecus*) *prometheus*

A slightly later classification (Mayr, 1951) goes to the opposite extreme. In this, all the australopithecines are lumped with fossil and modern man in a single genus with three species, one of which (*Homo transvaalensis*) includes all the australopithecines. Broom's classification is that of a determined splitter and Mayr's that of an equally determined lumper. Washburn and Patterson (1951) have suggested that the facts can be most accurately expressed by placing all the australopithecines in a single genus of their own, *Australopithecus*.

.   .   .   .

[1] I wish to record my grateful thanks to the Nuffield Foundation, London, for a grant, the receipt of which resulted in the discovery of some of the specimens on which the conclusions are based.

Reprinted by permission of The Wistar Institute Press from the American Journal of Physical Anthropology, n.s. 12:181–200 (1954). See note to preceding article.

The correct classification of the South African forms is complicated by the small number of specimens from Taungs, Kromdraai, and Makapan. However, all the specimens appear to fall clearly into two main groups. It is convenient to compare the samples from Swartkrans and Sterkfontein first, after which the smaller samples from the other sites may be considered. For the sake of convenience the Sterkfontein sample will be regarded as representative of "group A" and the Swartkrans sample of "group B."

One of the most useful characters separating the two groups is the structure of dm_1. The two types of tooth are illustrated in Figure 1. The type belonging to group B, of which there are 6 specimens from 4 mandibles, is a fully molariform tooth with 5 well developed cusps. The tooth is very much like an ordinary permanent lower molar. The cusps are all closely applied to each other and a well defined, transverse anterior fovea is present. The mesial buccal groove is deeply incised and ends abruptly, sometimes terminated by a small tubercle—a feature characteristic of the permanent molars of the Swartkrans form. The width across the posterior half of the tooth is greater than that across the anterior half, e.g., in SK 64 (least worn tooth) the anterior breadth is 7.9 mm while the posterior one is 8.7 mm. On the buccal face the enamel line is approximately horizontal.

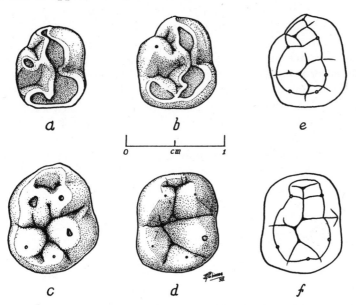

FIGURE 1. First and lower deciduous molar from (a) Sterkfontein, (b) Taungs, (c) Swartkrans, and (d) Kromdraai. The first two belong to Group A and this tooth type is represented in (e). The second two belong to Group B and this tooth type is represented in (f).

The group A form of this tooth is very distinct in appearance. The tooth is smaller than that of group B and is essentially 5-cusped, though the hypoconulid is very small. The entoconid is a small cusp well separated from the protoconid which is sharp and not as well developed as in group B. The major cusp is the metaconid which is well developed and its apex is situated almost on the longitudinal midline of the tooth. In group B the cusps are of approximaely equal size except for the smaller hypoconulid. Here the protoconid and hypoconid are the largest cusps and are subequal. In the group A tooth the anterior fovea is a large depressed area lingual to the metaconid. The latter cusp has a large, sloping buccal face which results in the enamel line being much lower down below this cusp than it is below the hypoconid. The width across the anterior half of the tooth is slightly greater than that across the posterior half.

Unfortunately only one intact specimen of this tooth is known from Sterkfontein but the Taungs child has the same type. Furthermore this tooth form is very similar indeed to that characteristic of euhominids. The group A and B tooth types are so very different that they can be distinguished at a glance.

A second feature which distinguishes clearly between the two groups is the structure of the anterior part of the nasal cavity floor. In group B the facial plane of the maxillae passes smoothly into the pyriform aperture without any sharp demarcation. There is a small anterior nasal spine in the form of a small roughened area with an apex which points upward and backward. The area surrounding the spine is depressed so that the latter is not visible in lateral view. The anterior extremity of the vomer inserts into a small cleft in back of the anterior nasal spine. In group A there is also no sharp line of demarcation between the lower margin of the pyriform aperture and the facial plane of the maxillae— as there is in *Telanthropus* and euhominids—but the distinction between the two is nevertheless considerably clearer than it is in group B. The

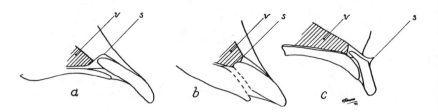

FIGURE 2. Sagittal section through the palates of the ape-man from Sterkfontein (*a*) and Swartkrans (*b*) and that of a modern Bushman (*c*). The vomer, V, is shaded and S indicates the anterior nasal spine. The condition in *Telanthropus* resembles that depicted in (*c*).

FIGURE 3. Transverse sections through the roots of P³ of (*a*) the Swartkrans form and (*b*) the Sterkfontein form. The sections were taken at a point a third of the root length from the apex.

a   *b*

anterior nasal spine is smaller than in the latter group and is sometimes divided into two by a groove for the septal cartilage. The vomer does not insert directly against the back of the spine but inserts in an equivalent position lower down. There is thus a sharp slope from the back of the anterior nasal spine a short distance down to the anterior end of the vomer.

A third feature separating the two groups is the nature of the roots of P³. It seems clear that early hominids had three-rooted upper first premolars, and the evolutionary tendency is toward a condition where only a single root is present. In one specimen from Sterkfontein a single root is present but in all other known australopithecine specimens there are at least two roots. Of 13 Sterkfontein specimens only one has a double buccal root, i.e., three roots altogether, while of 19 Swartkrans specimens 14 have double buccal roots. This difference takes on even greater significance when it is remembered that the geologically older form is the more advanced in this respect.

Another point of difference between the two groups is in the size and structure of the canines. In group B upper and lower canines are small, often being easily matched in both size and structure among the homologues of modern euhominids. There is a clear distinction between the upper and lower canines in structure. In the maxillary tooth the lingual grooves converge sharply onto the gingival eminence and the borders lateral to the grooves are thickened. In the mandibular tooth the thickened borders are not present and the lingual grooves do not meet on the gingival eminence. The crown is slightly asymmetrical in that the cingulum extends higher up the distal face of the crown than it does on the mesial. This feature is not strongly developed, is not present in the upper canine, and is also detectable in the mandibular canine of modern euhominids. The canines of group B therefore have a remarkably modern euhominid appearance. Those of group A on the other hand are larger and exhibit some exaggerated features not met with in euhominids. The maxillary canine is robust, symmetrical, and has the lingual grooves roughly parallel and without the swollen marginal ridge of group B.

These differences are easily seen and no example of this group B type tooth has been seen in a group A specimen. Except for size the structure of this tooth is more easily found among euhominids—even the size is duplicated in *Pithecanthropus*—than is that of group B. However the mandibular canine is markedly different from the group B type. The crown asymmetry is very evident, as can be seen from the illustration (Figure 4). The lingual ridge is always present and, except for one instance (Figure 4 c), is very strongly developed. Although the basic structure of the canines is the same in both groups there is an absolute distinction between them so that one could not mistake the one for the other. There is just about as much difference between a lower canine of group A and one of group B as there is between one of group A and one of modern man.

Skull shape also differs between group A and B. In the former the skull is small, narrow, has a small but unmistakable forehead and the supra-orbital torus is not marked, i.e., there is no platform in the glabella region. In group B the skull is slightly larger, is broad across the ear region, has no real forehead and the supraorbital torus is well developed in the region of the glabella so that a flattened platform is present. There is never more than a small degree of maxillary prognathism and the face is flat and broad. In group A prognathism is sometimes no greater than in the former group but may be marked, as in the case of Sts. 5.

Apart from the more important differences cited above there are others

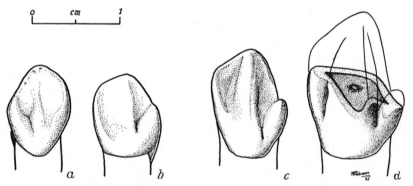

FIGURE 4.   Australopithecinae mandibular canines. (*a*) SK 96 from Swartkrans. This tooth is from the left side and is the smallest canine in the collection from this site. (*b*)SK 87, from the right side, is the largest isolated tooth in the collection and has a module of 9.5 while the largest canine known has a module of 9.7. This tooth also is the tooth with the strongest resemblance to the group A type. (*c*) and (*d*) are respectively the smallest and largest mandibular canines from Sterkfontein. Both are from the right side. (*c*) is also the tooth with the least strongly developed lingual ridge. These teeth therefore represent the full range of both size and structure in the known canines of these two groups.

of lesser significance. The crown shape and structure of P_3 differs in the two groups, as does, to a lesser extent, that of P^3. It appears from the size of the innominates and femurs of the two groups that group A had a body size approximately comparable with that of African pygmies while group B comprised much more robust creatures which were, probably, a bit larger than the average modern man but not large enough to be considered giants. This is mentioned only as a point of interest because comparable size differences are present in modern man and given no taxonomic significance—though such size differences are often accorded some significance in other animals. Sexual dimorphism is apparently more marked in group A than in group B. In the latter it can be demonstrated, but is manifestly only slight. In the former variation in size and in structure is appreciably greater than in group B and this seems to be associated with a greater degree of sexual dimorphism.

So far this discussion on group A and group B is based only on the Sterkfontein and Swartkrans specimens respectively. It is now necessary to see if and how the other specimens fit into these categories. Starting first with the Kromdraai specimens: these exhibit the dm_1 pattern, crown and roots of P^3 and crown of P_3 typical of group B. All the features of the skull shape cannot be ascertained, but those that are available also are typical of this group. The relations of the vomer and anterior nasal spine are not known but the conformation of the lower part of the pyriform aperture, as far as it is preserved, is of the Swartkrans type. The Kromdraai form fits easily into group B. There are no features which contra-indicate referring it to this group.

The Taungs specimen, being immature, gives information on only a few of the diagnostic features outlined above. However the structure of dm_1 is so obviously like that of group A and so different from that of group B that there can be no question as to which group it belongs. There are no factors inconsistent with its being placed in group A.

The Makapan form requires rather more consideration, not so much because of the nature of the available material but because of the views which have been expressed by Dart and Broom. In my opinion it is indistinguishable from the Sterkfontein form but both Dart (especially 1948a) and Broom (1950b) considered it to differ in a number of points. Broom especially regarded it as so much more advanced than the other australopithecines that he was inclined to give it euhominid status. Dart regarded the occiput from Makapan as belonging to a larger-brained form than that from Sterkfontein, the only complete and undistorted skull of which has an endocranial volume of some 480 cm³. On the Makapan occiput the areas for muscle attachment are plainly visible and Dart identified the highest point reached by muscle, in the midline, as the maximum occipital point, with the inion some distance below it.

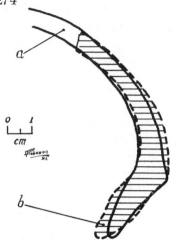

FIGURE 5. Comparison of sagittal sections of the occiputs from Sterkfontein and Makapan. (*a*) section of occiput of Sts. 5. (*b*) section of the original specimen from Makapan.

Orienting the skull fragment on this assumption gave a horizontal occipital plate and a contour that could only have belonged to a fairly large skull. It seems to me, however, that if one assumes the maximum occipital point to coincide with the point identified by Dart as the inion, then this occiput is virtually indistinguishable from that of Sts. 5 from Sterkfontein. Both specimens have an unmistakable occipital torus which is situated in an almost identical position in both specimens. The slight overlap of muscle markings over this, in the Makapan specimen, is not uncommon in modern man. In none of the Sterkfontein specimens is the outer table of the skull sufficiently well preserved in this region to show muscle markings. If a sagittal section of the Makapan occiput is superposed over one of Sts. 5 the fit is almost exact (see Figure 5). No special significance need be attached to the complicated system of sutural bones in the Makapan occiput, as a mark of taxonomic distinction from other forms, because this is a very variable feature in hominids and the second calvarial fragment from Makapan does not have it.

Broom was particularly impressed by the differences in the innominate from Makapan and that from Sterkfontein, more especially in the structure of the ischium. The Sterkfontein innominate is that of an adult while the Makapan one belonged to an adolescent in which the three elements of the bone had not yet fused. The ilium of the latter is almost exactly like that from Sterkfontein in size and structure. When adult this ilium would have been a little larger than that from Sterkfontein but the difference would have been so small as to be easily explicable as a sexual difference. The ischium, which Broom considered so critical, in my opinion would closely resemble that from Sterkfontein after the remaining small amount of growth had occurred along the acetabular margin and over the ischial tuberosity. There are thus no critical differences between this specimen and that from Sterkfontein in either size or structure.

Unfortunately no dm$_1$ is known of this form but the single buccal root of P^3, crown structure of P$_3$, and what is known of the lower canine and skull shape and size all mark this form as belonging to group A.

To sum up: on the strength of a series of relatively independent characters the South African australopithecines are here shown to fall into two natural groups, each representing a separate phyletic line. Group A comprises the specimens from Taungs, Sterkfontein, and Makapan, and group B those from Kromdraai and Swartkrans.

.   .   .   .

The prehominid classification here being presented may be expressed as follows:

Family: Hominidae
Subfamily: Australopithecinae
Genus (1):   *Australopithecus*
            Species: *africanus africanus* (Taungs)
                       africanus transvaalensis (Sterkfontein, Makapan, and East Africa)
Genus (2):   *Paranthropus*
            Species (1):   *robustus robustus* (Kromdraai)
                       robustus crassidens (Swartkrans)
            Species (2):   *palaeojavanicus* (Sangiran)

In this classification the australopithecines are placed in a separate subfamily from euhominids. Mayr's classification requires the australopithecines and euhominids to belong to the same genus and hence to the same subfamily.

It has been shown (Robinson, 1953d) that euhominids exhibit some characters not shown by the australopithecines. That is, there is a morphological distinction between an australopithecine and a euhominid grade of organization. Among the more obvious of these differences is the fact that the former group walked erect while the latter not only walked erect but also had a large brain and all that follows from this fact. Furthermore it is clear that the Swartkrans prehominid could not be ancestral to euhominids because a much more suitable ancestor, *Telanthropus*, lived synchronously with it. The Sterkfontein prehominid lived slightly earlier than *Telanthropus* but could not be ancestral to the latter because of certain specializations—for example the later and more advanced *Telanthropus* had a more primitive upper premolar root system, the Sterkfontein form had very specialized canines, etc., and the time interval between them was very short.

Not only are there morphological distinctions between the prehominids and the euhominids, but it is clear that not all of the former reached

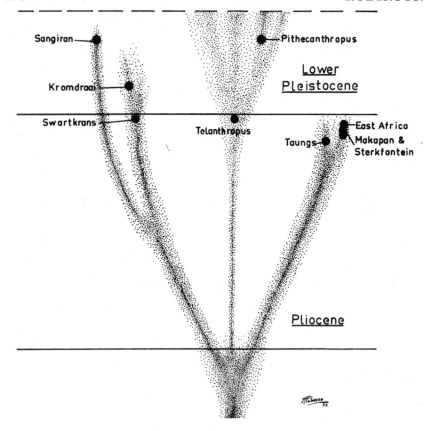

FIGURE 6. Suggested evolutionary relationships of the australopithecines, *Telanthropus* and *Pithecanthropus*. The relative lengths of the lower Pleistocene and the Pliocene are not to scale. The exact position in time of the separation of the three phyletic lines of australopiths is not known, nor is it known whether there were more than three. Probably there were more lines in the early stages of the history of the group. Insufficient material of the Sangiran form is known to judge whether it is nearer the euhominid group than the Swartkrans and Kromdraai forms.

the latter grade of organization. Consequently taxonomic distinction between the two groups is required, hence their separation into two separate subfamilies.

The genus *Plesianthropus* is sunk, being synonymous with *Australopithecus*, and also *Meganthropus* which is synonymous with *Paranthropus*.

The genera may be defined as follows:

Australopithecus:

dm$_1$ incompletely molarized, protoconid most strongly developed cusp (including anterior accessory cusplet) with large, sloping buccal face; vomer does not insert directly against back of anterior nasal spine; P^3 usually having a single buccal root; canines large with mandibular canine strongly asymmetrical and lingual ridge present, normally strongly developed; skull narrow, forehead present, supra-orbital torus not strongly developed.

The specific characters, in this case, are the same, as only one species is known at present.

Subspecies: *africanus africanus:* tuberculum sextum present on M_1; deciduous canine without mesial cusplet.

africanus transvaalensis: M_1 without tuberculum sextum; protostylid common and may be large; deciduous canine with mesial cusplet.

Paranthropus:

dm_1 strongly molarized, metaconid and hypoconid largest cusps, protoconid without large, sloping face; vomer does insert against back of anterior nasal spine; P^3 usually with double buccal roots; canines small, mandibular one not strongly asymmetrical, lingual ridge never strongly developed; skull broad across ear region, no forehead, supraorbital torus well developed near midline.

Species (1): *robustus:* crown of P_4 appreciably larger than that of P_3. Root of P_4 double.

Subspecies: *robustus robustus:* deciduous maxillary canine symmetrical with very small distal cusplet; dm_1 with no mesiobuccal cusplet anterior to anterior fovea.

robustus crassidens: deciduous lower canine markedly asymmetrical with distal cusp well developed; dm_1 with mesiobuccal cusplet.

Species (2): *palaeojavanicus:* crowns of P_3 and P_4 subequal; roots of P_4 partially fused.

Telanthropus from Swartkrans has been dealt with at length elsewhere (Robinson, 1953d). For this reason and the fact that it is not regarded as a prehominid but a euhominid, it is not discussed here. Its characters are such that it does not fall into either of the genera defined above. It is a product of a third phyletic line of the prehominids, distinct from the above two, of which specimens could only be discovered by finding geologically earlier australopithecine-bearing deposits than those now known. This line must have been a higher-rate line than either of the two others.

CONCLUSIONS

1. The prehominids, by the lower Pleistocene, were a group with a long evolutionary past.

2. The group was not simply a short-lived, highly variable one, transitional between pongids and euhominids.

3. All the known australopithecines fall easily into two genera, *Aus-*

tralopithecus and *Paranthropus,* each representing a separate line of evolution.

4. *Australopithecus* contains a single species with two subspecies, containing the specimens from Taungs, Sterkfontein, Makapan, and East Africa.

5. *Paranthropus* contains two species, one with two subspecies, distinguishing the specimens from Kromdraai and Swartkrans, the other containing the Javanese specimen hitherto referred to as *Meganthropus palaeojavanicus.*

6. *Telanthropus* is a euhominid descended from the prehominids but not from either of the above phyletic lines.

7. The prehominids therefore include at least three phyletic lines of which at least one progressed to the euhominid grade of organization.

The Australopithecines and Their Bearing on the Origin of Man and of Stone Tool-Making

J. T. Robinson   1961

South Africa has played a significant part in the piecing together of the story of the evolution of man by providing a large proportion of the known evidence relating to the very early chapters of this story. The evidence has been of several sorts, but here I refer chiefly to fossil remains of early members of the family of man. In this address I shall be concerned to outline some of the major features of what has so far been learned about the australopithecines and how they fit into the evolutionary story of man.

The first australopithecine specimen came into scientific hands 36 years ago—the story of this and later discoveries has been told often and will not be repeated here. For roughly thirty of those years considerable controversy existed as to the nature of these creatures. In the last few years fairly general agreement has been reached that the australopithecines truly belong with the family of man and not among the apes. Emphasis has now shifted to attempts to evaluate the nature of the relationship to true man and from the early majority view that they were nothing but apes, the pendulum has now swung almost to the other extreme with the rapidly growing tendency to regard them as the earliest true man. I shall put before you a view which is less extreme than either of these.

FROM the South African Journal of Science, 1961, vol. 57, pp. 3–13, reprinted by permission of the author and of the South African Association for the Advancement of Science. Originally delivered in July, 1960, as Presidential Address to Section F of the South African Association for the Advancement of Science. Dr. Robinson has supplied some references and minor additions which do not appear in the original publication. See note to second preceding article.

THE MAJOR PREHOMININE FEATURES

The australopithecines are roughly intermediate in grade of organisation between the small-brained pongids and the large-brained, bipedal hominines. They were erect-walking but had small brains. Well over 300 specimens, representing nearly a hundred individuals, are now known from South Africa. A small amount of material; less than a dozen specimens, is known from East Africa and the Far East. This is a good sample, palaeontologically speaking, and has given much information about variation and other population characteristics. This is important since it is not individuals that evolve but populations and it is the business of the palaeontologist to try to get back from the bits of individuals which comprise his material to the characteristics of the populations to which those individuals belonged.

The evidence for erect posture in the prehominines[1] is good. The pelvis is known from one almost complete specimen as well as a number of incomplete ones and it differs markedly from the pongid or monkey type but only very insignificantly from the hominine type. The lumbar region of the spinal column, the proximal and distal ends of the femur, and the nature and orientation of the occiput all add to the evidence which shows that the australopithecines were functionally and structurally well adapted to erect posture and locomotion.

The dentition provides considerable evidence of hominid affinity. The anterior teeth are small and compact and built closely on the hominine pattern. Even the canines are within the size range of hominines. Other teeth which are especially diagnostic are the first lower premolar, first lower deciduous molar, and deciduous canine. In pongids the first two are semisectorial teeth usually having one prominent cusp, though a second may be partially developed. In the prehominines and hominines the premolar is bicuspid and the deciduous molar well molarised, with five cusps, as in the permanent molars. Sophisticated statistical analysis of the deciduous canines has shown that the prehominine teeth are easily and sharply distinguished from the pongid form while they closely resemble, and in some cases are indistinguishable from, the hominine form.

These—and other—telling morphological features clearly indicate close affinity with hominines. But the small brain indicates a more primitive condition. The endocranial volume appears to be only about 500 cm³— I know of no sound evidence at present indicating a brain significantly larger than this. The range was evidently about 450–550 cm³ and there-

---

[1] Editor's note: for closer conformity to rules of nomenclature, Dr. Robinson here uses "prehominine" and "hominine" in preference to the earlier "prehominid" (= australopithecine) and "euhominid" of the preceding papers.

fore well below the pongid maximum of 685 cm³. The early hominines appear to have had endocranial volumes averaging from about 900–1100 cm³, though estimated volumes as low as 755 cm³ have been given.

Along with this small endocranial volume in the prehominines the braincase is relatively small and the face relatively prognathous. It is therefore evident that an important feature of hominines—the enlarged brain and the consequent modifications in skull architecture—was not yet significantly developed in the known prehominines.

TAXONOMIC DIFFERENTIATION WITHIN THE PREHOMININES

It is common at present to regard the prehominines as comprising a single rather variable group without any significant differentiation. A considerable volume of evidence exists which shows that this is not the case. Two different forms are known in South Africa at present: *Australopithecus* occurs at Taung, Sterkfontein, and Makapansgat, and *Paranthropus* at Kromdraai and Swartkrans. It is important to realise that the largest *Paranthropus* sample, 160 specimens from Swartkrans, occurs less than a mile from Sterkfontein which yielded the largest sample of *Australopithecus*—108 specimens. Geographic variation can therefore be disregarded in this case.

Australopithecus has a dolichocephalic skull with a good hominine shape. A distinct, low forehead is present and the vertex rises well above the level of the brow ridges. The latter are poorly developed and the postorbital constriction is moderately developed. The face is fairly wide, the nasal region is slightly raised above the surrounding level of the face, which is distinctly prognathous. The skull is gracile, without any heavy bone or strong development of ridges or crests. The mandible is robust with a moderately high ramus and an almost vertical chin region. The dentition is morphologically very similar to that of early hominines. Molars and premolars are well developed and the canines are fairly large but do not protrude because they are recessed into the jaw to a greater extent than the other teeth. The proportions along the tooth row are typical of early hominines.

Paranthropus is very different. Although the endocranial volume appears to differ insignificantly from that of *Australopithecus*, the skull architecture is markedly dissimilar. The skull is brachycephalic, with no trace of a forehead; the frontal passes straight back from the well developed supraorbital torus in a manner reminiscent of the condition in the gorilla. The vertex rises very little above the upper level of the orbits. Le Gros Clark (1949b) devised an index to measure this feature in primate skulls and it places *Paranthropus* right in the middle of the pongid range while *Australopithecus* is well outside this position and very near to modern man. In all known adults with the appropriate area preserved a sagittal crest is present—occupying roughly the middle third of the distance from glabella to inion. The degree of postorbital constriction is relatively greater than in *Australopithecus* and the zygomatic arches stand out well away from the braincase. The face is massive and wide. The enormously robust cheek bones actually project further forward than does the nose, which is completely flat. The face is appreciably less prognathous than in *Australopithecus*. The lower jaw is massive with a very high and vertical ramus. A most curious situation is found to exist in the dentition. The postcanine teeth are massive, being distinctly more robust than those of *Australopithecus,* but the canines and incisors are distinctly smaller than in the latter form. There is thus a sharp change in proportion between the anterior teeth and the postcanine teeth which is unique in the hominids.

Paranthropus thus has a very robust skull with enormous development of bone and a curiously spheroidal braincase with strong development of rugosities and crests, a very wide, dished face, and the dentition is specialised quite differently to that in *Australopithecus.* These descriptions are based on female skulls in both cases, but sexual dimorphism does not appear to be well developed. Furthermore *Paranthropus* was a very heavily built, muscular animal which probably stood over five feet in height and must have weighed a few hundred pounds. *Australopithecus* clearly was very small and slenderly built—the female apparently being no more than about four feet in height and weighing only some 40–50 lbs.

Besides these differences—which are obvious enough—there are other important dental differences. The first lower deciduous molar in *Australopithecus* is of the same type as is found in all known hominines, having a characteristic specialisation of the anterior half of the crown. *Paranthropus* is unique in the primates in having a completely molarised deciduous first lower molar without any trace of the specialisations seen in *Australopithecus* and all hominines. The deciduous canines also differ considerably in the two forms.

The differences in skull architecture can be explained primarily in terms of differences of dental and dietary specialisation. *Paranthropus* has very heavy crushing and grinding cheek teeth and the anterior teeth are less important, being appreciably reduced in size. This implies a vegetarian diet which requires considerable bulk to provide the necessary nutritive value. Much chewing is required to comminute the often tough plant material. Enlargement of cheek teeth with specialisation for crushing and grinding are common features of creatures adapted to vegetarian diet. *Paranthropus* apparently also ate roots and bulbs since there is clear evidence of grit in the diet, in the form of small chips and

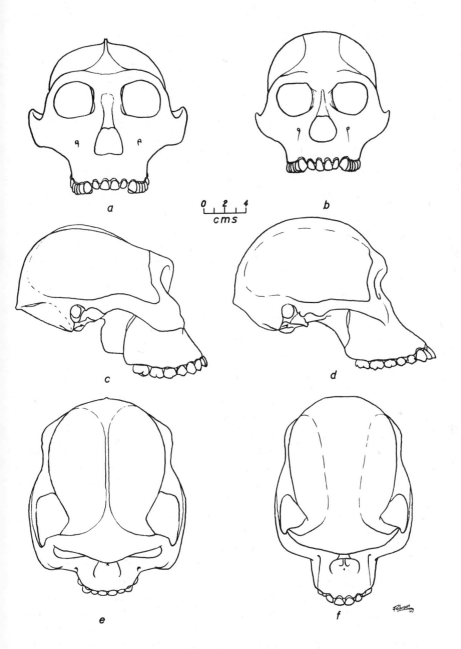

FIGURE 1. Comparison between skulls of females of *Paranthropus* (*a, c, e*) and *Australopithecus* (*b, d, f*). The former series is based largely on SK 48 from Swart-krans; the latter on Sts 5 from Sterkfontein.

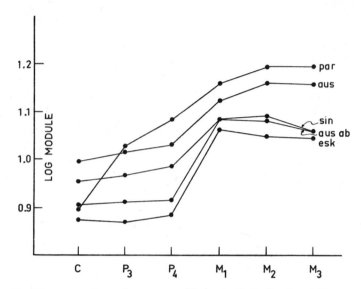

FIGURE 2.   Size comparison of some mandibular teeth in five hominids. *par* = *Paranthropus,* aus = *Australopithecus,* sin = Pekin man, aus ab = Australian aborigine, and esk = East Greenland Eskimo. This illustrates very clearly the aberrant nature of the *Paranthropus* dentition in which a marked change of proportion between the anterior and post-canine teeth occurs between the canine and first premolar.

flakes of enamel which have broken off from the occlusal margins of the tooth crowns. The powerful chewing forces which must have been involved have resulted in great thickening of the bone in which the cheek teeth are set and along the avenues through which the chewing forces are dissipated—such as the palate, the cheek bones, and jugal arches, lateral parts of the supraorbital torus and the pterygoids. Also the heavy jaws needed powerful muscles, hence there is further robustness introduced in such areas as the origin and insertion of the masseter and pterygoid muscles. The relation of large temporal muscles to small braincase was such that even females apparently normally had a sagittal crest. On the other hand the very small anterior teeth result in a face which does not protrude forwards at all markedly.

   Australopithecus, on the other hand, has none of these extreme modifications. Both skull shape and structure and especially dental morphology are closely comparable to the early hominine condition. It therefore seems reasonable to conclude that the diet of this form was essentially the same as that of early hominines—i.e., they were omnivores eating both flesh and vegetable matter. This was probably the sort of diet still found in hunters and food-gatherers of today.

   The adaptive difference between these two forms is thus considerable.

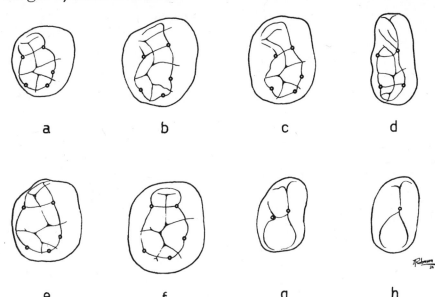

FIGURE 3. Basic cusp and fissure patterns in mandibular first deciduous molars of (*a*) European (Netherlands); (*b*) Bantu; (*c*) Bush; (*d*) baboon (*Papio*); (*e*) *Australopithecus;* (*f*) *Paranthropus;* and (*g, h*) chimpanzee. All to same scale. The specialised pattern of the hominines (*a, b, c*) is also present in *Australopithecus* but not at all in *Paranthropus*. The pongid teeth (*g, h*) are very different from those of hominids.

Their ecological requirements and direction of evolution were quite different. The degree of difference between them in these respects was of a distinctly greater order than that between any two of the living pongids. This is precisely the sort of difference which is regarded by modern mammalian systematists as excellent grounds for generic separation. It is interesting to notice that there is good evidence indicating that the vegetarian *Paranthropus* was present in the Sterkfontein valley in times when the climate was apparently significantly wetter than when the more carnivorous *Australopithecus* lived there.

Recently Leakey has found a fine australopithecine skull at Olduvai in East Africa and has given it a new generic name, "Zinjanthropus" (Leakey, 1959). He regards it as more advanced than either of the australopithecines already dealt with. However it is very clear that this form has all the major features already described for *Paranthropus*. The same pattern of modification of the skull architecture as a consequence of a specialised vegetarian diet is clearly developed. No valid grounds appear to exist for regarding this form as anything other than a typical *Paranthropus*. (Robinson, 1960).

Some mandibular fragments from Sangiran in Java, which have been called "Meganthropus" and regarded as members of the Pithecanthropus group, seem to me manifestly also to belong to the genus *Paranthropus*. They agree very closely with the equivalent parts of *Paranthropus* from South Africa—in almost every known feature the morphology is identical with that in *Paranthropus*—up to and including the greatly reduced anterior teeth coupled with very large cheek teeth (Robinson, 1953a, 1955).

Paranthropus therefore appears to have been spread across the width of the Old World with little modification. *Australopithecus* is not known from quite so far afield yet, but it is also known from near Olduvai and probably from Olduvai as well. One specimen found in 1938 by Kohl-Larsen in the Laetolil beds near Lake Eyassi is fairly clearly an *Australopithecus* (Robinson, 1953a, 1955). Some recent finds by Leakey at Olduvai, especially the adolescent mandible from the bottom of Bed I, appear also to belong to this genus.

TELANTHROPUS

From among the large number of *Paranthropus* remains which have come from Swartkrans I found a fragmentary upper and lower jaw of apparently the same individual and another almost complete mandible with a few other fragments of what clearly is a different type of hominid. This has been called *Telanthropus* and in my opinion represents a homi-nine, not an australopithecine (Robinson, 1953d).

The teeth are distinctly smaller than those of either australopithecine and agree in size very closely with those of the hominine from Java and Pekin now generally known as *Pithecanthropus*. The canine crowns were about the size of those of *Paranthropus*, but the roots were much reduced compared to those of either of the australopithecines. As well there are a few important characters which are found only among hominines but not among australopithecines. These are: (1) the structure of the nasal cavity floor and the premaxillary face of the maxilla, (2) the wide U-shape of the mandibular contour with wide interramal distance, (3) the small distance between the occlusal plane and the mandibular articulation with the skull, and (4) the slender construction of the mandible. None of these features can be matched in the australopithecines. In some respects *Telanthropus* is actually more advanced than the Pekin hominine. On the other hand, in no known feature is *Telanthropus* less advanced than the australopithecines. If the science of comparative morphology means any-thing, then *Telanthropus* must be classed with that group with which it shows closest and most fundamental resemblance, the hominines. *Telan-thropus* is often passed over lightly on the grounds that since so few

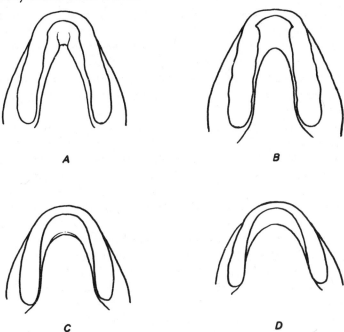

FIGURE 4. Contours of the mandibular body in A, *Australopithecus;* B, *Paranthropus;* C, "Telanthropus" (*Homo erectus*); and D, *Homo sapiens* (modern American white). Both australopithecines have a narrow interramal distance anteriorly; "Telanthropus" has the hominine condition in this respect.

specimens are known its affinities cannot be determined. It should be remembered that these few specimens occur right among the two largest australopithecine samples known and therefore in the most favourable possible situation for determining whether this form is an australopithecine or not. Here again geographic variation does not enter into the matter and apparently time differences are also not involved. Furthermore, although not much is known about the variation in *Telanthropus,* a great deal is known about that of both *Paranthropus* and *Australopithecus from that locality.*

STONE TOOLS ASSOCIATED WITH AUSTRALOPITHECINES

The cultural level attained by the australopithecines is of great interest. Professor Dart has argued that much evidence points to the australopithecines having used bones, horns, and teeth as implements and weapons (e.g. Dart, 1957, 1958, 1960). One may, I think, accept this in principle, but with two reservations: (a) the case should not be carried beyond the legitimate evidence; (b) the evidence so far available is primarily concerned with *Australopithecus* and does not necessarily apply equally to *Paranthropus*. It seems fair to conclude, therefore, that at least *Australopithecus,* and possibly also *Paranthropus,* were tool-users, bearing in mind that upon occasion the distinction between tool-using and tool-making can be rather fine.

But in 1956 Dr. Brain found some evidence of a stone industry in loose breccia at Sterkfontein and in 1957–8, in two seasons of excavation there, I was able to demonstrate for the first time the direct association of an australopithecine (*Australopithecus*) and a true stone industry (Robinson and Mason, 1957). This placed a different complexion on the matter; most students accepted that *Australopithecus* must have been a stone toolmaker. The recent discovery by Dr. Leakey of a stone industry with his Olduvai *Paranthropus* seems to have clinched the matter in the minds of most workers, who are now convinced that the australopithecines were stone toolmakers and state so without reservation.

However it seems to me, as I have pointed out elsewhere (in Robinson and Mason, 1957; Robinson, 1958), that this is far too facile a view of the situation. At Sterkfontein there is a considerable depth of deposit, which has yielded a hundred specimens of *Australopithecus* and not a trace of stone artifacts or even foreign stone. Unconformably overlying this is breccia which is demonstrably more recent by both faunal and lithological evidence. It nevertheless still contains *Australopithecus* but also a genuine stone industry, mainly in rock foreign to the immediate neighbourhood of the excavation. Furthermore, this industry is not of extreme primitiveness—it is not the very beginnings of tool-making, but appears to belong to the earliest levels of the handaxe culture, as Dr. R. Mason of the Archaeological Survey, Johannesburg, has shown (in Robinson and Mason, 1957; Mason, 1961). So at the same site we have evidence of considerable depth of deposit with the largest sample of *Australopithecus* specimens known but no evidence of a stone industry, followed by a small time gap, after which *Australopithecus* still occurs but with a fully fledged stone industry. The time gap appears to correspond closely in age with the *Australopithecus* deposit at Makapansgat, where tons of breccia have so far yielded no such stone industry as that at Sterkfontein. So roughly 96 per cent. of the known South African material of *Australopithecus* is not associated with stone implements, but suddenly a clear stone industry, representing an early stage of the Chelles-Acheul culture, appears towards the close of Sterkfontein time. Where did it come from? It seems to me that the only explanation can be that a toolmaker invaded the Sterkfontein valley during the time represented by the unconformity—and that invader could not have been *Australopithecus* as he had already been there for a long time.

It seems anything but coincidence that the stone artifacts turn up in the Sterkfontein valley at just about the time that the remains of *Telanthropus* also appear in the valley, less than a mile away at Swartkrans. As we have seen, *Telanthropus* has some major features which can be matched only among tool-making hominines, but not among the australopithecines. What more logical then that *Telanthropus* was the invading toolmaker? It is of interest to note that at Sangiran in Java, *Pithecanthropus*, a tool-maker, occurs side-by-side with *Paranthropus*, the vegetarian and least manlike australopithecine. At Swartkrans we find *Telanthropus*, also a hominine and in my opinion a toolmaker, side-by-side with *Paranthropus*. In North Africa at Ternifine *Pithecanthropus* is again present with a slightly more advanced form of the Chelles-Acheul culture than that at Sterkfontein. This is the opinion of Dr. Mason, who has examined both industries.

What, then, of the Olduvai specimen and the stone artifacts found with it? This site is directly on the migration route south to the Transvaal and the Sterkfontein valley and it seems impossible for the tool-making hominine, *Telanthropus*, to be present down here without it having been present at some stage in East Africa also. If *Australopithecus* occurs with stone tools and is not their maker, then this can as easily be true of the Olduvai individual. A powerful argument, in my opinion, against the Olduvai *Paranthropus* being a stone toolmaker is that it is a specialised vegetarian and vegetarians have little need for manufactured stone tools. If either of the australopithecines were to be toolmakers it is far more likely to be the partly carnivorous *Australopithecus*. If *it* is not, as clearly seems the case from the Sterkfontein evidence, it is improbable in the extreme that the vegetarian *Paranthropus* would be. Australopithecines, it will also be recalled, had small brains well within the pongid size range. Finally, a characteristic feature of the earlier levels of the stone age culture sequence is the exasperating fact that remains of the makers of the tools are so exceedingly rare. Why then, if the australopithecines were toolmakers, should their remains be so common and stone tools rare when the normal experience is exactly the reverse? This seems a further argument against any of the australopithecines being toolmakers. On the other hand *Telanthropus* remains *are* very rare and this fits in with the general picture.

I submit therefore, that there is no good evidence in support of the thesis that australopithecines were stone toolmakers but that there is very pertinent evidence against it, favouring the idea that this group consisted essentially of tool-users.

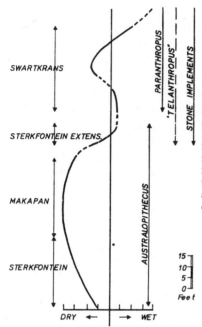

FIGURE 5. Climatic curve for Sterkfontein, Makapan (Limeworks), Sterkfontein Extension, and Swartkrans sites, modified after Brain. The curve is based on porosity, reflecting degree of rounding of the sand grains in the breccia from these sites. Central line indicates present rainfall conditions. The distribution of *Australopithecus, Paranthropus,* and "Telanthropus" is shown along with that of stone implements.

One may conclude that *Australopithecus* occupied the Sterkfontein valley over a long period when the climate was rather arid. Then *Telanthropus* moved into the valley, already a toolmaker. Since the ecological adaptations of these two forms were very similar, the more advanced *Telanthropus* will presumably have displaced or eliminated *Australopithecus*. Meanwhile the climate was becoming appreciably wetter, as has been shown by analysis of the breccia itself, and soon the vegetarian *Paranthropus* moved into the valley. Since the *ecological* requirements of *Paranthropus* and *Telanthropus* differed far more than those of the latter and *Australopithecus*, there will have been much less competition between them and they could occupy the same area as successfully as the gorilla and man have for long enough in Central Africa. This is demonstrated also by just the same sort of association from roughly the same time period at Sangiran in Java, right at the other end of the Old World from the Sterkfontein area, where *Pithecanthropus* and *Paranthropus* occur together.

TELANTHROPUS AND THE HOMININES

We have seen that *Paranthropus* and *Australopithecus* are very different creatures, ecologically quite differently adapted and morphologically very distinct. *Telanthropus* must be classed with the hominines, not the australopithecines, on morphological grounds. But is the genus *Telan-thropus* valid? Answering that question involves a reconsideration of the whole hominine group. It seems to me clearly impossible to make the sort of distinction within the hominines that is so clear in the australopithecine group. There is no evidence of which I am aware which suggests that any major adaptational differences existed which could conceivably be of a generic magnitude. The morphological differences also are of a low order. Probably the chief variable is brain size, the early *Pithecanthropus* forms being relatively small-brained and hence with slightly differently shaped braincases. The dentition was also relatively robust in the early forms and so the face was still fairly robust and prognathous. But the known range in brain size of the earliest hominines can be accommodated within the observed range of variation in modern man. The dental and facial changes appear to be part of a continuous sequence of modification of no great magnitude. These differences and the lack of any significant divergence of ecological requirements, fit well into the picture of species differences within a good and well defined genus among modern vertebrates. Furthermore, it is clear that as soon as hominines were well launched on their path of cultural development, the character of their evolutionary mechanism would have been modified. As Mayr (1951) has pointed out, man occupies a wider range of environments than any other animal. This is a result of his capacity for artificial adaptation. He can adapt himself to arctic conditions or to tropical conditions without significant change in his morphology or physiology—which is what occurs in other animals in such cases.

This capacity for artificial adaptation reduces his capacity to speciate. Natural adaptation, under the control of natural selection, to different environmental conditions is the normal basis of speciation and hence also of the achievement of any greater level of taxonomic distinction. Reduced rate of speciation and the more recent increasing tendency to interbreed over a wider area, have reduced appreciably the possibilities of significant adaptive radiation within the hominines. This and the very short time in which hominines have existed argue against such radiation.

For all of these reasons it seems to me that the hominines must all be included within a single genus, *Homo*. This was suggested ten years ago by Mayr (1951) as part of a taxonomic scheme which included other aspects which do not appear to me to be valid. It therefore appears that *Pithecanthropus* should be reduced simply to a species of *Homo-H. erectus*. *Homo sapiens* appears to be the only other valid species, including Neandertal man as no more than a subspecies. However, there is no time now to go further into this aspect of the matter save only to say that in this scheme *Telanthropus* would become *Homo erectus* and I therefore now formally sink the genus *Telanthropus* (originally created by Broom and me in 1949) and transfer the specimens hitherto contained in that genus to *Homo erectus*.

This scheme reduces the contents of the whole family Hominidae to three genera only, *Paranthropus*, *Australopithecus*, and *Homo*—and I trust that university students of the future will be grateful for this nomenclatural simplification! But it should be clearly recognised that these genera are not all of the same sort. *Paranthropus* and *Australopithecus* are validly distinct on any grounds. They were divergent, adaptively well separated stocks which represented an adaptive radiation within the prehominines and could successfully have occupied the same territory for a long time. But *Australopithecus* and *Homo* are probably two phases of the same phyletic sequence, though evidently at least one species of *Australopithecus* was contemporaneous for a short time with an early *Homo erectus* in the Sterkfontein valley. But there is no sharp discon-

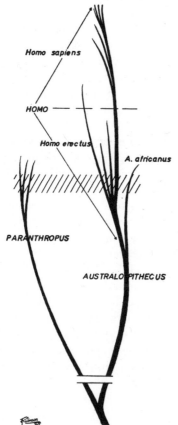

FIGURE 6. Schematic representation of relationship between *Paranthropus*, *Australopithecus*, and *Homo*. The hatched zone represents approximately the time period from which the australopithecines and "Telanthropus" are known. This period appears to be entirely in the Middle Pleistocene.

tinuity between *Australopithecus* and *Homo*, except, in the known specimens, in brain size. But clearly there was at least one phyletic line in
which this gap was bridged. So while it is convenient to keep a generic
distinction between the two groups, it should be recognised that this is
not a distinction of the same type as that between *Paranthropus* and
Australopithecus. This "vertical" type of arbitrary taxonomic distinction
within a single evolutionary sequence is one of the troublesome things
which the palaeontologist has learned to live with, about which the
neozoological taxonomist with his "horizontal" distinctions does not have
to worry.

HOMINID EVOLUTION

Hominids apparently arose from an apelike form more closely related
to pongids than to any other known primates. This was probably a vegetarian stock. The dentition of the early Miocene pongids is closely similar
to that of the modern ones, and presumably therefore there has been no
major change in diet during that time. The monkeys and pongids of today
are, with very minor exceptions, vegetarians of one sort or another and
carnivorousness is not characteristic of them. In such a stock, then, an
adaptive shift of enormous importance occurred—the acquisition of erect
posture. It seems likely that changes in the pelvic region, especially in the
innominate, occurred for some reason not primarily concerned with erect
posture. But when this change had, as a prospective adaptation, got to the
point where gluteus maximus could function as an extensor of the thigh
rather than as an abductor, the animals would find that erect posture
became far more easy to use than is the case in pongids. The nature of
selection would then have changed markedly and this would probably
have led to what has been called quantum evolution—the rapid re-
adaptation of a group, producing a very distinct change in the population.

This would have given rise to the prehominid group and the first primate bipeds. I visualise these as more nearly *Paranthropus*-like with an
essentially vegetarian diet, perhaps with an insectivorous element as well.
But a second adaptive shift must have occurred, probably in a more arid
environment—the adoption of a more specifically carnivorous element in
the diet. This resulted in the emergence of the *Australopithecus* line.
Definite carnivorousness would have placed a premium on tools in the
absence of large canines and this probably led to a well developed phase
of tool-using—sticks, stones, bones—whatever came to hand conveniently.
But freed hands resulting from erect posture and the premium on tools
resulting from carnivorousness, would certainly have resulted in appreciable selection pressure in favour of increased intelligence. This would
result in increase of brain size, with consequent skull changes, a shift

from tool-using to tool-making, etc.—in short, in the emergence of *Homo*. Meanwhile *Paranthropus*, a large animal, perhaps as expert at intimidation tactics as is the gorilla, and probably a moderate tool-user—e.g., digging "stick"—lost its previously larger canines, which reduced to modern size, while selection maintained the size of the dietarily more important cheek teeth. *Paranthropus* is basically less distinct from the hominid ancestor than is the more progressive *Australopithecus*.

The study of this phase of the evolution of man is of relatively recent origin and I hope that we shall have the opportunity to learn as much in the next 25 years as we have in the last 25.

ACKNOWLEDGEMENTS

The work on which this address is primarily based has been possible because of financial aid from various bodies or persons and I hereby make very grateful acknowledgement to the Nuffield Foundation, London, and the Nuffield Liaison Committee, Johannesburg; the Boise Fund and Professor Sir Wilfrid Le Gros Clark, F.R.S., of Oxford University; the Council for Scientific and Industrial Research, Pretoria, South Africa; the Wenner Gren Foundation for Anthropological Research, New York; Mr. and Mrs. L. Donnelly, Johannesburg, and Col. J. Scott, Johannesburg.

The Hominization of the Masticatory Apparatus, and Modifications of Diet

G. H. R. von Koenigswald   1958

I

Of all parts of the skeleton, it is the dentition which permits us to draw the most important conclusions as to the zoological position and the affinities of a given species. For a long time much attention has been paid to the dentition of modern man, as well as that of the living higher primates, man's closest relatives in the zoological sense of the term. Far less is known on the subject of the teeth of primitive man and fossil anthropoids, for whom we must often draw our conclusions from the study of a single specimen.

The principal difference between the dentition of men and of modern anthropoids lies in the form of the canines and the first premolars, the morphology of the latter being strongly influenced by the growth of the canines. In man, the canine is small and the teeth are disposed in a generally parabolic arc. In the anthropoids, on the contrary, a simian diastema is usually present opposite the upper canines, so that, at least in the upper jaw, the arrangement of the teeth is discontinuous. Related to the large upper canine, the first lower premolar often presents a simple pointed cusp, the "sectorial" type (unicuspid, or heteromorphic) while in man

Originally entitled "L'hominisation de l'appareil masticateur et les modifications du régime alimentaire," from Les Processus de L'Hominisation, 1958, a symposium (Colloque Internationale du Centre Nationale de la Recherche Scientifique) held May 19–23, 1958, at Paris. Published by Les Editions du C.N.R.S., 15 Quai Anatole France, Paris; reprinted by permission of the author and of the C.N.R.S. The author, who is identified with the recovery of many human fossils from Java and South China (Pithecanthropus, Meganthropus, Solo man, Gigantopithecus, and a southern variant of Sinanthropus, to use the familiar generic names), here presents his views of relationships among early hominids based primarily on molar patterns and sizes. He is Professor of Paleontology at the University of Utrecht.

this tooth is biscuspid (or homorphic) with the principal cusps of more or less the same height. It should, however, be noted that in the anthropoids, especially chimpanzees and orangs, one may also find a less developed cusp on the lingual side, so that there is no fundamental difference in the number of cusps between hominids and pongids, but rather in their development only. "The first lower premolar of all great apes, living and extinct, is a distinctly sectorial tooth, that is to say, the buccal cusp is elevated and pointed whereas no lingual cusp can be recognized, at least in most of the characteristic cases. Nevertheless, a lingual cusp exists but is concealed by a prominence caused by the lingual ridge there where in descending from the tip of the buccal cusp it meets the long lingual edge." (Weidenreich, 1937, p. 57)

The surface of the human molar is generally smooth, with few or no wrinkles. This is true, however, mainly for the dentition of Europeans, who have been the principal object of this kind of study; in African negroes, in Melanesians, in Chinese, and particularly in Malaysians, we often find a more wrinkled surface. Wrinkles are typical of anthropoids: wide coarse wrinkles in gorillas; fine, numerous furrows in chimpanzees; and a complicated system of wrinkles associated with low cusps in orangs, who possess the most specialized type of molar of all the higher primates. In the modern human dentition, the first molar (upper and lower) is generally the largest. This condition changes somewhat in the anthropoids, in whom the second upper molar is generally largest. In modern man, the first lower molar is always the largest of the series, as it is in approximately 10 per cent of chimpanzees (according to Remane). The third lower molar is the largest in approximately a third of gorillas and in a smaller proportion of orangs and chimpanzees. In relative dimensions of the molars, the chimpanzee comes immediately after man. We should remark here that all fossil anthropoids have a third molar larger than the second; accordingly, this situation should be considered as the original one.

The upper molars invariably retain the primitive trigone in their pattern. The *crista obliqua*, a crest joining the peak of the protocone to that of the metacone, which is well developed in gorillas, chimpanzees, and orangs, is often indentifiable in man. Furthermore, we find a fourth cusp, the hypocone, which is generally at its largest in the first molar. In the second molar, this cusp is already reduced in the majority of cases, particularly in individuals of the white race, and to a lesser degree in Melanesians. Usually, the third molar no longer has this cusp. We find striking differences between various human races in the reduction of this element. We cannot go into details here, and I refer the reader to tables given by Dahlberg (1949). In anthropoids, the hypocone of the second and third molars is generally much better developed than in man.

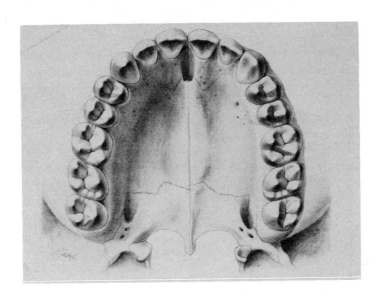

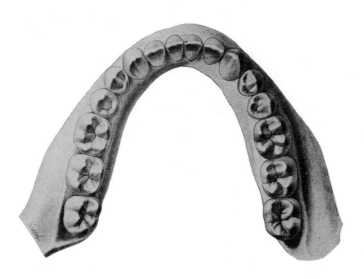

FIGURE 1. *Homo sapiens* L., recent; normal dentition after Röse). Natural size.

Modifications in the arrangement of cusps are generally more marked in the lower molars. Here, the fundamental type is denoted the "dryopithecus pattern," or "Y 5," of Gregory and Hellman. The first term derives from *Dryopithecus* of the Tertiary, which exhibits this arrangement on its three molars; the second term relates to the system of furrows on the surface. It is characteristic of this arrangement that the hypoconulid is well developed and is displaced to the vestibular or buccal side, and that the metaconid has a broad contact with the hypoconid. The lower molar consequently has five principal cusps, three on the vestibular side and two on the lingual side. A marked tendency is to be noted toward the elimination of the hypoconulid, so that, in the most reduced forms, this tooth has four cusps only, associated with a system of furrows; this is the cruciform or +4 type. According to the form of furrows and the number of cusps, there are two intermediate types known as "Y 4" and "+5."

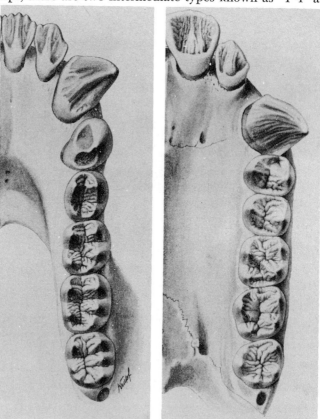

FIGURE 2.   Orang; normal dentition (after Selenka). Natural size; d = diastema.

Here also we find considerable differences in different human races. It is evident however that the "Y 5" type predominates on the first molar: 100 per cent in Chinese, Mongols, and Australians, and somewhat less in other races. In the second molar, type "+4" already predominates: 94 per cent in white Europeans. The form of the third molar is very irregular and does not exhibit the "Y 5" type. All these observations lead us to conclude that, in man, the first molar is the least reduced, and that the dryopithecus type should be considered as the primitive one. This is equally true for the anthropoids of the present day.

We very often find, in the mesiolingual part of the upper molar, a supplementary cusp, known as Carabelli's cusp. This cusp appears preferentially on the first molar, but may also be present on the second or on the third. The cusp is apt to be widespread in individuals of the white race: 72.3 per cent of the American army (according to Dietz, 1944), while in certain races, such as Eskimos, it may be completely absent. This structure is rare in anthropoids, and is most commonly indicated not by a cusp but by a groove.

We should make it plain here that there is no structure nor any formation of the molars in the anthropoids which is not present in the human dentition. In the lower molars, there may be found the paraconid, the metastylid (Bennejeant, 1936) and the "tuberculum sextum"; in the upper molars, the "fovea anterior" and the "parastyloid tubercle" (Bennejeant). There is not a single trait—possibly making exception for the exaggerated size of the canine for certain anthropoids—which will allow the two groups to be distinguished. There is, rather, an assemblage of relationships and an evaluation of metrical and morphological details which reveals the true nature of a dentition under discussion.

In order to discern the evolutionary trend of the human dentition, one should first of all examine the dentition of fossil man. The molars of Neanderthal man exhibit, in particular, a more complex system of wrinkles. We shall see that this is equally characteristic of older types, and that a relatively complicated system of wrinkles is typical in the ancestors of man. We should emphasize this fact, considering that for a long time Adloff has viewed the smooth surface of human molars—specifically molars of the white race—as actually primitive, and wrinkled molars as extremely specialized. This hypothesis has been contradicted by observation of the facts. Neither the molars of Neanderthal man nor those of Heidelberg man differ essentially from man of today. Furthermore, the reduction in number of cusps, characteristic of modern man, is to be seen as already present to a certain degree in the Krapina race of Neanderthal man, where approximately half of the second molars have but four cusps.

We find, preceding the period of Neanderthal man, a group which comprises Heidelberg man, *Pithecanthropus erectus* (whose dentition is practically unknown), *Atlanthropus,* and *Sinanthropus.* For the last, probably the most primitive of the group, we are acquainted with abundant specimens of jaws and isolated teeth, which have been studied very carefully by Weidenreich (1937). Here, also, the surface of the molars exhibits a complicated system of wrinkles. The molars, and especially the premolars, are larger than in modern man. Generally, the third molar is reduced; however, the maximum length known for this molar (13.8 mm) is higher than for the second (13.2 mm) so that, at least in some cases, the third molar is the largest of the series. The first molar is always smaller than the second. The dimensions, relative and absolute, of the lower premolars are important. In modern man, the first premolar is often slightly smaller than the second: De Jonge gives means of 6.6 mm for the first lower premolar and 6.9 for the second. In *Sinanthropus,* the mean mesiodistal diameters of the two premolars appear to be similar, with, however, a maximum of variation for the first premolar. In mandible G 1, the anterior premolar measures 9.1 mm and the posterior 8.5 mm. Lengths of the first premolar in modern man vary from 5.2 to 8.1 mm, showing that the mean in *Sinanthropus* is higher than the maximum in modern man. This indicates a marked reduction of this tooth in the latter. In Heidelberg man and in *Meganthropus* the first premolar also predominates, something which is still to be seen in several modern human races.

In regard to the canines, particularly the upper, the crown seems already reduced, whereas the root is disproportionate as to size and weight. This led Weidenreich (1937, p. 59) to conclude:

"Although I believe that the appearance of the lower first premolar suggests the probability that a still larger upper canine must have existed in the fore-runner of *Sinanthropus,* yet there is no distinct evidence proving that the lower canine also must have been essentially larger in the preceding stage of evolution. As noted above, the lower canine of *Sinanthropus* looks much more like an incisor than like the upper canine. It is quite probable that this peculiarity also represents a primitive character."

In Java, under the Trinil beds containing *Pithecanthropus erectus* (with a first lower premolar identical to that of Heidelberg man), lie the Djetis beds containing *Pithecanthropus modjokertensis* and *Meganthropus palaeojavanicus.* Both of these are individuals of large size which, for convenience, we will here place in the *Pithecanthropus* group. We know very little about the dentition of *Meganthropus* (type specimen: lower jaw with two premolars—of which the first predominates—and first molar), but we possess a part of the lower jaw of the *Pithecanthropus* form, as well as a fine palate.

The molars of the lower jaw exhibit the dryopithecus pattern and an

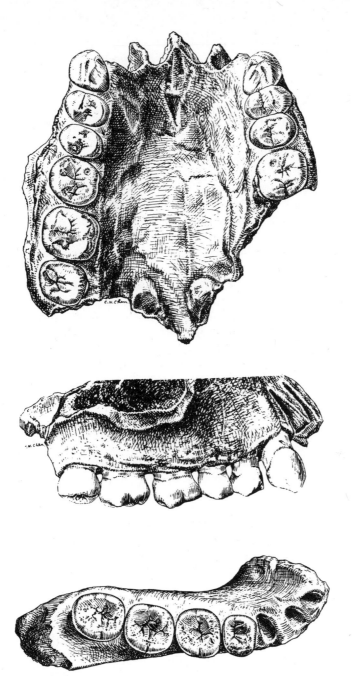

FIGURE 3. *Pithecanthropus modjokertensis* v. K., Lower Pleistocene, Sangiran, Java. Upper jaw (see Figure 6 for reconstruction) and mandible in original condition. Natural size.

increase of the mesiodistal diameter from front to back. In this case, the third molar is not reduced: the primitive disposition. This is equally true for the upper molars, in which the second dominates.

In the palate, the molars, premolars, and canine are disposed in a straight line; the dental arcade is not parabolic as in modern man, but instead is a characteristic "divergent dental arcade" as defined by Hellman (1918). Furthermore, the canine, although well worn, still projects below the level of the occlusal plane. This tooth is pointed, with two wear facets, one in front, the other behind. Opposite the canines, on both sides, there is a well marked diastema, 4 mm wide.

Can the jaw be considered as "hyperspecialized," placing this form of *Pithecanthropus* on a lateral branch? Certainly not, since the relative dimensions of the molars indicate primitive, "pithecoid" conditions. Besides, this type of canine was more or less predicted by Weidenreich (1937, p. 60), and a close examination of the deciduous dentition had already led Remane (1924) to conclude that the first ancestors of man must have possessed larger canines.

Pithecanthropus modjokertensis belongs to this type. The dentition might easily be confused with that of a "relatively advanced anthropoid" but, since we possess significant fragments of the skull of the same individual, there can be no doubt as to the human nature of this fossil. Furthermore, we may note that the nasal aperture has the same form as in man while, in the Australopithecinae, it is invariably patterned as in the anthropoid apes.

Pithecanthropus modjokertensis possesses the most primitive known human dentition.

The human types so far examined represent stages of evolution as well as morphological stages, since they also fall into order by geological age; the oldest specimen, *Pithecanthropus modjokertensis,* comes from the Djetis beds, corresponding to the Villafranchian. This suggests trying to determine the evolutionary trends, which, since the lower Pleistocene, have gradually brought the human dentition to its present form.

These trends may be summarized as follows:

With the reduction of the canines, a loss of the primitive diastema ("simian diastema"), terminating in the continuous dental arcade characteristic of man.

Reduction of the mandibular premolars, of which the first was primitively the largest. Inversion of the primitive relations of the molars (first molar smallest, last molar largest), and disappearance of the fundamental dryopithecus type, which persists longest in the first molar. At the same time, reduction of the number of cusps from five to four and formation of the "+ pattern."

The reduction in dimensions is indicated in the following:

Length of Three Lower Molars

Pithecanthropus modjokertensis	40.0 mm
Sinanthropus pekinensis (G 1)	37.7
Homo heidelbergensis	36.5
H. neanderthalensis (Krapina J)	35.5
H. sapiens (mean according to De Jonge)	32.4

that is, a reduction of approximately 20 per cent.

The second upper molar is still predominant in *Pithecanthropus;* in more recent specimens, it is the first. Reduction of the hypocone, particularly on the second and third molars, is characteristic in *Homo.*

Finally, reduction of wrinkles on all molars and premolars.

We have not yet mentioned the Australopithecinae of South Africa, since they are considerably removed from ancient human types such as *Pithecanthropus* and *Sinanthropus.* An important body of material, composed of jaws, skulls, and other parts of the skeleton, deriving from South Africa (Taungs, Sterkfontein, Kromdraai, Makapan, and Swartkrans), has been described by Dart, Broom, and Robinson. While the molar series exhibits primitive characters in dimensions—the fact that the third molar of the upper jaw is larger than the second is doubtless due to a hyperspecialization—the series of incisors, canines, and premolars is much reduced, to a degree which is almost ultrahuman. The diastema has disappeared. In the lower jaw, the first premolar is already shorter than the second. In *Australopithecus crassidens,* the mean difference in the length of these two teeth is 1.3 mm. In spite of this, the second premolar always has two roots as in the anthropoids, rather than a single one as in *Homo, Sinanthropus, Pithecanthropus,* and *Meganthropus.* This is one of the reasons why the last named cannot be considered as an australopithecine, as Robinson has attempted to suggest.

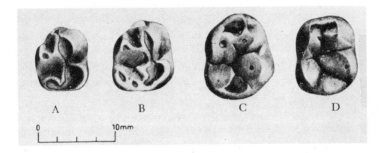

Figure 4. First lower deciduous molars of Australopithecinae, arranged by degree of "molarization": A, Taungs; B, Sterkfontein; C, Swartkrans; and D, Kromdraai (after Robinson).

The degree of reduction may be estimated by comparison with *Sinanthropus*. Thus, while in the first lower premolars the mesiodistal diameters overlap, the first lower molars show a marked difference; this may be taken to illustrate the degree of specialization.

	Mesiodistal Diameter	
	1st lower premolar	1st lower molar
Australopithecus (Swartkrans)	9.3–10.5	14.0–16.1 mm
Sinanthropus	7.9– 9.8	9.9–13.6 mm

The age of the *Australopithecus* specimens is Lower Pleistocene or Villafranchian (Oakley, 1955a). There are five deposits, ranked as follows by increasing age:

Kromdraai: *Paranthropus robustus* Broom
Swartkrans: *Paranthropus crassidens* Broom
Makapan: *Australopithecus prometheus* Dart
Sterkfontein: *Plesianthropus transvaalensis* Broom
Taungs: *Australopithecus africanus* Dart

In a recent publication Robinson (1956) distinguishes two genera only, *Australopithecus* and *Paranthropus*, each with two subspecies: *A. a. africanus* from Taungs, *A. a. transvaalensis* from Sterkfontein and Makapan, *P. r. robustus* from Kromdraai, and *P. r. crassidens* from Swartkrans. Although he considers *Meganthropus* of Java as a species of *Paranthropus*, it has nothing to do with that group.

As may be seen from Robinson's classification, *Australopithecus* belongs to a lower level and *Paranthropus* to a higher. The two distinct types of deciduous lower molars distinguished by that author (1956, p. 135) are not essentially different, but they may be separated by the degree of molarization, this being greater in the Kromdraai specimen. There is no difference, excepting as to size, between the first and the second deciduous molars, a condition which has not even been reached in modern man.

Since it is possible to classify the australopithecines according to the degree of molarization of the first deciduous molar, which also reflects their geological age, it is hardly to be doubted that they all belong to the same genus. If we consider them all as subspecies, the type becomes *A. africanus*. It seems preferable, however, while calling them all *Australopithecus*, to keep the old species names in order to distinguish them according to their respective deposits.

The skeleton furnishes proof that the Australopithecinae should without any doubt be classed among the *Hominidae;* Heberer has proposed the name "Praehomininae" for the group. For morphological and geological reasons, however, they cannot be ancestors of the *Pithecanthropus* group; the common ancestor of these, as we have seen above, could not conform to the definition given for the Australopithecinae, but would

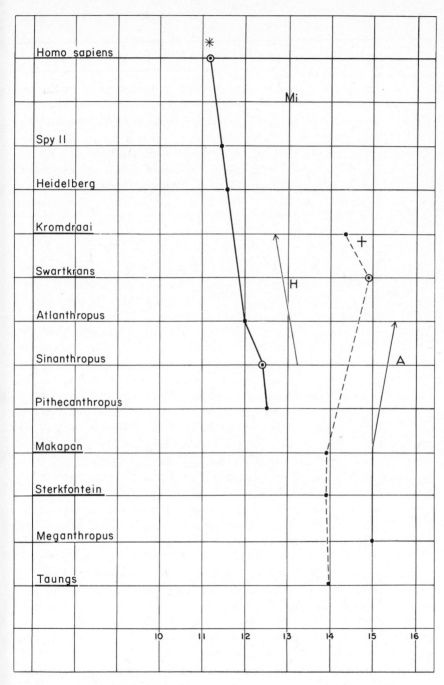

FIGURE 5. Length of the first lower molar. Note the trend to reduction in *Homo* (H), but not in *Australopithecus* (A). The species are arranged by geological age.

approach *Pithecanthropus* more closely. The Australopithecinae should accordingly be considered as a lateral branch of the genealogical tree of man rather than as an ancestral type.

Having examined the evolutionary trends of the human dentition, we will now try to state the characters which should be found in the immediate Tertiary ancestor of man, as we might imagine him in the Pliocene (and perhaps the Miocene): canines of medium size; in the lower jaw, large first premolar, bicuspid (nonsectorial), with a talonid; the second premolar smaller, bicuspid with talonid; molars of the dryopithecus pattern, five principal cusps and wrinkles only slightly accentuated, increased size of the mesiodistal length; in the upper jaw, a diastema; second molar larger than the first.

II

There are two different groups of higher primates which have been designated as being the ancestors of man: the Dryopithecinae, by Gregory, and the Oreopithecinae, by Hürzeler. Let us begin with the latter.

The Oreopithecinae comprise a single species, *Oreopithecus bambolii* Gervais, of the Lower Pliocene (Pontian). Known principally from deposits in Tuscany (Italy), the species has been reported, though never described, from Bessarabia. *Oreopithecus* has been considered as an anthropoid by Gervais, as a member of a distinct family by Schwalbe and Schlosser, and as a cercopithecid by Abel (1931) and Simpson (1945, p. 187: "*Oreopithecus* . . . is certainly a cercopithecoid primate, but with certain peculiarities that make its position uncertain.") Hürzeler, having recently made a close study of the then known remains (1949a), not only placed *Oreopithecus* in the "Hominoidea," but even considered it as belonging to the Hominidae: "this is the proof of a Tertiary man" (1954, p. 94).

The arguments and conclusions of Hürzeler have not been generally accepted and form the basis of a discussion which is far from being ended (Remane, Robinson, Vallois, von Koenigswald). It is impossible to treat all the details of this here; if we reject his final conclusion, this is principally due to the strange morphology of the molars, which are different from those of all the higher primates known from the Miocene and the Pliocene. The first lower molar—which ordinarily has the most conservative traits—as well as the second, has only four principal cusps, and a rudimentnary hypoconulid, always placed centrally. The elongated third molar exhibits a very prominent and well developed hypoconulid, removed from the hypoconid and not united by a crest to the entoconid. This tooth has many points in common with the corresponding tooth of certain cercopithecids. None of the molars has the dryopithecus pattern,

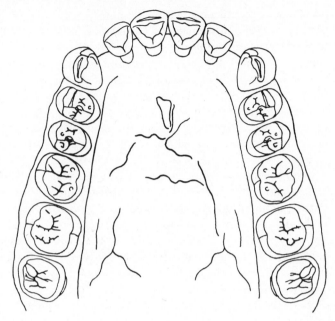

FIGURE 6. *Pithecanthropus modjokertensis* v. K. Reconstruction of upper jaw. Natural size.

which is nevertheless present in much older species of higher primates. There is no way to derive this type from *Oreopithecus:* the hypoconulid of the first and second molar would have to be enlarged (and displaced to the buccal side); in the third molar, the same cusp would have to be reduced, two opposed tendencies which it is difficult to imagine being combined in one and the same dentition!

The upper molars also exhibit certain peculiarities. There is a crest, the *crista obliqua*, which, when present in the Hominoidea, unites the point of the protocone to that of the metacone. In the Oreopithecinae, this crest starts from the point of the protocone, and terminates on the mesial slope of the metacone, a disposition never seen in other higher primates.

Oreopithecus possesses small canines and consequently has no diastema; one may ask if this indicates a primitive or a specialized condition. The first lower premolar is bicuspid and oval, with an attenuated talonid. The second premolar is larger than the first, as in the Australopithecinae. As far back as 1881, Forsyth Major regarded the poor development of the canine as evidently responsible for the form of the anterior premolars; he wrote (p. 41, note): "*Oreopithecus* exhibits analogy with man in the nature of its anterior premolar, which in this case is also influenced by the weak development of the canines."

Even while taking account of a certain resemblance in relative dimensions between the Australopithecinae and *Oreopithecus,* their fundamental morphological differences are too numerous to admit a relation between the latter and the hominids in general. In our opinion, the morphology of the molars has greater weight than the differentiation of the canines and the premolars.

Coming now to examine the Dryopithecinae (following the definition of Simpson, 1945), we must recognize, to begin with, that we are not dealing with a single species, or with a clearly defined group, but with a great variety of forms, ranging from the Lower Miocene to the Upper Pliocene. The Dryopithecinae are distributed over vast regions, from France to China and from Germany to East Africa. This subfamily comprises at least ten different genera and some thirty species, of which many are not clearly defined. They all exhibit the fundamental dryopithecus pattern in the upper molars, and no variation in the form of these upper molars, except perhaps in the secondary crests and wrinkles. Considering the morphology of the molars, this group, in its totality, approaches the hominids more than *Oreopithecus.*

The majority of the Dryopithecinae with well developed canines appear to be anthropoid apes, such as *Dryopithecus fontani carinthiacus* Mottl (1957, fig. 7), in which the first lower premolar is bicuspid but pointed and short. There are, however, two species which we shall examine in detail, because they have some relationship to the origin of man.

The first is *Gigantopithecus blacki* von K., from China, which was originally known only from four isolated molars, discovered in Chinese apothecary shops in Hong Kong and Canton. These teeth are of considerable size (larger than the teeth of a gorilla); their form, very similar to that of human molars, so struck Weidenreich that he considered them as belonging to a giant hominid. Taking account of the reduction of the human dentition, he gave *Gigantopithecus* a central position, and considered it as the common ancestor of *Pithecanthropus* and *Sinanthropus.* This is however impossible from the stratigraphic point of view, since *Gigantopithecus* can be dated only to the Middle Pleistocene, and is contemporary with *Sinanthropus.*

Pei has recently described a mandible (1957) and a certain number of isolated teeth (1956). The mandible is of enormous size, with relatively small canines. The first lower premolar is bicuspid and moderately sectorial, with a well developed talonid, and is longer than the second. Pei concludes (1956, p. 490), "The morphological pattern of *Gigantopithecus* indicates that it may belong to a side branch of the Anthropoids, but the point where it took off is nearer to the hominid line than any other fossil Anthropoid so far found."

Because of its gigantic size and recent geological age, *Gigantopithecus* can in no wise be considered as an ancestor of man. However, this type, with a Carabelli cusp on one of the upper molars, and much elongated third lower molars offers, as does *Hemanthropus peii* von K., smaller in size, found in the same deposits, and probably related to *Gigantopithecus,* a certain resemblance with the Australopithecinae, so much that it may be asked if the Gigantopithecinae should not be considered as an Asiatic equivalent of the South African Australopithecinae, classed among the "Praehomininae" rather than among the anthropoid apes.

The second species is still more interesting. This is *Ramapithecus brevirostris* Lewis, from the Pliocene of the Siwaliks of India. Even in the first publication (1934, p. 162), *Ramapithecus* was classed by its describer in the family of "Simiidae (*Hominidae?*)." The type specimen consists of a right maxilla and premaxilla, with an almost complete dentition, but without the third molar, the canine and the incisors. The alveoli of the molar and of the central incisor are present; the lateral incisor is broken.

"There are no diastemata in the dental series." This is not quite accurate; there is a small diastema of about 3 mm which was probably covered by the crown of the lateral incisor; since the specimen in question is considered to belong to a female, one may suppose that the diastema in the male was larger. "The cheek teeth of opposite sides of the jaw are more widely separated posteriorly than anteriorly, rather than approximately equidistant from M^2 to P^3." The dental arcade would have been "divergent" and only slightly different from that to be seen in *Pithecanthropus.* We may cite following remark from Hrdlicka (1935, p. 35), who is not favorable to Lewis's interpretation: "the canine, if the damage to its alveolus be discounted, was not small in relation to the jaw or the rest of the teeth, but of fair though not large proportions (mouth of alveolus $8.5 \times .6$ mm.) . . . *Ramapithecus brevirostris* was a moderate-sized anthropoid ape, the upper denture of which reached, at least in the individual under examination, a greater resemblance to the human than that of any other known fossil or living anthropoid ape."

We should add to this a few details regarding a lower jaw attributed to *Ramapithecus* cf. *brevirostris* described in 1937 by Gregory, Hellman, and Lewis. In this jaw may be seen the alveolus of a canine of medium size; an elongated premolar, almost bicuspid, not sectorial and with a well developed talonid, oriented in the axis of the mandible (and not obliquely as in the anthropoids); followed by a shorter second premolar, also possessing a well developed talonid. "The lower cheek teeth are worn transversely in a flat surface without projecting lingual cusps" (p. 21). The symphysis forms a flattened elipse with no simian shelf, and the low angle of inclination is little different from that to be seen in *Pithecanthropus* and *Meganthropus* (see Weidenreich, 1945, fig. 12g). The length of the first molar is 9.1 mm. Of all known fossil higher primates, this *Ramapithecus* is closest to the type representative of hominids in the Pliocene, as far as we are able to imagine it.

The study of the teeth of different "hominoids" leaves us with the impression that not only the anthropoids but also the hominids as well have evolved in several different directions, although only one of the latter has survived: the one which was destined to be transformed into *Homo sapiens.*

Morphological and Phylogenetic Problems of Taxonomy in Relation to Hominid Evolution

W. E. Le Gros Clark   1955

It is well recognized by comparative anatomists that there is a biological relationship between man and the anthropoid apes, in the sense that, by a process of gradual diversification, both have been derived in the distant past from a presumed common ancestral stock. When, in the early days of evolutionary studies, this inference was first made, it was based almost entirely on the totality of the anatomical resemblances between man and apes. Similar degrees of resemblance between other groups of mammals had been accepted as evidence of an evolutionary relationship; and in some cases this relationship had been further demonstrated and confirmed by the discovery of fossil remains of extinct creatures of intermediate type. But at the time of the publication of Darwin's book on the *Descent of Man* in 1871 the fossil record of human evolution was almost nonexistent, and the evidence for the relationship of man and apes—although it seemed convincing, even then, to many biologists—was only indirect. In more recent years, the fossil record bearing on human ancestry has accumulated to a remarkable extent. It is still meager in comparison with that of the evolution of some other mammalian groups, but it has provided much more direct and concrete evidence for the relationship of man and apes than was previously available. It is particularly noteworthy how closely some of these fossil types

FROM The Fossil Evidence for Human Evolution: An Introduction to the Study of Paleoanthropology, *Chapter I (pp. 1–47). Reprinted by permission of the author and of the University of Chicago Press. The author reviews certain principles in the interpretation of fossil hominids generally, based to a considerable extent on practical experience of recent years (compare the preceding article by Breitinger, 1959, which deals with principles deriving from evolutionary theory, and relating to the earliest hominids); particular attention is paid to fallacies and sources of error in interpretation. Sir Wilfrid Le Gros Clark is Dr. Lee's Professor of Anatomy in the University of Oxford.*

conform to intermediate stages of human evolution, which had been postulated and predicted on the basis of the indirect evidence of comparative anatomy. Discoveries of such fossil relics, indeed, provide a remarkable vindication of the well-established methods of comparative morphology which have been used for the assessment of systematic affinities and phylogenetic relationships. As Watson (1951) has noted, in arriving at a natural classification "individual animals . . . are allotted to their groups by structural similarities and differences, determined by observations directed by ordinary morphological reasoning. And the methods of morphology are shown to be valid because they enable us to make verifiable predictions." The progress of paleontological discovery has led to the verification of many of the predictions (based on the study of the comparative anatomy of Recent types) regarding the phylogenetic relationships and evolutionary origins of different groups of Primates. In this sense, indeed, paleontology might almost be called an experimental science, that is, if "experiment" is defined (as it is in the *Oxford Dictionary*) as "a procedure adopted for testing an hypothesis." Comparative anatomical studies of living forms may demonstrate a gradational series of morphological types, and such a series may suggest an actual temporal sequence of evolution. But the inference of a temporal sequence based on indirect evidence of this sort can be validated only by the direct evidence of paleontology.

1. COMPARATIVE ANATOMY AND TAXONOMY

Before considering the fossil evidence for the zoölogical relationship between man and ape, a brief reference may be made to the indirect evidence of anatomical resemblance. In spite of superficial appearances, these resemblances are actually very close. The bony skeleton, for example, is constructed on the same general plan; and in the case of some of its elements it may hardly be possible to make a clear distinction without a careful scrutiny of morphological details or the comparison of biometric data. It is precisely for this reason, of course, that quite sharp controversies in the past have occasionally been aroused over the identification of certain fossil fragments of a doubtful nature—whether they should be referred to ape or man. The muscular anatomy of man and apes is astonishingly alike, even down to some of the smaller details of attachments of many of the individual muscles. The similarity in the structure and disposition of the visceral organs suggests that apes have a closer relationship to man than they have to the lower Primates. The human brain (though larger in relation to body size) in its morphology is little more than a magnified model of the brain of an anthropoid ape; indeed, there is no known element of the brain in the former which is not also to be found developed to some degree in the latter. All these facts, together with observations recording similar metabolic processes, serological reactions, blood groups, and so forth, are well known. It is because of such a striking complex of resemblances that in schemes of zoölogical classification man and the anthropoid apes have for many years been placed quite close together, and in recent years the tendency has been for a still closer approximation.

Even the antievolutionary biologists of past days classified man in the Mammalia (they could hardly do otherwise), but they emphasized their conception of his apartness by placing him in a separate order, or even in a separate subclass, of mammals. More detailed and less subjective studies later placed him in the order Primates, according him a family status (Hominidae) which is equated with the Pongidae (anthropoid apes) and the Cercopithecidae (catarrhine monkeys). Today, the detailed morphological resemblances between man and the anthropoid apes are believed by many authorities to be more accurately expressed by grouping the Hominidae and Pongidae in a common superfamily, Hominoidea, and thus contrasting them both with the catarrhine monkeys— Cercopithecoidea (Simpson, 1945). The closer association in a zoölogical classification of man and apes is no doubt due partly to the stricter application of taxonomic criteria, particularly as the result of the work of those authorities who are specially qualified by practical experience to apply the principles of vertebrate taxonomy to the Primates. But it is also due to the discovery of the fossil remains of primitive hominids in which the morphological distinctions contrasting *Homo sapiens* with the Recent anthropoid apes are not nearly so obtrusive.

Notwithstanding the numerous anatomical resemblances between Recent man and Recent apes, there are, of course, quite pronounced differences, and in the past these have all been duly emphasized by one anatomist or another. In some cases they have certainly been over-emphasized, partly (it seems) because the human anatomist tends by the nature of his studies to focus attention on the minutiae of morphology and is thus inclined to exaggerate their taxonomic significance. Perhaps, also, the very personal nature of the problem has led some authorities to lay more stress on differences between man and apes than they would do on equivalent differences in other mammalian groups. The lists of morphological characters which from time to time are put forward as evidence of man's "uniqueness" among mammals often give the strong impression that the authors are straining the evidence to the utmost limit (and sometimes a considerable way beyond it) in order to substantiate their thesis. It does not always seem to be fully realized that some of the unique features of *H. sapiens* on which these authors lay stress are merely distinctions at a generic or specific level, or that they represent little more than an extension of morphological trends which are quite apparent in other Primates. Nor is adequate account taken of the fact that similar claims for uniqueness might be equally valid for many other mammalian species. The giraffe, for example, possesses a number of anatomical characters which establish it as "unique" among all other living mammals, but its taxonomic position in the Giraffidae (equated with related families of the same infra-order, Pecora, such as the Cervidae and Bovidae) is accepted as a reasonable interpretation of its evolutionary status. Anatomically, *H. sapiens* is unique among mammals only in the sense that every mammalian species is in some features unique among mammals.

It is instructive to consider a sample of those anatomical differences which have been claimed to be so exclusively distinctive of the Hominidae as to demand an unusual degree of taxonomic isolation, and to see how these equate with differences found among other mammals which are accepted as forming natural groups in the phylogenetic sense. In *Homo* the large size of the brain relative to the body weight is certainly a feature which distinguishes this genus from all the other Hominoidea, but it actually represents no more than an expression of the trend toward a progressive elaboration of the brain shown in the evolution of related Primates (and also of many other groups of eutherian mammals). In its morphological pattern, indeed, the human brain shows much less contrast with that of the large anthropoid apes than is found among the various families of an equivalent taxonomic category of Primates, the super-family Lemuroidea; and even in its absolute size it shows less contrast than is to be found between the primitive and advanced genera of the single family Equidae. Several patterns of articulation between the bones of the skull have been claimed as quite distinctive of the Hominidae, but they also occur as variants (in some instances quite commonly) in the skulls of apes. In any case, however, the differences in pattern of articulation which are claimed to distinguish the Hominidae from the Pongidae are no more pronounced than those which are found to occur between different groups of (say) the single family Cercopithecidae. The dentition of the Hominoidea, in spite of differences between the Hominidae and Pongidae such as those of the relative size and shape of the canines and first lower premolars, actually shows far closer similarities than are to be found in the several families of (for example) the Feloidea. The linear proportions of the limbs in *H. sapiens* show certain well-recognized differences from those of the Recent anthropoid apes, but again these differences are not more marked than they are in (say) the several families of the Muroidea. Even the form of the glans penis and the fact that the female is characterized by a permanent, well-developed "bosom" have been adduced as evidence of "man's" uniqueness among mammals. But these may be no more than specific characters of *H. sapiens* and not characteristic features of the Hominidae as a whole (for, of course, we have no idea at all what the penis and the female breast may have been like in extinct types of man such as *Pithecanthropus*). These examples (which could well be multiplied) appear to indicate that anatomists who have laid such stress on differences of this sort as emphasizing the morphological "uniqueness" of *H. sapiens* have perhaps introduced a personal and subjective element into their assessment of the taxonomic status of their own species.

2. MAN, *Homo sapiens,* AND THE HOMINIDAE

In order to eliminate the subjective factor as far as possible in discussions on hominid evolution, it seems quite essential to avoid colloquial terms such as "man" and "human." In recent controversies on the taxonomic position of fossil hominids, as so frequently in the past, their too common use has been a very obvious source of confusion. The fact is that these terms may not properly be used as though they were equivalent to the zoölogical terms *Homo* and Hominidae or to the adjectival form "hominid," in the same way that (for example) the term "horse" can be substituted for "equid." In the latter case, although the primitive equid *Hyracotherium* is so markedly different superficially from the modern *Equus*, it can be called a "primitive horse" without real danger of misunderstanding, for the term "horse" (or "horse family") still remains elastic enough in the minds of most people to permit its extension to relatively remote ancestral forms. Similarly, the fossil Hominoidea of Miocene age may appropriately be called "primitive anthropoid apes," even though they had not acquired all the specialized features which are accepted as characteristic of the anthropoid apes of today. But the terms "man" and "human" have come to assume, by common usage, a much narrower and more rigid connotation, which for most of us (however we may try to persuade ourselves otherwise) also involves a real emotional element. There can be little doubt that if these colloquial terms were to be rigidly excluded in strictly scientific discussions of the evolutionary origin of *H. sapiens,* and only the terms proper to taxonomy employed, such problems could be approached on a much more objective plane than often appears to be the case.[1]

[1] The confusion to which the loose use of the term "man" may give rise is well illustrated by those comparative studies in which the skeletal elements of a fossil hominoid are compared with only the Recent anthropoid apes and with only *H. sapiens* (or perhaps even with only one or two racial varieties of *H. sapiens*) and the conclusion is then drawn that in certain features the fossil agrees more closely

Homo sapiens is the terminal product, or one of the terminal products, of an evolutionary radiation which also led to the development of other types which have now become extinct, all of which are included in a natural group, the family Hominidae. If this familial term is to be used as it is in the definition of equivalent mammalian groups (i.e., with due reference to the fundamental concepts of evolution and to the taxonomic designation of other equivalent radiations), it must include not only *H. sapiens* but all those representatives of the evolutionary sequence which finally led to the development of this species (and of collateral lines) from the time when the sequence first became segregated from the evolutionary sequence of the Pongidae. Similarly, the family Pongidae logically includes not only the Recent anthropoid apes (gorilla, chimpanzee, orang, and gibbon) but also the fossil and extinct related types to which this particular line of evolutionary development gave rise after it had become clearly segregated from the common ancestral stock which also gave rise to the Cercopithecidae. It is of the utmost importance that those taking part in discussions on phylogenetic sequences and zoölogical classification should recognize the implications of these taxonomic terms and make proper use of them. So far as the Hominoidea are concerned, they are illustrated diagrammatically in Figure 1. From this diagram it will be seen that (as will be discussed in later chapters) three genera of the Hominidae are here provisionally recognized: *Homo*—represented by the two species *H. sapiens* and *H. neanderthalensis; Pithecanthropus*—an extinct type which is known to have existed in the Far East during Early and Middle Pleistocene times; and *Australopithecus*—a primitive hominid whose fossilized remains have recently been recovered in such quantity from travertine deposits in South Africa. It still remains uncertain whether *Pithecanthropus* and *Australopithecus* are represented by more than one species. The phylogenetic relationships of these genera to one another and to the anthropoid ape family (Pongidae) indicated in the diagram are to be regarded as provisional interpretations based on the fossil evidence so far available. But the main intention of the diagram here is to make it clear that the Hominidae include all those genera which represent the earlier and later developments of a single evolution-

---

with the "anthropoid apes" than with "man." The fallacy of such a statement is obvious, but it may nevertheless be very misleading to the casual reader. Clearly, the authors of such studies are using the term "man" as though it were equivalent to *H. sapiens,* or perhaps only one racial variety of *H. sapiens.* But the term "man" must presumably be taken also to include extinct types, such as Neanderthal man and the various representatives of the *Pithecanthropus* group (including "*Meganthropus*"). These should be taken into consideration and also, of course, the extinct types of anthropoid ape. The fallacy of extrapolating from single species or genera to larger taxonomic groups is not uncommon in the literature of paleoanthropology.

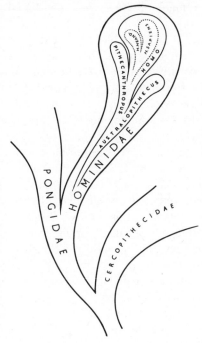

FIGURE 1. Diagram illustrating the probable phylogenetic relationships of the known genera of the Hominidae, and the relationship of the latter to the Pongidae. This diagram is also intended to emphasize that, as paleontological records in general clearly establish, representatives of an earlier genus may survive and persist long after other representatives of the *same* genus have given rise to a later genus. In other words, an ancestral genus may for some time actually be contemporary with its derivative genus.

ary radiation, the latter being distinguished from the other radiation of the Hominoidea—the Pongidae—by a clear divergence of evolutionary trends. Similarly, the genus *Homo, Pithecanthropus,* or *Australopithecus* includes those species which represent in each case a common line of evolutionary development diverging from other genera of the Hominidae. In other words, these terms are taken to connote a "vertical" classification of the Hominoidea, in the sense that they are indicative of separate main and subsidiary evolutionary sequences, ascending and diversifying from common basal stocks.[2] It is particularly urged that this simple and now generally accepted scheme of classification of the Hominoidea should be adhered to and that fancy terms invented from time to time by individual authors (such as Euhominids, Prehominids, Prehominians, Archanthropinae, Presapiens, and so forth) should be strenuously avoided. In so far as none of these terms has ever been properly defined, they remain en-

[2] It is to be observed that mammalian classifications are not entirely of the "vertical" type. Where the fossil evidence is still wanting and in some cases where it is a matter of greater taxonomic convenience, terminal products of different lines of phylogenetic development may be grouped together in a "horizontal" type of classification. For example, in the Primates the Old World monkeys and the New World monkeys are at present grouped in a common suborder, the Anthropoidea, although there is some evidence (still far from complete) that these two groups of monkeys had their evolutionary origin in different groups of Eocene prosimians.

tirely obscure, and, in so far as they remain obscure, their continued use is bound to lead to confusion.

One of the most important desiderata of a workable classification is that it should meet with a general (even if only provisional) adoption for common usage. Taxonomic systems usually involve a compromise of vertical and horizontal classifications, the former coming to predominate more and more as the fossil evidence of phylogenetic lines gradually accumulates; while this evidence remains incomplete, no two students of a particular mammalian groups are likely to agree on all points of their classification. But they can, and should, agree to use a common system even if they do not accept all its implications, provided that the system represents at least a reasonable approximation to probable phylogenetic relationships and that it is broadly conceived in its basic plan. In the present work we make use of Simpson's classification of the Primates (1945), not because it is the only possible classification, or on the assumption that it represents the last word on phylogenetic relationships (which no system of classification can do with the present paucity of the fossil record). We use it because (1) it is based on recognized authority and experience, (2) it has the merit of simplicity, (3) it appears to reflect reasonably closely such phylogenetic relationships as can be inferred from the evidence at hand (and as far as this can be done in any system of classification without seriously affecting convenience of reference), and (4) it has been provisionally accepted and recognized by other authoritative workers in the same field. It is well to emphasize this last consideration, for only by the provisional acceptance of a common scheme of classification (with common and well-understood taxonomic terms) is it possible for zoölogists or anthropologists to engage in mutual discussions on problems of Primate evolution without misunderstandings and misrepresentations.

One of the most remarkable sources of confusion in recent discussions on hominid evolution is the tacit assumption by some writers that a large brain is an essential character of the Hominidae; this example is referred to here because it serves to illustrate rather forcibly the misuse of taxonomic terms. Now it is, of course, obvious that one of the outstanding characteristics of *H. sapiens* is the relatively large size of the brain. But some of those anatomists who lay most stress on this distinction also maintain that the Hominidae (i.e., the family comprising the evolutionary radiation leading, *inter alia*, to *H. sapiens*) separated from the other radiations of the Primates at a very remote geological period—at least by the Early Miocene. On the other hand (as we shall later see), there is no evidence to show that the precursors of *H. sapiens* acquired a brain size approaching modern dimensions before the Early Pleistocene and certainly not before the Upper Pliocene. Consequently, there must presumably have been a very lengthy period in the hominid sequence of evolution during which the brain still retained a size approximating to that of the modern large apes. In other words, while a large brain may be accepted as one of the diagnostic characters of the species *H. sapiens* or the genus *Homo*, it is not a valid criterion of the family Hominidae. In a recent essay it has been suggested by Oakley (1951), following a well-reasoned argument, that the term "man" (and presumably "human" as well) should be reserved for those later representatives of the hominid sequence of evolution who had reached a level of intelligence indicated by their capacity to fabricate implements of some sort. Man, that is to say, is essentially a tool-making creature. If this definition is accepted, then the earlier small-brained representatives of the Hominidae who had not yet developed this capacity may conveniently be referred to "the prehuman phase of hominid evolution."

The assumption that a brain of large dimensions is a distinctive feature of the Hominidae as contrasted with the Pongidae is certainly in part the result of a terminological confusion resulting from the loose usage of the terms "man" and "human" as though they were equivalent to "hominid." But it has also been argued (again mainly on the basis of comparative anatomical studies of living forms) that the primary factor which led to the evolutionary divergence of the Hominidae from the Pongidae was the rapid enlargement of the brain and that other distinctive characters, such as those related to posture and gait, were secondary developments. However, apart from the fact that functional considerations make such a speculative hypothesis unlikely or, indeed, impossible, it is rendered untenable by the paleontological data now available.

It has been necessary to divaricate on the significance of the taxonomic terms used in discussions on hominid evolution, for the reason that much fruitless argument has evidently been expended for the want of careful definitions, and it may be well to re-emphasize briefly one or two of the major points discussed. The purpose of zoölogical classification, as Simpson has pointed out, is primarily a matter of practical convenience; but the basis of a taxonomic system is phylogenetic, and the criteria of the definition of taxonomic terms should, as far as is consistent with practical convenience, be consonant with the evidence of phylogeny. It is for this reason, of course, that zoölogical classifications must necessarily be provisional and tentative in the absence of a substantial paleontological record, and they need constant revision as this record becomes more and more complete. In the absence of any fossil remains, the family Equidae would presumably be defined (as Cuvier, indeed, defined his equivalent of this family) on the basis of the existing species of *Equus*—that is to say, by characters such as the single complete digit on each foot and the complicated pattern of the cheek teeth. But, with the accession of fossil material, the definition of Equidae has come to be widely extended to include such primitive representatives of the equid sequence of evolution as *Hyracotherium* and *Mesohippus*. In defining the Hominidae and contrasting this family with the Pongidae, considerations of phylogeny must also be taken into account. In other words, a satisfactory definition is to be obtained only by a consideration of the fundamental factors of structural evolution which determined the initial segregation of the Hominidae and the Pongidae from a common ancestral stock, and of the divergent trends which the two evolutionary sequences followed in their later development.[3] The former consideration is no doubt of more direct importance in the identification of fossil remains of early hominoids whose taxonomic status may not be immediately clear, for in such primitive types some of the later evolutionary trends will not yet have manifested themselves to any marked degree. Those anatomical features which probably have no more than a specific value for the definition of *H. sapiens* (such as the combination of a large brain with a vertical forehead, small teeth, reduced jaws, presence of a chin, and so forth) must obviously be avoided in the definition of the Hominidae.

3. THE EARLY DIFFERENTIATION OF THE HOMINIDAE AND PONGIDAE

As we have already noted, the expansion of the brain to the large dimensions characteristic of *H. sapiens* was evidently a relatively late

---

[3] While in any system of classification the lower taxonomic categories, such as genera and species, may be defined in more or less static terms (at least in so far as they concern divergent rather than successional types), it is impracticable to draw up any comprehensive definition of larger categories, such as families and orders, except on the basis of evolutionary trends. The latter may be inferred indirectly by a consideration of the various end-products of evolution in each group, but they can be ultimately demonstrated only by paleontological sequences. For example, the order Primates is particularly difficult to define by reference to fixed characters, mainly for the reason that, as a group, it is not distinguished by any gross forms of adaptive specialization possessed by all its members in common. The evolutionary progress of the Primates, as Simpson (1949) has well said, has been in the direction of greater adaptability rather than of greater adaptation. Thus the order can be defined only by reference to the prevailing evolutionary trends which have distinguished it from other groups—such as the progressive development of large and complicated brains, the elaboration of the visual apparatus and a corresponding reduction of the olfactory apparatus, the abbreviation of the facial skeleton, the tendency toward the elimination of the third incisor tooth and of one or two premolars, the preservation of a relatively simple pattern of the molar teeth, the replacement of sharp claws (falculae) by flattened nails (ungulae), the retention of pentadactyl limbs with an accentuation of the mobility of the digits, and so forth (Le Gros Clark, 1954). Not all Primates (even those that exist today) have developed all these characters or completed their development to the same degree. And still less so, of course, was this the case with the earliest Primates of the Eocene period.

phenomenon in the sequence of hominid evolution. What, then, are the basically distinctive characters whose development initiated the evolutionary radiation of the Hominidae in the first stages of its segregation from the Pongidae and which might therefore be expected to be of importance for the differentiation of the *earlier* representatives of these two families? From a consideration of the details of comparative anatomy of living forms and from the evidence now available from fossil hominoids, it appears reasonably certain (and, indeed, is agreed by authorities who hold widely differing views on the phylogenetic details) that the most important single factor in the evolutionary emergence of the Hominidae as a separate and independent line of development was related to the specialized functions of erect bipedal locomotion (Washburn, 1951a). Herein the Hominidae showed a most marked evolutionary divergence from the Pongidae, for in the latter the strongly contrasting brachiating mode of locomotion was developed. In the one case the lower limb increased in length in relation to the trunk length and to the length of the upper limb; in the other it was the upper limb that increased in relative length. In other words, in the relative growth of the limbs the Pongidae and the Hominidae have followed two opposing allometric trends. In the Hominidae the bony elements of the foot and the knee joint became modified in shape and proportions to permit the structural stability required for bipedal progression; in the Pongidae the mobility of these parts was enhanced for specialized prehensile functions. In the Hominidae the pelvic skeleton underwent quite far-reaching changes directly related to the erect posture; in the Pongidae it retained the general shape and proportions found in lower Primates generally. These divergent modifications of the limbs and pelvis are related to very different modes of life in the two families. They involve more than just those proportional differences in linear dimensions which can be determined by over-all measurements and about which so much detailed and accurate information has been accumulated by the patient studies of Schultz (1931, 1936, 1950b), for they are also accompanied by quite marked structural divergences in muscular anatomy (as Straus, 1949, has emphasized). The total morphological pattern of the limbs and pelvis in the known representatives of the Hominidae thus presents a criterion by which these are distinguished rather abruptly from the known representatives of the Pongidae. If, as now appears probable, this distinction was the factor responsible for the primary segregation of these two evolutionary radiations, it provides a most important clue for assessing the true taxonomic position of their early representatives.

Another criterion of special importance in paleontology is provided by the total morphological pattern of the dentition. In all the Recent

Pongidae the primitive features of the Primate dentition have been modified by the widening of the incisor series, the replacement of a converging molar-premolar series by parallel (or slightly divergent) tooth rows, the accentuation of powerful overlapping canines (with a pronounced sexual dimorphism), and the development of a more strongly sectorial[4] character of the anterior lower premolar. In all the known Hominidae the incisors remain small, the molar-premolar series converge in a rounded arcade, the canines have undergone a relative reduction in size and do not overlap to any marked degree (and not at all after the early stages of attrition, except in some individuals of the Pleistocene genus, *Pithecanthropus*), and the anterior lower premolar is of a bicuspid, nonsectorial form. These differences in the dentition may have been secondary to those of the limbs and pelvis, but the paleontological evidence indicates that they also become manifested relatively early in the evolutionary history of the two families.

4. TOTAL MORPHOLOGICAL PATTERN

Reference has been made earlier to the "total morphological pattern" presented by limb structure or the dentition. It seems desirable to stress this concept of pattern rather strongly because the assessment of the phylogenetic and taxonomic status of fossil hominoid remains must be based, not on the comparison of individual characters in isolation one by one, but on a consideration of the *total pattern* which they present in combination.[5] Undoubtedly, many of the conflicting opinions expressed in the past by comparative anatomists regarding the relationship of the Hominidae and other Primates have been the result of the separate comparison of *individual* characters. In fact, however, it is doubtful whether any single structural detail or measurement by itself can be accepted as providing a clear-cut distinction which would permit a positive identification of a single specimen of a fossil hominoid. For example, the mere presence of a measurable gap (diastema) between the upper canine and lateral incisor teeth is not by itself sufficient to determine that a frag-

[4] A sectorial type of lower premolar, which is characteristic of all known anthropoid apes, is a predominantly unicuspid tooth, the main cusp having anteriorly a cutting edge which shears against the upper canine.

[5] Vertebrate taxonomists are, of course, well accustomed to taking account of groups of characters in their assessment of the zoölogical status of an animal, and they are quite conversant with the phrase "character complex." But anthropologists and human anatomists (perhaps from lack of experience in the practice and principles of taxonomy) often tend to focus their attention rather on single characters in their discussion of relationships; or, if they take into account a list of several characters, they tend to treat them as an assemblage of separate individual units, without recognizing that in combination they constitute a pattern which must be treated as a whole. It is in order to emphasize this most important principle that the term "pattern" is put forward as somewhat equivalent to (but actually meaning more than) the term "complex."

ment of a fossil hominoid jaw is identifiable as that of an anthropoid ape rather than a hominid (though a diastema is very rarely absent in the completely erupted dentition of anthropoid apes and is very rarely found in a hominid jaw). But if a well-marked diastema forms one element of a complicated morphological pattern which also includes conical, projecting, and overlapping canine teeth, a laterally compressed lower first premolar tooth of sectorial form, forwardly placed incisors, and so forth, it becomes an important feature in the taxonomic identification of a fossil specimen, for such a pattern is diagnostic of the Pongidae in contradistinction to the Hominidae. Or, to take another example, the mere presence in one specimen of a primitive type of skull of a "mastoid process," considered simply and solely as a bony eminence, does not by itself identify it as hominid rather than pongid, for a mastoid process *of a sort* may occasionally be found in the skulls of mature gorillas (as Schultz, 1950a), has noted). But if a mastoid process of typical hominid shape, disposition, and proportions is found *consistently* in a number of skulls in a common collection of fossil hominoids (immature as well as mature) and if it also forms a component part of a total morphological pattern of associated parts normally found in hominid, but never in pongid, skulls (including a clear-cut digastric fossa and a well-marked occipital groove, and a characteristic relationship to the nuchal area of the occipital bone and to a tympanic plate of a particular conformation), its significance for taxonomic purposes evidently becomes enormously enhanced. Many similar examples could be adduced (and some will later be noted) of a coincidence of total morphological pattern which has been overlooked or obscured by treating in isolation only one or two features of the pattern and assuming that these are by themselves adequate for the assessment of taxonomic affinities.

5. CONVERGENT AND PARALLEL EVOLUTION

It is a fundamental principle of taxonomy that a closeness of resemblance in total morphological pattern is an indication of a corresponding closeness in zoölogical relationship. On the other hand, it is also generally recognized that structural resemblances of a sort can be produced by convergent and parallel evolution, and in this case they are not of equal value in the assessment of relationships. Taxonomists are well aware of these complications and of the need to take account of them. But the potentialities of convergence and parallelism have been much overestimated by some comparative anatomists, who have sought to discount the structural resemblances between *H. sapiens* and the anthropoid apes by attributing most (if not all) of them to these processes. That some degree of convergent and parallel evolution has occurred in the Hominidae and Pongidae is not in doubt; but to attribute all those similarities

which form component elements of a highly complicated total morphological pattern to long-standing convergence or parallelism reduces the
morphological principles underlying taxonomy to an absurdity. By the
skilful manipulation of such extreme misapplications of well-known evolutionary processes (and, incidentally, taking no account of the statistical
improbabilities at once made evident by a consideration of the principles
of genetics), it is possible for any one to draw those conclusions regarding systematic affinities which conform most with his personal predilec-
tions. There is no need here to enlarge on this matter of convergence and
parallelism in relation to taxonomy (or on the misconceptions which
some authorities have held on the degree to which evolution is irreversible), for such questions have recently been dealt with in a thoroughly
reasonable manner by paleontologists well qualified to do so by long
experience and recognized distinction. But it is worth while quoting
Simpson (1951a) that "the basis of parallelism is initial similarity of
structure and adaptive type, with subsequent recurrent homologous
mutation"; that the initial similarity and the homology of mutations
themselves imply phylogenetic relationship; that "closeness of parallelism
tends to be proportional to closeness of affinity"; and that "it is improbable that convergence ever produces literal identity in structure and
certainly no such case has ever been demonstrated." The extensive data
of comparative anatomy and vertebrate paleontology now available justify the assumption (at any rate as a reasonably secure working hypothesis) that species and genera which show a preponderance of structural
resemblances are genetically related forms, unless some flagrant discrepancy exists in one or more features such as could be explained morphologically only by a long period of independent evolution from an
ancestral form of a much more primitive type (and not, as may, of
course, occur, by mutational variations of a geologically more recent
date). It may not always be possible to exclude finally the factor of convergence as an explanation of a similarity in individual structural features; but it is not permissible to dismiss a complicated pattern of
morphological resemblances as merely the expression of convergence,
without presenting evidence in support of such an arbitrary "explanation."
As Colbert (1949) has pointed out, "parallelism should not be invoked
to explain resemblances among related animals unless it can be proved,
for to do this is to make the whole concept of evolution largely meaningless."

6. THE MULTIPLICATION OF GENERA AND SPECIES

Among the more vexing taxonomic problems of Primate paleontology
is the somewhat arbitrary multiplication of genera and species on the
basis of skeletal remains which in some cases are very fragmentary. This,

of course, is also a problem of vertebrate paleontology in general. Skeletal elements by themselves do not always reflect to the same degree those differences which are apparent enough in the living animal to warrant distinction at a specific, or even a generic, level. For example, in the Recent Cercopithecoidea the comparative odontologist might not always find it easy to justify—on the basis of the dentition alone—some of the specific distinctions which are clearly justified by a study of the animals as a whole. On the other hand, these very examples may lead him to attribute an exaggerated importance to trivial details of the dentition in *other* groups of Primates in which they may be no more than an expression of individual (or subspecific) variation. Particularly is this the case with the study of fossil remains of the Hominoidea; for the individual, sexual, and subspecific variations in this group of Primates are rather considerable. There is thus an almost inevitable (and perhaps, therefore, excusable) tendency among Primate paleontologists too readily to multiply species or genera among the fossil remains which they study, if these are only few and fragmentary, for the obvious reason that the extent of the individual and group variability can hardly be assessed until a much more complete record becomes available. But this initial tendency toward "splitting," provided that it is recognized, is perhaps not of great importance; and it is often a matter of convenience to accept provisionally and temporarily the generic and specific differentiations which have been made by a paleontologist in the first instance, even though there may be some doubt about their taxonomic validity. Later on, as more fossil material becomes available or as the result of a more detailed comparative analysis of the relevant structural details, the initial taxonomic distinctions may need to be revised. The genus *Sinanthropus* ("Pekin man") was at first based on a single tooth, and the name was retained and employed for many years, even by those who felt dubious about its validity. With further discoveries in China and Java, it became clear that *Sinanthropus* was really not distinguishable generically from *Pithecanthropus* ("Java man"), and it is now included in this genus of early hominids. The Chinese representative of the genus is usually still distinguished specifically from the Javanese representative (*Pithecanthropus erectus*) as *P. pekinensis*, though even this distinction may eventually prove to be unwarranted. But it is a distinction which is convenient to retain, pending the accession of further material which may allow a more complete study of the limits of variance in the two groups. Another example illustrating the difficulties of taxonomy in the study of fossil remains is furnished by the discovery of *Australopithecus* in South Africa. The first skull to be found was described by Dart (1925), who created for it the species *Australopithecus africanus*. Subsequently, Broom found many more remains of individuals belonging to the same group and

thought that he was able to distinguish other genera and species—
Plesianthropus transvaalensis (found at Sterkfontein), *Paranthropus robustus* (found at Kromdraai), *Paranthropus crassidens*, and *Telanthropus capensis* (both found at Swartkrans). Lastly, Dart (1948a) described yet another specimen from Makapansgat under the name of *A. prometheus*. It is probably true to say that most authorities would agree that a convincing case has not yet been made out for separating these fossils generically; but, as already noted, it may be a matter of convenience in preliminary discussions to refer to these provisional taxonomic terms, though, of course, this does not commit those who do so to their final acceptance. On the other hand, where there is a large element of doubt, the wisest procedure (pro tem) is to use place-names referring to the site of discovery and to speak (for example) of the "Sterkfontein skull," of the "Kromdraai mandible," or of the "Swartkrans pelvis."

It is a matter of great difficulty to formulate precisely the criteria by reference to which specific or generic distinctions are recognized in fossil material. Particularly is this so when the material is scanty and it is not possible to determine the limits of individual, sexual, and age variability. In such cases the paleontologist can only proceed on the assumption that these limits are of much the same order as in closely related groups where they are reasonably well known. For this purpose a sound knowledge of such related groups (as well as a considerable taxonomic experience) is obviously a prerequisite, for different skeletal and dental characters show different degrees of variation in different groups.[6] Thus even considerable variation in the size of the molar teeth and jaws or in the cranial capacity in a group of fossil hominids should not delude the paleontologist into making specific distinctions on the basis of such characters alone, for the latter are known to show a very wide range of variation in the single species *H. sapiens*. On the other hand, similar degrees of variation found among the fossil remains of certain lower Primates may justify a specific distinction in so far as the same characters are known to be less variable in these types. On the basis of such analogies, it is legitimate to make specific or generic distinctions as a provisional taxonomic device (even when the fossil material is scanty); but the validity of these distinctions

[6] It may be suggested that paleoanthropologists, by an international convention, should agree to refrain from creating any new species or genus on the basis of a fossil specimen unless it can be demonstrated with reasonable assurance that the skeletal and dental characters of the specimen deviate from those already known to an extent at least equivalent to the differences between recognized species or genera in Recent representatives of the same or allied groups. It should also be agreed that no new species or genus be created without a formal diagnosis (for it is only by reference to formal diagnoses that taxonomic determinations of similar material can be made by other workers and that the latter can judge whether a new species or genus is "true" or not).

can, of course, be finally determined only when sufficiently abundant material is available for comparative study.

It seems sometimes to be assumed (in referring to fossil specimens) that specific or generic distinctions are disallowed if intergradations between these taxonomic categories are demonstrable. However, such a criterion is clearly not applicable to a temporal sequence (nor, indeed, is it always so in a contemporary series of geographically or ecologically segregated groups). If a complete fossil record of the Hominidae were available, there would presumably be complete intergradations from the earliest to the latest representatives of this evolutionary sequence. This would not eliminate the need to make taxonomic distinctions in order to give expression to the various subsidiary radiations of the sequence, though naturally the distinctions become less and less obvious as the paleontological record leads back to the *initial* stages of evolutionary segregation of each radiation. Intergeneric gradations in a temporal sequence are well exemplified in the Equidae, for Simpson (1951b) remarks, in reference to *Hipparion* and related forms, that the difference from the ancestral type *Merychippus* "is clear-cut and, indeed, obvious when the most characteristic forms are compared, but the change was gradual and even an expert is puzzled as to where to draw the line in the continuous series from advanced *Merychippus* to primitive *Hipparion, Neohipparion,* or *Nannippus.*" On the other hand, the discovery of intergradations in the fossil record may be of some importance, in so far as they facilitate (or confirm) natural groupings in the major taxonomic categories, such as families, suborders, and orders, for they may betray systematic affinities which are not always fully apparent when the terminal products of phylogenetic lines are alone considered. For example, in the classification of the Primates a comparison of the living tarsier with the existing lemurs suggests a contrast so pronounced as to justify a subordinal distinction between tarsioids and lemuroids. But a study of prosimians of Eocene date has demonstrated that, in their dentition and skull, these early Primates may present such a mixture of characters as to suggest that tarsioids and lemuroids have originated (independently of other groups of Primates) from a common ancestral stock. This inference finds expression in the inclusion in Simpson's classification of tarsioids and lemuroids in the same suborder, Prosimii; but their early evolutionary segregation is at the same time reflected in their taxonomic separation into different infra-orders. So far as the Hominoidea are concerned, the taxonomic association of the Hominidae and the Pongidae in a common superfamily, Hominoidea, depends partly (as already noted) on the discovery of fossil remains showing what appears to be a considerable degree of structural intergradation between the two families.

7. THE QUANTITATIVE ASSESSMENT OF TAXONOMIC RELATIONSHIPS

Apart from the problem of assessing general taxonomic relationships by reference to morphological resemblances so far as these may be determined by direct comparisons, attempts have from time to time been made to estimate degrees of resemblance (and thus, it is assumed, degrees of affinity) on a quantitative basis. This biometrical approach is an attempt to facilitate and place on a strictly objective basis the comparison of one type with another. But unfortunately it is fraught with the greatest difficulties, the main one of which, no doubt, is the impossibility by known methods of weighting each individual character according to its taxonomic relevance. If the measurements of every single morphological character of skull, dentition, and limb bones were of equal value for the assessment of zoölogical affinities, it might be practicable to assess the latter in strictly quantitative terms. But it is very well recognized that this is by no means the case. It is well known also that the products of convergent evolution may lead to similarities (particularly in general over-all measurements and indices derived therefrom) which, if expressed quantitatively, would give an entirely false idea of systematic proximity. Generally speaking, it is true to say that statistical comparisons of over-all measurements and indices are of the greatest value in assessing degrees of affinity in forms already known to be quite closely related— e.g., subspecies or geographical races—but they become of less and less practical value as the relationship becomes more remote and the types to be compared become more disparate. This was made clearly evident in the pioneer studies of Pearson and Bell (1919) on the femur of the Primates. For while their comparisons of the dimensions and indices of the femur in Recent man (*H. sapiens*) and his Paleolithic precursors (e.g., *H. neanderthalensis* and *Pithecanthropus*) clearly provide data of considerable value for assessing their relative affinities, the phylogenetic interpretations which they give to their comparisons with lower Primates not only are very meager and tentative in relation to the vast amount of work which their analysis has entailed but are not always in accord with the paleontological evidence which has since become available.[7]

[7] But this is not to depreciate the importance of the studies of Pearson and Bell. If there are faults in their work, they are the faults of pioneers applying their technique to a field with which they were not thoroughly conversant, and, of course, their statistical methods have now in some cases been superseded by more reliable techniques. They specifically stated that their studies were to be regarded as experimental—to see how much could be ascertained (in regard to systematic affinities) by the intensive biometrical study of single bones. It will probably be agreed that the results of this experiment, relying on only a few indices based on over-all measurements and not taking into full account such factors as body size, were largely negative. But it will also be agreed that it was an experiment well worth trying.

Since the original studies of Pearson and his colleagues, the application of biometrics to taxonomic inquiries has become commonplace. But, because statistical methods are sometimes applied uncritically and without due appreciation of the morphological and phylogenetic basis of taxonomy or of the fundamentals of the phenomena underlying the data to be measured, they have been open to criticism and are in serious danger of becoming discredited. For this reason it seems worth while drawing attention to a number of fallacies which are often overlooked by workers in this field, particularly by anthropologists who are not morphologists by training or who are not statistical experts. They are listed here, not in any spirit of criticism, but in the earnest hope that, by their careful avoidance in the future, some common sources of confusion may be avoided in discussions on the evolutionary origin of man.

The Fallacy of Relying on Inadequate Statistical Data

One of the limitations of the biometric analysis of taxonomic characters depends on the fact that, if adequate statistical methods are employed, the analysis of even a few measurements entails a very considerable amount of work. Consequently, there is a danger of relying on too few measurements, a danger which is, of course, very seriously increased if these happen to have little taxonomic relevance. The comparison of such measurements may lead to the statement that (say) a fossil bone or tooth shows no significant difference from that of *H. sapiens*, or perhaps from that of the Recent anthropoid apes. But, clearly, such a statement is of doubtful value (and may actually be very misleading) if at the same time account is not taken of other morphological features which may, in fact, be much more relevant for assessing affinities. An example of this difficulty is provided by the famous case of *Hesperopithecus*. This generic name was given to a fossil tooth found in Nebraska in 1922, on the assumption that it represented an extinct type of anthropoid ape. Part of the evidence for this assumption was based on a comparison of the overall measurements of the tooth with a series of ape teeth, for these metrical data established clearly that in this respect the fossil tooth falls within the range of variation shown in Recent apes (Gregory and Hellman, (1923). However, it was the critical eye of a comparative anatomist, with a long experience of the examination and discrimination of paleontological material, which drew attention to certain "nonmetrical" morphological details throwing serious doubt on the original interpretation. As is well known, the tooth proved later to be that of a fossil peccary. This example, which has a certain historical interest in the field of Primate paleontology, is quoted here not in criticism of those who were responsible for the mistaken identification (there can be few paleontologists who have not erred in this way at some time or another!), but to emphasize that two or three over-all measurements of a tooth can express only an insignificant proportion of all those metrical elements which contribute to its shape as a whole. This applies also, of course, to skulls or individual bones.

The Fallacy of Treating all Metrical Data as of Equal Taxonomic Value

It has already been emphasized that morphological characters vary greatly in their significance for the assessment of affinities. Consequently, it is of the utmost importance that, in applying statistical methods, particular attention should be given to those characters whose taxonomic relevance has been duly established by comparative anatomical and paleontological studies. This *principle of taxonomic relevance* in the selection of characters for biometrical comparisons is one of great importance, but it is also rather liable to be overlooked. It may be asked how the distinction is to be made between morphological characters which are relevant or irrelevant for taxonomic purposes. The answer to this question is that each natural group of animals is defined (on the basis of data mainly derived from comparative anatomy and paleontology) by a certain pattern of morphological characters which its members possess in common and which have been found by the pragmatic test of experience to be sufficiently distinctive and consistent to distinguish its members from those of other related groups. The possession of this common morphological pattern is taken to indicate a community of origin (in the evolutionary sense) of all the members of the group, an assumption of which the justification is to be found in the history of paleontological discovery. But, as a sort of fluctuating background to the common morphological pattern, there may be a number of characters, sometimes obviously adaptive, which not only vary widely within the group but overlap with similar variations in other groups. Such fluctuating characters may be of importance for distinguishing (say) one species from another within the limits of the family, but they may be of no value by themselves for distinguishing this family from related families. In other words, they are taxonomically irrelevant so far as interfamilial relationships are concerned. The same applies to other major taxonomic categories such as superfamilies, subfamilies, and so forth. For example, among the lemurs the over-all dimensions (length and breadth) of the molar teeth may provide useful criteria for distinguishing between the various species and subspecies of the Galaginae or between those of the Lorisinae, but they could not be expected to be of any value in differentiating between these two subfamilies.

So far as the Hominidae are concerned, the principle of taxonomic relevance may be illustrated by reference to the extinct genus *Pithecanthropus*. The available evidence indicates that in this type the morphological features of the skull and jaws are very different from those of *H. sapiens*, while the limb skeleton is hardly distinguishable. Clearly, therefore, if the question arises as to whether the remains of a fossil hominid are those of *Pithecanthropus* or *H. sapiens*, for taxonomic purposes the morphological features of the skull and jaws are the relevant characters to which attention should be primarily directed. In the study of fossils representing early phases in evolutionary radiations, their affinities must be determined by a study of those characters whose taxonomic relevance may be inferred from a consideration of the main trends of evolution and demonstrated by comparative anatomical studies and by extrapolation from the fossil record, so far as the latter is available. For example, as we have already seen, the initial evolutionary segregation of the Hominidae from the Pongidae was almost certainly dependent on modifications related to the development of an erect bipedal gait (see Washburn, 1951a, on this point). Hence, in assessing the affinities of the *earlier* representatives of the Hominidae (whose taxonomic position may be in some doubt), the skeletal characters of the pelvis and hind limb are likely to be of much greater importance than those of the forelimb. As we shall see later, also, the morphological details of the dentition are likely to be of much greater taxonomic relevance than the actual over-all dimensions of the teeth and jaws or the cranial capacity. As a further example of the principle of taxonomic relevance, we may refer to the dentition of some of the fossil representatives of the Pongidae. In these the incisor teeth are so similar to those of *Homo* (and even *H. sapiens*) as hardly to be distinguishable. On the other hand, in all known pongids the canine teeth are quite different. Obviously, therefore, in determining as between the pongid or hominid affinities of a fossil hominoid, the canines have a much higher degree of taxonomic relevance than the incisors.

It perhaps needs to be emphasized that the principle of taxonomic relevance must also, of course, be taken into account in any attempt to assess the affinities of a fossil type from the biometrical study of a single skeletal element. For not all the dimensions or indices of such a specimen will have the same taxonomic relevance, and some may have none at all for the particular comparison under consideration. The pelvic bone of the fossil Australopithecinae from South Africa provides a good example of this point, and it also illustrates the essential importance of distinguishing between those morphological characters which may be similar in two divergent evolutionary groups simply because they are inherited from a common ancestry and those characters which represent adaptive modifications peculiar to, and are thus distinctive and diagnostic of, either one or the other of the two groups. The former type of character is obviously not taxonomically relevant for distinguishing the two groups (at least in the earlier stages of their evolutionary development); the latter type evidently has a high degree of taxonomic relevance. The australopithecine pelvic bone presents a most interesting combination of characters. Some of these are quite distinctive of the hominid (as opposed to the pongid) line of evolution, such as the width-height ratio of the ilium, the development of a strong anterior inferior iliac spine, the orientation of the sacral articulation, the formation of a deep sciatic notch, and so forth; and together they comprise a morphological pattern which is evidently an adaptation to the mechanical requirements of an erect posture. On the other hand, there appear to be no characters which are definitely distinctive of the pongid (as opposed to the hominid) line of evolution. It is true that in certain features the pelvic bone is rather more primitive than that of modern man, and in these particular features it does show some degree of resemblance to that of the modern anthropoid apes. But such a resemblance is clearly due to the retention of primitive features derived from a common hominoid ancestry and is thus not indicative of any real affinity with the modern anthropoid apes; this is made quite clear by the fact (as we have just noted) that, in those features in which the australopithecine pelvis *has* undergone modification away from the primitive ancestral type, the modification has followed the direction of hominid evolution and not of pongid evolution. It is these latter (positive) features, therefore, which are relevant for determining the taxonomic status of the Australopithecinae so far as the pelvic bone is concerned.

In order to keep within reasonable limits the number of measurements to be used for the statistical comparison of a fossil bone or tooth with related types, the rational procedure is first to make direct visual observations, selecting for comparison just those features which are known to have taxonomic value for the problem in hand. In many cases differences or resemblances may be so obtrusive as to obviate the need for statistical methods altogether. On the other hand, if differences and resemblances are not immediately apparent on visual inspection, special *ad hoc* measurements and indices may then be devised in order to test those characters which can reasonably be expected to be of value in the assessment of systematic affinities in any particular case. Only negative results are to be anticipated if routine measurements of little or no taxonomic value are employed.

The Fallacy of Treating Characters Separately and Independently, Instead of in Combination

This fallacy has recently been treated in some detail by Bronowski and Long (1951, 1952). They point out that a bone or a tooth is a unit and not a discrete assembly of independent measurements and that to consider their measurements singly is likely to be both inconclusive and misleading. The right statistical method, they emphasize, must treat the set of variates as a single coherent matrix. This can be done by the technique of multivariate analysis, which is essentially a method (not possible with more elementary techniques) that can be used for comparing morphological *patterns*. In principle, the application of the technique is straightforward enough, but it requires care and discrimination, a sound knowledge of morphology, and also a considerable experience of statistical methods. A number of measurements or indices of a bone or tooth are selected, which are judged on morphological grounds to be taxonomically significant; and from these the averages, variances, and correlations for a number of specimens are calculated. It is then possible to construct a numerical picture of the size and shape of the bone or tooth (and of the extent to which they vary), and to express this as a discriminant function. Such functions may be used for deciding whether (say) a fossil hominoid tooth is more likely to belong to a pongid or a hominid type, provided, of course, that the particular discriminant functions already calculated for the two families are sufficiently distinct. Bronowski and Long have emphasized the value of multivariate analysis by applying it to a controversial issue which had arisen in regard to certain teeth of the South African fossil genus *Australopithecus*, and they were able to resolve the controversy by demonstrating very positively their hominid character.

The Fallacy of Inadequate or Inaccurate Statistical Treatment

This fallacy has been dealt with in part in the preceding section. The possibility of inaccuracies of computation is one which needs to be borne in mind, for cases have occurred in which such errors have led to rather serious misstatements and misunderstanding. The amateur statistician needs to check and recheck his calculations so that there can be no possible doubt about the accuracy of his final figures. One of the disadvantages of scientific papers which incorporate elaborate statistical analyses is that, since only the end-results of the calculations are usually published, the latter cannot be checked by the reader. It is not a little disconcerting to contemplate the possibility that simple errors of calculation have occasionally occurred in the biometrical work of the nonprofessional statistician, leading to results the falsity of which may not become apparent for some time.

The Principle of Morphological Equivalence in Making Statistical Comparisons

Failure to understand this principle is perhaps one of the most serious sources of fallacy likely to affect statistical studies by those who are not thoroughly acquainted with the morphology of the skeletal elements with which they are dealing. A simple (but rather crude) example may be offered by referring to a measurement often employed in craniology —the auricular height. This is commonly taken by measuring the maximum height of the skull (in the Frankfurt plane)[8] from the auditory aperture; and in comparing different racial groups of *H. sapiens* it gives an index of the height of the brain case at this particular level. But, in comparing *H. sapiens* with (say) the gorilla, it would clearly be misleading to employ the same technique, for in male gorillas the height of the skull is often considerably extended by the development of a powerful sagittal crest. If such a comparison were made, it would be a comparison of the height of the brain case in *H. sapiens* with the height of the brain case *plus* a sagittal crest in the gorilla and would have no meaning from the morphological viewpoint. This is, of course, an extreme example, but it is perhaps not fully realized that similar (if less obvious) fallacies may be incurred in other craniometric work in which over-all measurements of the skull are commonly equated with one another. In comparing skulls of closely related groups, such measurements may be sufficiently equivalent morphologically to make direct metrical comparisons valid. But if they are used to compare, say, a modern European skull with the skull of the fossil genus *Pithecanthropus*, quite serious difficulties are involved. For example, in the European the glabello-maximal length is an approximate measurement of the maximal length of the brain case. But in the *Pithecanthropus* skull it measures a good deal more, for the glabello-maximal length is complicated by the exaggerated development of a massive supra-orbital torus, the great thickness of the skull, and the projection backward of an exaggerated occipital torus. The over-all glabello-maximal measurement is thus not strictly comparable (in the

[8] The Frankfurt plane, and also some of the anatomical landmarks of the skull to which reference is made in the text, are illustrated in Figure 2.

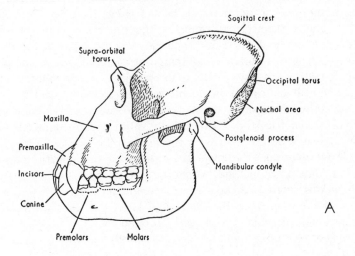

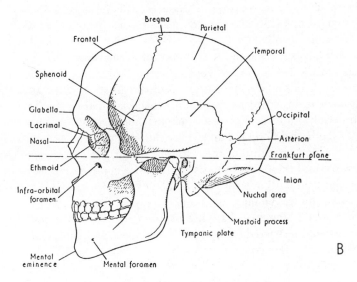

FIGURE 2. The skull of a male gorilla (A) and of modern *Homo sapiens* (B) seen from the side, to illustrate some of the anatomical landmarks to which reference is made in the text.

morphological sense) with that of a European skull—in both cases it involves a number of different elements which may be independently variable among themselves. Again, in the European skull the maximal width is commonly situated in the parietal region, while in the *Pithecanthropus* skull it is situated in the temporal region. Thus to compare the maximal width in the two skulls is to compare measurements which are also not morphologically equivalent. In fairness to physical anthropologists generally, it must be stated that these sources of fallacy in comparative osteometric studies are usually quite well recognized, but this may not always be the case with the less careful workers. As a further example we may take the lower front premolar tooth in the Hominidae and Pongidae. One method which has been used for measuring the length of this tooth is to take the maximal anteroposterior diameter in the axis of the tooth row. But, as is well known, in the anthropoid apes the front lower premolar is commonly rotated on its vertical axis, so that the axis corresponding morphologically to the transverse axis of the hominid premolar is directed obliquely posteromedially. Thus, to compare the maximal anteroposterior diameters in the axis of the tooth row in the two groups is to compare dimensions of the premolar itself which again are not morphologically comparable. What is actually being compared in this case is the maximal anteroposterior *space* occupied by the premolar in the tooth row—a very different thing. In comparing over-all measurements of skeletal elements, it is of the greatest importance that the morphological basis of the dimensions to be compared should be stated very precisely indeed.[9] For the amateur biometrician, when comparing bones or teeth of different shapes, may fall into the trap of comparing dimensions which (because of the different shape) are not morphologically comparable and then, on the basis of this false comparison, may conclude that because these dimensions are similar the bones or teeth are actually of the *same* shape. We may reiterate here (what has already been pointed out) that, while biometrical studies of immediately related forms belonging to the same restricted group (such as a species or subspecies) may be expected to give fair comparisons which approximate sufficiently closely in their morphological equivalence, the statistical comparison of different

---

[9] It may be argued that the fallacy of morphological nonequivalence must almost necessarily be involved in any over-all measurement of a skeletal structure, since such a measurement is bound to include a number of different components which may vary independently. For example, two skulls may show the same thickness of cranial wall, but the latter may actually be composed of different proportions of the outer table, inner table, and diploë. This, of course, is perfectly true, but it only serves to emphasize still more strongly the need for care in stating the morphological fundamentals of the biometric data employed.

genera which show a greater disparity of form needs to be carried out with a very critical appreciation of the technical difficulties involved.[10]

The Fallacy of Comparing Skeletal Elements in Individuals of Different Age, Sex, and Size

This is a fallacy which is perhaps hardly likely to occur in the hands of careful workers—and yet it does occur from time to time. It is well recognized that age changes may lead to quite considerable modifications in the structural details and proportions of skeletal elements. In the skull, for example, they are so marked that it would clearly be fallacious to compare a few measurements of the adult skull of a primitive hominid with those of juvenile skulls of an anthropoid ape and to infer from such a comparison that the former is not markedly different from anthropoid apes in general. In regard to sex differences, again, it would obviously be misleading to compare the dimensions of the canine teeth in fossil hominoids of presumably male sex with the relatively small teeth of a female gorilla and to conclude therefrom that, in these particular dimensions, the fossil teeth fall within the range of variation of those of Recent apes. The sex variation needs to be taken into account in such a case, as it does also in comparisons of morphological and metrical features of the skull and skeleton in general.

The factor of body size in statistical comparisons is perhaps of even greater importance, for the reason that it has been overlooked much more frequently by physical anthropologists. Differences of proportions in the skull and skeleton in Primates of different size may be merely an expression of allometric growth, or they may be related to the mechanical requirements dependent on differences in body weight. In either case, of course, they may be of very little taxonomic importance (except perhaps in the determination of specific or subspecific distinctions). Thus in quadrupedal mammals the relative thickness of the leg bones is a function of the absolute size of the animal, for the strength of a bone as a supporting structure varies as its cross-sectional area (i.e., as the square of the linear dimensions of the animal), while the weight of the animal varies as the volume (i.e., as the cube of the linear dimensions). In heavier mammals, therefore, the leg bones are relatively thick, and their actual shape may thus be markedly different from those of lightly built (but still quite closely related) types. Clearly, then, it may be very misleading to compare the "robusticity index" of (say) the femur in Primates of very

[10] The fallacies which may arise from the comparison of over-all measurements in types which are not closely related have previously been emphasized by Washburn (1942b).

different body size (e.g., hominids, apes, and monkeys) and then assume degrees of affinity or divergence without any reference at all to the body-size factor. The differences in shape of bones may be even more accentuated by the fact that in larger animals the muscular ridges, tuberosities, and so forth are much more powerfully developed. Nor does this difficulty apply only to limb bones. In the skull it is well known that in closely related animals account must be taken of the factor of allometry in comparing relative size of brain case and relative size of jaws; and variations in the proportion and indices of these structures may again be reflected in differences depending on the degree of development of muscular ridges or of bony features which have developed in response to mechanical stresses. Thus, for example, it would be futile to compare cranial indices of a gorilla with those of a small monkey, with any idea of drawing taxonomic conclusions, unless factors of body size are first taken into account. For the same reason (though at first sight the case is a less obvious one) it would be misleading to make a direct comparison of cranial indices in the small and delicately built skull of a pygmy chimpanzee with those of a large and massive skull of a fossil *Australopithecus*. And even in comparisons of modern human skulls of a single homogeneous series, account needs to be taken of absolute size, for it is well established by biometrical studies that there is a significant correlation between form (as expressed in cranial indices) and absolute size.

It can hardly be overemphasized that in comparing dimensions and indices of skull, limb bones, pelvis, or other skeletal elements of Primates generally, taxonomic conclusions must first be preceded by an inquiry into all the complicating factors related to body size, an inquiry which may need elaborate statistical studies and which most certainly requires an intimate knowledge of the structural responses of skeletal elements to functional demands.

The Fallacy of Comparing Measurements Taken by Different Observers Using Different Techniques

The dangers of this fallacy have been emphasized again and again by biometricians, and the only excuse for mentioning it here is that it is still overlooked by some writers. If it is certain that the different observers are using identical techniques for recording their measurements, the latter may be employed for comparative studies; but they still need to be used with the greatest circumspection (particularly in the case of very small objects, where measurements need to be accurate to a fraction of a millimeter). Where it is apparent that different observers are not employing precisely the same techniques, statistical comparisons must necessarily be stultified. In anthropological craniometry attempts have been made (with some success) to secure general agreement on the definitions of points and planes which serve as a basis for statistical measurements (see, for example, Buxton and Morant, 1933). In regard to other elements of the skeleton and also the dentition, the virtual absence of standardization of metrical technique renders comparisons between different observers very hazardous indeed.

The Fallacy of Relying for Assessment of Affinities on Biometrical Analysis of Characters Which May Have No Genetic Basis

It is not always recognized by anthropologists that, during the period of growth, bone is a very plastic material. That is to say, its form may be readily modified by the mechanical effects of pressure and traction of the soft parts immediately related to it and also by the effects of dietetic deficiencies or constitutional disturbances of one sort or another. This needs to be taken into account as a possible source of fallacy in the attempts which have sometimes been made to assess the affinities of the various racial groups of *H. sapiens* on the basis of osteometric data, particularly in those cases where differences are so slight as to be detected only by statistical methods. So far as paleoanthropology is concerned, also, it is a factor which always needs to be taken into account when seeking evidence for the differentiation of geographical variants of the same general type. For example, it has been argued that the Javanese and Chinese representatives of the Pleistocene genus *Pithecanthropus* are taxonomically distinct because (*inter alia*) the thigh bone of the latter shows a flattening of the shaft (*platymeria*) which is not present in the former. But, apart from the fact that this is a feature which shows considerable variation within the limits of the single species *H. sapiens*, there is some suggestive evidence of an indirect nature that the degree of flattening of the shaft may depend on nutritional factors (Buxton, 1938). If this is so, it is not a genetic character which can be properly used for taxonomic reference. How far nutritional or other postnatal influences may determine minor differences in cranial or facial proportions is still quite uncertain. It is for this reason, of course, that in the study of modern populations physical anthropologists are now placing less reliance on the comparisons of traditional anthropometry and are concentrating their attention on characters whose genetic composition is directly ascertainable and by reference to which racial groups can be classified objectively on the basis of gene frequencies.

8. The Importance of Geological Age for Determining the Evolutionary Position of Fossils

It is necessary to recognize the distinction between a morphological series linking one taxonomic group with another and a geological series representing a true temporal sequence. A graded morphological series, by itself, may be of direct importance in the determination of major taxonomic groupings, and it may also provide indirect evidence of great value for a provisional assessment of phylogenetic relationships. But evolutionary lines of development can be finally determined only by the demonstration of an actual temporal sequence, and the latter can be established only if geological dating is secure. It is necessary to emphasize that anatomical studies *by themselves* can, of course, provide no basis for assessing geological age—this must depend on the studies of geologists based on stratigraphic data, of paleontologists based on faunal evidence, and of archeologists based on cultural sequences. Of these different lines of evidence, that of geological stratification is undoubtedly the most important, for paleontological and archeological evidence of the antiquity of fossilized remains is essentially derivative, being itself ultimately based on stratigraphic data. So far as hominid paleontology is concerned, it is unfortunate that the geological evidence of antiquity has so often been equivocal, mainly for the reason that the fossil remains have been discovered by chance and the stratigraphic evidence obscured before there has been an opportunity for a systematic study of the site, or they have been found in the course of excavations by workers who were not qualified by training and experience to assess the geological evidence.

Undoubtedly many of the unsatisfying controversies which in the past have been aroused by the discovery of hominid fossils might have been avoided, had it been possible in the first instance to establish a dating with reasonable certainty. In the absence of any degree of certainty, there has been a tendency for some anatomists to select that evidence for antiquity which seems best to fit in with the morphological status of the fossil. But this is a tendency which must be strenuously avoided, for it introduces a very obvious subjective element. Naturally, if the anatomist finds from the study of a skeleton assigned to a great antiquity that it shows no significant difference from that of modern *H. sapiens,* he is entitled to issue a caveat or perhaps to demand a more rigorous inquiry into the evidence for geological age, but he is not entitled to ignore the evidence simply because it conflicts with his preconceived ideas of evolutionary history. On the other hand, if a fossil of primitive type is found in a deposit which is *later* in geological age than might be expected on the general evidence already available, this need not disturb conclusions previously accepted regarding its evolutionary position, for it is quite well recognized that archaic types may persist for long periods in some parts of the world after they have given rise to more advanced types elsewhere (see Figure 1). For example, individuals of the genus *Pithecanthropus* certainly persisted into the Middle Pleistocene in the Far East, that is to say, at a time when *H. sapiens* (or the immediate precursor of this species) was already in existence in Europe. A parallel example is also to be found in the evolutionary history of the Equidae, for some representatives of the genus *Parahippus* are known to have survived into the Upper Miocene, although other representatives of the *same* genus had already given rise to the succeeding phase of equid evolution (*Merychippus*) by the Middle Miocene.

These considerations have reference to a very common source of confusion and needless argumentation in discussions on evolution (and particularly on hominid evolution) when the suggestion is made that a particular fossil type may be "ancestral" to a later type. Thus, if the proposition is put forward that *Pithecanthropus* is ancestral to *H. sapiens*, this does not, of course, mean (though some critics have evidently supposed it to mean) that the particular individuals whose remains have actually been found in Java or China are claimed to be the direct ancestors of *H. sapiens*, or even that the local group or species of which they are representatives included direct ancestors. It means only to suggest that the genus as a whole provided the matrix which gave rise— perhaps elsewhere in the world and perhaps at an earlier time—to the precursors of *H. sapiens*. Or, to put it another way, it means that, so far as their probable morphological characters can be inferred indirectly from comparative anatomical and paleontological studies and also by analogy with what is known of the evolutionary history of other mammalian groups, the ancestors of *H. sapiens* would have resembled the known individuals of the *Pithecanthropus* group so closely as not to be generically distinguishable (though they might be specifically distinct). Similarly, when it is suggested that *Australopithecus* may be ancestral to later hominids (and on the purely morphological evidence the suggestion is a perfectly valid one), it is not implied that the representatives of this genus found in South Africa are themselves the actual ancestors. The fact is that in their anatomical structure the South African fossils conform so closely to theoretical postulates for an intermediate phase of early hominid evolution (based on indirect evidence) as to lead to the inference that the actual ancestral group could hardly be *generically* distinct. It is here a question of weighing the available evidence and estimating probabilities. Only when the paleontological record becomes much more fully documented by further discoveries, will it be permissible to make more definite statements on these particular problems. But, in any case, the chances of finding the fossil remains of *actual* ancestors, or even representatives of the local group which provided the actual ancestors, are so fantastically remote as not to be worth consideration.

9. PRIMITIVE (OR GENERALIZED) AND SPECIALIZED CHARACTERS

In discussions on possible relationships of certain fossil hominids to *H. sapiens,* the argument is sometimes advanced that they are too specialized in one or another anatomical feature to have provided an ancestral basis for modern types. The suggestion here, of course, is that the development of some morphological character which is not present in *H. sapiens,* and wherein the latter appears to preserve a more primitive condition, implies an aberrant specialization which precludes any consideration of an ancestral relationship. In order to discuss the validity of such arguments, it is clear that we need some definition of the terms "primitive or generalized" and "specialized," and we also need to consider whether a structural specialization by itself necessarily implies the impossibility of reversion to a supposedly more primitive condition.

In studies of phylogenesis the distinction between morphological characters which are essentially primitive or generalized and those which may be regarded as divergent or specialized is commonly based on several considerations. In the first place, a study of the comparative anatomy of living types, particularly of those which, on the whole, are the most simply organized and occupy the most lowly position in a scale of increasing elaboration, may give an indirect indication of the relation between primitive and specialized features. A reference to the earlier fossil representatives of the group will provide further evidence which may, indeed, be conclusive if the fossil record is sufficiently complete to provide a closely graded sequence of evolutionary development. Detailed anatomical studies of the morphological characters concerned, with special reference to their embryological development, may add still further information. As a simple and very obvious example, we may take the morphological character of pentadactyly. This is judged to be a primitive and generalized condition in mammals which has in some cases been replaced by specializations depending on the loss of one or more digits; the reasons for this assumption are as follows: In living mammals of a simple organization, and also in Reptilia (from which mammals were originally derived), pentadactyly is the general rule; paleontology has demonstrated that in the early precursors of those mammals which today have less than five digits pentadactyly was also a characteristic feature; and, lastly, a detailed anatomical study of mammals with less than five digits may reveal, in the adult, vestigial remains of those which have been lost in the course of evolution or, in the embryo, transient traces of these vanished structures.

By the application of criteria such as these, it is usually possible to determine which characters can be designated as primitive or generalized and which are obvious specializations. For example, so far as the Hominoidea are concerned, it is certain that the gross elongation of the forelimbs in the Recent anthropoid apes (associated with retrogressive changes in the pollex and modifications of the limb musculature) are specializations from the primitive or generalized Primate condition. The same may also be said of the profound modifications of the skull and skeleton for erect bipedalism in the Hominidae. It may also be accepted, by the same line of reasoning, that the brachydont canine or the retrogressive changes in the last molar of *H. sapiens* are specialized features.

The importance of making a general distinction between primitive and specialized characters depends on the fact that the latter may be taken to indicate divergent trends of evolution, giving rise to more or less aberrant groups, and such aberrant groups, of course, are unlikely to bear an ancestral relationship to later-evolved groups in which similar specializations are absent. This consideration introduces us again to the much discussed question of the irreversibility of evolution. As already mentioned, there is no need to debate this question here, for it has been adequately discussed elsewhere. The important point to recognize is that, while the principle of the irreversibility of evolution is perfectly sound in its general application, it is not legitimate to use it as an argument against ancestral relationships in reference to isolated characters which may have quite a simple genetic basis and which are not obviously related to any marked degree of *functional* specialization. It is well known that some mutational processes may be reversible, for this has actually been demonstrated by genetic studies in the laboratory. It is also certain that individual morphological or metrical characters considered as isolated abstractions may undergo an evolutionary reversal; for example, the size of a tooth may increase and subsequently undergo a secondary reduction again (as demonstrated in the paleontological record of the Equidae), or muscles may be developed as new morphological units and later disappear when the functional demand for them ceases to exist (as demonstrated by vestigial or atavistic appearances sometimes seen in the human body). Instances of the loss of a character previously acquired are common enough in paleontology and may be termed "negative reversals" of evolution. On the other hand, a "positive reversal," that is to say, the re-acquirement of a complicated or composite morphological character in its *exact* original form after it has been lost in the course of evolution must certainly be a rarity. For if the initial development of such a character has been the result of a multiplicity of mutations or of a prolonged sequence of successive mutations, and if it has also been dependent on a great complexity of selective influences, the chances of its redevelopment will be so entirely remote as to be discounted altogether as a possibility. Reference may also be made to the line of argument followed by Ford (1938), who points out that, as any evolving group becomes more and more specialized in adaptation to one particular mode of life, the possible variations which could be of use to it become progressively restricted. "Finally," he goes on to say, "it attains a state of 'orthogenesis' in which the only changes open to the species are those which push it along the path it has already pursued."[11] In other words, it becomes more and more difficult, on the basis of the natural selection of heritable variations, for an evolving line to retrace its steps and thus reverse its evolutionary trends.

But, while it is legitimate to exclude from ancestral relationship to modern types any fossil group which provides clear morphological evidence of an aberrant development obviously related to any extreme functional specialization, it is equally important to avoid the assumption that any minor deviation from a supposedly primitive condition must necessarily also be exclusive in the same sense. For example, it has been suggested that the development of a sagittal crest on the skull of some of the Australopithecinae from South Africa would debar these fossil types from consideration as possible ancestors of *Homo*. But there is no evidence that a sagittal crest is a morphological entity having a separate genetic basis; it is no more than the secondary result of a growth process depending on the combination of a small brain case with large jaws and large temporal muscles (it is "built up" by the further extension upward of these muscles when they have reached the limits of the cranial roof at the mid-line of the skull). Indeed, it is a character which would be expected to be present in the earlier, small-brained representatives of the Hominidae, for only as a result of the later expansion of the brain (and the concomitant reduction of the jaws), would the temporal muscles during growth find adequate accommodation on the brain case itself without the need to build up a sagittal crest. It has also been argued that the Pleistocene hominid genus *Pithecanthropus* could not be ancestral to *H. sapiens* because it was characterized by prominent supra-orbital ridges which are absent in *H. sapiens* and were presumably absent in the evolutionary precursors of the Hominoidea. But it is too hazardous to draw such conclusions on such slender evidence; for, again, there is no theoretical or practical reason why, in the hominid sequence of evolution, the development and subsequent disappearance of prominent supra-orbital

---

[11] It need hardly be said that, in using the term "orthogenesis," Ford is not referring here to the effects of an inherent tendency within the organism to evolve in a certain direction, but to the effects of what has been called "orthoselection."

ridges should not be correlated with changing proportions of the jaws and brain case. And, in any case, nothing is known of the genetic basis of this particular morphological character.

Granted that single mutations are reversible in direction and that negative reversals are common phenomena of evolution, the question arises —how are we to determine from the study of the fossilized remains of a group of hominoids whether it has already attained to such a degree of specialization in its anatomical structure that it must be regarded as a divergent or aberrant group having no ancestral relationship to modern types? Surely, here it is a matter of assessing the total morphological pattern in terms of the probable complexity of its genetic constitution and of gauging the degree to which morphological changes may have committed the group to a mode of life which has restricted too far the opportunities for selection in other evolutionary directions. Thus, for example, the structural adaptations of the modern anthropoid apes for a brachiating mode of arboreal life—as shown in the modifications of the limb skeleton and musculature—have evidently become too extreme and too complex to permit them (with any probability) to revert to the more generalized structure which would be a necessary prelude for modifications in the opposite direction of erect bipedalism. On the other hand, the large size of the molar teeth of the Australopithecinae and the heavy supra-orbital ridges of *Pithecanthropus* could certainly not be regarded as functional specializations of this type.[12]

We may formulate the general proposition, then, that if a fossil group shows structural changes which are evidently related to (and responsible for) functional specializations, and if the latter appear to have definitely committed it to one special mode of life, it is to the highest degree unlikely that the group would be capable of a true evolutionary reversal. That is not to say, of course, that a specialized group of animals is incapable of changing its mode of life. For example, in the course of evolution an arboreal group may become adapted for terrestrial life and

[12] The functional aspect of specialization is perhaps more important for taxonomy than is often realized; for, in the assessment of phylogenetic relationships, taxonomists have sometimes tended to lay more stress on what are presumed to be nonadaptive characters than on obviously adaptive characters. But, in the first place, it has been questioned whether a character ever is nonadaptive in the sense that it has no relation whatever to the functional demands on the environment. It is true that *by itself* a character may have no selective advantage, but it may be linked genetically with some other character which has. Second, a character which has no selective advantage may much more easily undergo a rapid change by mutational variations than one which is directly adapted to a special environment, for any sudden disturbance of the second type of character might be presumed to place the animal at an immediate disadvantage. In other words, it might be expected that, in a given environment, obviously adaptive characters would actually be more stable and therefore of more importance for assessing affinities.

subsequently become adapted again for arboreal life. But in doing so, it does not revert to the more primitive or generalized structure of its arboreal ancestors. Its terrestrial specializations are preserved and still further modified away from the primitive condition to allow such a functional transformation. Apart from functional considerations, however, it is also legitimate to discount the possibility of an evolutionary reversal if the morphological divergence from a'more primitive condition can be assumed, on the basis of paleontological evidence, to be the cumulative effect of a long succession of small mutational variations exposed to selective influences of a complex nature, or if there is reason to suppose (by analogy from genetic studies of living forms) that the morphological character concerned is the phenotypical expression of a genotype which is so complex that an evolutionary reversal could occur only as the result of a multiplicity of mutational reversals.

In spite of what has been said, it needs to be emphasized that the ultimate decision as to whether a fossil genus is ancestral to a Recent genus or not must be determined by the paleontological record, and this can be done only when the latter is known in sufficient detail. On purely morphological grounds (and without reference to the paleontological sequence), there is no certain argument why *H. neanderthalensis* could not be ancestral to *H. sapiens*. But, in this particular instance, the fossil record shows clearly that such was not the case. Some of the early Miocene genera of the Pongidae may have been ancestral to the Hominidae—there likewise appears to be no valid morphological argument against this. But the solution of this particular problem must depend on the amplification of the fossil record by further discoveries.

10. GENERAL CONSIDERATIONS

We have been concerned in this chapter to draw attention to some of the more obvious sources of confusion which all too commonly lead to misunderstandings and misrepresentations in discussions on hominid evolution. Undoubtedly, the failure to recognize the phylogenetic implications of taxonomic terminology has been responsible for much of this confusion, for the reason that there has been a tendency to use this terminology as though it were based on morphological definitions applied to living forms only. The loose employment of colloquial group terms is an even greater source of confusion. It is a remarkable fact that even in strictly scientific papers authors frequently use the terms "man" and "human" without any attempt to define them, and it is clear, also, that they are used with very different meanings not only by different writers but also by the same writer in different contexts. The term "hominid," again, seems to be used quite frequently as though it referred only to the large-brained genus *Homo,* whereas it should be strictly employed only as the adjectival form of the taxonomic term "Hominidae." In other words, as we have tried to emphasize, it should be equated with the other familial categories of mammalian classification and apply to the whole sequence of evolution which led to the development of *Homo* (and other hominid genera) from the time when this sequence became segregated from the related family Pongidae.

The assessment of genetic affinity by the comparison of morphological details of no more than portions of a fossilized skeleton (particularly if these are very fragmentary) obviously poses a most serious problem, for in many cases such comparative studies can lead only to inconclusive results. Yet, because of their rarity, it is a matter of importance that all fossil Primate material should be subjected to intensive study and that some attempt should be made to assess the taxonomic status of each specimen, even though this may lead to no more than a provisional interpretation of its affinities. In the absence of an abundant fossil record, conclusions regarding lines of phylogenetic development must always be provisional; and, as the evidence accrues with new discoveries, they will need constant revision. Paleontologists themselves are quite aware of this, but it would be well that those less experienced in the study of fossils should recognize it also. For it is interesting to note in the literature of paleoanthropology that the polemical articles which seem so often to be evoked by new discoveries of primitive hominid fossils are contributed not so much by those with practical experience of paleontology as by those in allied fields who may even have no personal acquaintance with the fossil material under discussion. In any case, however, it can hardly be emphasized too strongly that, in assessing the taxonomic position of a fossil specimen, account must be taken of the total morphological pattern (and not its individual units) which provides the reliable morphological evidence on which zoölogical relationships can be determined. The comparison of individual characters independently as isolated abstractions, instead of treating them as integrated components of a complex pattern, is perhaps one of the main causes of the multiplicity of systems of classification of the Primates which are still to be found in the literature.

Finally, lest some paleoanthropologists should gain from this chapter an impression of an unduly critical attitude, it should be stated that not a few of the criticisms which have been enumerated apply as well to some of the writer's own work as they do to that of others.

Bones of Contention

W. E. Le Gros Clark   1958

When Darwin published *The Descent of Man* in 1871, he affirmed his conviction that "Man is descended from some lower form, notwithstanding that connecting links have not hitherto been discovered," and, as may be supposed, the opponents of the idea of evolution were very quick to make play with the absence of such links. It is true that the archaic fossil skull and associated limb bones of Neanderthal, discovered in 1856, had been described by Professor D. Schaaffhausen of Bonn University (1861) as exceeding all modern types "in those peculiarities of conformation which lead to the conclusion of their belonging to a barbarous and savage race," and, in fact, Darwin did make a passing reference to the skull in his book, but only to note that in this ancient type of man the size of the brain was evidently quite considerable. Huxley (in whose memory I have the honour of giving this lecture) made a special study (1906, pp. 111–50) of the Neanderthal skull, of which the results were published as one of his essays in *Man's Place in Nature* in 1863. He was very cautious in expressing his opinions on the significance of this fossil material, for, in spite of the fact that he refers to its "most extraordinary characters" and believed it to be "the most pithecoid of human crania yet discovered," he doubted whether it differed to such a degree from the skull of primitive modern races such as the Australian aboriginal to merit a taxonomic distinction. Referring to the Neanderthal remains as a whole, he concluded that "at most, they demonstrate the existence of a man whose skull may be said to revert somewhat towards the pithecoid type." This particular remark is an excellent example of Huxley's insight, for the accumulation of remains of fossil man since his day has now made it

FROM *the* Journal of the Royal Anthropological Institute, *1958, vol. 88, part II, pp. 131–145, reprinted by permission of the author and of the Royal Anthropological Institute of Great Britain and Ireland. This article adds some special viewpoints and comments to the preceding one. It was originally given as the Huxley Memorial Lecture for 1958.*

probable that the extreme, or specialized, Neanderthal type of later Mousterian date was indeed the result of a retrogression from an earlier and more generalized type which was more closely akin to *Homo sapiens*. But, in spite of his careful and judicious appraisal of the evidence, Huxley (1864) very quickly found himself involved in the controversies which ensued and which gave expression to a diversity of opinions advanced by other anthropologists. Quite extreme views were expressed by some of these authorities—for example, that the man of Neanderthal was a microcephalic idiot or suffered from some pathological deformity, or even (according to Professor Mayer of Bonn) that he was only "a rickety Mongolian Cossack belonging to the hordes driven by Russia, through Germany, into France in 1814." With the evidence now available of numerous remains of the Neanderthal type of man (found at different sites in Europe, the Near East, and North Africa), it may seem perplexing that eminent authorities offered such contrary interpretations of the original specimens found in 1856, and also that they expressed their opinions with such vehemence. In fact, however, it is the case that discoveries of fossil hominids which appear (at any rate in some respects) to fulfil Darwin's predictions of connecting links always have aroused controversies of a polemical nature, and the controversy in which Huxley found himself involved was merely the first of a long series of contentious disputes of a similar type. We may recall that the remains of *Pithecanthropus*, discovered by Dubois in 1891, were at one time claimed by some critics to be not human at all, but those of an extinct and hitherto unknown type of giant ape. And in more recent days, the early discoveries of *Australopithecus* in South Africa were almost immediately followed by conflicting claims of an extreme kind, too hastily put forward on insufficient or mistaken evidence. Thus, on the one hand it was claimed that these primitive hominids were so advanced as to be acquainted with the use of fire, while the disputants of the opposing camp claimed with equal vehemence on the basis of inadequate, and in some cases faulty, statistical data that they were not to be differentiated from the apes.

Undoubtedly, one of the main factors responsible for the frequency with which polemics enter into controversies on matters of palaeo-anthropology is a purely emotional one. It is a fact (which it were well to recognize) that it is extraordinarily difficult to view with complete objectivity the evidence for our own evolutionary origin, no doubt because the problem is such a very personal problem. Even scientists of today may not find it easy to clear their minds entirely of an emotional element when they come to consider the evidence in detail, and this emotional element is only too frequently betrayed by the phraseology with which disputants claim with equal insistence to be assessing the same evidence dispassionately. It is partly for this reason (as I shall mention later) that it is an advantage, in discussing the earlier stages of hominid evolution, to avoid altogether the colloquial and unscientific terms "man" and "human" (which have a wide and not easily definable connotation), and to use only those terms (such as *Hominidae*, *Homo*, and *Homo sapiens*) proper to the zoological nomenclature of taxonomy. Naturally, the problem of human origin is of quite compelling importance, so much so that each fossil discovery which appears to throw light on it immediately arouses interest to the extent that interpretations of its possible significance tend always to be advanced before detailed and systematic comparative studies (which may take a long time) have been completed. This tendency for premature appraisals has the further unfortunate effect that, should the author's first interpretation of a fossil specimen prove by subsequent and more extended analysis to be mistaken, he may well find it difficult to retract unconditionally his original opinion. And so the controversies are apt to be prolonged far beyond their limits of usefulness.[1]

Apart from these general considerations (which have reference to defects of human nature rather than defects of scientific methodology), it has become apparent in recent years that much of the controversial character of discussions on fossil man is commonly based on misconceptions of well-recognized principles of palaeontology, or even on quite simple terminological confusions. I should like to take the opportunity offered me by this lecture to draw attention to some of these sources of misunderstanding, with particular reference to certain relevant remarks of Huxley's which we should do well to remember. It is my hope that, by so doing, some of the confusion of ideas which still complicate discussions on the evolutionary origin of Man may be avoided.

Type Specimens and Typical Specimens

Probably the one single factor which above all others has unduly, and quite unnecessarily, complicated the whole picture of human phylogeny is the tendency for the taxonomic individualization of each fossil skull or fragment of a skull by assuming it to be a new type which is specifically, or even generically, distinct from all others. As a result, the species and genera of fossil hominids have been multiplied far beyond the limits which would be regarded as justifiable in any other equivalent group of Primates, and this has introduced a complexity into problems of human

[1] Perhaps the most remarkable example of the reluctance to discard previously expressed views was provided by the first reactions to the exposure of the Piltdown forgery. In spite of the overwhelming evidence demonstrating the fraudulent nature of the Piltdown jaw and teeth (Weiner, Oakley, and Le Gros Clark, 1953), some anatomists quite seriously questioned the validity of our conclusions.

evolution which is quite illusory.[2] Possibly one of the reasons for this tendency is the misunderstanding of the term "type specimen" by those not fully conversant with the principles of taxonomy. When a fossil specimen is found which is adjudged on morphological evidence to represent a new species or a new genus, it is given an appropriate specific or generic name, and the specimen is taken to be the "type" on which the new name is based. But, as Simpson (1945) has emphasized, "Types are almost never really average specimens within a species, or fully central species in a genus. Types were formerly, and still are by many students, supposed to be not only name-bearers but also the bases on which group concepts are erected and the standards of comparison for those concepts." Anthropologists and others have undoubtedly tended to fall into this error of assuming a type specimen to be a typical specimen, so that any newly discovered fossil which deviates even to a slight degree from the "type" has commonly been assigned to a supposedly new species or genus. Thus, for example, within the limits of what is evidently a common taxonomic group comprising the genus *Pithecanthropus* there have been arbitrarily created a variety of "types" such as *Pithecanthropus, Sinanthropus, Meganthropus, Homo modjokertensis,* and so forth. Again, the remains of Early Mousterian man have by several authorities been split up into an astonishing diversity of "types" such as *Homo krapinensis, Homo steinheimensis,* and *Palaeoanthropus palestinus.*[3] Apart from the fact that there is no sound morphological evidence for making such taxonomic distinctions, the common practice of doing so has had the unfortunate result of obscuring the all-important principle that populations, and not individuals, are the units of evolution, and that it is fundamentally the variation within a population which provides the raw material available for evolution. Thus, there has been an inevitable tendency, in attempting to construe the course of human phylogeny, to focus attention on the arbitrary individual "type" and not on the broad range of populations of which they are merely individual representatives (and in some case, perhaps, rather extreme variants). The general outline of human evolution becomes at once simplified, and more intelligible, if the fossil record is considered in its proper perspective, bearing in mind that the evidence now available

[2] It is interesting to refer in this context to a remark by K. A. Kermack (1956) on the unfortunate multiplication of types in other fossil vertebrates. He writes, "palaeontology in general suffers from too many species rather than too few. The study of the Karroo reptiles, for example, has been made needlessly difficult due to the whole-hearted creation of new species and genera."

[3] Those who are tempted prematurely to accept specific distinctions on the basis of some of this limited material might well emulate Huxley's cautious reluctance to accept a specific distinction for Neanderthal Man on the basis of the limited material then available to him.

makes it increasingly apparent that at each phase of evolution the hominid population then existing included a sufficiently wide range of variants to provide the opportunity for selective processes to lead on to the next phase. For example, the *Pithecanthropus* group, as we now know from their remains in Java and China, showed a high variability in features such as the relative development of the frontal region of the skull and the size of the jaws and teeth, and their cranial capacity actually ranged from 775 cc. to as much as 1,200 cc. So high a variability may be correlated with the fact that in the Early and Middle Pleistocene the rate of hominid evolution was proceeding rather rapidly with the deployment of relatively small (and often contiguous) populations into widely dispersed areas with contrasting and changing environments.[4] A population displaying the wide variability of *Pithecanthropus* would clearly have provided a particularly favourable opportunity for selective processes to modify its genetic constitution, and thus to produce a systematic shift in the total range of variation to the point where the transition to the more advanced genus *Homo* would be effected. The unfortunate splitting of the australopithecine fossils into numerous genera and species has also had the effect of introducing quite a spurious complexity into what may be termed the "*Australopithecus* phase" of hominid evolution, for, again, there is no valid morphological basis for recognizing in their variety more than one genus. Like *Pithecanthropus*, they show a considerable range of variation in skull form and cranial capacity and, while broadly contemporaneous in the geological sense, they probably represent a sequence of regional varieties of a local nature (the equivalent, perhaps of the racial varieties of modern *Homo sapiens*) which may actually have occupied the Transvaal region over a period of a hundred thousand years or more. As a matter of fact, it is now generally agreed that the initial multiplication of australopithecine genera and species made on the basis of the earlier discoveries was unwarranted, but there still remains some disagreement regarding the validity of the genus *Telanthropus*. It was on the basis of small jaw fragments found at one of the australopithecine sites, which in their size and dental morphology appear to approach more closely to more advanced hominids, that the separate genus *Telanthropus* was created, and on anatomical grounds Robinson (1957) has suggested that it is "an australopithecine which had reached euhominid status."[5]

---

[4] It is reasonable to suppose, also, that with the first development of social organizations in the Hominidae, the range of individual variation would immediately be increased simply because the selection pressure on *individuals* would be relieved by group responsibilities.

[5] Incidentally, it is to be hoped that the term "euhominid" may be discarded since, in so far as it has not been strictly defined by morphological criteria, it has no validity as a taxonomic term.

It seems doubtful, however, whether a generic distinction is justified even in this case (at any rate by reference to such fragmentary material), for it is not clear that the morphological differences between *"Telanthropus"* and *Australopithecus* exceed those known to exist in other hominid genera.[6] One of the main points of interest of the australopithecines, surely, is just the very fact that as a generic group they do display such a high degree of variability, for this obviously could account for a relatively rapid transition to a more advanced phase of hominid evolution by selective processes.

In the case of the Early Mousterian populations of Europe, if it is recognized that such differences as their individual remains may show in skull structure and so forth are merely the expression of the variability of a single taxonomic group (and not indicative of so many different genera and species), it again becomes clear at once that they could have provided the genetic material for a subsequent diversification on the one hand into the extreme (or "classical") Neanderthal type of later Mousterian date, and on the other into the modern races of *Homo sapiens*. It seems now almost certain that this actually did occur, particularly on the evidence of the high variability of the sample of the Upper Pleistocene population found at Mount Carmel. The suggestion that this population consisted of different taxonomic groups living in close association, or that it represents the results of cross-breeding between two different species, *Homo neanderthalensis* and *Homo sapiens,* seems much less plausible and less probable. At any rate, such an interpretation is perhaps hardly justified on the basis of such limited material.

The multiplication of species on the basis of other fossil skulls which it now seems clear are not morphologically distinguishable from *Homo sapiens* has been due simply to the failure to recognize the range of variation to be found in modern races of mankind, and it has had the unfortunate effect of distorting considerably the perspective of Upper Pleistocene man. For example, the designation of the Combe-Capelle skull, found in Aurignacian deposits in the Dordogne, as a separate species *Homo aurignaciensis,* as well as other instances of similar specific distinctions, has tended to obscure the important point that our own species *Homo sapiens* is in fact very ancient, and that Aurignacian man and his immediate predecessors, who lived about 30,000 years ago, were not different ana-

[6] My friend Dr. J. T. Robinson has done so much by his excavations and careful comparative studies to elucidate the significance of the australopithecines that I regret to find myself not quite in agreement with him on this particular point. However, the disagreement is perhaps not very fundamental, for Dr. Robinson (1953b) has emphasized that the proposed new genus *Telanthropus* has "some australopithecine affinities"; and that it "is manifestly very closely related to the australopithecines" (1953a).

tomically from ourselves. Such specific designations, similarly based on no valid evidence, have also tended to obscure the fact that *Homo sapiens* was very widely spread over the Old World in those early times.

Apart from other considerations, it is an interesting but not generally recognized fact that practically none of the genera and species of fossil hominids which have from time to time been created have any validity at all in zoological nomenclature. A newly named genus or species only becomes valid if it is accompanied by a formal diagnosis which clearly states in what respects the new type differs from other known genera or species, and it is perhaps rather surprising that palaeo-anthropologists have not been in the habit of conforming to this important principle of taxonomy. There is little doubt that the fossil record of the Hominidae would be immediately and immensely clarified if all those taxonomic terms which have not been validated by a formal diagnosis should once and for all be discarded (unless, indeed, it should be found possible by detailed comparative studies to validate them in this way).

In order to avoid the confusions of thought which result from the unwarranted multiplication of new species and genera, it should be accepted that, in future, no new species or genus is to be created on the basis of a fossil specimen unless it can be demonstrated with reasonable assurance *that the morphological characters of the specimen deviate from those already known to an extent at least equivalent to the differences between recognized and already well-established species or genera in allied groups.* Further, in presenting the formal diagnosis which is necessary for the validation of a new species or genus, the diagnosis should be so framed as to cover a range of variation at least equivalent to that found in allied groups.[7] In this connection, it is well to bear in mind the remarkable range of variation common to all the higher Primates, that is to say, in both the Hominidae and the anthropoid ape family, a characteristic of these groups which has been sufficiently emphasized in the numerous publications which have been recorded in the systematic studies of Professor A. H. Schultz. Indeed, these studies raise serious doubts whether even the range of variation observed in the extinct genera *Australopithecus* and *Pithecanthropus* is really as exceptional as some have supposed.

Only by careful attention to these desiderata will it be possible to give expression to the hope implied in a recent statement by Dr. Ernst Mayr (1958) that "the time has now come . . . for bold hypotheses aiming to make sense of the diversity of remains of fossil man. Such hypotheses can

[7] The palaeontologist, of course, is not able to apply genetic tests for the determination of specific categories. But, as K. A. Joysey (1956) rightly remarks, in practice even the neontologist rarely applies a genetic test. "He accepts that genetic discontinuity is reflected by morphological discontinuity, and there is a very high probability that his decisions are correct."

be made only through analogy with the variation, in space and time, of other species of mammals." As I have tried to make clear, the "diversity" to which Dr. Mayr refers is to a large extent quite illusory as far as their generic and specific labels are concerned.

EVOLUTIONARY TRENDS AND LINEAR SEQUENCES

When Huxley first studied the fossil evidence for the evolution of the horse family, he suggested that the European fossil genera *Palaeotherium* —*Anchitherium*—*Hipparion*—*Equus* represent a temporal series marking the gradual evolution of the modern horse. He was actually very careful in giving expression to this interpretation, however, for he regarded it as "highly probable that many forms of *Anchitherium*-like and *Hipparion*-like animals existed . . . and it is highly improbable that the particular species of *Anchitherium* or *Hipparion* which happen to have been discovered should be precisely those which have formed part of the direct line of the horse's pedigree." The fact that the direct line of the evolution of the modern horse was later found to be represented by American fossil genera such as *Miohippus, Merychippus*, and *Pliohippus*, and that Huxley's genera were collateral offshoots of the main line, was not really of very great importance from the point of view of the objective demonstration of equid evolution, for the latter demonstrated clearly enough the main trend of evolutionary development which had characterized the group. It may be put this way. Trends of evolution can be inferred from a consideration of the end-results. Fossil evidence may confirm the fact of these trends and, if sufficiently complete, may demonstrate an actual evolutionary sequence in terms of successive types. It is useful to recognize this difference between an evolutionary trend and an actual linear, or ancestor-descendant, sequence, for it is only rarely that the fossil record of any taxonomic group is sufficiently abundant to permit the establishment of a true linear sequence. In the case of hominid evolution, the fossil record is still not adequate to allow firm conclusions regarding the entire linear sequence of the Hominidae which culminated in the emergence of *Homo sapiens*, but it is sufficiently adequate to demonstrate some of the main evolutionary trends which have occurred in human phylogenesis.

The importance of recognizing the distinction between the fossil evidence of trends and the evidence of sequences has reference to those controversies aroused by the discovery of fossil hominid remains which seem to be based on a confusion of the two conceptions. Huxley himself (1876) put the matter very clearly when he wrote "it is convenient to distinguish those intermediate forms between two groups, which do not represent the actual passage from the one group to the other, as *intercalary* types, from those *linear* types which, more or less approximately, indicate

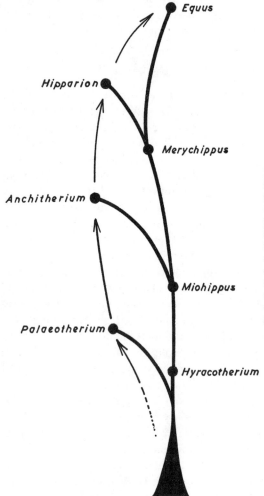

Figure 1. A diagram illustrating the essential difference between Huxley's "intercalary types" (left) and his "linear types" (right) in the fossil record of the Equidae. Note that the intercalary types do provide objective evidence of the main *evolutionary trend* of the Equidae, even though they do not comprise the actual *linear sequence* of successive ancestral genera.

the nature of the steps by which the transition from one group to the other was affected." So far as the later stages of hominid evolution are concerned, the series *Australopithecus—Pithecanthropus—Homo* may well represent a linear sequence, for, in fact, the gradations from the one type to the other are quite close, and also, as it now appears, they comprise a temporal succession; such a proposition therefore, is a perfectly reasonable interpretation of the evidence *at present available*. Even so, however, it must be regarded as no more than a provisional interpretation until a more complete fossil record of these genera has accrued. On the other hand, there can be no question but that this series represents an evolutionary *trend*.

BRAIN SIZE AND INTELLIGENCE

Following the publication of Darwin's *Origin of Species*, much of the ensuing anatomical controversies on the question of man's relationship to lower animals naturally concerned the differences in the size and proportions of the brain. The large brain of modern *Homo sapiens* is such an obvious and distinctive human trait, and is in such strong contrast with the smaller brain of the large apes, that some authorities were tempted to regard it as sufficient justification for the widest separation of man in any scheme of classification. But apart from the size factor, attempts were made to prove that in certain structural details the human brain was also quite distinct from the ape's brain and, as is well known, one of these features (the hippocampus minor) provided the central theme for a celebrated debate in which Huxley took part. In the second edition of Darwin's *Descent of Man* there is included an appendix by Huxley on the comparative anatomy of the human and ape brain in which he demonstrated that they are constructed on the same basic pattern, and that the differences between the two are not greater than those which occur between the large apes and the Catarrhine monkeys. He went even further, and in considering the gradations in cerebral development which are shown in the whole series of modern Primates he notes that "it is a remarkable circumstance that though, so far as our present knowledge extends, there *is* one true structural break in the series of forms of Simian brains, this hiatus does not lie between Man and the man-like apes, but between the lower and lowest Simians; or, in other words, between the Old and New World apes and monkeys and the Lemurs."

With our present knowledge, it has become evident that even in modern man the size of the brain shows an extraordinary variability; for example, the cranial capacity (which is closely correlated with brain volume) ranges in individuals of "normal" intelligence from less than 900 cc. to about 2,300 cc. And yet, so far as it has been possible to apply appropriate tests, there is within such limits no marked correlation between the brain size and intelligence.[8] To the palaeo-anthropologist this lack of correlation is particularly disconcerting, for it means that he has no sure method of assessing the mental capacity of extinct types of hominid simply by reference to cranial capacity. Incidentally, Darwin himself remarked that "no one supposes that the intellect . . . of any two men can

---

[8] Perhaps the smallest brain of an apparently normal individual so far recorded on good authentication is that described by B. G. Wilder (1911). The brain was that of a man aged 46, with a height of about 5 ft. 6 in. and a weight of 145 lb. On removal from the skull it weighed 680 grams, which is equivalent to a cranial capacity of about 720 cc. For a recent discussion on brain size in relation to intelligence, see the article by Professor Dart, "The relationship of brain size and brain pattern to human status," S. Afr. J. Med. 21, pp. 23–45.

be accurately gauged by the cubic content of their skulls." In the extinct genus *Pithecanthropus* the cranial capacity (as already noted) was also highly variable, but the mean volume was about 1,000 cc. which is considerably lower than that of modern *Homo sapiens* (1,350 cc.), and the capacity of the smallest skull of *Pithecanthropus* so far found has been estimated to be not more than about 775 cc. Since the largest cranial capacity recorded for a gorilla is 685 cc., the actual volume difference between apes and *Pithecanthropus* seems to bear no relation to the difference in mental powers, for it is known from archaeological evidence that those representatives of *Pithecanthropus* which inhabited China could fashion stone implements, and they even knew the use of fire for culinary purposes. From what has been said, it seems evident that actual brain mass by itself (at any rate up to certain limits) can hardly be used as a direct index of intelligence in the study of fossil hominids. This question became one of great importance when skulls of *Australopithecus* were excavated at various sites in South Africa. One of the outstanding features of this Early Pleistocene hominid (which was recognized from the first) is the remarkably small size of the brain; indeed, it was this very ape-like feature which led Dart to propose the generic name *Australopithecus* (i.e., Southern "Ape"). We still have no accurate data indicating the range of variation in its cranial capacity; on the available evidence it probably ranged from about 450 cc. to about 700 cc.—that is to say, at its upper limits the cranial capacity was closely comparable with the largest figure for the gorilla.[9] Unfortunately, however, while the cranial capacity can provide an indication of the brain size, it can tell us nothing of the intrinsic neural organization which may be supposed to be much more closely related to intellectual functions than mere mass of nervous tissue.[10] The importance of recognizing this point is relevant to the evidence, lately accumulated, suggesting the possibility that the australopithecines may have been capable of fashioning stone implements of a very primitive kind. Such implements have been found *in situ* in

[9] Except in a few isolated specimens, it has been possible to get only very rough estimates of the cranial capacity of the australopithecine fossils, either by direct measurement on reconstructions of damaged skulls or by attempts to establish statistical correlations of some sort on the basis of certain extra-cranial measurements. Both these methods involve preliminary assumptions the validity of which it is not possible to assess with accuracy.

[10] In a recent monograph (Haug, 1958), Dr. H. Haug has demonstrated that not only is the relative brain weight (cephalization coefficient) greater in man than in anthropoid apes, the *grauzellkoeffizient* (i.e., relation of volume of cortex to volume of its contained nerve cells) is also greater—at any rate in the visual cortex. This observation emphasizes the importance of considering the intrinsic structure of the cortex (as well as its total volume) in relation to its functional efficiency. So far as the australopithecine brain is concerned, unfortunately we have not the data whereby we can calculate either of the two coefficients to which Dr. Haug refers.

consolidated breccia deposits also containing the remains of *Australo-pithecus* (but containing no remains, so far discovered, of a more advanced type of hominid). The association of skeletal relics of hominids with stone artifacts would in most cases lead to a reasonable supposition that the former were responsible for making the latter. But there has quite naturally been an element of doubt in the case of *Australopithecus*, partly because of preconceived (but as yet unsubstantiated) assumptions regarding the minimum size of the brain requisite for the ability to fabricate tools, and it will be necessary to await further evidence before it can be definitely decided whether this primitive hominid was a toolmaker. However, apart from this question, in discussions on the taxonomic status of *Australopithecus* there has been a curious misunderstanding based on the *non sequitur* that a large brain is an essential feature of "true man," therefore *Australopithecus* is a "true ape." This type of argument at once makes clear the essential need either to define these colloquial terms in scientific phraseology or, preferably, to replace them by scientific terms proper to zoological nomenclature. Of course, a large brain is a distinctive feature of modern man, and indeed of the genus *Homo* as a whole. But, as we have already seen, it was not so characteristic of *Pithecanthropus*, for even the totally inadequate sample of this extinct type includes one specimen with a cranial capacity of less than 800 cc. Further, it may be assumed on *a priori* reasoning that in the immediate evolutionary precursors of *Pithecanthropus* the cranial capacity would have been still less expanded and, indeed, could hardly have exceeded that of the modern large apes. The fact is, then, that while a voluminous brain is characteristic of the genus *Homo*, it is not characteristic of the family Hominidae as a whole, and it has become clear from recent discussions on hominid phylogeny that a good deal of misunderstanding has arisen simply because these taxonomic terms have been confused with the colloquial (and unscientific) terms, "man," "human," "humanity," and so forth.

We may perhaps clarify the matter in the following way. Probably most students of human evolution agree that the evolutionary line which led to the emergence of *Homo* separated from that which led to the modern large apes somewhere about the Early Pliocene or the Miocene period (or perhaps even earlier). Translated into taxonomic terminology, this is equivalent to saying that the Hominidae (comprising the hominid sequence of evolution) became segregated as an independent lineage from the Pongidae (comprising the anthropoid ape sequence of evolution) as far back as the Early Pliocene or the Miocene. Since there is no evidence that in the hominid sequence of evolution the brain began to expand to the dimensions characteristic of *Homo* before the Lower or Middle Pleistocene, it seems clear that there was a prolonged period during which the earlier Hominidae were not to be distinguished from the anthropoid apes on the basis of brain size. Once it is recognized that a large brain has only been characteristic of the *later* phases of hominid evolution, some of the misunderstandings regarding the phylogenetic status of *Australopithecus* immediately become clarified.[11]

The discussions on the comparative anatomy of the brain of man and apes, in which Huxley played such an important part, were complicated by the tacit assumption that human intelligence must be based on quite outstanding structural differences in the brain, and that these assumed differences by themselves would imply a very remote relationship to the anthropoid apes. It is interesting to note Huxley's commentary (1906, pp. 1–51) on this type of argument: "The argument, that because there is an immense difference between a man's intelligence and an ape's, therefore, there must be an equally immense difference between their brains, appears to me to be about as well based as the reasoning by which one should endeavour to prove that, because there is a 'great gulf' between a watch that keeps accurate time and another that will not go at all, there is therefore a great structural hiatus between the two watches. A hair in the balance-wheel, a little rust on the pinion, a bend in a tooth of the escapement, a something so slight that only the practised eye of the watchmaker can discover it, may be the source of all the difference." In making these comments Huxley was of course speaking as a comparative anatomist, and he took the view that the assessment of phylogenetic relationships is primarily a morphological problem, the data for which are to be acquired from the study of the anatomy of living and fossil types. But it is interesting to note his suggestion that the efficiency of the brain as an organ of intelligence may be related not to any major structural feature demonstrable by anatomical studies, but perhaps to some other factor of quite a different order.

THE PITHECOMETRA THESIS

Huxley (1906) made the statement that "the structural differences between Man and the highest Ape are of less value than those between the highest and the lower Apes." Stated in such general terms this proposition has not only stood the test of time—it has been considerably reinforced by the accumulation of comparative anatomical studies since Huxley's days. But it was given the somewhat spurious title of the "pithecometra thesis" by Haeckel (1898), who thus implied that degrees

---

[11] It is relevant to comment on the fact that the primitive Eocene equid *Hyracotherium* (= *Eohippus*) is not excluded from the family Equidae because its brain was only a small fraction of the size of the brain of the terminal genus *Equus*.

of affinity could readily be quantified simply by the direct metrical comparison of structural resemblances and differences. Now it is one thing to compare selected measurements, for example of the skull, teeth, or limb bones, and quite another to evaluate the taxonomic significance of such measurements. Clearly, the comparison of dimensions which have little or no taxonomic significance for deciding degrees of affinity is likely to give rise only to negative (and sometimes very misleading, results. I have elsewhere indicated (Le Gros Clark 1950; 1955) the numerous pitfalls which may entrap the unwary biometrician who attempts, without adequate knowledge of the biological fundamentals of his material, to apply statistical methods to the assessment of phylogenetic relationships, and I will not repeat these warnings in detail here. But I would like to draw particular attention to a paper by Bronowski and Long (1952) demonstrating the importance of employing statistical methods which treat a set of variates as a single coherent matrix; such a method is the technique of multivariate analysis which permits the comparison of morphological *patterns* rather than the comparison of individual measurements as though they were independent and isolated abstractions. Another important paper demonstrating the application of the technique has more recently been contributed by Ashton, Healy, and Lipton (1957), in which they were able finally to resolve certain conflicts of opinion which had unhappily arisen over the very obvious hominid features of the australopithecine dentition (incidentally confirming the results of my own earlier statistical studies and also those of Bronowski and Long).

In general, the statistical comparisons of a few selected measurements or indices may be of considerable value in assessing degrees of affinity in forms already known to be closely related, e.g., geographical varieties, subspecies, or even species, but they become of less and less practical value as the relationship becomes more remote and the types to be compared become more disparate. This is because factors of parallelism and convergence greatly complicate the situation, and also because the more fundamental contrasts which differentiate the more distantly related types make it difficult or impossible to adhere to the important "principle of morphological equivalence" in making metrical comparisons.

So far as I am aware, zoologists have not found it practicable to apply statistical data for the assessment of evolutionary affinities except for the differentiation of local varieties. But anthropologists have attempted to do so. That great pioneer of biometrical enquiry, Karl Pearson, made a brilliant attempt to find out how far metrical analysis would provide evidence of relationship in the phylogenetic sense, and subsequent attempts to apply this method of approach have led to a realization of its inherent difficulties. For example, Seltzer (1937), applying Pearson's

"Coefficient of Racial Likeness" to several series of skulls, found that it showed the greatest racial differences among three English series, and the least racial difference between a group of Tibetans and a group of Central African negroes! In their comparative study of the femur, also, Pearson and Bell (1919, p. 225) were led to make the statement that their statistical evidence "indicates the great divergence of the Galley Hill femur from that of Recent Man." We now know (from the evidence of fluorine analysis) that the Galley Hill skeleton was of comparatively recent date, and certainly not distinguishable from *Homo sapiens*. It must not, of course, be inferred from these examples that biometrical methods are not at all applicable to the study of phylogenetic relationships, but they do serve to emphasize the difficulties involved in their application, even in the most expert hands. The well-known aphorism "Science is measurement" is strictly true, but it by no means follows that all measurements are scientific. In this connection, it is worth while drawing attention to the caveat in a recent review (Blochwelder and Hoyme, 1955) that "Statistics can enter the picture only after biologically valid measurements have been obtained."

In any assessment of the phylogenetic status of fossil types, and particularly in attempts to determine whether those which show an unusual combination of characters belong to one or other evolutionary sequence of two major taxonomic groups, it is essential to recognize that while species (and to some extent genera) can be defined morphologically in static terms, the larger categories such as families are only to be defined in dynamic terms of evolutionary trends. For example, the family Equidae is not to be defined simply by reference to the terminal products of its evolutionary history—this history is itself fundamental to its definition. The general principles of classification are intended to reflect evolutionary sequences of this kind; herein lies the difference between the so-called "vertical classifications" based on phylogeny, and "horizontal classifications" which, so to speak, merely serve to compare and catalogue in arbitrary fashion the end-products of evolution without direct reference to their phylogeny. The contrast between these two lines of approach is emphasized by Simpson's remark (1945) that "the linking of *Hyracotherium* [i.e., *Eohippus*] with *Equus* in the Equidae is solely on the basis of temporal variation and is flatly contradicted by any horizontal criteria."

Let us now briefly consider the sort of problem which arises when the phylogenetic status of a fossil hominoid is in question—whether it is the product of an early phase in the evolutionary sequence of the Hominidae or in that of the Pongidae. We may assume with confidence that the grouping together of these two families in the common superfamily Hominoidea accurately reflects the fact that they had their origin in a

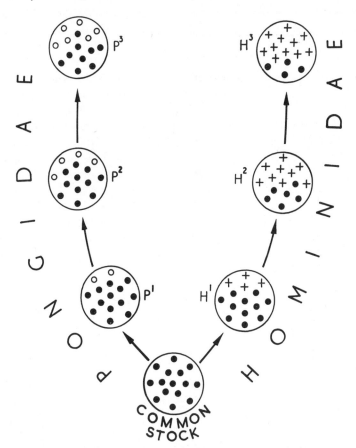

FIGURE 2. A diagram representing the divergence of two evolutionary sequences, the Pongidae (anthropoid ape family) and the Hominidae (the family which includes Recent and extinct types of man). The two sequences inherit from a common ancestry *characters of common inheritance* (black circles). As the lines diverge each one acquires its own distinctive features, or *characters of independent acquisition;* those distinctive of the hominid sequence of evolution are represented by crosses and those of the pongid sequence by white circles. For further explanation, see text.

common ancestral stock (though authorities differ in their estimates of the geological date at which they became segregated from this stock). In the accompanying diagram are represented schematically the two diverging lines of evolution, and the morphological characters of the common ancestral stock are indicated by black circles. Now, some of these ancestral characters are of course inherited and retained in common by both families—such characters may be termed *characters of common inheritance.* But when the lines of evolution segregate and branch out to form the two separate groups, each of the latter gradually acquires its own special and peculiar pattern of morphological characters by which it comes to be distinguished from the other. Characters of this sort may be called *characters of independent acquisition.* In the diagram those which are distinctive of the Hominidae are indicated by crosses, and those of the Pongidae by white circles. Since the pongid sequence of evolution has been much more conservative than the progressive hominid sequence, its terminal products (the modern anthropoid apes) have preserved more of the original characters of the ancestral stock. As divergent evolution proceeds, characters of common inheritance will become progressively supplemented or replaced by characters of independent acquisition in each line. Conversely, if the lines are traced backwards in retrospect they will be found to approximate more and more closely to each other in the characters of common inheritance which they share. Thus, for example, in representatives of an early stage in the hominid sequence (H^1 in the diagram) it may well be found that characters of common inheritance predominate over characters of independent acquisition, the latter being as yet relatively few in number or only showing an incipient development. If, now, the remains of an individual corresponding to the stage H^1 are examined and the morphological characters compared quite indiscriminately—if, that is to say, the characters are simply enumerated without giving to each one an appropriate weighting according to its evolutionary significance, the erroneous conclusion may be reached that because in the *sum* of its characters it shows a closer resemblance to apes than to modern *Homo sapiens,* therefore it is taxonomically a pongid. But this would be to ignore the highly important principle of taxonomic relevance in comparing morphological characters. Haldane (1956) has succinctly stated the position in his remark that, in constructing a natural system of classification, "palaeontologists rightly lay more stress on differences which at a later date become the basis of familial or ordinal distinctions," that is, on differences which by their progressive development later become important diagnostic characters of major taxonomic groups. The decision as to the taxonomic status of a previously unknown fossil—whether it is a primitive representative or one or other of two divergent lines of evolution corresponding to two related families—must therefore depend on a recognition of the fundamentally different trends which have distinguished the evolution of the two families and which are thus diagnostic of each of them as a natural taxonomic group. In the particular case which we are considering, the taxonomically relevant characters on which the diagnosis of "pongid" or "hominid" depends are the characters of independent acquisition which serve to distinguish the divergent trends in the two sequences, the nature and direction of the trends of each sequence being at once made evident by a consideration of the objectives actually reached by its terminal products. The stage H^1 of hominid evolution might be exemplified by the fossil genus *Australopithecus*, which is a particularly apt illustration for our present purpose. In the early discussions following the discovery of this primitive hominid, some anatomists, basing their judgment exclusively on the characters of common inheritance (such as the relatively small brain-case and large jaws), were led to suppose that it really was an ape in the taxonomic sense. But more careful studies soon made it clear that many of the characters of independent acquisition distinctive of the Hominidae (particularly in the dentition and pelvis), but none of those distinctive of the Recent Pongidae, had already been developed in *Australopithecus* and super-imposed on the characters of common inheritance. In other words, in those characters in which this fossil type has undergone modification away from the ancestral stock of the Hominoidea, the direction of change has been in that of the hominid sequence and divergent from that of the pongid sequence.[12]

Another serious difficulty which complicates any attempt at a quantitative assessment of the taxonomic position of fossil types is related to what has been termed "mosaic evolution." This principle has recently been emphasized by de Beer (1954) with particular reference to his new studies of the famous fossil *Archaeopteryx*. As he pointed out, there has been a common assumption that the evolutionary process ordinarily involves a gradual and general transformation of the whole animal. But this is by no means the case, for different morphological characters may evolve with apparent independence at different rates, so that the representative of one particular phase of evolution may be compounded of a mosaic of characters, some of which still preserve almost entirely archaic characters while others have achieved almost entirely the terminal stage of their development. In the palaeontological study of hominid evolution it is hardly possible to overstress the importance of this principle. Following Darwin's reference to connecting links, and the invention of the popular and much abused phrase "the missing link," the conception seems to have been widely held that such an intermediate phase must be represented by a creature almost exactly half-way in every major character between modern man and modern apes. Thus arose what may be termed the "half-way illusion," which even today appears to colour the judgment of some anthropologists. But almost a hundred years ago Huxley (1860)

[12] It needs to be emphasized that the terms "hominid" and "pongid" should be strictly limited to their use as the adjectival equivalents of the taxonomic terms Hominidae and Pongidae. Because of the confusion which has arisen in some of the discussions on *Australopithecus*, it is obviously essential, also, that authors should define precisely what they mean by these terms.

drew attention to this type of fallacy when he said, "the stock whence two or more species have sprung, need in no respect be intermediate between those species." It follows from the concept of mosaic evolution that a fossil type representing a connecting link in an evolutionary series may not be recognizable as such by the statistical comparison of isolated morphological characters. This is made very clear by reference to the discussions which followed the discovery of the skull cap and femur of *Pithecanthropus* in Java. A metrical study confined to the frontal region of the skull might appear overwhelmingly to favour the suggestion that this extinct genus was an ape in the taxonomic sense, and a similar study of the femur would find no essential difference from *Homo sapiens*. Indeed, the contrast between the skull and thigh bone led some authorities to suppose they belonged to different creatures altogether. Mosaic evolution in the Hominidae is equally well shown in *Australopithecus*, in which the dentition and pelvis are fundamentally of the hominid type, while the brain and brain-case still retain archaic proportions closely approaching those of the large apes. Clearly, the relevant features for the phylogenetic assessment of *Australopithecus* are those in which this type had already advanced some considerable way in the direction of terminal characters distinctive of, and diagnostic of, the hominid sequence of evolution.[13]

I mentioned above that statistical comparisons of morphological features for establishing taxonomic affinities involve the most serious difficulties except in rather closely related groups. But there is another means of quantitative comparison which does not involve similar complications —the technique reported in the classic work of Nuttall (1904) on Blood Immunity and Blood Relationship. The precipitin reaction which formed the basis of Nuttall's work (and which has been considerably developed since by Dr. A. A. Boyden) has the advantage of being able to provide an objective and quantitative assessment of affinities and has thus proved of the utmost value for testing the validity of conclusions based on comparative anatomy. It is also a test which may help in some degree to overcome one of the main difficulties which the morphological taxonomist has to meet—the difficulty of determining whether a similarity in structure really betokens a correspondingly close relationship, or whether it is the result of convergent evolution, for according to Boyden (1953) so far

[13] The example of *Archaeopteryx* happens to be very apposite to this particular problem. Its taxonomic position is determined not by the archaic reptilian characters which it still retains in abundance, but by the incipient development of a few definite avian characters which are clear evidence that it represents an early stage of avian evolution. It is thus placed not in the Reptilia, but in a sub-class (Archaeoptyerygiformes) of the class Aves. Clearly, it would be easy to "prove" that *Archaeopteryx* is taxonomically a reptile if attention is focussed on its archaic characters; by a similar selection of characters it might also be "proved" that *Australopithecus* is taxonomically a pongid.

as serological convergence is concerned there is "as yet no proven case for protein antigens. As further work is undertaken, they may appear, but it is unlikely that they will be frequent." We may note, incidentally, that the serological test shows a close relationship between man and the anthropoid apes, a less close relationship with the quadrupedal Old World Monkeys, and no more than a distant relationship with the lower Primates. Perhaps one of the most interesting aspects of this test is that it provides the final justification for grouping the Pongidae and Hominidae in a common superfamily, Hominoidea.

CHRONOLOGY AND HOMINID EVOLUTION

There is one other source of misunderstanding in discussions on hominid evolution to which I should like to draw attention; it has reference to the importance of the time factor in the interpretation of fossil remains. In the past it sometimes happened that a great antiquity was assigned to the skeletal remains of *Homo sapiens* on the basis of what we now know to have been quite inadequate geological data. Today the situation is very different, partly because of the development of technical methods for arriving at a relative or absolute dating, and partly because of progressive refinements in the methods of analysing stratigraphical evidence. Consequently, it is now possible to state with much more assurance the temporal sequence of the various types of fossil hominids at present known, and it is only by reference to this time factor that conclusions can safely be drawn regarding their evolutionary position. It was during the Pleistocene period that the later stages of hominid evolution occurred, leading finally to the emergence of the genus *Homo,* and in this connection it is important to recognize that as the result of the redefinition of the term Pleistocene in recent years this period has been quite considerably extended into what was previously regarded as late Pliocene. The Pleistocene, as it is now understood, includes the so-called Villafranchian period, the greater part of which preceded the first major (Günz) glaciation of the Ice Age. This means, in effect, that the duration of the preglacial Pleistocene may have been almost as long as the whole of the rest of the period. With the redefinition of the Pliocene-Pleistocene boundary, there has been a significant revision of the subdivisions of the Pleistocene, a revision which has perhaps not yet been fully recognized by anthropologists. For example, much of what was generally termed the Lower Pleistocene is now included in the Middle Pleistocene. For a brief summary of the relation of these now accepted subdivisions to fossil hominids, reference may be made to a recent lecture by Dr. K. P. Oakley (1956–7). According to this authority the genus *Homo* is known to have extended back into the upper part of the Middle Pleistocene, the remains of the genus *Pithecanthropus* so far discovered are probably not older than the lower part of the Middle Pleistocene, while the earlier group of australopithecine fossils found in South Africa are definitely of Villafranchian, or Lower Pleistocene, antiquity. In other words, so far as we know from the scanty records at present available (and it needs to be recognized that they still are scanty), there is no evidence that any more advanced type of hominid was in existence at the time when the earliest known representatives of *Australopithecus* existed, or that there was any more advanced type of hominid in existence at the time when the earliest known representatives of *Pithecanthropus* existed. The genera *Australopithecus—Pithecanthropus—Homo* thus appear to fit into a temporal sequence, even though they almost certainly overlapped in time in different parts of the world. But the fact that some later representatives of *Pithecanthropus* (for example) may have been contemporaneous with early representatives of *Homo* in other parts of the world does not, of course, exclude the possibility (which seems likely enough on purely morphological grounds) that the one genus was ancestral to the other. It is well known from the vertebrate palaeontological record that a genus may survive in one region long after the same or a closely related genus has given rise by progressive evolution to a more advanced type in another.[14] It is well to bear this in mind, for it has sometimes been argued, on the basis of the few fossils so far discovered, that *Pithecanthropus* was too late in time to have been ancestral to *Homo*. But a genus (as distinct from a local population) commonly has a wide distribution in time, and very often in space as well. In the evolutionary history of the Equidae there was a sequence of probably not more than nine genera from the Eocene *Hyracotherium* to the modern *Equus*, covering a span of fifty million years or so. It may be, of course, that hominid genera, at any rate in the later stages of evolution, succeeded each other more rapidly. It is not to be supposed, however, that their temporal range was limited to the geological time during which their local representatives so far known happened to have lived. The genus *Australopithecus* was already in existence in South Africa during the Lower Pleistocene, and (apart from extreme ideas of "explosive evolution") it may be presumed, as a genus, to have extended back at least into the immediately antecedent period of the Upper Pliocene.[15]

---

[14] These are, of course, examples of the "persistent types" to which Huxley drew attention in his lecture at the Royal Institution on 3 June 1859.

[15] It still remains questionable whether *Australopithecus*, *Pithecanthropus*, and *Homo* are properly to be separated as distinct genera, equivalent in the *degree* of their morphological difference (for example) to the genera of the Equidae. Even so, it may be felt preferable, as a matter of practical convenience, to make provisional use of the generic terms which have been rather widely accepted.

Subscript

Lest it might seem that the title of my lecture is itself of a contentious nature, let me insist that it is not meant to be so. Every discovery of a fossil relic which appears to throw light on connecting links in man's ancestry always has, and always will, arouse controversy, and it is right that this should be so, for it is very true that the sparks of controversy often illuminate the way to truth. After all, Huxley himself was a noted controversialist in many fields of thought, and in every one of them he brought to bear a penetrating insight which did much to clear away confusion of thought. My own modest intentions have been simply to draw attention to certain recurring patterns of disputation in the field of palaeo-anthropology which, because of the evident misunderstandings they involve, still tend to becloud, rather than to clarify, the atmosphere of controversy. By so doing, it may be that I can to some degree help to ensure that the illumination from controversial sparks is less diffused over irrelevancies and more firmly focussed on fundamentals.

Statistics of Discrimination
in Anthropology

J. Bronowski and W. M. Long   1952

One important step in anthropological research is to assign a new find to a known group, or to decide to which of several groups it is most nearly related. How does an anthropologist decide that a fossil bone is like a human bone, and unlike an ape bone? The shape and size of the bone may provide the answer at once: they may be quite different in the various species, and no mistake is possible. The evidence of the eyes, matched with previous experience, is enough. At other times this may not be so; the decision may be a close one, and mere visual judgments unreliable. In such cases, various dimensions of the individual may be measured, and compared with corresponding dimensions in the possible species, using statistical tests to estimate the importance of observed differences. The use of statistical tests in this way does not differ in principle from the judgment based on inspection coupled with experience. For in his appraisal of size and shape the anthropologist has in mind, consciously or unconsciously, some measurements which influence his decision, both singly and by their relation to one another, and these measurements seem to him to make it much more probable that the fossil belongs to one group rather than another. Statistical methods substitute a precise scale in terms of which these probabilities may be expressed.

Reprinted by permission of The Wistar Institute Press from the American Journal of Physical Anthropology, n.s. 10:385–394 (1952). This article, cited in the preceding papers by Le Gros Clark, illustrates certain of the latter's points as to the avoidance of statistical fallacies, and demonstrates how measurements can be used in finding morphological relationships, in this case of the australopithecines. Dr. Bronowski and Mr. Long are with the National Coal Board of Great Britain; Dr. Bronowski is Director General of the Process Development Department of the Board and in addition is a well known mathematician, scientist, writer, and radio and television speaker.

One difficulty seems at first to present itself, however. How are the measurements which have been taken to be combined? A bone or a tooth is a unit, not a discrete assembly of independent measurements. To consider these measurements singly, as certain workers have done, is likely to be both inconclusive and misleading. It is inconclusive because nothing is decided when it is shown that, say, the height of an incisor tooth lies in the range of heights of gorilla incisors, and the breadth lies in the range of breadths of chimpanzee incisors; for this state of affairs may well be characteristic of a species different from both. And it will be misleading for a different reason, which is that all the measurements of such a set are correlated with one another: if the height of a tooth is above the average, its breadth and other dimensions are also likely to be above average, and the evidence, as one test is piled upon another, tends simply to repeat itself—the tests do not furnish entirely separate pieces of evidence, as at first sight they might appear to do.

The right statistical method must treat the set of variates as a single coherent matrix. This is the technique of multivariate analysis. As a case in point, consider for example the problem of deciding to which of two species a bone should be allocated. The multivariate technique can, ideally, be pictured to work as follows. The dimensions of this bone in every conceivable direction are measured, in many members of the two species; the averages of each dimension in each of the two species, the variance of each dimension, and finally the correlations between the dimensions are then calculated, giving a complete numerical picture of size and the shape, and the manner in which they vary, in each of the two species. The next step is not to compare the dimensions one by one, nor even to single out those dimensions which, as single dimensions, are most critical. Instead, it is to construct *that function of the complete matrix of dimensions which is more critical than any other in discriminating* between the bone in one species and the other.

In practice, an endless set of measurements of a specimen cannot be taken. There would in any case be little point in doing so, for as more and more measurements are taken, after a while each fresh one inevitably bears an increasing physical resemblance to, and thus becomes more and more highly correlated with, some previous measurement. The additional information contributed by the new measurements, after a certain stage, becomes negligible. Likewise with the discriminating function: the sharpness of the discrimination, as more and more dimensions are incorporated in the function, rises more and more slowly. There is a limit to the sharpness of discrimination which can be obtained, a limit which represents the complete and ultimate appreciation of all the differences in size and shape of the bone, between the two species. In practice, provided the measurements are judiciously chosen, a small number of them is often enough to approach fairly nearly to this ultimate limit. The limited set then summarizes the whole configuration of measurements which makes the bone a unit.

As an example of topical interest, consider the problem of deciding whether a particular lower milk canine tooth belonged to a man or to a chimpanzee (Bronowski and Long, 1951). Let us take 4 measurements, x_1 the height, x_2 the maximum anterior-posterior length of the upper half, x_3 the maximum breadth of the upper half, and x_4 the maximum anterior-posterior length at the level of the basal cingulum, all measured in millimeters. The discriminant function, as it is called, is of the very simple type

$$a_1x_1 + a_2x_2 + a_3x_3 + a_4x_4;$$

and the function we have obtained, using values of the means, variances, and correlations of the measurements obtained from 40 human and 44 chimpanzee milk canines, is

$$X = x_1 - 7.49\, x_2 + 2.34\, x_3 + 4.70\, x_4 \qquad (1)$$

This has on the average the value

$$X = +\ 17.6 \text{ for the chimpanzee,}$$

and has the average value

$$X = -\ 5.0 \text{ for man.}$$

The standard deviation of X is 2.45, so that the range of X, taken at 2½ times the standard deviation, is 6.1 on either side of the average. In order to classify a tooth, which is supposed to be either a chimpanzee or a human lower milk canine, x_1, x_2, x_3, and x_4 are measured in millimeters, and the measurements inserted in the discriminant function (1) above. If the result lies between $+ 23.7$ and $+ 11.5$ the tooth is chimpanzee; if between $+1.1$ and $- 11.1$ it is human.

Sometimes the classification problem is wider, and it may be necessary to distinguish between several possible groups. Extensions of the method allow such problems to be dealt with in the same unambiguous and logically satisfying manner.

In the case of the fossil teeth 4 alternatives present themselves: man, the chimpanzee, the gorilla and the orang-utan. The main problem is, however, to distinguish between the human family on the one hand and the three anthropoid apes on the other, and as it happens the function (1) serves admirably for this purpose. Using further measurements from

40 gorillas and 34 orangs, we find that the range for the ape family as a whole is $+ 31.5$ to $+ 5.0$, and since the human range is as we have seen $+ 1.1$ to $- 11.1$, effective discrimination is ensured.

As an application, we have calculated the values of this function for the Kromdraai and Taungs milk canines found in South Africa. The values are $- 2.6$ and $- 7.9$ respectively. They prove conclusively that these teeth do not belong in the ape categories. More than this, they fall precisely in the human range. It would be wrong to conclude positively that they are human teeth—there still remains the possibility that they come from another realm or species not considered in setting up the function. Even if this is so, however, the discriminant analysis indicates that the two fossils bear a closer resemblance (in a sense we shall describe later) to human than to ape teeth.

The discriminant function, as we have said, is designed for the especial purpose of sorting individuals which are initially assumed to belong to one of the families under consideration. In many cases this assumption is not open to question, for instance in the sexing of material from a known species. At other times it may not be certain that an individual does belong to one of the species under consideration. This brings us to another type of problem, that of deciding whether the size and shape of the individual are such as would be found in a certain species, allowing for the variation which is always present.

To meet this problem we again obviously need a technique which treats any set of measurements which may be taken as a coherent whole. If the dimensions are tested separately, some of them may show differences from the average for the group in question which, considered alone, would appear significant; others may not. When many tests are carried out, there is always an increased chance of finding a difference which, considered by itself, would be regarded as significant—on the principle that the more shots we make, the more likely we are to hit some target. It is very difficult to make allowances for this type of accident when the dimensions are correlated. Moreover, even when no single dimension shows a significant variation from its group mean, the total configuration may still be wrong. Multivariate methods attack this problem from a standpoint similar to that which led to the discriminant function. Ideally, one imagines a large number of individuals from the given species to have been measured in every conceivable direction. A function is then constructed which on the basis of these measurements expresses the *total* deviation in size and shape from the average for the species. In practice, of course, one uses a summary of size and shape based on a few major dimensions.

Using the same 4 dimensions, x_1, x_2, x_3, and x_4 which formed the basis for the discriminant function, we have constructed such a function for human milk canines. It turns out to be

$$S = (y_1 - 6.53)^2 + (y_2 - 11.96)^2 + (y_3 - 4.99)^2 + (y_4 - 1.91)^2 \quad (2)$$

where y_1, y_2, y_3, and y_4 are quantities obtained from the x's by the relations[1]

$$y_1 = x_1$$
$$y_2 = -0.345\,x_1 + 2.605\,x_2$$
$$y_3 = 0.078\,x_1 - 0.586\,x_2 + 2.337\,x_3$$
$$y_4 = -0.124\,x_1 - 1.159\,x_2 - 0.119\,x_3 + 2.050\,x_4$$

The function S, as we have already indicated, expresses in a numerical form the combined divergence of the set of measurements x_1, x_2, x_3, and x_4 from the average for human teeth, and as their configuration departs more and more from the human average, so does the value of S grow. In about one human lower milk canine in twenty, on the average, will it exceed the value of 6.0: and in only one in a hundred, on average, the value 8.4. For practical purposes we may take it that if an individual gives an S-value greater than 8.4 it is not human; if the S-value is between 6.0 and 8.4 the matter is open to doubt; but if the value is less than 6.0 then the configuration of the 4 measurements is such as would be found reasonably often in human teeth.

We selected three ape teeth at random from our basic sets, one chimpanzee specimen, one orang, and one gorilla: the S-values they gave were 62.7, 50.3, and 113.9, respectively. The Kromdraai and Taungs specimens on the other hand give S-values of 1.0 and 5.9 respectively, thus confirming their hominid character.

We must emphasize again the difference between the S-function (2) and the discriminant (1): the S-function is used to test whether the set of measurements is such as we would reasonably expect to find in human specimens, whereas the discriminant is designed to give an immediate decision to which family, man or the apes, the individual belongs, assuming that it does belong to one of them. In the former case, we are concerned with absolute probabilities, in the latter with relative probabilities.

Functions of the S-type can play a useful part in examination of the relations between different groups. As we have already seen, the value of S for an individual expresses, ideally, its divergence in size and shape from the average for the group to which the S-function relates— in a sense, the "distance" of the individual from the average or "center" of the group. A natural extension in dealing with a number of groups is

---

[1] The significance of the y's is more fully explained in the appendix.

to consider the distances between different groups, that is, the distances between their centers; it is sometimes possible to divide up an assembly of groups into constellations of the group, or "super-groups," the members of any one constellation being in general closer to one another, that is, resembling each other more, than members of different constellations. An interesting application of this technique to a number of Indian castes and tribes may be found in the Report on the United Provinces Anthropometric Survey (1941) by Mahalanobis, Majumbar, and Rao, published in Sankhyā (1949).

The above very brief outline of some of the uses of multivariate analysis will, we hope, show that it is an instrument of considerable potential value in physical anthropology. It is interesting to note that the method was developed, in the first place, largely to meet problems in biological classification. It has been rather slow to take hold: perhaps co-operation between statisticians and anthropologists has not been as good as it might have been. Improvement in this respect should be of advantage to both.

To those who may wish to apply the technique, the best advice we can give is to call in the help of a trained statistician. The discriminant function should be within the scope of those with a little knowledge of statistics (for details see R. A. Fisher, 1948) but some of the other techniques need a fairly advanced training.

The authors are indebted to Prof. W. E. Le Gros Clark and Prof. J. T. Robinson for supplying them with the measurements of fossil, human and ape teeth which they have quoted.

Appendix

The purpose of this appendix is to show in simple terms what reasoning underlies the construction and use of the statistical functions mentioned in the text. We shall use the language of geometry.

In everyday solid geometry a point is specified by three co-ordinates. Let us take the 4 dimensions x_1, x_2, x_3, and x_4 of our milk canines as specifying points in a 4-dimensional space. Each tooth will then be represented by one point. If we have a large number of teeth of one species, say the chimpanzee, we shall find that the points corresponding to them tend to cluster around a certain central point or centroid, in such a way that the concentration or density of points in the space (that is, the number per unit volume) falls off with increasing distance from the centroid. Similarly, the points corresponding to human lower milk canines will cluster round another point, the human centroid. Suppose now that we have to decide to which of the two species a certain specimen should be allocated. A reasonable procedure would appear to be to find which centroid was nearer to the point representing the specimen, and to allocate it accordingly. Again, if we have to decide whether the 4 measured dimensions of a specimen are such that it can reasonably be taken to be human, we might use the distance of the corresponding point from the human centroid as a guide.

This idea of distance is indeed the key to the solution in each case, but first we have to make allowance for the fact that the points of each population or group are not symmetrically distributed around the centroid. The loci of equal point densities are not concentric spheres (as they would be if the distributions were similar in every direction) but ellipsoids, partly because of the correlations between the dimensions and partly because their variabilities are not all the same.

This difficulty is overcome by transforming the original variates to new ones which are uncorrelated and whose variances are all equal. The loci of constant point densities are then spheres, and the probability associated with any set of dimensions is directly related to the distance from the centroid of the point representing the set.

The significance of the equations in the text will now be more fully understood. They transform the original correlated variates x_1, x_2, x_3, and x_4 to uncorrelated variates y_1, y_2, y_3, and y_4, and the y's all have the same standard deviation. The S-function is simply the square of the distance of the point (y_1, y_2, y_3, y_4) from the point $(6.53, 11.96, 4.99, 1.91)$, the latter being, in terms of the y's, the human centroid. The critical values 6.0 and 8.4 are the squares of the radii of spheres which enclose respectively 95 per cent and 99 per cent of the human population.

In this geometrical scheme the discriminant function appears as a device for the rapid comparison of distances: with two populations the value of the discriminant for a specimen shows at once which centroid is nearer to the point representing the specimen. This could also be done by calculating the value of the S-function for the specimen with regard to each population in turn, and, as one would expect, the discriminant function is related to the S-functions and can readily be deduced from them.

Since the distance from the centroid of a population to a point representing a specimen is in a sense a mathematical expression of the resemblance between the specimen and the average of the population, the discriminant affords a direct answer to the question of which of two groups a specimen resembles more cloesly. It remains, however, a relative measure—the resemblance in each case might be small. The S-function, being an absolute measure, is thus in a sense a more fundamental quantity.

The method of obtaining the transformation to uncorrelated variates may be found in an Appendix to the Report on the United Provinces Anthropometric Survey, already cited. The calculation is straightforward, if a little tedious, and once the transformation is obtained the S-function is easily constructed, being

$$\sum_i (y_1 - \bar{y}_1)^2$$

the y_1's being obtained by substituting the means of the x's in the equations of the transformation. The critical limits for the S-function may be found from the fact that if the y's are expressed in standard measure, that is, are converted to variates with unit standard deviation by dividing by their original standard deviation, the S-function given by the standardized y's, for members of the population to which it relates, is distributed as χ^2 with degrees of freedom equal to the number of dimensions involved. This assumes that the basic distributions of the populations are mutivariate normal, which with material of this kind is usually sufficiently accurate.

The discriminant function can also be obtained from the transformation equations, being simply

$$\sum_i d_i y_i$$

where the d_i's are the differences of the $\bar{y}_i$'s of the two populations in question.

Ecology and the Protohominids

George A. Bartholomew, Jr., and Joseph B. Birdsell   1953

Although the word ecology is used in both the biological and the social sciences, attempts to bring the biologist and students of human society together by analogical reasoning are beset with traps for the unwary. The biological world lies primarily within genetic and physiological limits while that of the social sciences lies within cultural limits. However, whatever else man is, he is first an animal and hence subject, although usually indirectly, to environmental and biological factors.

It is generally agreed that the ecological generalizations and points of view which have proved helpful in interpreting the natural history of most mammals can be applied virtually intact to all primates except man. It should, therefore, be possible to extrapolate upward from ecological data on other mammals and suggest the biological attributes of the proto-hominids and to extrapolate downward from the ethnological data on hunting and collecting peoples and suggest the minimal cultural attributes of the protohominids.

We propose first to discuss in general terms some aspects of mammalian ecology which appear to be applicable to the protohominids; second, to apply these ideas to the available data on the australopithecines; and third, to discuss the application of a few ecological ideas to preagricultural humans. A history of the development of ecology and suggestions for its applications to anthropology which has recently been published

FROM *the* American Anthropologist, *1953, vol. 55, pp. 481–498, reprinted by permission of the authors and of the American Anthropological Association. This and the next two articles consider various aspects of the life of hominids at an australopithecine stage and the transition to more advanced forms, with particular attention to the role of tool-using and tool-making. The present paper is a suggestive hypothetical reconstruction of the relations and interactions of primitive hominids and their environment. Dr. Bartholomew is Professor of Zoology and Dr. Birdsell is Professor of Anthropology, both at the University of California at Los Angeles.*

by Bates (1953) provides basic historical orientation and perspective for such an effort.

Protohominids and tools. In retrospect, the vast sweep of evolution appears to lead inevitably to the appearance of man, but a rational interpretation of the evidence refutes this. During the Cenozoic there have been three separate mammalian evolutionary complexes, one in Australia, one in South America, and one in Eurasia, Africa, and North America. Of these complexes, only the last has produced organisms of the hominid level. Further, since the major orders of mammals were already distinct in the Eocene, each has had a separate genetic history for approximately 70,000,000 years, and only one, primates, has produced an organism at the hominid level of organization.

Since a number of mammalian orders have shown a strong independent evolutionary trend toward a large brain size, this trend is by no means peculiar to the order primates (Edinger, 1948). This striking parallelism is presumably related to the fact that large brain size favors varied behavior and learning as supplements to genetically fixed responses. Why then did not the primates, like the other mammals, reach an apparent evolutionary dead end in the Pliocene? The familiar and reasonable ideas concerning the importance of arboreal life in setting the stage for the appearance of man, i.e., dependence on vision, grasping hands, and the lack of restrictive skeletal adaptations, need not be labored here, but the importance of bipedalism can profitably be reexamined.

The primates comprise the only major order of mammals which is characteristically arboreal. There can be no doubt that this arboreal heritage has been of vital importance in human evolution, but the critical stage in the transition from ape to protohominid involves the assumption of a unique terrestrial mode of life. A number of cercopithecids have successfully invaded the terrestrial habitat, but these all show quadrupedal adaptations. This level of adaptation, while obviously effective if one may judge by the fossil record and by present abundance, appears to represent a stable, long-surviving, adaptive equilibrium.

The terrestrial adaptations of the hominid line represent a step into a new and previously unexploited mode of life in which the critical feature was bipedalism. Among mammals changes of this magnitude have occurred only rarely since the middle Cenozoic. Aside from the saltatorial rodents such as the jerboas and kangaroo rats, all placental terrestrial mammals other than man use both hind and front legs for locomotion. The extreme rarity of bipedalism among mammals suggests that it is inefficient except under very special circumstances (Hatt, 1932; Bartholomew and Caswell, 1951). Even modern man's unique vertical bipedal locomotion, when compared to that of quadrupedal mammals, is relatively ineffective, and this implies that a significant nonlocomotor advantage must have resulted from even the partial freeing of the forelimbs. This advantage was the use of the hands for efficient manipulation of adventitious tools such as rocks, sticks, or bones. Of course, the terrestrial or semi-terrestrial living primates have their hands free when they are not moving, but only man has his locomotion essentially unimpeded while carrying or using a tool. Man has been characterized as the "tool-using animal," but this implies a degree of uniqueness to man's use of tools which is unrealistic. Not only do other primates use tools—the use of sticks and rocks by chimpanzees and baboons is generally familiar—but such unlikely animals as the sea otter (Fisher, 1939) and one of the Galapagos finches (Lack, 1945) routinely use rocks or sticks to obtain food. Indeed, the natural history literature is replete with instances of the use of tools by animals, and there really is no clear-cut boundary between web-spinning, nest-building, and stick-wielding on the one hand, and tool use at the simplest human level on the other. However, in contrast to all other mammals, the larger arboreal primates are, in a sense, tool users in their locomotion. As they move through the maze of the tree tops, their use of branches anticipates the use of tools in that they routinely employ levers and angular momentum. The grasping hands on which the locomotion and feeding of primates depends, are of course obviously preadapted for tool use.

Rather than to say that man is unique in being the "tool-using" animal, it is more accurate to say that man is the only mammal which is continuously dependent on tools for survival. This dependence on the learned use of tools indicates a movement into a previously unexploited dimension of behavior, and this movement accompanied the advent of bipedalism. With the assumption of erect posture regular use of tools became obligatory; the ability occasionally to use tools must have preceded this in time.

Protohominids and body size. The conditions of terrestrial life for a bipedal tool-using mammal virtually demanded that the protohominids be big mammals, i.e., at least in the 50 to 100 pound range, for large size of itself offers important biological advantages (Carter, 1951: 293). In the case of the protohominids two such advantages at once suggest themselves: First, large size would remove them from the category of potential prey for all carnivorous birds, reptiles, and all mammals except the big cats and the pack-hunting dogs; second, it would allow them to utilize, without restrictive anatomical specialization and with simple instrumentation, virtually the entire range of food size utilized by all other terrestrial mammals.

Sociality. Social behavior is inextricably interwoven with ecology, and although it is not possible to review the subject in detail here, certain aspects of it are basic to the development of later ideas.

The transitional protohominids must have been social to the extent of forming relatively stable family groups. Even in the absence of direct evidence, such a statement can be made with complete confidence from knowledge of the other members of the suborder Anthropoidea. First, there is the absence of seasonal sexual periodism in man and the great apes. Thus sexual ties form a bond of sustained and continuing attraction which provides a biological basis for the long-surviving family unit. As has frequently been pointed out this is a central element in human sociality. Second, there is a long period of growth and maturation. The long childhood of man and the great apes is not a mere function of size —the blue whale, the largest mammal that has ever lived, grows to sexual maturity and to a length of 70 or more feet in two years (Mackintosh and Wheeler, 1920)—but it is related to the unique dependence for survival on learning in the higher primates. The acquisition of competence for independent life demands several years of parental care in the chimpanzee and a decade or more in man. Hence, survival requires a mother-offspring relation which is sustained through many years and, like sexual attraction, is not just a seasonal interlude as in other social mammals. Since these factors shape the social behavior of both the great apes and man, they must have shaped the social life of the protohominids.

Other cohesive forces, by analogy with living primates, must have supplied integration to the social organization of the protohominids. Important among these must have been dominance-subordinance relationships. The concept of social dominance has proved to be a touchstone to the understanding of the social behavior of vertebrates. It is a key factor in the social behavior of mammals as diverse as deer (Darling, 1937), seals (Bartholomew, 1952), and primates (Yerkes, 1939).

In every case in which it has been studied in mammals, dominance is established at least in part on the basis of aggressive behavior (Collias, 1944), of which a large component is either directly or indirectly dependent on reproductive physiology. In mammals the male sex hormones stimulate aggressive behavior and contribute to greater body size, while the female sex hormones inhibit the former and do not contribute to the latter. Consequently, males tend to be dominant over females in most situations. In the higher primates, as in many other social mammals, sexual dimorphism in size reinforces the greater aggressiveness of the male and insures his superior social status in situations where force is involved. In most social mammals, gregariousness overcomes the disruptive effect of dominance-subordinance relations and maintains the social unit. In primates dominance is not an exclusively disruptive force, since the dominant animal may protect the subordinate animal which looks to it for protection as well as leadership (Noble, 1939).

In nonprimate social mammals, the resolution of the forces produced by dominance and gregariousness typically produces à seasonal breeding unit which consists of a dominant male and a harem of females and which usually excludes the young of previous years.

The social unit in nonhuman primates is variable, and too few detailed field studies have been published to allow extrapolation from living anthropoids to the protohominids. In modern hunting and collecting groups of man the smallest unit is the biological family including immature offspring, and in many cultures the most important functional group is the extended family, or band. In the case of man, even at the simplest level, social dominance is not based exclusively on successful aggressive behavior. The distance between nonprimate mammals and man is too broad to be spanned by the bracketing technique previously used, but the semi-permanent biological family, including offspring, must have been a basic unit among the protohominids. Integration on any more extensive scale must have depended upon the degree of cultural attainment. It should be observed however, that fairly large groups have been reported for living nonhominid anthropoids (Carpenter, 1942; Nissen, 1951).

Territoriality. No aspect of the social behavior of wild vertebrates has attracted more attention than territoriality, a concept which includes the entire complex pattern of behavior associated with the defense of an area. The display of ownership of places and objects is very highly developed among human beings, but this behavior pattern is not peculiar to modern man. It is almost universally present in terrestrial vertebrates, either on a permanent or seasonal basis. The large literature on the subject with regard to birds has been reviewed by Nice (1941). Its status in mammals has been discussed by Burt (1943), and its relation to vertebrate populations has been examined by Errington (1946).

Territoriality springs from the necessity for finding and maintaining environmental conditions suitable for survival and reproduction. The techniques of territory maintenance, the precise factors immediately responsible for it, and the immediate significance of it vary from species to species.

The maintenance of territories either by individuals or by social groups has profound effects on distribution. Birds and mammals tend to be neither continuously distributed nor irregularly grouped, but to be spaced at more or less regular intervals through ecologically suitable habitat.

This spacing is determined by conflicts between pairs of individuals or between interacting groups of animals. Thus, territorial boundaries are learned and vary in time and space. If anthropologists were willing, this might almost be considered protocultural behavior at a subhuman level; in any event, it emphasizes the continuity of human behavior with that of other vertebrates.

As a result of the centrifugal effects of aggressive behavior, territory maintenance forces animals to disperse into adjacent areas. It distributes the individual organisms or social units of a species throughout the entire accessible area of suitable habitat. Should the population increase, local population density does not continue to build up indefinitely. Instead territorial defense forces individuals out into marginal situations, and thus the resources of the optimal habitat are not exhausted. Most of the displaced individuals do not survive, but some may find unexploited areas of suitable habitat and thus extend the range of the species. The result is that a population tends to be maintained at or below the optimum density in the preferred habitat, and the excess individuals are forced to marginal areas to which they must adapt or die.

Thus territoriality is one of the primary factors which determine the density of population. It organizes a local population into a well-spaced array that allows adequate living conditions for all successful individuals. It limits the breeding population which can exist in suitable habitats and thus helps to prevent increase beyond the long-term carrying capacity of the range. This dispersive effect of territoriality can hardly help but be an important causal factor both in migration and in the spread of genes through a population. Hence, it must contribute importantly to rate of evolutionary change (Burt 1949).

The question of the importance of territoriality to the biology of proto-hominids at once presents itself. Carpenter (1934; 1940) has demonstrated that howler monkeys and gibbons maintain territory by group action. It is clear that territoriality exists in all complex human societies, and it is clearly established that group territoriality is also important at the simplest levels of human culture. It is, therefore, reasonable to assume that protohominids similarly possessed a well-developed territoriality, presumably on the basis of the family or extended family.

Population equilibrium. One of the most critical ecological factors which can be determined about an animal is the density of its population. The number of variables which contribute to the determination of population density is enormous; a complete analysis for even the best known of living wild mammals is difficult, perhaps impossible. Nevertheless, the framework within which such an analysis can be made is known, for the factors involved in population dynamics have been studied intensively in recent years. A useful discussion of populations from the point of view of the ecologist is given by Bodenheimer (1938), and Allee *et al.* (1949).

Since organisms are transient biochemical systems which require continuous expenditure of energy for their maintenance, the struggle for existence becomes, in one sense at least, a struggle for the free energy available for doing physiological work. This fact offers a point of view from which to approach the problem of estimating the population of protohominids, or any other mammal.

There exists a series of nutrient or trophic levels that expresses the energy relations which tie together the various organisms of the terrestrial environment. The primary trophic level is that of the green plants, for only they can use radiant energy to synthesize significant quantities of organic material. The trophic level of the herbivores includes all animals directly dependent on plants for food. The next higher trophic level, that of the meat-eaters which may be primary carnivores (eaters of herbivores), secondary carnivores (eaters of other carnivores), and so on. The final trophic level, the eaters of dead organic material, eventually returns materials to the inorganic state depleted of biologically available energy.

Materials which are used as building blocks and sources of energy by organisms cycle continuously through these trophic levels, and at each level there is an endless competition for them. There are a number of obvious corollaries which follow from these relationships. An important one is that nutrition plays a primary role in determining the major functional adaptations of animals. Life demands a continuous expenditure of energy, and this energy is available only through nutrition. These energy relations involve a sustained long-term pressure sufficiently constant to maintain and give direction to the major evolutionary trends apparent in the adaptive changes of the sort shown by hoofed mammals and the canrnivorous mammals. As Simpson (1944: 31) and others have pointed out, these nutritive adaptations have for the most part led not only to greater efficiency but also to more and more specialization, with a consequent reduction in potentiality for new major nutritive adaptations. Thus adaptations toward increased efficiency in food getting, or toward avoidance of becoming food for other organisms, are largely restrictive from the standpoint of future evolutionary change.

The total weight of biological materials produced by one trophic level must necessarily be less than that of the level below it on which it depends, and greater than that of the level above, which it supports. Each nutritive level must in the long run live on the interest, not the capital, of the trophic level below it. From this there follows a maxim which allows of no exception. On a long-term basis the mean population of a species is in equilibrium with the trophic levels both above it and below it, as well as with the total limiting effects of the inorganic environment. This means that the birth rate must be great enough to balance the death rate from disease (a nutritive phenomenon from the standpoint of the disease-causing organism), predation, and accident. Consequently, birth rate is a factor subject to natural selection, and all natural populations represent approximate equilibria between biotic potentials and total resistance of the biological and physical environments. Shortlived mammals of high fecundity, such as rabbits and mice, are sometimes characterized by drastic short-term fluctuations in population size, the causes for which are still subject to active controversy (Cole, 1951). However, in this paper we shall ignore the problem of population cycles, for drastic cyclic fluctuations have rarely been observed in large tropical mammals with low reproductive potentials.

It has beeen generally appreciated since the time of Darwin that animals despite their capacity to increase in numbers, tend to maintain a population which fluctuates around some equilibrium figure. This idea is of such a basic nature that it forms a foundation for the concept of natural selection which now appears to be an omnipresent evolutionary force. The factors involved in the maintenance of these equilibria are complex and variable. Since, as pointed out above, an animal population cannot possibly permanently exceed its food resources, these fix an upper limit. The determination of the actual equilibrium figure is a subtle problem which must be solved independently for each population. A thoughtful analysis of the factors limiting population in a nonhominid primate under natural conditions is presented by Collias and Southwick (1952) in their study of howling monkeys. For a population to maintain itself above that lower critical level which means inevitable extinction (Darling, 1938), many factors (which may vary independently) must be simultaneously satisfied. Such things as a suitable habitat which will include adequate food resources, water, and home sites, and climatic conditions that do not exceed the tolerance of the group must be present.

Since biological factors vary with time, values for population equilibria are not to be measured at a given point in time. They fluctuate about a balance which is determined, not by the mean condition, but by the extremes. Indeed, one of the most firmly established ecological generalizations is Liebig's law of the minimum, which states that a biological reaction at any level is controlled not by the factors which are present in excess, but by that essential factor which is present in minimal quantity. Since, as was previously pointed out, population density is the most critical single ecological datum, anthropologists studying the simpler cultures characterized by few storage techniques would do well to search for these critical limiting factors which do determine density. Such limiting factors are not necessarily either obvious or conspicuous at all points in time, and even when they occur their expression may be subtle or apparently indirect. A semi-arid area may have many fruitful years in succession, but a single drought year occurring once in a human generation may restrict the population to an otherwise inexplicably low density. For example, the Papago Indians of the lower Colorado River were forced in drought years to revert to a desert hunting and collecting economy for survival (Castetter and Bell, 1942). Thus, their population density appears in part to have been strongly affected by the preagricultural carrying capacity of this area. In some cases the size of a population will be determined not by the availability of an abundance of food during ten months of the year but by a regular seasonal scarcity in the remaining two months.

The reproductive potential of animals is such that under favorable conditions, such as having available a previously unexploited habitat, the size of a population can increase at an essentially logarithmic rate. This capacity for rapid increase makes possible the recovery of populations following drastic population reduction. In a stable population, on the other hand, the reproductive potential is expressed only as a one-to-one replacement of adult individuals.

Anthropologists are properly impressed with the complexity of learned behavior in human groups, but may fail to appreciate its significance among other mammals. Even on the nonhuman level, population density may be controlled by behavioral factors, either genetic or learned. Territoriality and dominance relations, which are dependent on learned behavior, contribute to the determination of group relations and population density. Under certain circumstances behavioral factors may be more important than nutritive factors in determining population density. For example, recent work discussed by Calhoun (1952) has shown that the Norway rat under controlled experimental conditions, in which food is present in excess at all times, reaches a population equilibrium that is determined by strictly behavioral factors related to territoriality and competition for suitable homesites. Thus, experimental work confirms extensive field observations on a variety of vertebrates. Since learned behavior operates as an important factor determining density in all terrestrial mammals which have been studied, and in modern man, it must have been an important factor in determining the population density of the protohominids. The importance of learned behavior increases directly with its complexity, and in man at cultural levels above the hunting and collecting stage of economy it becomes increasingly difficult to identify the ecological factors affecting population size.

Ecology and the Australopithecines

The dating of the australopithecines has proved troublesome, and final decision is not now possible. Dart and Broom have suggested that these protohominids lived during a period extending from the Villafranchian into the Middle Pleistocene. This time span overlaps the datings of early man in other parts of the world, and implies a collateral relationship with more evolved hominids. Another view has recently been given by Teilhard de Chardin (1952), who places the australopithecines in Villafranchian time, and thus removes them from contemporaneity with known African hominids. Breuil (1948) seems to reflect a similar point of view. In the former case the australopithecines would have been competing in their closing phase with more advanced forms of man, and hence would have been decreasing in numbers and range. In the latter instance the australopithecines would apparently have been the sole occupants of the protohominid niche over wide areas in South Africa, with the resultant possibility of having an expanding population and range. For purposes of an ecological discussion it is necessary to assume one dating or the other; it is not important to decide whether or not the australopithecines were in fact ancestral to more advanced hominid types, but it is important to determine whether or not they were the sole occupants of the hominid niche in South Africa.

As Tielhard de Chardin (1952) points out, the australopithecine-bearing breccias and the human industry-bearing deposits have never been found conformably associated in the same site. This assumes, as did Tielhard de Chardin, that *Telanthropus* is but a variant of the australopithecine type. Therefore, for purposes of discussion we shall assume that the australopithecines are Villafranchian in date and hence earlier than the makers of the pebble-cultures of South Africa. By analogy with the ecology of other animals it would be surprising if man and the australopithecines had remained contemporaries in the same area over very long periods of time, for closely related forms with similar requirements rarely occupy the same area simultaneously.

Use of tools. Neither the archeological nor morphological evidence concerning australopithecines suggests an alternative to the assumption, which we made earlier, that protohominids were dependent on the use of tools for survival. It is generally agreed that the australopithecines were bipedal. Referring to our previous discussion, this strongly implies that the australopithecines routinely utilized adventitious or perhaps even slightly modified tools. Dart's evidence (1949b) for the use of ungulate humeri as clubs offers empirical support for this theoretical position. Unmodified rocks used as tools can rarely be identified except by context.

Familiar evidence from both archeology and ethnology shows that at the simplest level, rough tools commonly are discarded after initial use. Hence, a lack of recognizable stone tools in the breccias does not indicate that these were not used. Time alone precludes the survival of wooden implements such as clubs and digging sticks, although their use by australopithecines is certainly to be expected, for even the living great apes use sticks spontaneously.

The dentition of the partly carnivorous australopithecines (see section on food size) is uniformly characterized by reduced canines and incisors, and by nonsectorial premolars and molars (Le Gros Clark, 1949b). These dental characteristics are unique to them among all the large carnivorous mammals. The absence of teeth adapted for stabbing or shearing clearly implies the killing of game by weapons and butchering by simple tools. This observation would hold true even if the assignment of carnivorous habits to australopithecines were based only upon the abundant evidence that baboons were an important item in their diet. It is not dependent on the controversial question of their killing large hoofed mammals.

The dentition of australopithecines offers further evidence concerning their dependence on tools. As pointed out previously, intrasexual combat is characteristic of the males of virtually all strongly dimorphic mammals. Australopithecines are dimorphic, but they do not have the large piercing canines so characteristic of most of the larger living primates. This striking reduction of canines strongly implies that even in intrasexual (and intraspecific) combat, the australopithecines placed primary dependence on tools.

Scale of food size. It should be possible on theoretical grounds to fix the approximate upper and lower size limits of the food which could economically be handled by the australopithecines with nothing more elaborate than a crude stick for digging and a limb bone for a club. Their capabilities would allow the utilization of the following animal foods: virtually all terrestrial reptiles and the smaller aquatic ones; eggs and nesting birds; some fish; fresh-water mollusks and crustaceans; insects; all of the smaller mammals including some burrowing forms, and larger mammals up to and including baboons. It is difficult, perhaps impossible, to determine whether or not the remains of the large giraffids and bovids reported from the bone breccias (Dart, 1948b), represent kills by australopithecines or their scavenging from the kills of the larger cats. Since few meat eaters are loath to scavenge, and the implementation which would allow the australopithecines to kill such large animals is not apparent, we suggest that scavenging from the kills of the larger carnivores may have been sytematically carried out.

Like most present-day hunting and collecting peoples, the australopithecines probably used plants as their major source of food. Without imputing to the australopithecines any cultural capabilities beyond the use of a simple stick for digging, at least the following types of vegetable food would be available to them: berries, fruits, nuts, buds, and shoots, shallow-growing roots and tubers, and fruiting bodies of fungi. Some of the very small vegetable foods exploited by modern human groups were probably not extensively used. Effective utilization of grass seeds and other hard-shelled small seeds require specialized gathering implements and containers, and processing by grinding or cooking.

Such activities imply technologies which cannot be assigned *a priori* to the australopithecines, and for which there is no archeological indication until much later times. In this connection it may be noted that the evidence for the use of fire by *Australopithecus prometheus*, though impressive, is still regarded by some as controversial (Barbour, 1949b; Broom, 1950b). In summary, it seems reasonable to treat the australopithecines as generalized carnivorous animals for which the freeing of hands and the use of simple implements enormously broadened the scale of food size to include a surprisingly large proportion of the total food resources of the terrestrial environment.

Social behavior. The biological bases for the family and social organization at the protohominid level which have already been discussed should apply to the australopithecines. Group organization beyond the family level is not indicated by the archeological context of the finds, because the rather large number of individuals recorded from Swartkrans and Sterkfontein might result from sampling of family-sized groups over many generations. However, there is at least one line of archeological evidence which suggests social organization beyond the simple family level. Since baboons travel in large aggregations and were a significant item of australopithecine diet, it would seem likely that the latter hunted in bands. A single australopithecine, even armed with a club, would not be a serious threat to a band of baboons (Dart, 1949b). Such group hunting does not necessarily imply a high level of communication, such as speech, or permanence of organization, for it is characteristic of a number of nonprimate carnivorous vertebrates—many canids, some fish-eating birds, and killer-whales. Broom (1950b) has shown that the australopithecines were characterized by sexual dimorphism, a widespread trait in the primates, including man. In social mammals, sexual dimorphism is almost invariably a product of sexual selection associated with competition between males for females. Characteristically this sexual selection produces males which are larger, and more aggressive than females, and which have specialized structures for offense and defense. Although these dimorphic characters are a product of competition between males, they usually result in the males assuming the role of group defender. We propose that the sexual dimorphism of the australopithecine males may have favored a secondarily-derived function related to aggressive behavior, namely the hunting of large prey, including perhaps other australopithecines (Dart, 1949b). Thus it may be that a sexual division of labor such as is present in all known hunting peoples was foreshadowed at this early level of hominid evolution.

The primates which first began to exploit a bipedal tool-using mode of life were establishing a level of adaptedness of enormous potentiality which had previously been inaccessible. They were entering a period of rapid change leading to a new kind of adaptedness. In the terminology of Simpson (1944) they were a group undergoing quantum evolution. It is to be expected that, like other similarly rapidly evolving groups, they would be represented in the fossil record not by a uniform long-persistent type, but by a variable group of related forms. The australopithecines, which probably occupy a stage near the end of a step in quantum evolution, fit this theoretical prescription nicely. The various australopithecine forms which have been named can be considered representatives of a highly polymorphic assemblage. Their polymorphism is consistent with the idea of a rapidly evolving and radiating group and thus favors the probability of the Villafranchian dating.

It is reasonable to assume that most of the recovered australopithecine fossils date from a period prior to the time they faced competition from more highly evolved hominid types. When, as they inevitably must have, the australopithecines came in contact with culturally advanced hominids, they must have been subject to rapid replacement in terms of geological time.

DISCUSSION

A paper such as this necessarily can be of only temporary utility. We feel that its principal contribution lies in raising questions, the answering of which may require orientation toward new points of view, the collection of new kinds of data, and perhaps the use of new techniques.

Students of animal ecology have developed a number of points of view which could be profitably applied to the study of preagricultural man. Two are particularly attractive. The first of these is that the basic problem of human behavior, like the behavior of other animals, is the obtaining of food, for the human body requires a continuous input of energy both for maintenance and for propagation. The second point of view involves the idea that population density normally is a complexly maintained equilibrium, dependent upon environmental as well as behavioral (and in the case of man, cultural) forces.

Anthropologists and archeologists to date have shown great ingenuity in utilizing the meager data for paleolithic and mesolithic man to establish tentative chronologies and outline cultural relationships. However, at the simplest level, the significance of material culture lies neither in the establishment of chronology nor as a measure of relationships, but as an indicator of efficiency in obtaining food. The lack of data concerning the food-getting effectiveness of the various items of material culture primarily results from preoccupations with typology rather than function. Even the best of typological labels tend to restrict functional interpretations and to ignore the role of varied behavior and human ingenuity in extending an implement's utility. Furthermore, functional interpretations can be determined only by studies of living peoples, and the ethnologist has not yet generally been stimulated to the realization of the basic importance of such data.

It is of interest that some food-getting devices which we presume to have been available to the australopithecines remain important today in the economy of hunting and gathering peoples. But there is little systematic quantitative information concerning the proportion of food obtained through the use of the hands alone, or that added by the use of the simple digging stick, club, or wooden spear. Nor at a more culturally sophisticated level are there quantitative data available to measure the increase in efficiency made possible by the invention of such devices as the spear-thrower and the bow and arrow. In making such analyses it would be useful to distinguish between the contributions of the relatively limited variety of primary tools and the more varied secondary tools. For example, the ecological significance of the fist-axes of the lower and middle Pleistocene varies enormously depending upon whether they are to be interpreted as primary tools used to make wooden implements such as clubs, digging sticks and spears, or whether they are regarded in the unlikely light of hand-held striking implements (see, for example, Tindale, 1949).

As pointed out previously, all animal populations, including human populations, depend on radiant energy stored chemically by photosynthesis. Animals compete endlessly among themselves for the one per cent of incident solar energy which plants are able to capture. The competitive success of an individual animal can be determined from its metabolism and the success of a population can be expressed quantitatively as the product of population density times individual metabolism.

If one can obtain even approximate figures for (1) the production of organic material by plants, (2) population densities and, (3) metabolism, one can evaluate from one point of view the biological success of different organisms. One can compare lions and elephants, earthworms

and mice, humans and all other organisms, or more pertinent to anthropologists, one can compare simple cultures existing in either similar or
different environmental situations. Since human beings comprise a single
species, inter-group comparisons can be made on the basis of weight
per unit area. An instructive analysis of this sort for small North American mammals has been made by Mohr (1947).

To our knowledge this quantitative approach to human ecology has
not been exploited by anthropologists; indeed, few attempts have been
made by zoologists. Pearson (1948) has gathered figures which allow a
comparison of Indians of northeastern United States with other animals
common in the same area. Indians had less metabolic impact than deer,
about the same impact as long-tailed shrews. Deevey (1951) presents
calculations which show the amazing trophic impact of the present
human population of the world. Both these efforts are frankly exploratory
and depend on approximations, but they point up an approach which
merits consideration by anthropologists. If one could obtain for given
areas even crude figures for human population density and for the production of organic material by the flora, he could compare the nutritive
efficiencies of rainforest and grassland cultures, or the efficiency of Great
Basin Indians and Australian Aborigines even though the two peoples
live in arid regions of a very different character. Similarly one could
obtain quantitative estimates for the effects of rivers, lakes, sea shore,
and particularly vegetation types (i.e., oak woodland) on the capacity
of an area to support human populations at a simple cultural level.

As discussed earlier, natural populations tend to fluctuate about some
equilibrium figure. This fact has long been recognized by biologists, but
to date, despite the perspectives which it supplies, it has not significantly
influenced the approach of most anthropologists. From a short-term point
of view, populations are in only approximate equilibrium, but viewed
from the time scale of the Pleistocene, slowly expanding populations of
man can be considered as being essentially in equilibrium. It appears to
us that the idea that the populations of early man were in approximate
equilibrium with the environment can supply a point of view from which
to interpret the dynamics of technologically simple human populations.
It should greatly facilitate qualitative exploration of such considerations
as spatial variation of population density; growth or decline in numbers;
rates of movement as influenced by migration and gene flow; and, shifts
of populations into new climatic situations which demand new modes of
life and may involve biological as well as cultural changes in adaptedness.
As such qualitative interpretations are refined it may be possible to
develop models which depict these processes semi-quantitatively and
thus allow crude predictions.

Population density is a key to these dynamic processes, for either directly or indirectly it controls all of the others. As discussed in the sections on territoriality and population equilibrium, the density of early human populations, while immediately determined by a complex of variables in which behavior plays a central role, was ultimately controlled by the environment. Even in the most favorable environments the equilibrium density attained by natural populations is somewhat below the maximum which the environment can support. The factors restricting density are behavioral in an immediate sense and involve such things as aggressive behavior and territoriality. These behavioral factors must have brought dispersive forces to bear on Pleistocene man just as they do on other mammals. The existence of such dispersive forces suggests that the evolving australopithecines must have spread with great rapidity (i.e., almost instantaneously in terms of geological time) throughout the continental tropics and subtropics of the old world. Such an expansion would leave no suitable and accessible areas unoccupied. Consequently all subsequently evolved hominids in these regions must have expanded at the expense of already established populations. The replacement of the australopithecines by somewhat more advanced but related hominids may have followed the usual mammalian pattern of the gradual expansion of the more efficient form, and the slow reduction of the numbers of the less efficient. In many instances, however, population change must have resulted from gradual genetic penetration, and much of human evolution in the Pleistocene could easily have been powerfully affected by introgressive hybridization. In this regard it should be remembered that anatomical differences do not necessarily indicate genetic incompatibility between groups, and that there is no evidence of reluctance to hybridize even between widely different human types. If rapid and dramatic group replacement did occur it must have been a rare event occurring in special circumstances.

Although mammals are less affected by climate in a direct physical sense than are most organisms, physiological differences among mammals adapted to different climatic conditions have been clearly demonstrated (Scholander, *et al.*, 1950). Distributionally the primates are an order characteristic of the tropics or subtropics. Modern man himself appears to be unable to invade the higher latitudes without fairly elaborate cultural accoutrements. It may therefore be concluded that during the Pliocene, the evolving protohominids occupied only the tropics, subtropics, and perhaps the fringes of the temperate zones. The only place in which human populations could have expanded into a vacuum was at the margins of the then habitable areas. Thus changing cultural, and possibly changing biological, adaptedness would have allowed hominid expansion from the tropics into the temperate regions and ultimately into the arctic regions of the Old World. Aside from the initial continental expansion of the Old World protohominids, man expanded into major vacuums in populating Australasia, the New World, and much later, Micronesia and Polynesia. Once entered, these areas must have become filled rapidly, so that subsequent immigrants were faced for the most part with the problem of replacing established populations. Migrations, although spectacular, were probably of less importance in the Pleistocene than the processes discussed previously, which proceed normally without local catastrophic environmental change.

The anthropologists' lack of concern with the idea of population equilibrium in the simpler and more static human cultures is explicable in historical terms. Anthropologists, reacting to the claim by some anthropogeographers that extreme environmental determinism was operative on man, soon demonstrated that details of culture were not controlled directly by the environment. This broad denial overlooked man's nutritive dependence upon the environment, and long inhibited quantitative investigation of the relationship between man's population density and environmental factors.

The present interpretation of the mechanism of evolution is based upon natural selection which demands that populations be in a state of approximate equilibrium at a given time. To unravel the evolution of Pleistocene man, inevitably hampered as one is with inadequate data, one must necessarily use the idea of a population in equilibrium with the carrying capacity of the environment.

Most ecologists agree that no data are more crucial than those bearing upon population size, structure and density. Anthropologists, even though generally unconcerned with population equilibria, in some instances have been aware of the concept (Krzywicki, 1934; Steward, 1938; and Evans-Pritchard, 1940). But in general the importance of an ecological approach has not been appreciated. Some archeologists have hoped to reconstruct preagricultural population figures from studying the temporal and spatial distribution of sites, but the inescapable sampling errors in this approach render it unreliable. We suggest that an analysis of the energy relationships and the efficiency of the techniques for obtaining food offer a promising approach.

For several years it has been apparent that an ecological approach is imperative for all studies in population genetics, including those pertaining to man. It also offers a potentially useful point of view to the physical anthropologist, the ethnologist, and the archeologist, and it should provide an important integrative bridge between the various fields of anthropology.

SUMMARY

An attempt is made to apply ecological concepts which are widely used by vertebrate zoologists to protohominids in general and to australopithecines in particular.

Various aspects of the biology of protohominids are considered: tool use, bipedalism, body size, scale of food size, sociality, territoriality, population density and equilibria, dispersion, and nutrition.

Energy relations to the environment and population equilibria are discussed with regard to human preagricultural populations.

The Villafranchian
and Human Origins[1]

F. Clark Howell   1959

〜〜

Few people lack curiosity about their ancestors, their genealogy, and the ways of the world in the past. This curiosity extends to the ancestry and history of all mankind. In the last hundred years theological explanations have—especially in countries of Western cultural tradition—tended to be replaced by a more rational approach to the matter. This approach is the concern of human paleontology, and its inception is closely linked with the name of Darwin.

A century ago only a few early human skeletal remains were known, and these only from Western Europe. These represented either the approximately 35,000-year-old Cro-Magnon people or the (then scarcely recognized) 50,000-year-old "classic" Neanderthal folk. Much understanding of the course of human evolution has been gained since Darwin's time, and especially within the past quarter century. There are still some extraordinary gaps in the fossil record of the family Hominidae with respect both to specific ranges of Pleistocene time and particular geographic areas. Some such gaps, like the middle Pleistocene range in

[1] Editor's Note: This paper was documented by an exhaustive technical bibliography. Author and editor have agreed to eliminate all these references (except footnotes remarking on matters in the text); the bibliography may be found in the original publication.

〜〜

FROM Science, 1959, vol. 130, pp. 831–844, reprinted by permission of the author and of the American Association for the Advancement of Science. Dr. Howell combines a detailed first-hand knowledge of hominid fossils with an equally thorough knowledge of the implements of early man and of the paleontology and geology of the important sites, especially in Africa, many of which he has examined personally. In this careful, if technical, article, he surveys the significance of the geological background in the rise of tool-making man. Dr. Howell is Associate Professor of Anthropology at the University of Chicago.

Mediterranean Africa, have become known only in the last decade, as investigations have been vigorously pursued in the field. However, fossil specimens are still almost entirely unknown from this range of time in Western Asia and in sub-Saharan Africa. The most striking hiatus, particularly since stone artifacts are far from uncommon, is the complete absence of hominid skeletal remains from the Pleistocene in the Indian subcontinent.

In spite of these deficiencies in knowledge, a good deal is known of the major evolutionary stages in hominid phylogeny for the latter half of the Pleistocene. Several distinct, largely geographically restricted lineages are recognized to have existed during the middle, and to have persisted into the early upper, Pleistocene; these probably represented paleospecies, although some workers consider them to have been generically distinct. From a portion of one such (*not* Asian) lineage, anatomically modern man (*Homo sapiens*) evolved, but the details of this transformation are still largely obscure. This best documented aspect of human paleontological knowledge encompasses only the later phases of man's evolution. It is well known largely because of its recency and because there are apparently more abundant traces of human occupation in datable Pleistocene contexts, especially since these can often be linked with effects of the extensive continental glaciations of the Northern Hemisphere. This record thus begins, broadly, during the time of the first of these great continental ice sheets, variously named in Germany, Britain, Poland, and European Russia.

The main lines of hominid evolution were set during an earlier segment of the Pleistocene. The mammalian faunas of that time range, in Europe, Asia, and Africa, reveal the first appearance of new and modern genera in an otherwise often archaic assemblage. This was an extended period of fluctuating, but generally cooler and more temperate, climates compared with the late Tertiary (Pliocene), leading to mountain glaciation and changing biotopes and biotas. It was a time marked by extensive mountain building, faulting, and upwarping to the extent of several thousand meters, as seen in the Alps, Pyrenees, Caucasus, Atlas, and Himalayan ranges. This long interval, representing the lower Pleistocene and often termed the Villafranchian after its characteristic fauna, encompasses a time probably as long as the whole of the middle and upper Pleistocene. Half a million years is perhaps a modest estimate. The recent work by Emiliani, who employed oxygen isotopes in the analysis of climatic change from ocean-bottom cores, gives some promise of providing an "absolute chronology" for the Pleistocene. However, the published climatic curves appear to encompass only the latter half of the Pleistocene—that is, the three major continental glaciations and the intervening Great and Last interglacial stages, the stratigraphy of which closely parallels the core profiles.

The lower Pleistocene represents perhaps the most crucial period for future research in human paleontology. Such efforts promise results of great significance to the understanding of formative phases of hominid phylogeny and the elucidation of those distinctive associated patterns of behavior which differentiated the first hominids from other higher primate (pongid) antecedents and collaterals. I have attempted in this article to indicate a part of what is known of the Villafranchian stage from traces of hominids of this period.

The base of the Pleistocene is best defined by three lines of evidence: tectonics, climatic deterioration, and the appearance and distribution of new forms of animal life. In the majority of stratigraphic sections, an unconformity, representing an interval of uplift and erosion, separates terminal Pliocene deposits from overlying marine or continental (Villafranchian) sediments of the basal Pleistocene. The first signs of marked cooling are evident in the appearance of north temperate or arctic forms (such as *Cyprina islandica* in Mediterranean waters) in marine invertebrate faunas, and in vegetation changes demonstrated by palynology or by the particular conditions of sedimentation. Continental deposits of basal Pleistocene age contain mammalian assemblages referred to as Villafranchian, from the type locality of Villafranca d'Asti in the upper Po river drainage basin. Such faunas are characterized by the first appearance of the modern genera *Elephas* (*Archidiskodon*), *Bos* (*Leptobos*) and *Equus* (and, in some areas, *Camelus*), but in association with a number of other typically late Tertiary species.[2] The term *Villafranchian* has also often been extended to apply to this basal Pleistocene interval as well as to the fauna. The termination of the interval is ill defined; it is probably best taken as the base of the Cromerian "interglacial" stage or its marine equivalent in the Mediterranean basin, the Sicilian. This stage immediately precedes the first major continental glaciation.

In western and southwestern Europe,[3] evidences of fluctuating sea levels, both transgressive and regressive, and of variably cooler climates, unlike the preceding Pliocene, are recognized at a number of localities.

---

[2] Although several mammals are included as new arrivals in the Villafranchian, all are not *necessary* to prove a lower Pleistocene age; thus, *Equus* never reached Java and *Leptobos* is not present in sub-Saharan Africa.

[3] In France: Sâone basin (Bresse-Dombes region), Puy-en Velay (Haute-Loire), Allier valley (Perrier, Mont Coupet, Senèze localities), and Rhone valley (St. Vallier, Drôme); in Italy: Po valley (Piemonte, Emilia), upper Arno valley (Tuscany), Monte Mario (Rome), Puglia and Calabria, and Sicily.

The tilted deep-water Plaisancian and brackish Astian sediments of the (later) Pliocene sea, which flooded many areas of lowland southern Europe which are continental at present, are unconformably overlain in a number of regions (in southern France and Italy) by the marine deposits of the basal Pleistocene Calabrian sea. The Calabrian, a transgressive sea which was subsequently regressive (compare the Po valley; also the Emilian stage of *Emilia*), has, as its continental equivalent, developed in unsubmerged and emergent uplands, a series of fluviolacustrine sands and gravels with a markedly cool temperate flora and a characteristic Villafranchian mammal fauna. The contrast with the subtropical vegetation and archaic mammal faunas of the Pliocene is striking and clearly delineated.

The comparable successions afforded by the North Sea basin, in East Anglia and the Netherlands, and by the polliniferous clays and lignites of the lacustrine basin of Leffe (Bergamo, Tuscany) illustrate the main pattern of climatic change during the Villafranchian in western and southern Europe (Figure 1). The evidence would seem to indicate at least two major colder stages, the latter double, prior to the well-defined Cromerian interglacial stage. These two colder stages are separated by the still inadequately known Tiglian "interglacial" stage. This sequence is paralleled in the Rome region by the Acquatraversan and Cassian phases of colder climate which precede the transgressive Sicilian sea and the extensive eruptions of the Sabatino volcanoes. A very considerable body of evidence indicates several phases of fairly extensive mountain glaciation during this interval, very probably including the Donau and Günz stages in the northern Alps. The first Himalayan glaciation is perhaps the Asian equivalent. However, there is a dearth of evidence of direct correlation of these subalpine stages either with continental Villafranchian deposits in the lowlands or with equivalent marine horizons.

The European Villafranchian lacks any trace of higher primates, and there are no stone implements testifying to occupation of the continent by hominids.[4] This was probably a consequence of two factors: (i) Europe was not a primary center in the original hominid radiation, and (ii) the extent of the Mediterranean and Black seas, not only in the Pliocene but also during the Calabrian and Sicilian transgressions of the early Pleistocene, created impassable water gaps which effectively isolated Europe. The first evidence of hominid occupation of the European continent is well along in the earlier middle Pleistocene. It corresponds to the time of the Romanian regression of the Mediterranean, when eustatic

---

[4] Supposedly artificially flaked specimens have been reported from the East Anglian "Crags"; however, most workers are now convinced that these are natural specimens.

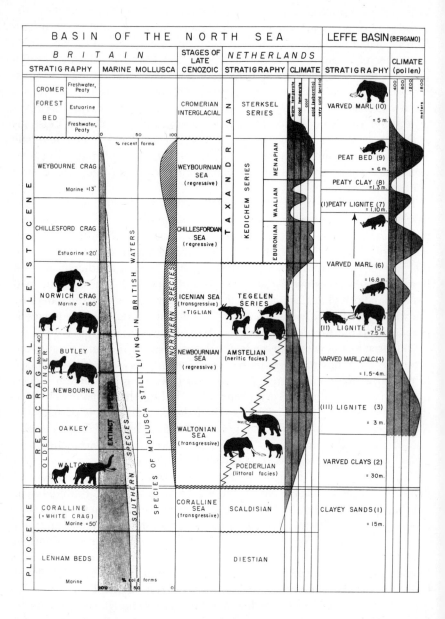

FIGURE 1. Villafranchian stratigraphy and climatic change in the North Sea basin and the Leffe lake basin (Tuscany). The silhouettes indicate some of the characteristic species in particular faunal assemblages. The Leffe climate curve, based on palynological evidence, is expressed in terms of present altitude corresponding to vegetation; Leffe is 400 meters above sea level. (Compiled from various sources.)

lowering of sea level attendant upon the first major continental glaciation evidently permitted expansion into Europe of those peoples [probably represented only by the Mauer (Heidelberg) mandible] responsible for the Abbevillian hand-axe industry.[5]

In eastern Asia the continental Villafranchian is best known in northern China and in the southern foothills of the Himalayas. In northern China, the Pliocene, a period of dry sub-tropical-to-tropical climate with extensive lakes between stretches of desertic country, was terminated by diastrophic movements resulting in extensive erosion (Fenho erosion interval). These formerly widespread lakes were consequently displaced, and rejuvenated rivers and streams greatly enhanced their fluviatile activities. In the synclinal basins of Nihowan (Hopei), Taiku, and Yûshe (Shansi), to mention only the best known, this erosion surface underlies a torrential lacustrine series of basal conglomerates overlain by sands, marls, and clays (lower Sanmenian series); the clays include a plant bed with cool dry flora (Taiku basin), and the series is capped with sands and silts which yield a characteristic Asiatic Villafranchian fauna. The entire series was tilted and is separated unconformably (by the Huangshui erosion interval) from the early middle Pleistocene red loams (upper Sanmenian series). No evidence of hominid fossils or of tool-making activities have been recorded from the earlier, Villafranchian, beds. The first evidence of hominid occupation is revealed at locality 13, Choukoutien, correlative with the upper Sanmenian series on faunal grounds, which has yielded a single small chert chopping tool but no human skeletal remains.

The entire Pliocene and lower Pleistocene succession is magnificently represented in sub-Himalayan northwest India, both in the Potwar region (Punjab) to the northwest and the Siwalik Hills to the east. The Pliocene, exposed in the middle Siwaliks series, is represented by fresh-water sandstones and shales, 6500 to 10,000 feet in thickness, deposited under tropical to subtropical climates trending toward increased aridity. The entire series was tilted during a major phase of mountain building followed by an interval of severe erosion at the end of the Pliocene. These movements, either through the development of anticlines or as a result of faulting, created a series of depressions trending northeast-southwest which were filled during the lower Pleistocene with great thicknesses of alluvial sediments (upper Siwaliks series) derived from the adjacent uplands. The earlier Tatrot zone of this series is characterized by a thick (100-foot) basal conglomerate overlain by nearly a thousand feet of coarse sand-

---

[5] It has been maintained that the Abbevillian, at least in the Somme valley where it is best known, is of "first interglacial" (Günz-Mindel-Cromerian) age. However, a variety of both geological and paleontological evidence indicates that assignment of a younger age is fully warranted, and that this was probably an ameliorative phase within or toward the end of the first major continental glaciation.

stone; interspersed silty or conglomeratic horizons contain a (still inade-quately known) fauna which is characteristically Villafranchian.[6] The overlying Pinjor zone, some 1000 to 1500 feet of laminated silts and sands, clearly distinguished lithologically from the Tatrot zone, appears to have been deposited under warmer and more temperate conditions by slug-gishly meandering streams, in contrast to the great alluvial activity that accompanied the deposition of the preceding Tatrot. A rich Villafranchian fauna is represented in the Pinjor zone. However, neither the Tatrot nor the Pinjor provide hominid remains, nor is there evidence of stone tools testifying to hominid occupation. Such tools first appear, as the "Pre-Soan" (Punjab flake industry) chopper–chopping-tool assemblage, in the over-lying boulder conglomerate, attributed to the second Himalayan glacia-tion, of early middle Pleistocene age.

Discussion of the southeast Asia area of the Sunda shelf, an extension of the mainland in middle and later Pleistocene time, is less pertinent here because of the extensive Pliocene submergence. Only isolated moun-tain peaks were emergent along the southern (Zuider Mountains) and northern (Kendeng Hills) coasts in eastern Java, and some few uplands in the western region. A Villafranchian fauna is known from fresh-water sandstones and coarse conglomerates at several localities where these overlie Pliocene marine beds. However, skeletal remains of two distinct hominids (*Meganthropus, Homo modjokertensis*) first appear only in the early middle Pleistocene. Sundaland, including Sumatra, Java, and Bor-neo, and much of the present ocean floor had become largely continental by that time as a result of further uplift and marine regression consequent upon continental glaciation in the Northern Hemisphere. There is no evidence to suggest hominid occupation of the Sunda shelf during the Villafranchian stage.

The present evidence would appear to indicate that continental Eurasia was not occupied by hominids during the lower Pleistocene—that is, the Villafranchian stage. The evidence is admittedly and necessarily of a negative nature, and further field investigations, particularly in the sub-Himalayan Siwaliks, are sorely needed. The important fact is that the available evidence does not bear out the opinions of certain earlier workers that Asia, or central Asia in particular, was a primary center for hominid (or higher primate) origin and dispersal. Such a conclusion is contradicted not only by our understanding of higher primate relation-ships, based on comparative anatomical and paleontological studies, but also by biogeographical and paleogeographical conditions. On the other

[6] The interesting and little known pongid *Ramapithecus* is the last Siwalik primate to occur in the Tatrot zone.

hand, a variety of evidence shows that the Villafranchian stage in Africa was crucial in the earlier phases of hominid evolution.

AFRICAN VILLAFRANCHIAN

Mediterranean Africa

Several lower Pleistocene localities with Villafranchian faunas are known in northwestern Africa[7] (Figure 2). One of the best stratified localities is Fouarat (near Port Lyautey, Morocco), along the southern border of the Rharb plain. A Villafranchian fauna is present here in coarse sands and sandstones representing a littoral facies of a Calabrian gulf which in places filled depressions in Pliocene marine sediments. Hominid occupation of the area is perhaps first recorded at a slightly later stage, probably corresponding to the regressive Emilian. Flaked pebbles, thought by some to represent primitive pebble tools, have been collected from the Arbaoua conglomerates, of basal Pleistocene age. These deposits, like the reddened Marmora sandy loams, mantle this region and (broadly) represent the continental equivalent of the Calabrian (Maghrebian) transgression. However, the artificial nature of the specimens is difficult to confirm when they are discovered in this gravel context.

The Villafranchian fauna of North Africa is more adequately known in Tunisia (Garaet Ichkeul), and particularly from old lake basins in northern Algeria (Bel Hacel; St. Arnaud). The base of Lake Ichkeul (near Ferryville) comprises southerly tilted deepwater Plaisancian and lagoonal Astian marine sediments which are overlain by fresh-water lake beds of basal Pleistocene age. The lower sands and gravels of the latter, separated from the Pliocene sediments by a thin conglomerate, are richly fossiliferous; a mild temperate flora, but with substantial boreal elements, occurs in intercalated, more or less sandy, clays. However, the full succession at Ichkeul is still poorly known, and the faunal assemblage is incomplete, since the beds are only partially exposed during times of low water, on the northern foreshore of the present lake. At Bel Hacel emergent dune sandstones, which concordantly overlie transgressive Plaisancian-Astian sediments, are eroded and filled with alluvial, weathered and reddened, conglomerates which contain terrestrial and fresh-water molluscs and a Villafranchian fauna. The more than 100-meter-high Sicilian beach rests horizontally and unconformably on the tilted and compressed series.

[7] Arambourg distinguishes lower (Ichkeul, Boucherit, Fouarat) and upper (Bel Hacel, Ain Hanech) Villafranchian faunas; the former is more archaic and includes *El. africanavus, Anancus, Stylohipparion, and Libytherium,* whereas the latter includes predominantly *El. meridionalis* and *Equus,* with *Libytherium* and, rarely *Stylohipparion.*

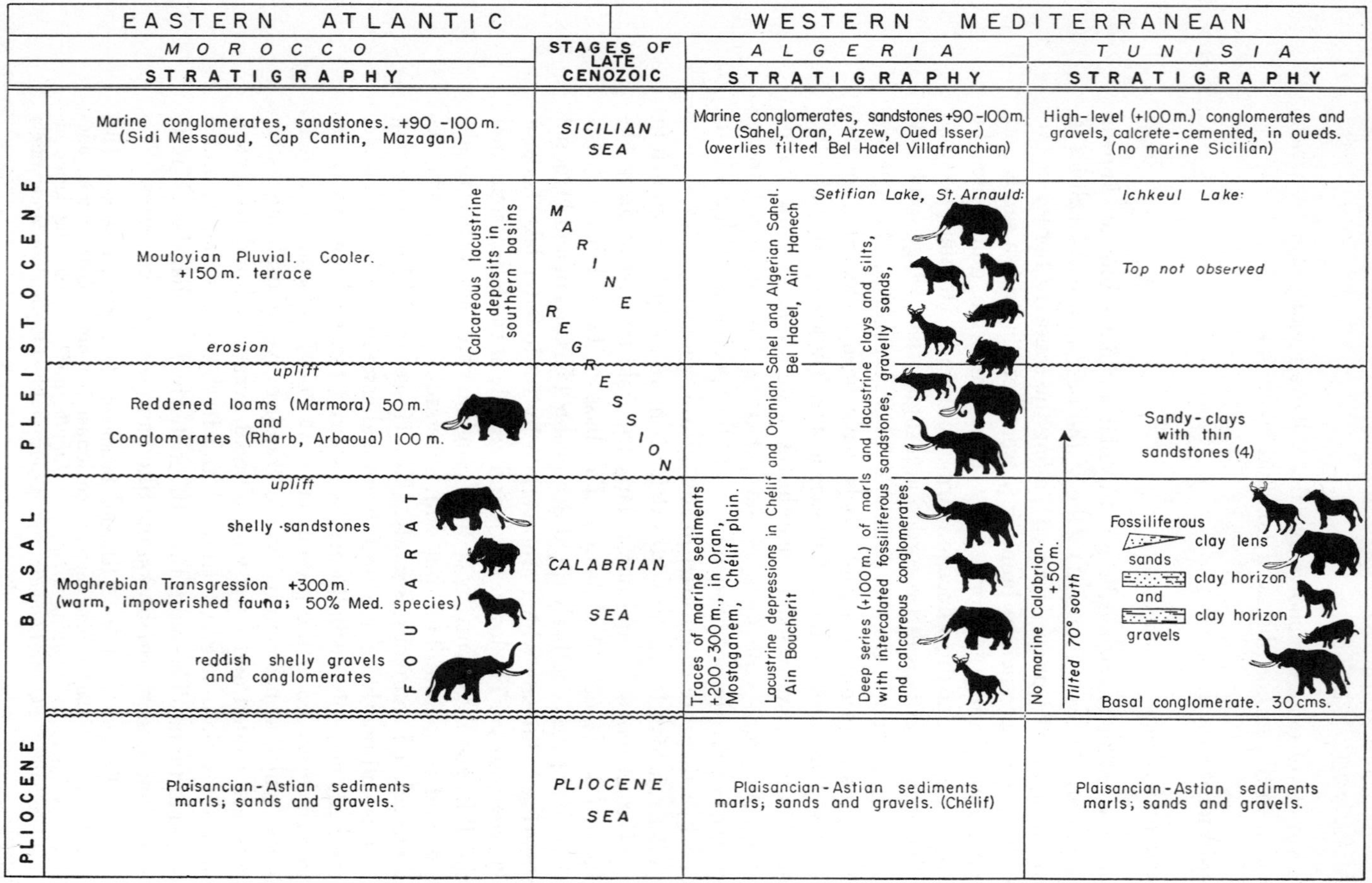

Figure 2. Villafranchian stratigraphy in northwestern Africa. The silhouettes indicate some of the characteristic species in particular faunal assemblages. (Compiled from various sources.)

On the Constantine-Setifian plateau near St. Arnaud the earlier Pleistocene is exposed in deep ravines dissecting thick marls and other calcareous clayey sediments, with intercalated gravel and conglomeratic
horizons, which fill old marshy or lacustrine depressions. In the Oued
Boucherit, two horizons, separated by a meter of sterile brown clay,
contain a Villafranchian mammal fauna. The lower horizon (Ain Boucherit) is a coarse calcareous conglomerate, and the upper horizon (Ain
Hanech), a cracked clay, rather sandy or with light gravels at the base.
A quantity of undoubtedly primitive stone implements have been recovered here, largely from the upper horizon.[8] These specimens (Figure
3) are fashioned from naturally worn dolomitic limestone pebbles, exhibiting fresh, concave flaking scars and ranging in size from that of a
tangerine to that of a good-sized orange. They are either battered over
most of the surface to a multifaceted polyhedral form (boules) or are

FIGURE 3. Pre-Chelles-Acheul implements from the site of Ain Hanech (Algeria).
(× ½) (Courtesy C. Arambourg.)

[8] Crude bifaces, referrable to a basal Chellean industrial stage, were discovered in
1952, derived from a higher level at the Ain Hanech site.

flaked along a margin unilaterally or bilaterally to produce an irregular sinuous edge characteristic of choppers or chopping tools. Unfortunately, the Ain Hanech site has been worked only briefly, since both political circumstances and the proximity of a Moslem cemetery have prevented extensive excavations.

No hominid skeletal remains have yet come to light in the formations of the North African Villafranchian. There is unquestionable evidence of hominid occupation of this region during the terminal phases of the Villafranchian, and a site such as Ain Hanech might one day provide fossilized remains of the creatures themselves.

Sub-Saharan Africa

The central African Pleistocene was initiated by prolonged and extensive uplift, 1000 to 1500 feet at least, accompanied by downwarping in adjacent areas and by fracturing along ancient troughs. Extraordinary volcanic explosions, especially of tuffs and ashes, also took place along the eastern Rift Valley. As a consequence, the mid-Tertiary surface of erosion, whose relief was relatively gentle even during the end-Tertiary phases of valley incision, was severely deformed, and drainage systems were disrupted and even reversed. Extraordinary depths of lacustrine deposits and subaerial, partially volcanic-derived, sediments were accumulated. These are particularly well preserved in the western (Albertine) and eastern (Gregory) rift valleys and represent good exposures of the continental Villafranchian.

The Villafranchian, with an overlying middle Pleistocene series (Rawe beds), is also represented along the southern shores of a minor rift valley trending east-west, now Kavirondo Gulf, an eastern embayment of Lake Victoria. At Kanam, along the north and northeast slopes of the extinct volcano which forms Homa mountain, a great thickness (more than 100 feet) of lacustrine brown clays, with intercalated fine, laminated stony tuffs from intermittent volcanic explosions, have provided a good Villafranchian assemblage. A few pebble tools have also been recovered from such horizons. A small fragment of a hominid mandible is also known; although it was once believed to date back to the lower Pleistocene, it is now known to be of considerably more recent age.

In the Albertine rift valley an extensive lake existed in the basal Pleistocene, as indicated by the massive (at least 1500 to 2100 feet, to judge from borings), tilted and contorted beds of the Kaiso series.[9] These are particularly well exposed along the margins of Lake Albert and its southern

[9] This series is named after the village of Kaiso, the type locality, on the eastern shore of Lake Albert.

tributary, the Semliki River, as well as along the northern shores of Lake Edward and in the region south of the latter adjacent to the volcanic highlands north of Lake Kivu. The beds seem to attain their maximum exposed thickness in the southerly reaches of Lake Albert and at the adjacent mouth of the Semliki valley; thinner exposures in the upper Semliki and the northern reaches of Lake Edward may merely reflect earlier, more prolonged and intense subsidence of the rift floor in this region.

The Kaiso series is complex, and three main stages of sedimentation have been distinguished. Only the basal stages are generally regarded as lower Pleistocene the upper stage is thought to be earlier middle Pleistocene. The lower stage (100 to 120 feet thick in the northern reaches of the valley) is largely silty, with some minor gravel horizons. In some localities this stage is found to overlie a basal ironstone horizon capped by unstratified sands; the ironstone seems to represent a laterite capping the down-faulted peneplain surface and provides an important datum point. This earlier stage is essentially nonfossiliferous. The middle stage (300 to 600 feet thick in the lower reaches of the valley) is predominantly clayey, with selenite evaporites and zones of gypsum. It is characterized by fine sands and sandstones and by discontinuous ironstone horizons and limonite lenses thought to represent desiccated pools. These horizons occasionally provide silicified wood and have yielded a typical, though small (13 species), Villafranchian mammal fauna. Several such ironstone "bone-beds" appear to be present, though they are restricted largely to the middle Kaiso stage.[10] However, another, perhaps lower, bed is also present in the lower Semliki valley. The site of Kanyatsi, along the northern shore of Lake Edward just east of the Semliki outflow, has yielded traces of worked stone implements adjacent to an ancient subaerial soil horizon within the middle Kaiso stage. The specimens represent fresh flakes of quartz and quartzite, but the cores from which these were struck are apparently absent, and no pebble choppers or chopping tools have yet been found.

The central region of the Gregory rift valley has failed to provide certain evidence of lower Pleistocene formations; this is perhaps because there was extensive uplift during the later Pleistocene, or because there was relatively little deposition but considerable volcanic activity. The northern and southern reaches of the valley do afford such exposures. The

---

[10] The particular horizon of the type Kaiso mammal fauna is not clear; possibly it corresponds to the middle or even the upper stage, but this problem may be settled by careful study and comparison of the molluscan faunas within the several stages of the Kaiso series. W. W. Bishop (Geological Survey of Uganda, Entebbe) is now carrying out systematic investigations in the Western Rift, both at Kaiso and in the Lake George-Lake Edward region.

tilted and step-faulted beds of the Omo series, just north and northwest of Lake Rudolph, testify to an ancient and extensive lower Pleistocene lake. A rich Villafranchian fauna occurs in extraordinary profusion in sandstone horizons intercalated in a massive succession of lacustrine volcanic clayey tuffs. Neither hominid skeletal remains nor primitive stone implements have been recovered from the Omo series, which, since their discovery by the Bourg de Bozas expedition in 1902–1903, have only been worked during one relatively brief field season. Further investigations in this most inaccessible region are surely warranted, especially since this year I recovered Pre-Chelles-Acheul artifacts from the eroded sandstones.

In the southern reaches of this rift valley the lower Pleistocene is exposed along the tributary Eyasi trough and the adjacent region to the west of the Crater Highlands. At Olduvai Gorge, which extends from Lake Lagarja on the Serengeti plains some thirty-five miles to the western boundary faults of the Balbal depression, the magnificent lacustrine series of the middle Pleistocene is underlain by a flow of olivine basalt, which buries or obscures earlier horizons. Slightly to the south, in the Vogel river region on the northwest escarpment high above the Eyasi graben, are the Laetolil beds, a series of upfaulted subaerially deposited tuffs. These appear to be earlier than, as well as in part contemporaneous with, the Olduvai series. The upper Laetolil beds have yielded a rich Villafranchian assemblage of mammals, including some microfauna. The lowest horizons are also fossiliferous, but the fauna is very poorly known. Pebble tools and a hominid maxilla fragment, the latter believed to resemble the australopithecine (*Australopithecus*), attributed to these beds may in fact be of later Pleistocene age. The basal bed (Bed I) at Olduvai Gorge is now known to contain a Villafranchian faunal assemblage comparable to that from Omo rather than of middle Pleistocene affinity. Pre-Chelles-Acheul stone implements of the Oldowan industry were first found here nearly 30 years ago. In July Dr. and Mrs. L. S. B. Leakey recovered a beautifully preserved skull of a new form of australopithecine from this bed in association with an occupation surface rich in such artifacts and with the bones of small game taken by this creature (announced at the 4th Pan-African Congress on Prehistory, Leopoldville, August 1959).

Central and eastern Africa afford some of the richest Villafranchian faunal localities in the world, coupled with an excellent Pleistocene succession. The faunas from these sites differ somewhat in composition, that from the Laetolil beds being probably the youngest, overlapping basal Olduvai, and that from Kaiso being perhaps the oldest. The Omo fauna overlaps both Laetolil and Kaiso, and that from Kanam is probably broadly equivalent. As yet it is impossible to determine the magnitude of the climatic change that occurred during the Villafranchian of central Africa because of the effects of tectonics in this unstable region. At present only a broad block correlation with other areas of the Old World, on the basis of faunal content, can be made. Future detailed investigations of the sediments in these basins, particularly of nonsequences and old soil horizons, coupled with palynological research, promise to throw some light on this problem.

At three such localities, Kanyatsi (Lake Edward), Kanam (Kavirondo, Kenya), and Olduvai Gorge, there is clear evidence of hominids, sometimes in the form of skeletal remains and, in all cases, in the form of deliberately fashioned stone tools. Few open habitation sites of the hominids themselves have yet come to light; however, this is largely a result of too little field work in difficult regions. There is every indication that such sites will be forthcoming in the future with concentrated work by prehistorians and Pleistocene geologists. Very complete evidence of such early hominid forms, including abundant skeletal remains, is afforded by the australopithecines of southern Africa.[11]

AUSTRALOPITHECINE SITES

The australopithecines now rank among the most numerous and best known of all Pleistocene hominids. Usually classified as a distinctive subfamily (Australopithecinae) of the Hominidae, but quite probably representing merely a distinct genus, *Australopithecus*, the group contains two probably subgenerically distinct forms, (*Australopithecus*) and (*Paranthropus*). On the basis of the associated faunal assemblages, it appears that the australopithecines are all probably late Villafranchian; however, there is a possibility that the younger form (*Paranthropus*) may have persisted into the early middle Pleistocene.

Australopithecines are known from five sites at three localities in southern Africa.[12] With one exception (Taungs) they occur in fossiliferous breccia, composed of calcite-cemented dolomite soil, which infills former caves, formed by solution or subsidence along ancient fracture

[11] Other riverine situations have provided *selected* assemblages of pebble tools referred to the Pre-Chelles-Acheul industries. The Kafuan industry, generally regarded as the oldest such manifestation, has been recovered from very high-level gravels of the Kafu and Kagera rivers in western and southeastern Uganda, respectively. The industry, in a more evolved facies it seems, is probably also represented in the Katanga, southeastern Belgian Congo, and in the calcified basal older gravels of the Vaal river in southern Africa. There is little question that some of the selected specimens are indeed artifacts of a very primitive stone industry although this is likely *not* true of those from the Kafu river; until larger assemblages are found *in situ*, preferably on old land surfaces, in clays or other fine sediments, there will always be a considerable measure of doubt concerning their full authenticity.

[12] Sterkfontein, Swartkrans, and Kromdraai are situated in a shallow valley about 6 miles northwest of Krugersdorp, southern Transvaal; Limeworks Cave is located in the Makapansgat valley, several miles northeast of Potgietersrust, central Transvaal; the limeworks at Buxton, near Taungs, is just west of the Transvaal border, adjacent to the Kaap escarpment bordering the Harts River, in Bechuanaland (Cape Province).

planes in dolomitic limestones of the Transvaal system. Studies of the mode of formation and the sequence of infillings of these caverns has demonstrated the significance of the degree of communication of the cavern with the outside in the accumulation of sediments. Travertines and intercalated bands of thin gray marly breccia, representing residual calcified material from dissolution of the dolomite, accumulate prior to the formation of any substantial opening to the surface. Subsequently, as the opening becomes progressively enlarged, surface-derived material collects in sufficient quantity to represent a state of equilibrium with outside conditions. Such breccia accumulations may serve as climatic indicators, through analysis of the sand fractions of breccia residues, minus the carbonate cement derived from roof drip, and comparison with modern dolomite soils in regions of differing rainfall in southern Africa. Very satisfactory results have been thus achieved for the Sterkfontein, Swartkrans, and Kromdraai (site A) sites; the method is not directly applicable to the Limeworks Cave site, Makapansgat, where alluviation or slopewash, in the higher levels, are complicating factors. In general, the climate appears to have been somewhat drier in this region when *Australopithecus* lived and somewhat, or even considerably, wetter when *Paranthropus* lived than it is now. Brain refers the three older Transvaal sites (Sterkfontein, Limeworks, Swartkrans) to a major dry interpluvial stage (with at least three separate peaks) and the youngest site, Kromdraai, to a succeeding, wetter pluvial stage.

The Taungs site, long since destroyed by quarrying activities, was a cave formed by solution in the capping carapace of a massive basal Pleistocene travertine banked up against a dolomite limestone cliff (Campbell Rand series). The filling of the cavity was calcified sandy breccia overlain by contaminated travertine with sandy lenses from which the type australopithecine remains were most probably recovered.

The fauna associated with the australopithecines is not only varied but differs from site to site. In general it comprises other primates (both rare monkeys and abundant baboons), numerous rodents, insectivores, hyracoids, lagomorphs, numerous carnivores, including hyaenids and sabretooths, suids, an extinct sivathere, equids, and numerous antelopes. The following frequencies were obtained from counts of over 7000 bone fragments, out of a much larger number, from remnants of the gray marly breccia at Limeworks Cave[13]: 92 percent, antelope (293 individuals; more

---

[13] The recent account by W. I. Eitzman of the original constitution of the Limeworks Cave and the mining activities which largely destroyed it suggests that there were probably three separate fossiliferous breccias, separated by travertines in the lower portion of this great cavern. He states that the lower and middle of these were densely packed with bone, whereas the upper horizon was more discontinuous and far less fossiliferous. It is clear that only a very small proportion of the bone accumulations have been salvaged from the mine dumps and that the great bulk of the fossil mammals (and australopithecines) were consumed in the lime kilns.

than two-thirds medium to small, the remainder large or very small varieties); 4 percent, other ungulates (four zebras, six chalicotheres, five rhinoceros, one hippopotamus, 20 pigs, six giraffids); 1.6 percent, carnivores (17 hyenas, one leopard, one jackal, one wild dog, one sabretooth, and nine other small and medium species); 1.7 percent, baboons (45 individuals), rare rodents (hares and porcupines), and very rare birds and reptiles (tortoise, water turtle). Five australopithecine individuals represent only 0.26 percent of the total assemblage.

The various segments of the skeleton are very unequally represented at this site. The frequency of cranial fragments is particularly high among the nonbovid ungulates (88 percent), the carnivores (75 percent), the rodents (100 percent), and the primates, including the australopithecines (95 percent). The proportions are lower (34 percent) among the antelopes (of all sizes), and there are interesting differences in frequencies of antelope postcranial elements: cervical vertebrae (7 percent), other vertebrae (5 percent), ribs, and so on (5 percent), scapulae (9 percent), innominates (8 percent), forelimbs (37 percent), hindlimbs (20 percent), feet (6 percent) (these figures do not apply to very small antelopes, which are represented exclusively by cranial elements).

Any consideration of the diet and life habits of the australopithecines must take into account the associated fauna and frequencies of preserved skeletal segments. Hence, such figures are important and are much needed from the other sites. Several possibilities exist as to the manner in which the australopithecines and the associated fauna came to be incorporated into the breccias. The sites might have been (i) natural crevices into which animals fell; (ii) crevices into which bone accumulations were swept by natural agencies; (iii) carnivore lairs into which prey or scavenged carcasses were carried; (iv) rubbish heaps; or (v) actual occupation sites of the australopithecines. There is no evidence at any of the sites to support (i) or (ii), although the gravelly breccia at Limeworks Cave was partly fluviatile in origin; there is also evidence of stratification in the upper brownish breccia at Swartkrans, probably due to deposition in isolated pools but certainly not the consequence of stream activity. It will always be difficult to decide between (iv) and (v), but the important and still unsettled question is whether the sites were occupied and the bones were accumulated by carnivores, in particular sabretooths or hyenas, or both, or by carnivorous australopithecines.

It is necessary to bear in mind that these sites are known because of commercial lime-quarrying activities. In most cases such efforts were directed toward the basal travertines, formed largely when the caves were still solution cavities. In the case of Taungs the cave was discovered as a consequence of such mining in the massive cliff-forming travertines at Buxton, in one of which the cave happened to be situated. All the fossil mammals at the Limeworks Cave, Makapansgat, have been obtained by sorting through the extensive dump heaps left behind by the miners. Only in the case of Swartkrans (in part) and some of the excavations at Sterkfontein have investigations been carried out which would permit some comprehension of the fossiliferous breccias as they existed *in situ*. However, the extreme consolidation of the fossil cave earths, a consequence of calcareous cementation, necessitates the use of explosives, so results are definitely limited with respect to details of the pattern of association and the arrangements of bones in the deposits. In the present state of knowledge it is indeed doubtful if the matter can be definitely settled until a new site can be excavated, with every attempt made not to disturb the stratigraphy and fossil associations.

Dart has repeatedly maintained that the extraordinary accumulations of mammalian skeletal remains in the fossiliferous breccias are a direct consequence of the predatory and carnivorous habits of australopithecines. Such remains represent in his opinion not only slaughtered prey but also scavenged carnivore kills; many of the bones were useful as tools and weapons for pounding, cleaving, scraping, stabbing, and slicing. On the basis of the preserved remains inventoried at Limeworks Cave, specialized functions have been attributed to specific bones and portions of animal skeletons that were put to use by those "flesh-eating, skull-cracking and bone-breaking, cave-dwelling apes."

There are in fact two distinct issues involved here. The question as to whether the bones were employed as implements and weapons by australopithecines presupposes that these creatures were carnivorous and were therefore responsible for the fossiliferous accumulations. The use of these bones is extremely difficult to verify, since none of the sites yield any trace of specimens which have been deliberately worked or shaped. There is no doubt that the jaws and teeth, horns, and shattered or damaged limb bones which Dart attributes to an "osteodontokeratic culture" might be employed in the fashions he has so exhaustively and imaginatively outlined. However, as in the case of the so-called "bone and antler industry" from the Choukoutien locality in northern China, attributed by Breuil to the middle Pleistocene hominid found there, this is extremely difficult to confirm scientifically, even though both claims may prove entirely valid.

The question of the carnivorous habits of australopithecines is a separate matter and one which should be resolved from existing evidence. The parts and proportions of the animal skeletons preserved do coincide closely with remains at carnivore kill sites in the open, even after the usual scavengers have been at work. Moreover, although contrary claims have been made, both brown and spotted hyenas may eat and accumulate bones in and about their lairs, at least at times. Nonetheless, this possibility does not account for the enormous concentration of bones at the sites. Also, there are discrepancies between the proportion of cranial and postcranial elements of the antelopes compared with the other ungulates, the carnivores, and the primates.

Two main points are important in connection with the dietary habits of these creatures: (i) the evidence from Taungs, Sterkfontein, and Limeworks Cave of baboon skulls bearing evident signs of localized depressed or radiating fractures, smashed-in walls or tops of the cranial vault, openings in the vault or base, and twisted facial skeletons all testify to predatory activities which are those of a hominid rather than any hyaenid or felid carnivore; and (ii) the substantial quantity of various antelope and other long bones which are not only broken and smashed but also split longitudinally, and which usually fail to reveal any traces of carnivore gnawing, is further testimony to hominid habits.

Such evidence has been convincing not only to me, but also to other workers who have examined the specimens in question. Moreover, it seems very likely, on the basis of the Taung evidence, that eggs, crabs, turtles, birds, rodents, and smaller antelopes were a not insubstantial part of australopithecine diet. The former such items are easily collected, and it is not particularly difficult to kill members of the other species of smaller mammals. The australopithecines were very probably carnivorous predators as well as scavengers of the kills of other carnivores (of which there was then an abundance of forms long since extinct). The marked disproportion between the bovid and nonbovid ungulates and the relatively few carnivores in the Limeworks Cave inventory may merely be a reflection of this latter fact and of the limited hunting capabilities of such creatures. Such a conclusion does not preclude the possibility that carnivores also, at least periodically, occupied such sites and contributed to the bone accumulations. This can hardly be denied until careful excavations have been carried out which prove the situation to have been otherwise.

Until recently none of the australopithecine sites were known to contain artifacts. Consequently, many workers asserted that such primitive creatures, although admittedly hominids, were incapable of making, and perhaps even of using, tools. Quite possibly this lack of stone implements has also convinced some workers that bone, horn, and teeth of other animals were used by australopithecines as weapons and implements. A few split and flaked dolomite pebbles from the calcified stony and sandy fluviatile horizon which overlies the pink and gray breccias at Limeworks Cave[14] suggest but do not afford conclusive proof of tool-making activi-

[14] This horizon has also yielded a fragment of an australopithecine maxilla

ties. However, there is no doubt about the validity of the implements (Figure 4), referred to a pebble-tool (Pre-Chelles-Acheul) industry, recovered recently from the Sterkfontein locality.[15] The specimens derive from a reddish-brown breccia at the extension site first thought to be broadly contemporary with the basal pink australopithecine-bearing breccia of the type site. Robinson's more recent investigations indicate, however, that these breccias are separated unconformably, as a consequence of subsidence, and that the latter pink breccia underlies the reddish-brown breccia of the extension site. The latter contains the foreign and worked stones as well as some fauna (including *Equus*, absent in the type site basal pink breccia) and some remains (isolated permanent teeth, a juvenile maxilla fragment with several teeth) referred to *Australopithecus*.

The specimens recovered from Sterkfontein include pebble- and core-choppers (8), a chopper-hammerstone (1), and rough retouched end-struck flakes (2). Quartz, quartzite, chert, and diabase pebbles foreign to the deposit were also found; about half (24) of these were plain, and the other half (23) exhibited evidence of fracture from use. The small flakes struck from the choppers and cores are missing and indicate that specimens were collected and worked elsewhere, near streams where raw material was available, prior to being carried to the site for use. Some of the specimens show extensive battering rather than careful flake removal, suggesting either hard use or, according to J. D. Clark, poor workmanship. The implements are fresh and unweathered and cannot have been washed in from the outside, since the breccias must have accumulated under an overhanging roof, and since the breccias fail to reveal such conditions of deposition. The artifacts seem to be concentrated at the western end of the site near the original entrance to the cave and were undoubtedly left behind by the hominids who occupied this end of the cavern.

The recovery of pebble tools in association with australopithecines is a momentous discovery. There now seems little doubt that these primitive creatures were already capable of using and manufacturing implements of stone and, presumably, of other nonpreserved materials as well. The extraordinary concentration of other mammalian bones would indicate that these creatures were capable of killing the moderate and smaller-sized species; probably they also scavenged carnivore kills. There is no indication that they had the ability, the equipment, or the organization necessary for killing very large mammals, in contrast to middle Pleistocene peoples. Such carnivorous habits would have required some sharpened stone implements, such as flakes and chopping tools, for cutting open

[15] Foreign pebbles were first reported from this region (at Kromdraai) by S. H. Haughton.

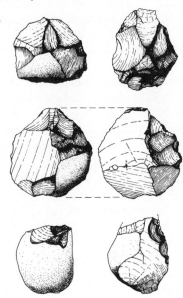

FIGURE 4. Pre-Chelles-Acheul implements from the australopithecine-bearing breccias at Sterkfontein (Transvaal). (After J. T. Robinson and R. J. Mason.)

the hide of kills to obtain meat. There is no trace of the use of fire at this early time.

Clark has recently suggested that the availability of water in the cave systems may have been an important factor in their having been occupied. Except for small and seasonally dry streams, cave and fissure systems, and springs related to them, provide the best source of water in such limestone country. Such sources of water would have attracted game and australopithecines alike and would have provided ideal conditions for the latter to prey on antelopes, pigs, baboons, and other animals which came to drink there. This also readily accounts for the profusion of animal bones accumulated in the cave and for the presence of implements necessary to butcher the slaughtered game.

AUSTRALOPITHECINE MORPHOLOGY

Hominids and pongids (apes) are generally regarded as closely related higher primate groups (hominoids). There are obvious and significant morphological and behavioral differences between the living representatives of the two families. Acceptance of the fact of evolution and the reality of such close affinity indicates, however, that such divergences were fewer and less sharply delineated in the remote past. The *primary* adaptation of the hominid radiation required transformation of the locomotor skeleton to permit fully upright posture and an efficient bipedal gait. This mode of terrestrial locomotion contrasts markedly with the arboreal or terrestrial quadrupedalism of the lower catarrhine monkeys or with the arboreal brachiation of the pongids, coupled, in the larger pongine (anthropoid ape) species, with semipronograde quadrupedalism. This basic locomotor adaptation of the hominids was doubtless preadaptive for subsequent evolutionary changes which affected the skull—reduction of the facial skeleton and extraordinary enlargement of the cerebral hemispheres and cranial vault. The latter has been linked with enhanced cultural capacities, although the manifold interrelationships between structure and function, and their behavioral significance, are still very largely obscure.

The pelves of four australopithecine individuals are now known. Three represent *Australopithecus* and were found at Limeworks Cave and Sterkfontein (at the latter site, much of an associated vertebral column was also found); *Paranthropus* is represented by one incomplete innominate bone from Swartkrans. These fortunate discoveries demonstrate conclusively that the pelvic structure of these creatures was that characteristic of primitive bipedal hominids. They also greatly add to our understanding of the hominid locomotor transformation, which involved a complex of interrelated structural modifications. These constituted a basic reorientation of the pelvis in relation to the trunk, interrelated changes which permitted an erect trunk and full extension of the lower limbs in stable upright posture (and in the female, maintenance of the bony birth canal).

Such changes involve (i) expansion of the iliac blade, especially the auricular area, coupled with sacral rotation and accentuated lumbar lordosis; (ii) shortening and anterior rotation or "twisting" of the ilium, with attendant development of a sigmoid curvature of the iliac crest; (iii) thickening of the outer bony table above the acetabulum (to aid in balance and weight support); (iv) development of an iliac cristal tubercle, in line with the strengthened supra-acetabular region (related to differentiation and expansion of the iliotibial tract as an aid in stabilization of the hip and knee joints in standing and walking erect); (v) enlargement and approximation to the acetabulum of the anterior inferior iliac spine (related to the size of the straight head of the *rectus femoris* muscle, as part of the general enlargement of the *quadriceps femoris* muscle group in bipeds); (vi) shortening of the ischium and altered form of the ischial tuberosity (the full significance of this is obscure, but it is apparently related to the position of the extensor, or hamstring muscle, lever arm); (vii) enlargement and displacement of the *gluteus maximus* muscle as a powerful extensor (rather than a lateral rotator as in apes and monkeys); and (viii) altered function of *gluteus medius* (and *minimus*) muscles as abductors (to maintain lateral stability in walking erect).

There are accompanying interrelated modifications in the proximal head of the femur. These include: (i) enlargement of the femoral head; (ii) development of the lesser trochanter (related to an altered disposition of the *psoas major* muscle); (iii) development of the anterior segment of the greater trochanter and the intertrochanteric line (related to the attachment of the Y-shaped ligament of Bigelow and the joint capsule); (iv) development of the *linea aspera;* (v) shift of *gluteus maximus* to a posterior rather than a lateral insertion, as in apes, in the place of *adductor minimus* and expansion of *vastus intermedius;* and (vi) notable reduction of the *quadratus femoris* muscle. Other modifications of the distal end of the femur, including the obliquity of the shaft, the marked depth of the patellar surface, the configuration of the intercondylar notch, and the enlargement of the lateral condyle, were apparently associated in large part with enhanced stability of the knee joint in orthograde progression.

The basic morphological pattern characteristic of hominid bipedalism is apparent in the australopithecine lower limb skeleton so far as it is known. There are a number of minor differences—for example, in the form of the ischial region—from the pelvic morphology of *Homo sapiens,* a not unexpected finding in a primitive lower Pleistocene hominid. The australopithecine lower leg and foot, except for a talus of *Paranthropus,* is still largely unknown.

The morphological pattern of the australopithecine dentition is also hominid rather than pongid. In the deciduous dentition this is evident in (i) the evenly curved dental arch, lacking diastemata; (ii) the small milk incisors; (iii) the small, nonprojecting spatulate milk canines; (iv) the quadricuspid upper first milk molar; (v) the nonsectorial, quinticuspid lower first milk molar with well-developed anterior fovea and cusps of approximately equal height. In the permanent dentition this is evident in (i) the evenly curved (parabolic) dental arch; (ii) the small incisors; (iii) the small, nonprojecting spatulate canines, lacking a talonid and with the internal cingulum forming a basal tubercle; (iv) the double-rooted upper first premolar; (v) the nonsectorial, bicuspid lower first premolar; and (vi) the replacement sequence, in which both the permanent canine and medial incisor tend to erupt relatively early.

The related structure of the facial skeleton is also primitively hominid, and this is paralleled in a number of structural details of the cranial base and the occiput. The brain, in proportion to body size, in certain aspects of its form and proportions, and in its tendency toward delayed maturation, approaches a primitive hominid rather than a pongid condition.

There are consistent morphological distinctions between the earlier form (*Australopithecus*) and the younger form (*Paranthropus*). These are evident not only in the deciduous and permanent dentitions and the facial skeleton but also in the structure of the cranial base and vault, as well as in the known portions of the postcranial skeleton. *Australopithecus* was a small, gracile bipedal creature, weighing certainly no more than 75 to 85 pounds in the larger males. *Paranthropus,* on the other hand, was a far more robust and massive creature of probably half again that body weight. Such, probably subgeneric, differences indicate a pronounced bifurcation within a primary australopithecine radiation, at least in the basal Villafranchian and possibly even in the later Pliocene. Unfortunately the general absence of fossiliferous Pliocene horizons in sub-Saharan Africa has thwarted investigation of the earlier evolutionary phases and primitive hominoid antecedents of the australopithecine group.

At Swartkrans another distinct hominid, designated *Telanthropus,* is found in direct association with the australopithecine *Paranthropus.* This form, which is still only very inadequately known, differs markedly from *Paranthropus* in dental and mandibular morphology and in certain features of the maxilla (in particular in the structure of the nasal floor). In all such characteristics, some of which reveal some resemblances to the earlier australopithecine *Australopithecus,* this hominid is further evolved morphologically than any known australopithecine and approaches therefore the phylogenetic status of certain earlier middle Pleistocene forms attributed to the genus *Homo.* The full implications of this conclusion cannot be properly evaluated until additional, more complete specimens have been discovered.

TERTIARY HOMINOIDS AND VILLAFRANCHIAN HOMINIDS

It is significant that the African Villafranchian hominids differ considerably in morphology from later Tertiary hominoids of eastern Africa and Eurasia. Four hominoid genera are recognized from the earlier Miocene of eastern Africa, three and possibly four genera[16] are recognized from the middle and late Miocene and the lower Pliocene of peri-Alpine Europe, and four genera are recognized from the (upper) lower and middle Siwaliks of Asia (Figure 5).

In both Africa and Europe primitive hylobatids (gibbons) are already evolved in the lower half of the Miocene. Most of the basic cranial and dental morphology of the group is already established in these forms; in fact the dentition is already basically hominoid in the Oligocene form *Propliopithecus.* However, in some features of postcranial structure and in limb proportions these forms differ significantly from their living

[16] G. H. R. von Koenigswald would distinguish *Paidopithex rhenanus,* of which a complete right femur is known, from the Pontian of Rheinhesse and the Schwäbian lignites, giving it as a separate genus (rather than as a species, as I have done here.)

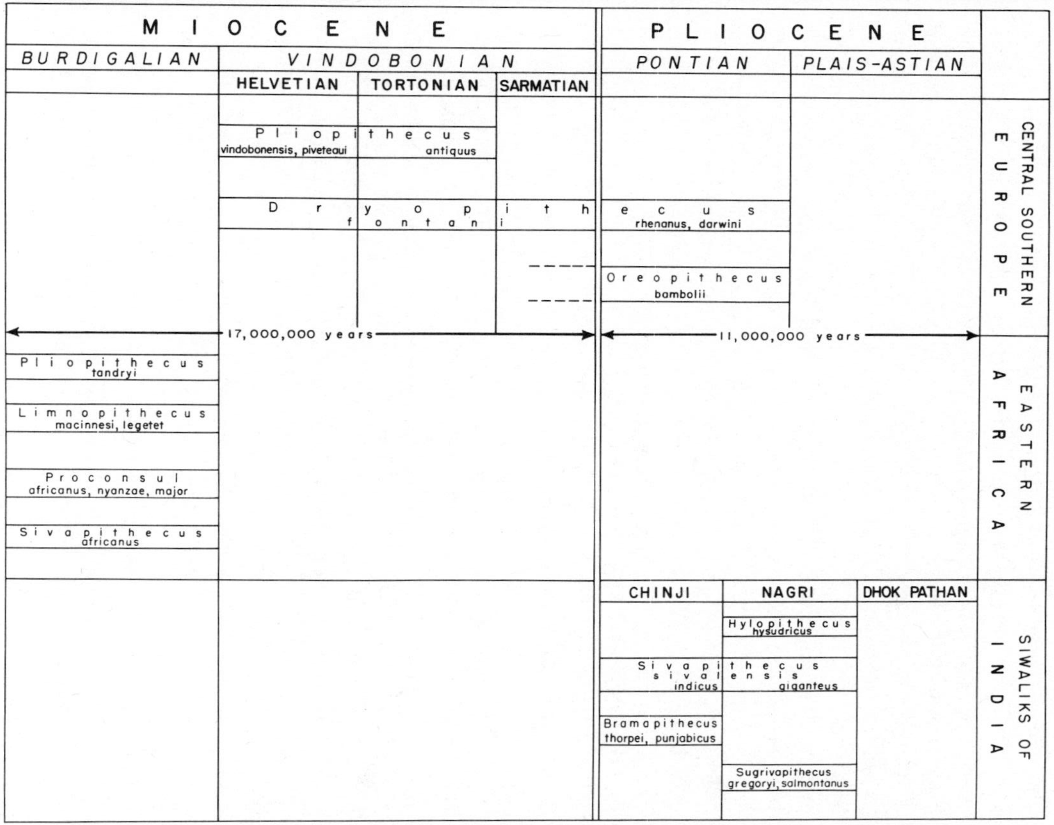

FIGURE 5. Temporal distribution of hominoids in the Neogene of Africa, Asia, and Europe.

representatives. Similarly, the basic dryopithecine (pongid) dental characteristics are manifest in the earlier Miocene hominoids of eastern Africa, although cranial and facial morphology is distinct from that of evidently specialized living varieties of the group. Moreover, the fundamental locomotor pattern of the recent large-bodied brachiator is evident in the morphology of shoulder and elbow joints, whereas the skeleton of the hand is distinctly primitive cercopithecoid or monkey-like. The later Miocene and Pliocene dryopithecine hominoids of Europe and their Pliocene counterparts of Asia, known nearly exclusively from jaws and teeth, are typically pongid in mandibular and dental structure and therein do not differ fundamentally from the living gibbons and great apes.

Oreopithecus, a form known for over three quarters of a century which has received much publicity and been much discussed recently, is a notable exception to this statement. This primate occurs in the Pontian (lower Pliocene) lignites of Tuscany. It is surely significant that *Oreopithecus* reveals features of dental morphology which are not *typically* pongid, although there can be no question that it is fully hominoid rather than primitive cercopithecoid (cercopithecid). A majority of workers tend to agree that the other hominoids of the later Tertiary are typical pongids, with all the attendant dental specializations which would effectively exclude such creatures from hominid ancestry. Hürzeler's painstaking reexamination of all the *Oreopithecus* material proves, however, that *all* later Tertiary hominoids were not typically pongid. Hence, the longstanding argument over the "cercopithecid" (Old World monkey) or "pongid" (anthropoid ape) origin of hominids can be clarified, since many of the more "generalized" hominid features which some workers have regarded as indicative of lower catarrhine affinity are present in either primitive or nonpongid hominoids. Consequently, an oreopithecine hominoid group might well provide the ancestral stage from which orthograde bipedal hominids were subsequently to evolve. It is still premature to assert the correctness of such a hypothesis to the exclusion of all others. The recent and truly important discovery of a nearly entire skeleton of *Oreopithecus* from the Grosetto lignites should provide most of the evidence necessary to resolve this problem.

It should be recalled that the whole of the African Pliocene, a span of over ten million years, is still either almost or entirely unknown.[17] Late

---

[17] In Mediterranean Africa the Pontian is little known in southern and northern Tunisia and practically not at all in Morocco. The richest locality, except for primates, is Qued el Hamman, Oran (Algeria). Findings from the later Pliocene are extremely rare; this period is known largely from the Constantine (Algeria) sites of Ain el Bey and Ain el Hadj Baba. A fairly substantial faunal assemblage, probably middle Pliocene, from the Gart el Moluk, Wadi Natrun, in Egypt, is known. The situation is even more discouraging south of the Sahara where a Pliocene fauna is known only from diamond diggings in Little Namaqualand, southwest Africa.

Tertiary hominoids surely occupied the more central area of the continent, although fossiliferous deposits of this time range are still unknown. Until some evidences of hominoid varieties are forthcoming from the upper Neogene of sub-Saharan Africa, any hypotheses of hominid origins will lack support. There is widespread evidence of extensive sub-Saharan desiccation, between 1°N and 20°S, from the late Miocene throughout the Pliocene. This was a period of desertification during which great distributions of fine, light, unstratified aeolian of the (upper) Kalahari system occurred. Conditions appear to have been such that, except for rare, and probably small, basins of sedimentation (proto-rift valleys), which are usually obscured by volcanic lavas and other deposits, the preservation of mammalian fossils was literally precluded.

This was certainly a crucial time for mammalian evolution in general as well as for higher primate evolution in particular. Thus, the origins of the incredibly rich eastern-central African grasslands fauna are literally unknown; yet this long interval was probably vital for such a radiation, since the Villafranchian antelopes appear largely referable to existing genera. For the pongid hominoids, whose ecological requirements and habits of locomotion were apparently becoming those of forest-dwelling, vegetarian (or frugivorous) brachiators, such desiccation had profound effects on distribution, which are fully evident today in the sparse and restricted habitats of the African apes. For those hominoids that were preadapted toward terrestrial bipedalism, it was a period of trial in a new and exploitable environment. The Villafranchian stage, as well as the later Pleistocene phases of hominid history, testify to the achievement of this primary radiation.

Tools Makyth Man

Kenneth Oakley   1959

Benjamin Franklin appears to have been the first to call man the "toolmaking animal,"[1] while Thomas Carlyle in Sartor Resartus (1833) declared: "Without tools he is nothing." In pre-Darwinian days the definition of man was no more than a philosophical exercise. That man might have evolved from lower animals was in the minds of very few people in those days. Certainly the question of how to draw a boundary between prehuman and human had not yet become a practical issue. Even the conception that man had a long unrecorded past had barely taken root a hundred years ago, although the seeds of the idea had been sown by a few men far ahead of their time, such as Isaac de la Peyrère, who published a book in Paris in 1655 on *Primi Homines ante Adamum*, and John Frere whose discovery of flint tools in brickearths at Hoxne in Suffolk led him to infer in 1797 that they had been "used by a people who had not the use of metals," and "belonged to a very ancient period indeed, even before that of the present world."

The idea that man had an extensive prehistoric past began to grow during the second quarter of the last century, largely as a result of stone tools being recognized in deposits containing the remains of extinct animals. Flint implements associated with bones of Diluvial (we should

[1] Quoted in Boswell's Life of Johnson, April 7, 1778.

FROM *the* Smithsonian Report for 1958 (*published 1959*), *pp. 431–456, originally published in* Antiquity, *1957, vol. 31, 199–209. Reprinted by permission of the author and of the Smithsonian Institution and the Antiquity Trust. The version appearing here contains some minor revisions and additions made by the author from recent information. Like Dr. Howell, Dr. Oakley combines knowledge of geology, of archaeology, and of the fossil men themselves; he is also noted for furthering the development of technical methods of dating. Of various articles he has written on the subject of the origins of human tool-making, this one is selected as best presenting his views. Dr. Oakley is Senior Principal Science Officer and Deputy Keeper in Charge of the Sub-Department of Anthropology in the British Museum (Natural History).*

now say Glacial) animals were reported from Belgian caves in 1832, and in 1840 from below a thick layer of stalagmite in Kent's Cavern, Torquay. At this time orthodox scientists, following the French naturalist Cuvier, were incredulous of such discoveries. When, in 1846, a French customs official, Boucher de Perthes, repeated his claim (first made in 1838) that he had discovered at Abbeville, in the ancient gravels of the river Somme, flints worked by man and associated with remains of Antediluvian animals, the majority of archeologists and geologists were frankly scornful. In 1854 one of his critics, a physician named Rigollot, was converted to the unorthodox view when he himself found similar chipped flints (hand axes) in fossil-bearing river gravel at St. Acheul, near Amiens. In November 1858, the English paleontologist Hugh Falconer visited Abbeville, and was favorably impressed by the evidence. In the following April, at Falconer's suggestion, the geologist Joseph Prestwich went to Abbeville and St. Acheul. After examining the collections and visiting the pits in company with the English archeologist John Evans, he returned to London and on May 26, 1859, presented a paper to the Royal Society announcing his acceptance of the claims made by Boucher de Perthes and Rigollot. This pronouncement, coming from a geologist of such high repute, had a great effect on scientific opinion throughout the world. The year 1859 was, as we now see, one of the turning points in human thought; the immense antiquity of man was established almost simultaneously with the publication in book form of Darwin's theory of evolution, *On the Origin of Species by Means of Natural Selection.*

Fossilized skeletal remains of man were found during the second half of the last century at a number of localities: Neanderthal (1856), Cro-Magnon (1868), Spy (1886), and Trinil in Java (1891). It was gradually realized that these provided concrete evidence that man had been subject to evolutionary change as deduced by Darwin in his "Descent of Man" (1871). However, none of these discoveries pushed back the antiquity of man, for the unquestionable flint tools from the Abbeville gravels had already indicated his existence in Europe before the arrival of the typically glacial fauna. As Boucher de Perthes expressed it (after translation): "In spite of their imperfection, these rude stones prove the existence of man as surely as a whole Louvre would have done."

How great is the antiquity of man? If he is defined as the tool-making primate, this problem resolves itself into the question of the geological age of the oldest known artifacts. Although the flint hand-axes (*palaeoliths*) dating from the earlier part of the Pleistocene period are crudely flaked, they are nevertheless standardized tools, and this has generally been regarded as indicating that a long tradition of slowly acquired skill lay behind them. This was the idea sustaining the search for traces of the handiwork of Tertiary man, in other words the hunt for *eoliths*.

I must here digress for a moment to recall that the Tertiary era, beginning 75 million years ago and distinguished by the rise of mammals, is divided into the Eocene, Oligocene, Miocene, and Pliocene periods. The Pleistocene period or Ice Age, with its postglacial appendage of Holocene or Recent time, constitutes the Quaternary era. Originally the Pleistocene was defined as coincident with the Quaternary Ice Age, but the International Geological Congress in 1948 recommended its redefinition to include the Villafranchian stage (formerly in part Upper Pliocene) distinguished by the spread of elephants of the genus *Elephas*, oxen (*Bos*), and one-toed horses (*Equus*). Owing to these changes in nomenclature, deposits which were formerly "Early" Pleistocene are now counted as Middle Pleistocene (e.g., the Abbeville gravels and the Trinil beds); while other deposits formerly counted as Pliocene, i.e., Tertiary, for example the Red Crag of East Anglia, are now regarded as Lower Pleistocene by the majority of geologists. The "glacial Pleistocene" is estimated to have been about half a million years in duration, but the addition of the Villafranchian stage has nearly doubled the length of the period.

The problem of eoliths, supposed artifacts of Tertiary man, was first raised by the discoveries of Abbé Louis Bourgeois, who found in 1867 a great quantity of chipped flints, in the form of alleged scrapers, knives, and borers, in a fresh-water deposit of Lower Miocene[2] age near Thenay (Loir-et-Cher). From time to time similar chipped flints were reported in other Tertiary formations: in Lower Eocene strata at Clermont (Oise), in Upper Oligocene gravels at Boncelles, Belgium, in "Upper Miocene" (now Lower Pliocene) deposits at Puy Courny, Cantal, in the so-called Pliocene plateau gravels on the North Downs in Kent, and within and below the Red Crag of East Anglia.

With the growth of knowledge on the evolution of the primates, based on a study of actual fossil remains, it has become clear in the present century that our forerunners had only the size range of bush babies throughout Eocene times. Man-sized apes did not emerge before the Miocene period, while the earliest manlike remains date from early Pleistocene times. Thus, pre-Miocene eoliths at any rate may now be dismissed as geological curiosities, with no bearing on the origins of tool making. The unreliability of the criteria used by the earlier archeologists who recognized "flints shaped by human agency" in the Tertiary formations is evident from the fact that Eocene eoliths are as convincingly artificial in appearance as many of those from later formations!

In some circumstances flint is very readily fractured, and the natural agencies which cause it to be chipped into shapes reminiscent of artifice

[2] Aquitanian: classified by some authors as Upper Oligocene.

are legion. The eoliths found in Tertiary river gravels are strikingly similar to flints broken by violent agitation in the water of chalk mills. This is understandable. An accumulation of flints of eolithic form was found in a river gravel in a valley in Würtemberg where the material carried by the main stream had evidently been drawn into whirlpools caused by the inflow of tributaries. Another agency which results in the production of pseudoartifacts is the pressure combined with movement occurring when flint-bearing strata founder through the solution of underlying chalk or other calcareous formation. This was the agency chiefly responsible for the Clermont eoliths. The Kent eoliths were mainly produced by the powerful friction of one stone against another which occurs in soil creep, particularly under subglacial conditions.

While it is reasonable enough to consider the possibility of tool-using primates having existed during Pliocene times, and even during the Miocene period, there are insuperable difficulties in the way of recognizing the particular pieces of stone or bone that may have been picked up and used. The earliest attempts at making tools from pieces of stone must have been all but indistinguishable from the accidents of nature (and we have already seen how "human" these can appear). Naturally fractured stones probably served as the first tools. Some Australian aborigines at the present day fashion wooden utensils with naturally shaped pieces of stone selected by virtue of their sharp cutting edges. As one French prehistorian expressed the problem of eoliths: "Man made one, God made ten thousand—God help the Man who tries to see the one in the ten thousand."

During the present century large numbers of flaked flints, including some strongly suggestive of intelligent design, have been found in the Stone Bed underlying the Norwich and Weybourne Crags in Norfolk and in the Bone Bed below the Red Crag in Suffolk. These flints show a number of features not found in the general run of Tertiary eoliths; and largely, I believe, because they date from the very interval of time when, according to many lines of evidence, tool making probably began, they have been widely accepted as human artifacts despite the relentless opposition of scientists who specialized in the study of flint fractures, such as the late Hazzledine Warren and the late Prof. A. S. Barnes. If one confines attention to the beautiful rostrocarinates, corelike forms, scraperlike flakes, and so on, laid out for exhibition in the Norwich Castle Museum and the Ipswich Museum, it is difficult to disbelieve in their human origin. Yet, collecting for oneself in the Sub-Crag Stone Bed, for example, one is bewildered by the high percentage of the component flints that have been bruised and chipped, the majority obviously in a random fashion. Now and again the flakes have been removed first from one side and then from another side in a way suggestive of design. By keeping only the best of the latter kind one can build a collection that is convincingly like a crude human industry; yet seen as part of a vast series of flakings, with gradation from obviously natural to seemingly artificial, the Sub-Crag "implements" are less convincing than when studied in isolation. Nevertheless, the late Reid Moir and others made a good case for accepting some of the assemblages of flakings in and below the Crag as the work of "pre-Palaeolithic Man," until belief in them was shaken by Barnes's demonstration that on statistical analysis the Crag flaking was of the high-angled type characteristic of the work of nature.

Out of 1,800 measurements of platform-scar angles in 18 different human industries, Barnes found less than 18 percent over 90°; but in flaked flints from Eocene deposits over 54 percent of the flake scars proved to have angles over 90°, while among flaked flints from the Crag formations over 62 percent of the flake scares are more than 90°. Professor Barnes concluded: "The high proportion of high-angle scars in the Tertiary flints contrasts sharply with the paucity of high angles in the human industries, and suggests that the Tertiary flaking was due to soil movements under pressure arising from solifluxion, foundering, or ice action" (1943).

Warren reached a similar conclusion after prolonged study of the character of the Crag flaking (1948) and, having reviewed the geological evidence, concluded that the Stone Bed and Bone Bed did not accumulate as beach deposits, but on a submarine floor, "which cannot reasonably be supposed to have been available for human habitation." As about 50 percent of stones in some parts of the Stone Bed are flaked, and as the deposit occupies several hundred square miles, a widespread natural cause was most probably responsible for them. The striations and bruisings which many of the Sub-Crag flints show are consistent with Warren's idea that the chief cause of flaking was the grounding of floating ice (mainly local pack ice) which would have jammed together patches of flints strewn on the floor of the shallow sea (1948). Certain flakings strewn on an alleged land surface within the Red Crag at Foxhall have been widely accepted as artifacts, even by those who do not accept the Sub-Crag chippings. To my mind the Foxhall "floor" is an enigma to be further investigated, rather than a proof of the existence of man in Britain during the Villafranchian stage.

If the Tertiary and Sub-Crag eoliths are unacceptable, what then are the oldest undoubted artifacts? Certainly not those of the "Cromerian industry" which has proved to be nonexistent, consisting apparently of flakings produced on the Cromer foreshore in recent times by the concussion of one stone against another in storms. These flakings occurred

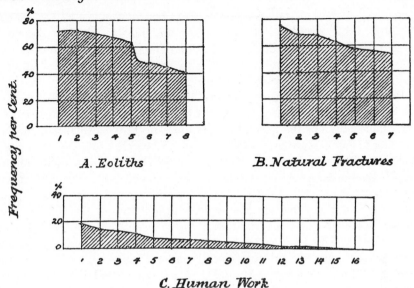

FIGURE 1. Percentages of obtuse platform-scar angles found in: A, eoliths in flint, including Sub-Crag (*1* and *3*); B, Naturally fractured stones, including flints crushed under cart wheels (*3*) or broken in foundering deposits (*4*), and chipped hard rocks in moraines (*7*); C, human flint industries, mainly early, including Abbevillian (*2*), Acheulian (*5–8*, *12*), Tayacian (*9*, *10*), and Mousterian (*13*). (After A. S. Barnes, by courtesy of the editor of *American Anthropologist*.)

among a spread of big stones which had the appearance of passing under the Forest Bed (Warren, 1940). The only flaked flints found in situ at this site appear to have belonged to the Stone Bed of the underlying Weybourne Crag. The ochreous patina of the foreshore flakes was at one time regarded as proof of their antiquity, but Warren found evidence that this patination is acquired in a few years on the Cromer coast, possibly on account of the action of some alga.

Recently Dr. Alfred Rust (1956) published an account of some sandstone pebbles with chipped margins found in the Mauer Sands of earliest Middle Pleistocene age which yielded the famous mandible of *"Homo" heidelbergensis*.[3] He kindly gave me the opportunity to examine his collection in 1956; but I must confess that I was unable to find any among those from the Mauer Sands which I could unreservedly accept as possibly worked by man. Most of the local sandstone, even before it was weathered, is too coarse and friable to make serviceable tools. Indeed, Heidelberg man could have cut more effectively with flakes of the hard limestone (Muschelkalk) available in the same valley.

In Europe we are left with the so-called Abbevillian hand-axes and

[3] Now regarded as the European equivalent of *Pithecanthropus*.

Clactonian flakes in the 40-meter terrace of the Somme as the oldest unquestionable artifacts. The only question here is whether the geological horizon of the "Abbevillian" is First Interglacial or an interstadial within the Second Glaciation, which is by no means impossible. (In fact, the same question applies to the Mauer Sands.)[3a]

When we turn to Asia we find that the oldest undoubted artifacts are in the same time bracket, either immediately antedating or contemporary with some phase of the Second Glaciation. The Pre-Soan flakes from the Boulder Conglomerate in the Punjab are not entirely convincing, for they may have been produced by glacial action; but there is no doubt about the chert chopping tool of Early Soan type found at Locality 13, Choukoutien (China), in association with fauna indicating a stratigraphic horizon within the period of the Second or Mindel Glaciation. The slightly later flake-and-chopper-tool industry associated with Peking man at Locality 1, Choukoutien, is now generally regarded as dating from the beginning of the Second Interglacial period. Some authors still claim that it is older, either inter-Mindel or even Günz-Mindel, but the associated fauna is clearly Middle Pleistocene in the modern sense.[3b]

In Africa, particularly south of the Sahara, high-level river gravels of Lower Pleistocene age have been found to contain large numbers of chipped pebbles, mainly of quartzite, which have been widely accepted as artifacts. These so-called pebble tools were first recognized in Uganda by the geologist E. J. Wayland in 1920, who referred them to a pre-Paleolithic stage of culture, later named Kafuan on the basis of their typical occurrence on the 175-foot terrace of the Kafu River. In a recent monograph on the prehistory of Uganda, the late Professor van Riet Lowe described no less than 27 constantly recurring forms of "Kafuan-type split and trimmed pebbles," and claimed that he and Wayland could trace the evolution of rostrocarinates from the simple split pebble, thus providing a link with the discoveries in East Anglia, where Moir found a gradation from rostrocarinates to Chellean (Abbevillian) hand-axes. Kafuan-type pebbles are even found in a layer of lateritic ironstone at the base of the 270-foot Kagera terrace which may be Lower Villafranchian or Pliocene. If there were no question about their being artifacts, these chipped pebbles would be the oldest evidence of a toolmaking hominid and would support the idea of an almost infinitely slow evolution of the earliest culture over some half a million years, from the end of the Pliocene to the first hand-axes.

[3a] The view that the Abbevillian horizon and the Mauer sands are interstadial ("Cortonian") had become widely held by 1959; see Howell, 1960.

[3b] Since this paper was written, Kurtén (1959b) has published evidence that the deposits at Locality I are probably of Mindel II age.

As doubts grew about the artificiality of chipped flints in the Tertiary and Villafranchian formations of Europe, belief waxed strongly in favor of the African pebble tools, because these were not in flint (which breaks so easily under a variety of forces), but in quartzite and the like. Moreover, they were for the most part in situations far removed from Pleistocene glaciers and pounding sea waves which have produced such quantities of pseudoartifacts in Europe.

Some prehistorians are now beginning to feel that the Kafuan pebbles[4] have been accepted as artifacts without sufficient consideration being given to the possibility that these also were fractured by natural forces. Should not quartzite gravels of, say, Triassic age be searched for similar forms, to see if they are produced in circumstances where no question of tool making arises? There is a great need, too, for experimental work on the lines of that by the late Professor Barnes and Mr. Warren, but designed to investigate the forces required to split quartzite pebbles. My own extremely limited observations in Africa suggest that at least some Kafuan-like flakings are produced when gravel is carried over waterfalls.[5] As for secondary chipping, it should not be forgotten that soil creep or solifluxion can occur under tropical conditions as well as under glacial.

One of my reasons for being skeptical about the Kafuan "pebble tools" is their prodigality. In the summer of 1955 I was with a party on safari through the Katanga Province of the Belgian Congo, and we were taken by Prof. G. Mortelmans to an exposure of gravels at Kafila near Elisabethville. Within a few minutes all the members of the party had found more "pebble tools" in this gravel than they could carry away. It is true that artifacts are astonishingly abundant at some African localities on the later hand-axe horizons, but the profusion of chipped pebbles in the Kafilan gravel reminded me of the profusion of eoliths in the Sub-Crag Stone Bed. Miles Burkitt evidently has similar reservations to make about the Kafuan pebbles, for he wrote recently: "From a study of the objects themselves it is not easy to find evidence to prove that they *must* be the handiwork of Man and that the fracturing cannot have been produced by natural forces." There has been an undeniable tendency among us all to argue subconsciously like this: "Man *could* have made these; they are of the right age for the beginning of culture; this is where we may expect to find artifacts; these *are* artifacts."

[4] Excluding the "advanced Kafuan" of some authors, which is synonymous with the unquestionably human Early Oldowan.

[5] Perhaps mainly when, under a semiarid climate, large masses of gravel are suddenly moved over falls at the commencement of the rains, with the result that a proportion of the stones collide out of water. Since this paper was first published, Dr. J. D. Clark (1958) has demonstrated that Kafuan-type flaking does occur through stones falling from the sides of gorges and striking other stones or rock surfaces out of water.

Fortunately there are certain situations in which fractured stones are acceptable as artifacts, even when the flaking appears random or accidental. For example, many of the fragments of quartz in the Choukoutien cave deposits would not be recognized as humanly struck if they were found on the surface away from their human context. The quartz found at Choukoutien is foreign to the site, and can only have been introduced into the cave by human agency. Another situation in which flaked stones are more readily acceptable as artifacts is where they occur isolated in an otherwise stoneless layer of lacustrine mud or sand.

If we discount the Kafuan pebbles, the oldest undoubted artifacts in the world are related to or equivalent to the Oldowan culture, first recognized by Dr. L. S. B. Leakey in the basal bed of the series of lacustrine sediments exposed in the side of the Oldoway (Olduvai) Gorge in northern Tanganyika. The associated fauna indicates that Bed I of Oldoway is of early Middle Pleistocene age.[5a] The typical Oldowan industry found in this bed consists of pebbles or other lumps of rock flaked by percussion to form crude chopping tools "varying in size from the dimensions of a ping-pong ball to that of a croquet ball." The chopping edges were made by removing flakes in two directions along one side of the pebble or lump, so that the intersecting flake scars formed a jagged cutting edge. The fact that occasionally these pebble choppers foreshadow bifacial hand-axes, and the fact that hand-axes appear and begin to replace pebble tools in Bed II, are indications that the Abbevillian-Acheulian sequence of cultures evolved from the Oldowan. The discovery of a few apparently Oldowan-type pebbles in the Laetolil Beds of Tanganyika and in the Kanam Beds of Kenya suggested that the beginnings of Oldowan culture were to be sought in the Lower Pleistocene (Villafranchian) beds of Africa, but until quite recently there has been an element of uncertainty about all pebble tools from Villafranchian deposits.

Unquestionable stone industries closely comparable with the Oldowan have now been found in North Africa and in South Africa in fossil-bearing deposits of Late Villafranchian age. The northern occurrence was discovered by Prof. C. Arambourg in lake-margin deposits at Ain Hanech in Algeria, and consisted of quantities of pebbles or stone lumps flaked in several directions to form subangular stone balls that would have served equally well as missile stones or multiedged pounders. A few hand axes of Abbevillian type are reported as coming from an immediately overlying layer. These Algerian industries are clearly the homotaxial equivalents of those in Beds I and II at Olduvai.

[5a] Since this was published, evidence has come to light suggesting that Bed I is of the same age as the Laetolil and Kanam beds which are regarded by some as Late Villafranchian.

The discovery in March 1953 of pebble tools of "advanced Kafuan" (I would now say Early Oldowan) type in the calcified surface of the Basal Older Gravels in the 200-foot terrace of the Vaal Valley in South Africa was the first positive indication that toolmakers existed in South Africa as early as the dry phase which terminated the First (or Villafranchian) Pluvial period. The discovery raised a most intriguing problem, because cave deposits that accumulated during this dry Late Villafranchian stage at Taung in Bechuanaland and at Sterkfontein and Makapan in the Transvaal had yielded remains of the subhuman *Australopithecus*. Was it possible that the pebble tools had been made by that creature? Analyzing the evidence available in 1954 I argued that it was possible, but I thought unlikely for two reasons. In the first place, although the Australopithecines walked upright on two legs and qualified structurally to be regarded as Hominidae, rather than as true apes or Pongidae, nevertheless in absolute size their brains were on an average no larger than those of apes. All the known tool-making hominids had brains considerably larger than those of apes. The earliest known toolmakers, the Chinese representatives of the genus *Pithecanthropus*, had skulls with average capacity about twice as great as that of *Australopithecus*. In the second place, Professor von Koenigswald had reported remains of an early *Pithecanthropus* in the Djetis Beds of Java which he claimed were of Villafranchian age. In other words, *Australopithecus* and *Pithecanthropus* evidently existed in the world contemporaneously, and at Peking at least there was evidence that the latter was capable of tool making. Thus it seemed most probable on the evidence available in 1954 that the pebble tools in the Vaal valley terrace had been made by true men, of the *Pithecanthropus* group, who had penetrated into South Africa before their more backward relatives the Australopithecines had died out. The above hypothesis seemed to be strongly supported by the absence of pebble tools from all the sites where remains of Australopithecines had been discovered, suggesting that although pebble toolmakers existed contemporaneously with the Australopithecines, the two groups frequented different environments.

The whole picture has now been altered by further discoveries. In 1955, some possible pebble tools, mostly of dolomite, were found in the gravel bed overlying the main Australopithecine deposit in the Limeworks Cave at Makapan in the Transvaal. These were commented on in Antiquity (Oakley, 1956c), and one of the chipped pebbles was illustrated (pl. II). There was considerable doubt as to whether these were artifacts, and the general opinion was that unless more convincing specimens came to light in the same bed they were better discounted as evidence bearing on the cultural status of *Australopithecus*.

In May 1956 Dr. C. K. Brain discovered indubitable pebble tools of

Oldowan type in the upper part of the Australopithecine breccias at Sterkfontein in South Transvaal. This is possibly the most important discovery in the field of paleoanthropology since the finding of implements with Peking man. Excavations at Sterkfontein carried out in 1957 by Dr. J. T. Robinson and Revil Mason have confirmed beyond all doubt that the artifacts observed by Brain are part of an industry occurring in situ in a layer of breccia containing teeth of *Australopithecus*.

It is worth reiterating that the hypothetical attribution of the pebble tools, not to Australopithecines themselves, but to some higher type of hominid living contemporaneously with *Australopithecus* in the Transvaal, has rather depended on the assumption that the two types would have occupied different ecological niches. As Bartholomew and Birdsell (1953) pointed out: "By analogy with the ecology of other animals it would be surprising if man and the Australopithecines[6] had remained contemporaries in the same area over very long periods of time, for closely related forms with similar requirements rarely occupy the same area simultaneously."

Brain's discovery has now shown that pebble tools were made at the very site where *Australopithecus* occurred.

At the present time there is general agreement among paleonotologists that the Australopithecine breccia at Sterkfontein is of Late Villafranchian (Lower Pleistocene) age. On the other hand Dr. D. A. Hooijer's further analysis of the fauna of the Djetis Beds in Java, which contained the remains of the earliest known examples of *Pithecanthropus*, has indicated that they are probably early Middle Pleistocene and not Villafranchian as previously claimed by von Koenigswald. While the last word on this question may not yet have been said, it is nevertheless true to say that there is no undisputed evidence that any hominids higher in type than *Australopithecus* were in existence in the world at the time when the Sterkfontein tools were manufactured.[7]

So it is only our belief that systematic tool-making requires a larger brain than the ape-size brain of *Australopithecus* (a belief which may prove to be ill founded), that makes us hesitate to infer that the Sterkfontein tools were probably made by that creature.

Another reason for doubting that the tools were made by *Australopithecus* is the fact that "they have no background" at this or any other Australopithecine site. No pebble tool or any kind of stone artifact has been observed in the series of underlying layers at Sterkfontein which

[6] The authors were assuming that the Australopithecines were nontoolmakers, in contradistinction to man.

[7] The antiquity and status of the fragmentary mandible of *Homo* cf. *sapiens* recorded from the Kanam beds of Kenya are now considered too doubtful to stand in the way of this generalization (see Oakley and Tobias, 1960).

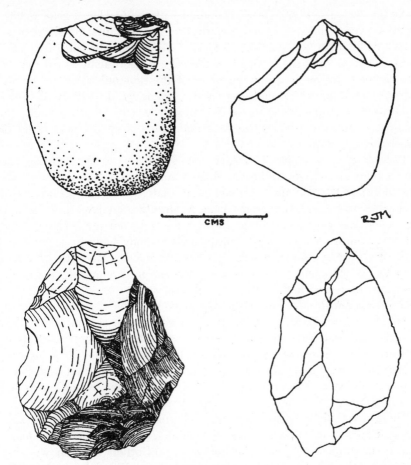

FIGURE 2. Two of the 58 stone artifacts found in layer of red-brown breccia containing teeth of *Australopithecus* at Sterkfontein, Transvaal. *Upper:* Pebble tool of Oldowan type, in diabase, described as utilized hammerstone. *Lower:* Bifacially flaked core in quartzite possibly used as chopper; prototype of hand-axe. It is noteworthy that diabase and quartzite are foreign to the site, and therefore were carried there. (After R. J. Mason, Archaeological Survey of S. Africa, by courtesy of the editors of *Nature*.)

yielded relatively abundant Australopithecine skeletal remains (traces of at least 16 individuals, including the skull known as Sterkfontein 5 and the associated spinal column and pelvic girdle). Robinson has suggested that the absence of pebble tools from the underlying layers is against *Australopithecus* being a toolmaker "since on all other Stone Age sites remains of the tool-manufacturer are extremely rare." I believe the relevant point is that, cannibalism aside, primates do not as a rule die or leave the remains of their dead at the living place (Oakley, 1954b, p. 66). In other words the substantial quantity of Australopithecine skeletal remains in the main bone-bearing breccia at Sterkfontein is consistent with the late Dr. Broom's suggestion that the cave was originally a carnivores' den rather than the actual living place of the hominid.[8] The red-brown breccia containing the stone tools (and a few isolated teeth of *Australopithecus* and fragmentary animal remains) was, on the other hand, accumulated at a time when the cave had temporarily become a site of hominid occupation.

There are many related issues to be considered in the light of the new evidence from Sterkfontein. For example, in the breccia of the nearby site of Swartkrans, accumulated at a later date, numerous remains of an aberrant Australopithecine named *Paranthropus* have been found, also some fragments, including a lower jaw, referred to a related form called *Telanthropus*, which Robinson believes may have been the toolmaker.[9] However, as the Swartkrans breccia is on a later time horizon than the Sterkfontein tools, one feels hesitant in attempting to explain the latter in terms of the former.

If in fact *Australopithecus* was the maker of the Sterkfontein tools, it would involve almost a revolution in our conception of "man." We have already seen that there is some doubt about the existence of "Kafuan culture." That is to say, there is no reliable evidence of tool-making before the Late Villafranchian time level. Is it possible that systematic tool-making arose, not gradually as most 19th-century evolutionists led us to imagine, but suddenly, and spread rapidly?

The Australopithecines must have originated as apes that became adapted to life in open country by walking upright. There are many reasons to suppose, as Dart, Bartholomew, and others have shown, that the earliest hominids must have been tool *users*. Bipedalism is initially disadvantageous biologically unless there is some compensating factor— in the case of the hominids this was the ability to use tools and wield weapons while moving. The early hominids survived in open country by becoming scavengers and hunters, and this they were enabled to do by developing "extra-corporeal limbs" (as O. G. S. Crawford once called tools and weapons), which could be changed or discarded as circum-

[8] The evidence collected in South Africa recently indicating that modern hyenas do not carry carcasses or bones into caves (Dart, 1957a) has little bearing on the activities of extinct species or varieties of hyena. Behavior of mammals is modified in response to environmental, particularly biotopic, changes. There is evidence that under subglacial conditions in Europe the hyena *Crocuta* took bones into caves, at least as long as competition by man did not preclude it.

[9] On the basis of this hypothesis Robinson has since referred "*Telanthropus*" to *Pithecanthropus;* but other authorities doubt whether it is separable from *Australopithecus* (Le Gros Clark, 1958, p. 133)

stances dictated. The earliest tools and weapons would have been improvizations with whatever lay ready to hand. Although the hominids must have begun as occasional tool users, ultimately they were only able to survive in the face of rigorous natural selection by developing a system of communication among themselves which enabled cultural tradition to take the place of heredity. At this point systematic tool-making replaced casual tool using, and it may be that this changeover took place in the Australopithecine stage.

It would not be surprising, in view of the close correlation between culture and cerebral development, if there had been at this stage intense selection in favor of larger brains, with the result that the transition from the small-brained *Australopithecus* to the larger-brained *Pithecanthropus* took place in a comparatively short space of time. The discoveries at Sterkfontein suggest that pebble tools may have been made by *Australopithecus*, while Professor Arambourg's finds at Ternifine (*"Atlanthropus"*) indicate that by the time culture in Africa had reached the beginning of the Acheulian stage the toolmakers had attained the grade of *Pithecanthropus*.

POSTSCRIPT

That systematic tool-making antedated any substantial enlargement of the brain in the evolution of the Hominidae has been confirmed by Dr. and Mrs. L. S. B. Leakey's discovery in July 1959 of an entire Australopithecine cranium associated with the broken-up bones of small animals, Oldowan pebble-tools and wasteflakes in Bed I, the lake-shore deposit now regarded as of Lower Pleistocene age, in the Olduvai Gorge, Tanganyika.

On the Phyletic Evolution of Homo sapiens

Emil Breitinger   1957

Conflicting views as to hominid phylogeny in general, and to the evolution of *Homo sapiens* in particular, arise from three kinds of cause, which are closely interrelated.

First is the inadequacy of the actual data which might give the key to the course of biohistoric development. The most important source, fossil finds, are from their very nature insufficient, since even in the favorable case of a complete specimen they convey only morphological information as to the bony framework, giving limited information or none at all on the no less important questions of physiological detail and of psychological and sociological factors. But even this limited glimpse into the morphological relations within the continuum of successive generations is in practice greatly hampered by the lack, quantitatively and qualitatively, of fossil finds: instead of finding generous representative samples from the web of prehistoric populations, there are available to us instead only a few, generally incomplete and fragmentary individuals, and these sporadic finds are distributed most unequally both geographically and over the time span of the Pleistocene. Moreover, fossil finds can usually be placed only within a given time range, and the chronologies of different continents must be compared with caution. As a consequence of all these insufficiencies of the data, every attempt at a biohistoric synthesis must take into account several possible interpreta-

Originally entitled "Zur phyletischen Evolution von Homo sapiens," *from the* Anthropologischer Anzeiger, *1957, vol. 21, pp. 62–83, this is the development of a paper given at the 1956 Tagung der Deutschen Gesellschaft für Anthropologie, Freiburg in Br. Reprinted by permission of the author and of the editor,* Anthropologischer Anzeiger. *A further application (see the previous paper by Breitinger) of the general rules of modern evolutionary theory, here to evolution in the later hominids and the relationships to them of modern man, the problem to which the remaining articles in this volume are also devoted.*

tions. Paleoanthropology shares this state of affairs with historical biology in general.

Consideration of problems in hominid phylogeny is rendered still more difficult from the fact that we ourselves are both students and specimens of the recent species of man, whose origin we wish to study. Consciousness of this peculiar "own-species" situation may in itself produce a certain degree of prejudice in the task before us. In particular, and often unconsciously, traditional notions as to the nature and origin of "man," convictions of a nonscientific kind, may intervene in questions of our own phyletic history. Fads or fashions exist in the systematic consideration of the genus *Homo*. For example, at the moment there is a tendency, as Remane (1956b) points out, to isolate "man" and to trace him back to a distant ancestral form. No one can entirely escape the influence of such factors of a personal or historic kind. So experienced an investigator as Le Gros Clark frankly declares, "however much we try to persuade ourselves otherwise, it is extraordinarily difficult to discuss it—(that is, the problem of the origin of our own species)—with complete objectivity" (1954b, p. 377).

The principal cause for the present confusion and disagreement in hypotheses relating to the derivation of our own species lies in the general arbitrariness of method. Insufficiency of source data and differences in personal approach to problems exist in other fields of human biology as well, for example, in human inheritance. But here, limits are put to untrammeled hypothesizing by basic principles and by methods of interpreting observations derived from experimental genetics. Such general consistent biological principles are urgently needed for concepts and ground rules in the phylogeny of hominids. Just as human inheritance, by reason of the special difficulties attendant on its investigation, was an unfavorable road by which to arrive at the fundamental recognition of the particulate nature of inheritance and at the rules by which the genetic material was handed on from generation to generation, so also the meager material of fossil human finds is ill-suited for the study of rules and regularities in the course of evolution generally. For the interpretation of its fragmentary source material, paleoanthropology must accordingly make use of the experience and conceptions which zoology and paleontology have achieved, under more favorable conditions and with much richer material.

1. PREMISES

A prerequisite for relating paleoanthropology to general evolutionary studies is a taxonomy corresponding to the principles and rules of zoological and paleontological classification.

At the moment, fossil hominids are still partly classified in a strictly formal manner; that is to say, given taxonomic names—species and genus —which are, however, used simply as labels, and the authors thereby renounce, often explicitly, the biological significance and the phylogenetic implications of these concepts. Such a misuse of taxonomic nomenclature leads only too easily to misunderstanding and biased meanings in phylogenetic relationships, even if one tries to compromise by saying "that species and genus designations in the case of hominids have quite a different content from that in other organisms" (Remane, 1954). It would surely be better to give up this pseudotaxonomic nomenclature entirely, and base names only on sites of finding. This would not, however, do away with the necessity of putting order and system into the material found, since the description of a specimen becomes scientifically meaningful only when it has been compared with information on known groups. Thus, there have appeared new systems for the hominids, with different divisions and names, of which none has so far been able to prevail generally; at times even similarly named groups vary considerably in the finds assigned to them by different authors. Such systems therefore cannot begin to fulfill the simplest purpose of a classification, which is to serve as a generally accepted aid to understanding. Much worse, however, is the fact that the groups in these systems lack a thoroughly clear biological definition, since without such foundations the way is open to unrestrained, loose formulations of hypotheses as to the meaning of phylogenetic relationships between the fossil finds.

From this Babel-like confusion of names and of ideas of groups for the hominids, so often deplored, we can escape only by subscribing to the following resolution: adopt the taxonomical standards valid in zoology and paleontology for the limits and meaning of categories, and give names according to the internationally binding rules of zoological nomenclature. This standardized classification guarantees both a common formal agreement as to the subject of investigation and a necessary consensus as to the principles of judgment. And thus, only in close association with zoological systematics, with genetics and paleontology, by whose cooperation the biological meaning of the central categories of systematics— species and genus—has in the last decades been made substantially firmer and deeper, can paleoanthropology achieve the biohistorical principles of general evolutionary study necessary for the solution of its problems. Ernst Mayr (1951) has correctly said, "The whole problem of the origin of man depends, to a considerable extent, on the proper definition and evaluation of taxonomic categories" (p. 109).

In the new systematics, a species is defined "as a group of actually or potentially interbreeding natural populations that is reproductively isolated from other such groups." (Mayr, 1942). These species are called polytypic, because they comprise a number of subgroups, races, demes, or whatever one cares to name these subspecific and local populations; and they are also called multidimensional because they possess a recognizable time dimension in addition to their geographical expanse.

In the horizontal dimension of the system, the present, the interfertility of many groups, geographically often widely separated and morphologically markedly different from one another, has been directly proved for man, and may also be accepted for those other populations in whose case this natural experiment is not known to have taken place, from the evidence of intermediate groups and contact zones, as well as on the basis of similarity of form. All of modern mankind thus represents a polytypic species in the genetic sense, which has been known since the time of Linnaeus (*Systema naturae*, Ed. X, 1758, vol. I, p. 2) by the species name *Homo sapiens*. Also inferring from morphological similarity, protohistoric and prehistoric groups of finds, or single skulls and skeletons with the characteristic traits of recent groups, may doubtless be included in this same species, especially since these finds in a given time horizon, may be considered as variants within a range of variation similar to that known for recent population groups. The oldest finds which in this sense may be without question assigned to the morphological group of the species *H. sapiens*, such as the Upper Paleolithic skeletons of Combe-Capelle and Grimaldi, are placed chronologically in the interstadial between the first and second advances of the last glacial period. Following the radiation curve of Milankovitch, this dating corresponds to an absolute age for the finds of about 80,000 years.

The problem is now how far back our species may reach in time, and where we may join it to the stream of evolutionary events.

2. Models for the Mode of Evolution

For the origin of new species, the primary problem of evolution, experimental and historical biology offer two models which, following G. G. Simpson (1953), we can designate as "splitting" and as "phyletic evolution."

A. Diagrammatically, splitting corresponds to the forking of a branch in a given phyletic tree. Just as two diverging twigs in a tree never again grow together, so also two species arising through splitting cannot unite once more phylogenetically. Splitting comes about through a process of gradual genetic differentiation, known as speciation, within the population nexus of a species, and this eventually leads, under appropriate conditions such as geographic isolation and other complicated interrelated factors, to genetic isolation between groups which once belonged to the same species. In the schematics, representation of such a speciation (Figure 1) demes or races of a polytypic species are indicated by

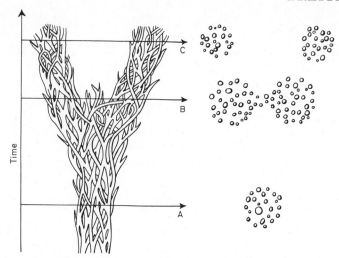

FIGURE 1.   Diagram of the splitting of a species (time horizon A) into two
species (time horizon C). After Th. Dobzhansky, 1955.

anastomosing or rejoining strands. Dobzhansky (1955) speaks of the
races of a given species as a genetically open system, because they may
flow together through renewed hybridizing, and, contrariwise, may once
more diverge into local populations and races (Figure 1, time horizon
A). Within the racial web of a species, genes may be exchanged without
hindrance, the more easily the smaller is the distance between the territory of the individual races. In the course of speciation, the racial web
divides gradually into two bundles which become more and more differentiated genetically from one another (Figure 1, time horizon B), and
between which there continues to be only a limited gene flow by way of
intermediate races. After the completion of speciation (Figure 1, time
horizon C), two new species will have arisen from the original one, these
being irreversibly separated from one another by reproductive barriers.
The appearance of such reproductive barriers is accordingly the decisive
stage of speciation. Through this event, the genetically open system of the
races of the one species gives way to the genetically closed systems of the
new species. Therefore, on the taxonomic level of species there is no further confluence in the phylogenetic future, but only phyletic continuity
and divergence.

These biological facts are of profound significance in the methodology
of evolutionary study. They provide the possibility of following a species
backwards into the past and, with sufficient material, reconstruct a
splitting—symbolized in Figure 2C by the forking line—as resulting from
the mode of evolution already described. Within the continuum of a polytypic species, on the contrary, shown in the diagram as a line but actually

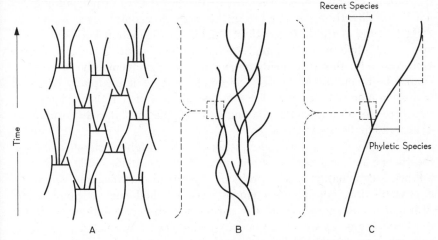

FIGURE 2. Diagram of the descent of individuals (A), populations and races (B), and two modes of evolution for a species (C). After Simpson, 1953.

to be represented (Figure 2B) on the taxonomically lower level of races as a web of actually or potentially anastomosing populations, an individual race usually can be followed only over a relatively short span of time, and the reversible converging and diverging of racial lines in the long run cannot be completely disentangled. Each line of this racial web has eventually, as its objective basis of phylogeny, a network of sexually reproducing individuals (Figure 2A); here the temporal connections of individual life cycles in a generation, symbolized by short lines, are the basis for the continuity of the community.

B. "Phyletic evolution" is diagrammed by the direction and length of a line in the family tree. Just as the distance between two diverging twigs of a tree usually increases, so the differences between two genetically isolated lines, originating through splitting, are normally greater and greater with increasing time (Figure 2C). And since the cumulative changes in the range of variation of one such phyletic line take place in a succession of populations, Simpson designates this situation as phyletic evolution. The phenotypic and genotypic changes within a phyletic line cannot be sharply distinguished in concept from the differentiation of newly arisen species directly attendant on speciation, which Simpson assigns to the mode of "splitting." Contrariwise, phyletic evolution seldom persists for long without again giving rise to speciation of subspecific groups. In the population web of a phyletic line, there naturally occur fluctuating and reversible changes by chance, but, nevertheless, its typical aspect is marked by progressive changes of an adaptive nature. Since the effect of phyletic evolution is manifest only on a time scale of geological magnitude, the phenomenon is principally the concern of paleontologists, not being directly approachable in the work of neontologists. S. Wright (1949b), one of the few geneticists making a distinction between speciation and phyletic evolution, terms the latter mode "transformation." Unfortunately, this technically satisfactory and conveniently short term cannot be recommended, since (as Simpson says) it is already reserved in paleontological literature for the special case of a radical change in structure, for example, the making over of the articular and quadrate bones into malleus and incus.

Phyletic evolution has consequences of the highest significance for the theory and practice of systematics. Simpson (1945, 1953) gives the following explanation in the problem of vertical classification: when, in a phyletic line, cumulative changes have reached such a point as to distinguish descendants from the earlier ancestral populations to about the same degree as we would encounter between two related contemporary species (Figure 2C), we say that one species has given rise to another. This phyletic progression has the same fundamental meaning for evolutionary history as the multiplication of a single species through splitting. By both processes there arise nominally new species, but the relation between two successive phyletic species is completely different from that between two recent or living species. These are contemporary, but reproductively isolated population groups, genetically completely separated from one another, cross sections of two different phyletic lines. Temporally successive taxonomic elements of phyletic evolution, on the contrary, are segments of a single line, sections of the continuum of reproductive communities spread out over geologic time.

The methodology of setting limits to vertical species is illustrated by Simpson with the example of the phyletic evolution of *Elephas plani-frons* → *E. meridionalis* from the work of Trevisan (1949). In this case (Figure 3), we have obviously a single species on each time horizon to be viewed as responding to the selective forces of secular changes in climate and biotype; the adaptive trait of number of enamel folds per 10 cm of molar length undergoes in the course of this a progressive increase from about 4½ in the Upper Pliocene to about 5½ in the Lower Pleistocene. The successive populations in this phyletic line constitute an evolutionary unit. However, since the geologically earlier and later groups differ to a degree recognized for species, it is taxonomically correct and expedient to set a vertical boundary between them. In the older typological systematics, in which individuals were classed by comparison with a type, all single finds approaching the *planifrons* type with a lamellar-index of 4½ were assigned to this species, and other specimens closer to the *meridionalis* type with a lamellar-index of 5½, to that

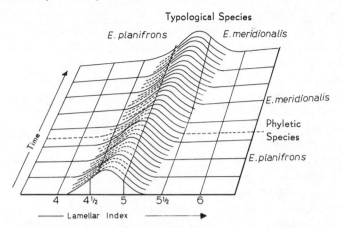

FIGURE 3. Vertical division of two species in a phylum of European fossil elephants. Following Trevisan, 1949, as modified by Simpson, 1953.

species. The phyletic line in this way would be divided into two co-existing species, of which one would be represented more and more rarely as time went on, while the other became more frequent. Since the natural populations of any time level are by this typological process arbitrarily broken down into two formal "species," the result suggests nothing of biological significance. The new systematics on the contrary recognizes no types, classifying not by individuals but by whole populations. In the present example, therefore, the vertical limit of species is placed at a time horizon in the phyletic succession; an apt stage of evolution to serve as this vertical boundary is the point at which the average lamellar-index of the elephant population was approximately 5. Of course, this procedure is also arbitrary, because phyletic evolution furnishes no genetic discontinuity as a basis for species boundaries. But the phyletic species bounded in this wise comprise only natural populations, which represent objective segments of an evolutionary series, and these species therefore have a definite biological and evolutionary significance.

The question of the origin of the species *H. sapiens* at once brings up the decision as to whether the correct mode of evolution is a "splitting" or a "phyletic evolution" from an older species of hominid.

3. SPLITTING IN THE COURSE OF HOMINID EVOLUTION?

A splitting would certainly be demonstrated if today there existed another hominid species in addition to *H. sapiens*. Since this is obviously not the case, it remains to be examined whether on one or another geological time horizon the existence of two or more species may be proven. In this case, the latest forking following a completed process of speciation would be considered as marking the origin of the surviving species *H. sapiens.*

Horizontal classification of approximately contemporary hominids is even today approached in very different ways. This is understandable in part from historical circumstances, since the question was first recognized as an important phylogenetic problem relatively late. As long as all the fossils could be counted on the fingers of one hand, the vertical, progressive division of the fossil men occupied the foreground of interest. This was because the pressing need was to find evidence for the validity of the evolutionary theory for the origin of "Man." The find from the Neanderthal, already named by W. King in 1864 as representing a species *H. neanderthalensis,* and the still more primitive and older find from Trinil, whose genus designation, *Pithecanthropus,* had been coined by E. Haeckel even before its finding, did duty as the first "links" in the line of development expected by the theory. Later discoveries of similar age and form were primarily evaluated as evidence for such a vertical series of steps for the hominids. It seemed less important how one might classify them relative to one another in the horizontal sense. If they were given individual designations of rank and order—new "species" alongside *H. neanderthalensis,* such as H. mousteriensis, H. rhodesiensis, H. soloensis, et cetera; or new "genera" alongside *Pithecanthropus,* such as Sinanthropus, Palaeanthropus, Africanthropus, et cetera—this was done more to emphasize the vertical position of the finds relative to *H. sapiens* than to bring out comprehensive comparative differences in the horizontal dimension of the system. To be sure, in the older systematics, in which the type specimen was the guidepost, it was permissible to use formal taxonomic rankings for the horizontal classification of finds since every new individual find naturally differed in some trait or other from the type. Moreover, the multiplication of such type-taxonomic names for finds of similar date and of approximately similar value, in a simple scheme of grades, served the practical purpose of giving expressive names for the material under discussion. The more matters remained limited to hominids, and the less there was known as to variations and the taxonomic implications thereof, so the less concern there was to make use, for the purpose, of the internationally agreed zoological nomenclature for properly grouping species and genera. Custom and tradition eventually fixed many of the names used for the different finds, so that today, in spite of better understanding, it is difficult to detach them once again. Many authors who accepted and made use of these designations, for example, Weidenreich, expressly stated that they by no means wished to use the names with the biological and taxonomic significance they would carry in the new systematics, but employed them only as designations of morphological types "without much concern for the kind of relationship to other types formerly known." In the case of many other authors, this is to be deduced from their positions on the phylogenetic evaluation of the finds. Even when such morpho-species and morpho-genera of fossil hominids are represented as extinct side-twigs in family trees (for example, Mollison, 1933, p. 98), these obviously should not be regarded as the result of so many splittings, since Mollison also represented the recent races of *H. sapiens,* which he clearly rates as subspecies, as a similar array of twigs.

The unsuitability of the museum classification should not, however, as already suggested, lead a total abstention from taxonomic nomenclature for the hominids, and the use in its place for new designations for different groupings of the fossil material, such as the terms introduced by Keith (1925) and Weidenreich (1946): Neoanthropi, Paleoanthropi, and Archanthropi; or the names used by Heberer (1948, 1950b): Preanthropi, Presapiens, Eusapiens, et cetera. Such "fancy terms," as Le Gros Clark, in his notable critical introduction to paleoanthropology (1955), asserts, should be completely avoided: "Insofar as none of these terms has ever been properly defined, they remain entirely obscure, and, insofar as they remain obscure, their continued use is bound to lead to confusion" (p. 9). The only safe way out of this dilemma means getting in step with the new knowledge and principles of taxonomy, which have led to a biologically based definition in place of the morphological definition of species. Zoological nomenclature, which takes care "that every unit should be given its special name" also furnishes the warning "that with every change of content (because of division, merging, or reassignment) the name should correspondingly be specifically altered" (Richter, 1948, p. 18).

In paleoanthropology it must be constantly emphasized that the basic unit of the new taxonomy is the population (Mayr, 1948). In such a natural breeding community, there is no type specimen but only a sometimes considerable individual variability (polymorphy). For such a population, the only things which can be called typical are the statistical values for the group in measurements and other morphological peculiarities. The most important practical unit for the student of systematics, the biological species, normally consists of a group of populations (subspecies, races), which exhibit greater or less geographic group variability (polytypy) and possess the capability of fertile hybridization.

According to this biological criterion in the definition of species, recent man constitutes a single polytypic species, divided into geographic races. This basic finding also serves as a point of departure in horizontal classification of the fossil hominids; it establishes the idea that we must also take account of divisions into geographic races in the geological past. This would appear to be obvious in any case. Still, this extension of view only actually became fruitful following the biological enrichment of the concept of species. Only a few decades ago the "origin of races" was viewed by noted authors as a differentiation appearing relatively late in our history. Witness Eugen Fischer (1936): "At the Sinanthropus stage humanity would seem to have been quite homogeneous. The formation of races had not yet begun." In the case of "Neanderthal Man," he also viewed "a marked division into races not yet" probable (pp. 253–254). Against this hypothesis which (speaking in present-day terms) imagines a monotypic hominid species until the Upper Pleistocene there weighs the broad geographic distribution of hominids which is known to have already existed in the Lower Pleistocene, since the relatively small groups of that period would have been far more isolated, and consequently the effect of local selective factors would have been more intense, than in the case of the fossil races of *H. sapiens.* Moreover, the morphological differences of approximately contemporary hominids found in geographically different places were, at a minimum, not less than the differences exhibited by the skeletons of recent races. On the contrary. Many authors —R. R. Gates (1948) most definitely—adjudged these traits to be the expression of a far-reaching division into true species and genera.

In answering this question, as to whether fossil hominids, generally equivalent as to date but differing in form, represent only geographical races or actual biological species, what diagnostic aids will the new systematics furnish? In studies of recent fauna, zoology also faces similar problems, when the decisive criterion of species—absence or presence of biological limitations on reproduction—is not available. In such cases, criteria are based on the fact that effective limitations on interbreeding are correlated with the degree of morphological differences between species, which is generally recognizable for any given genus (Mayr, 1958).

Since today we have knowledge of only one biological species, *H. sapiens,* we lack a standard, based on direct experience, by which to judge at what degree of morphological difference among fossil hominids we might give recognition to a genetic distinction between two species arising by splitting.

Another criterion, the demonstration of intergrading both in space and in form between geographically distant and morphologically different populations, as an index of their genetic relationship and membership in a single species, is scarcely applicable to the fossil finds, since chance plays so large a part in the recovery of material that populations, in the statistical sense, are seldom provided. Nonetheless, similarity in form between individuals from widely separated sites argues for membership in the same species.

Finally, we should give attention to the possibility of using the intra-specific variability of *H. sapiens* as a standard in the problem of species limits in the past. However, it is scarcely possible to do this so as to be generally representative, since the literature, though comprehensive, nevertheless provides a most unequal picture of the skeletal characteristics of different recent races. For many races, especially those living under primitive conditions, only a few ostelogical findings have been published; other, fuller skeletal series have been studied exclusively for their metrical traits; in most works, there is lacking the amount of illustration needed to make comparative judgments as to the variability of morphological features. As representing the intraspecific variability of *H. sapiens,* we must depend, as an unsatisfactory substitute, on the polymorphy shown by the larger skeletal series, usually European. On the other hand, few museums can provide the observer at once with skeletons of Pygmies and Fuegians, Australians and Lapps, Negroes and Eskimos, or other strongly contrasting races, a direct comparison of which allows the polytypy of *H. sapiens* to stand out most fully. To recognize the *vertical* distinction of the first Neanderthals found from the whole morphological group of recent races, comparison with a few European skulls sufficed. For *horizontal* classification of the fossil hominids, even a detailed knowledge of the variation of all the osteological traits of recent races cannot be used as a basis for judgment without reservation. For this would assume that intraspecific variability had always remained exactly the same in the course of hominid evolution.

Such an assumption is scarcely proper. Far more likely is the view of E. Mayr (1951), that geographical and individual variability, including sexual dimorphism, was greater in early hominids than we can tell from *H. sapiens* in the historic present. The high intraspecific variability of recent pongids, demonstrated by A. H. Schultz (1947, 1950c) points in the same direction. Remane (1954) deduces, on the basis of the fossil finds as well, that the Pongidae have possessed "at least since the Lower Miocene . . . an unusual range of individual polymorphism." Since in the splitting of a species it is always entire populations or subspecies which depart from the earlier species group, the earliest hominid species must already have been endowed with the high variability of whatever hominoid species served as its ancestor. "In the origin of the hominids we must assume a high individual variability in almost all characters from the time of their first separation" (Remane, 1954, p. 236). For the time period of the Pleistocene, moreover, the known hominid finds exhibit a consider-able geographic variation, such as would threaten to break up the unity

of the species. This centrifugal force appears, nevertheless, to have resulted in a completed speciation at no time and in no region, probably
because, as Mayr (1951) suggests, biological isolating mechanisms among
regional groups of hominids could not develop quickly enough.

From the evidence, a factual basis for a horizontal classification of
fossil hominids cannot be provided with a neat, convincing formula to
take care of all cases. This does not lead us, however, to pronounce a
resigned *"non liquet."* For, when we weigh the two taxonomic possibilities
under consideration, if the first and more radical possibility, that there
were two or more fossil hominid species arising through division, cannot be
ruled out, the very uncertainty favors the more conservative view, that we
have to reckon only with subspecific differences between contemporary
finds. Instead of an alternative which requires special arguments for its
proof, the view of subspecific differences among the regional fossils makes
the minimum taxonomic assumptions as to the morphological body of
fact. It is true that many anthropologists, like specialists in other fields of
systematics, are still inclined taxonomically to overestimate size and form
differences in fossil finds, creating horizontal species or even genera for
cases which in a broader view represent only extremes of intraspecific
variation. If, following Darwin's recommendation for situations of taxonomic evaluation, we consult biologists "having sound judgment and wide
experience," as to whether contemporary finds of fossil hominids ought to
be ranked as one or several species, we are told by Dobzhansky, E. Mayr,
Remane, and others (indeed, Weidenreich had already expressed the
view) that, with the possible exception of the so-called Australopithecinae, probably at no time did more than one species of *Homo* live.
Mayr (1951) sees in the ecological versatility of the hominids, who
have occupied more varied niches than any known animal, a concrete
indication that in the course of hominid evolution no case of complete
speciation took place.

4. PHYLETIC EVOLUTION OF *H. sapiens*

If, following this taxonomically conservative view that the morphological differences between contemporary hominids ought to be rated as
only subspecific in nature, then obviously the vertical chronological succession of all available finds corresponds to the model of a phyletic
evolution. "All the phyletic transformations in Hominidae were always
taking place within a single genetic system, a species consisting of
geographically, but not reproductively, isolated races" (Dobzhansky,
1944, p. 262).

This conception is all the more attractive, since it leaves all possibilities
open for the phyletic relations between the presently known fossil

hominids which, in view of obstacles both in data and method, we cannot now evaluate properly in detail. On the other hand, the more venture-some assumption, of contemporary species and their earlier splitting, demands that one or more of these species end as extinct side lines, and thereby definitely excludes them from having taken part in the process of evolution leading to the surviving species *H. sapiens*. It must be considered that, in the continuum of a phyletic evolution, the regional groups of a species at a given time level may all or only in part contribute to the formation of the characteristic trait complex and gene pool of that species at a later time horizon. Spatial expansion and temporal extension of particular regional races with well adapted gene combina-tions might, for example, lead to the contraction of other races, whether by partial destruction or by overrunning and mixture; in this way, viewed historically, an expanding race might undergo substantial changes in the constitution of its characteristics and genes, through mixture with local races and through the influence of local factors of selection in a new environment. Such processes would have taken place in different regions in a widely distributed species. And this in turn might have made it possible that expanding geographic races coming in contact with one another should combine evolutionary advantages which would come into being in different regions. Such a genetically open system is thus more plastic in the evolutionary sense (Dobzhansky) than a system composed of several parallel species genetically cut off from one another.

In the evolution of the hominids, there is only one *a priori* certain case of a completed speciation, that which marks their actual origin from another hominoid species. This original separation of the hominids from higher primates of the Tertiary is at the same time especially characterized by the fact that, with the development of the upright posture, a new adaptive plateau was achieved. The model representing phyletic evolution refers in the narrower sense to those changes and processes of deployment which took place in the population network of the phylum, or phyletic line, after the above completed separation.

This mode of evolution, of a phyletic hominid line as a unit—analogous to Figure 2C—seems seductively simple. The problems posed by its vertical divisions and subspecific interweavings in detail—analogous to Figure 2B—in the phylogenetic interpretations of the fossils are in fact manifold and confining.

Vertical classification of a phylum into segments, which is primarily called for by the need of more precise description, proceeds from the premise, as set forth in section 2, that morphological changes in chron-ologically ordered finds coincide with genetic changes in the continuum

of the population nexus, even if these are not strictly proportional. Therefore, it is taxonomically correct to designate such segments of a phylum,
which differ from one another in the same degree as known species, as
phyletic species. Being segments of an evolutionary unit, phyletic species
are not sharply distinguished from one another; it is possible to set limits
between phyletic species principally by agreement only. For this, it is
sufficient that new characteristics, or distinguishing grades of characteristics, shall have achieved a broad or general distribution in the evolving
web of populations of the phylum at a given time horizon.

In the fossil hominids, vertical classification is simplified, in part at
least, by the great gaps in information, since we are at once relieved of
the decision as to the time horizon in which two phyletic series are to be
distinguished from one another. The great differences in form between
the first known fossil finds, whose geological age was, to begin with,
decidedly overestimated, led directly to the conception of "stages" in
hominid evolution, and typologically oriented hypotheses have drawn
from this the naive expectation that further finds must fit neatly into such
a scheme of steps, or provide intermediate "links" in all characteristics.
In opposition, it cannot be too strongly emphasized that, in the evolution
of the hominid phylum from the beginning, we must reckon with parallel
subspecific groups, having a considerable individual and geographic
variation in their features. It must further be supposed that phylogenetic
changes in the course of time took place at unequal rates, that primitive
traits survived longer regionally, and progressive manifestations might
have disappeared once more in connection with migrations and mixtures,
or with the extinction of whole groups, and that in fact in individual traits
even a reverse development may be imagined. The more comprehensive
becomes the future knowledge of reliably dated finds from all time periods
and from the entire territory occupied by hominids, the more clearly
will appear the complexly subdivided continuum of the phylum, in
place of the older concept of "stages." If it should become constantly
more difficult to agree on a time horizon between phyletic species which
should be valid everywhere, at least we shall at the same time obtain a
view, from many cross sections at different times provided by random
representative populations in the material, such as will resolve at least
some of the more important phyletic relations in the network of subspecific groups, marking the course of the evolution of the phylum in
the concrete terms of morphology.

Such a comprehensive and at the same time detailed knowledge of
fossil groups would naturally furnish fruitful information for our special
question as to the phyletic roots of the species *H. sapiens,* whatever convention may finally be accepted as to its limiting point in the vertical

dimension. The material existing at the moment permits only a tentative first draft. With respect to the time dimension, on which *H. sapiens* is to be recognized as the terminal segment of the phylum, the frame of this pattern may be set widely or narrowly, and correspondingly the question of the phyletic roots of the species placed in a more recent or ancient phase of hominid evolution in the Pleistocene. Two contrasting viewpoints may be discussed.

A. The broader conception, taxonomically, of including in the phyletic species *H. sapiens* all the Neanderthals in the wider sense, including the Steinheim skull from the second interglacial, is represented by those authors who, like Dobzhansky (1944) and E. Mayr (1944, 1951) first attempted a vertical classification of hominids from the standpoint of the new systematics. Mayr classified recent and fossil hominids as a single genus *Homo* with three phyletic species: *H. transvaalensis* (South African man-apes)→*H. erectus* (Java man and Peking man)→*H. sapiens* (pre-Neanderthal group, Neanderthal group, modern man group). With Dobzhansky, he based this unusual extension of the phyletic species *H. sapiens* on the ground that recent finds belonging to the Neanderthal form group, especially the Mount Carmel skeletons, no longer permit a specific separation of the Neanderthals from the Upper Paleolithic races of "Modern Man," and perhaps render it impossible. Apart from the factual arguments for this view, there is the practical obstacle to its general recognition that the traditional conception connected with the term *H. sapiens*—corresponding systematically to the subspecies group "modern man" of Mayr—is strongly fixed in anthropology. For the rest, the phylogenetically important question, as to the genealogical relations of subspecific groups in consecutive time phases, is not affected by any agreement as to vertical species limits. It does not reduce the phyletic importance of the long discussed relation of the Neanderthals to the Upper Paleolithic men if, in Mayr's vertical classification, it is now brought within the phyletic species *H. sapiens* as a question of the origin of the subspecies group "modern man" (Mayr accepts the relation of this to the subspecies group of the "Preneanderthals"), while we now seek the roots of the more broadly conceived species *H. sapiens* geologically much earlier, in the population nexus of the species *H. erectus*. Mayr expresses himself only briefly on this problem, to the effect that, at least on Java, the finds of Ngandong and Wadjak "may have formed a practically unbroken chain of hominids leading from Java man to modern man" (p. 113).

Similarly addressed to vertical limits, although giving different taxonomic rank to the phyletic hominid groups, is the vertical classification of Le Gros Clark (1955). He divides the family Hominidae into three genera: *Australopithecus, Pithecanthropus, Homo.* The genus *Homo* comprises on the one side the phyletic species *H. sapiens,* ranging from recent races through the Upper Paleolithic men and the early, "generalized" Neanderthals, such as Saccopastore, Krapina, Mount Carmel, Ehringsdorf, and Steinheim—to take account only of moderately complete finds—and reaching back into the middle interglacial. From the last named "Premousterian or early Mousterian *Homo sapiens*" finds there arose on the other side "an actual evolutionary series," an "aberrant (and, in some respects, a retrogressive) collateral line" (p. 74), the "extreme" Neanderthals of the "cold" Mousterian of Europe, which Le Gros Clark recognizes with the rank of a species, *H. neanderthalensis.* However, he checkreins his conclusion "that *H. neanderthalensis* was a typical divergent radiation in process of speciation" by adding, "even if this process had not become quite complete in the genetic sense by the time this group of Paleolithic man became extinct" (footnote p. 71). With this reservation, the taxonomic difference from Mayr's ranking of the extreme Neanderthals—a subspecies group within the phyletic species *H. sapiens*—is virtually annulled. Le Gros Clark, analogously to Dobzhansky and Mayr, finds the roots of the species *H. sapiens,* as defined above, in the genus furnished by him for the Pithecanthropus group. "This does not mean . . . that the Far Eastern population of this genus was itself the actual ancestral group—it means, at the most, that the genus *Pithecanthropus* was probably ancestral to the genus *Homo;* if so, of course, the transition from one to the other may have occurred in some other part of the world" (p. 106). The specific difference between the Javanese and Chinese finds within the genus *Pithecanthropus* is obviously given only slight significance by Le Gros Clark: "There are certain minor differences . . . and . . . these are held by some authorities to justify a specific distinction. Provisionally, therefore, *P. pekinensis* of China may be regarded as a species quite closely related to *P. erectus* of Java" (p. 97). If these are regarded as true species, resulting from a splitting, naturally only one of them could have given rise to the phyletic species *H. sapiens.* This phyletic implication is not discussed by the author.

B. The narrow restriction of the species *H. sapiens* to recent and Upper Paleolithic races corresponds broadly with the traditional view of the content of this oldest systematic concept of anthropology, and need not be enlarged upon. A detailed osteological definition has been given by Le Gros Clark (1955) for the purpose of his vertical classification. In this, the form of the inferior frontal region is diagnostically important: "supraorbital ridges usually moderately developed and in any case not forming an uninterrupted torus" (p. 48). This feature, "arcus superciliares," is diagnostic for recent races as well as for skulls of Upper Paleolithic skeletons, whereas all older hominids, for whom the frontal bone exists in sufficiently complete form, allowing a definite judgment as to the form of this region, though certainly variable, exhibit in every case a torus supraorbitalis extending over the entire upper border of the orbit. This holds for the "classic" Neanderthals, in whom this trait, designated as "proscopiny" by Frassetto, was first recognized, as well as for the geologically (mostly) older "generalized" Neanderthals, particularly for the skulls of the Skhul skeletons from Mount Carmel, who have more lately been dated to the beginning of the last glacial phase. Naturally, then, one should not expect that this craniological difference, which is to be viewed primarily as a symptom of a deeper-rooted difference in the development of the frontal brain, and eventually thus in the grade of cerebralization, should, when more material is known, coincide almost everywhere with a narrowly circumscribed time horizon. In any case, at present the form of the lower forehead region serves to separate vertically the species *H. sapiens* from an older segment of the hominid phylum, a phyletic species known by the name given it by W. King (1864) from the type specimen from the Neander Valley, *H. neanderthalensis*. The original restriction of this designation to the "classic" Neanderthals of Europe, which are particularly similar to the holotype from Neanderthal, is understandable historically, but cannot be sustained from the standpoint of the new systematics. *H. neanderthalensis*, as a phyletic species, must be expected to exhibit a corresponding polytypy in space and time. It comprises the geographic races of the "extreme" Neanderthals in Europe, Africa (for example, Broken Hill, Eyasi, Saldanha), and Asia (for example, Ngandong), and in geochronological range all the populations represented by the "generalized Neanderthals" and the "Preneanderthals," which we can trace back to the latter part of the second or middle interglacial with the Steinheim find.

How, in this taxonomic approach, we may interpret the question of the phyletic roots of the species *H. sapiens* within the population network of the species *H. neanderthalensis*, is more easily made clear by using diagrams instead of words. In Figure 4, the geochronological divisions of the Middle and Upper Pleistocene are shown, following the data of Zeuner (1952). For choosing finds to be represented, the criteria were reliable dating and satisfactory condition of preservation. The two-dimensional representation suggested a restriction to Europe and hither Asia. In comparison with my first attempt (Breitinger, 1955, p. 39), the Steinheim and Mount Carmel finds have been adjusted as to date.

The anastomosing or rejoining web of lines (populations), as time goes on, corresponds to the model of phyletic evolution, that of a species,

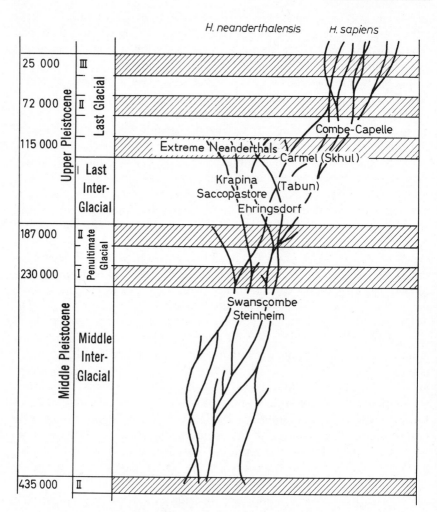

FIGURE 4.   Phyletic relations of *H. neanderthalensis* to *H. sapiens*.

polytypic at every time horizon, in process of evolutionary transformation. In particular, the confluence and the occasional dying out of lines signifies that races and local population cannot be followed back over major time spans. It would be a mistake to expect to find a direct relation for the earlier sapiens races going back nearly 200,000 years to populations of the middle interglacial, populations for which we have not yet satisfactory knowledge of a single individual, in spite of the finds of Swanscombe and Steinheim. By contrast, considering the time position and the morphology, it is not impossible that the skeletons from Mugharet es-

Skhul belong to one of those populations standing in genealogical relationship to the races of the Upper Paleolithic. And this group of finds in turn would have proceeded from populations of the last interglacial. For this, remains are known, in Palestine, of a few individuals, for example, Djebel Kafzeh, Mugharet el-Zuttiyeh, and Mugharet et-Tabun; and in Central Europe, from Ehringsdorf, Krapina, and Saccopastore. At the same time, these interglacial races are to be regarded as the starting point for the "classic" Neanderthals of Europe. If their special morphological differentiation came about, as F. C. Howell (1951) conjectures, during a climatically caused isolation at the beginning of the last glacial phase, this suggests the beginning of a process of speciation, which, however, came to a premature end with the extinction of this subspecies group (Mayr) before a genetically determined barrier to reproduction could develop. Any definite conclusion as to phyletic connections going further back in the population network of *H. neanderthalensis* are prevented by the all too meager material.

The picture outlined here, from inductive judgment on the basis of the finds, as well as deductions from the assumed mode of evolution, coincides in its essential points with the views of many authors although they make use in varying degrees of other terminology. Among the most recent writings, I shall mention only S. Sergi's (1953c) emphasis on polytypy in a sequence of "morphological cycles" of "Paleoantropi" and "Fanerantropi" and C. Arambourg's (1955a) transformation of the Neanderthals (as classified here) into the species *H. sapiens.*

Detailed discussion is not the purpose of this exposition, which is devoted primarily to principles. A little may be said, however, relative to the opposing hypothesis of a parallel evolution of *H. sapiens* alongside the other known hominids, a hypothesis (in essence an old one) put forward several times in recent years by Herberer as his "Entfaltung" or "deployment" hypothesis. Substance and terminology are most easily conveyed by comparing two diagrams of this author.

Until the year 1950, Heberer embodied his views in a "modern phylogenetic scheme of relationships of the Hominoidea" (Figure 5), according to which "modern man (Neanthropine type)" stems from the "Anthropus or Archanthropine stage," in part affected by the Neanderthal group (Paleanthropine type), which, however, essentially constituted a special differentiation and did not otherwise develop to the Neanthropine stage" (1950a, p. 20).

In the same year, Heberer (1950b) abandoned this "stage hypothesis," and in agreement with H. V. Vallois' (1949a) conception, developed following the discovery of the Fontéchevade skull fragments, propounded a "basically independent phylogeny of the Neanthropines"

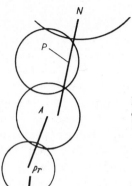

FIGURE 5. Extract from diagram of phylogenetic relations of the Hominoidea, from Heberer, 1950a.

which "may in fact be thought of as independent back as far as the Prehominine base" (1951a, p. 64). For this simplification, his diagram of the "Entfaltungshypothese" (Figure 6), first published in 1951 and since then republished with certain variations, gives the impression that several parallel phyletic lines are assumed, which arose by splitting from the australopithecine group. Heberer explains that, at present, it is not possible to decide whether the three twigs represented "are rooted in polyphyletic fashion in the Prehominines" or whether they possessed "phyletically and geographically an original homogeneity. The diagram

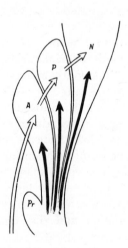

N NEANTHROPINES
P PALAEANTHROPINES
A ARCHANTHROPINES
Pr PREHOMININES

FIGURE 6. "Deployment" hypothesis (black arrows) and stage hypothesis (white arrows), after Heberer, 1951a.

favors the first version." However, note this sentence in the same section: "There was certainly a high degree of contact, and contact brings about gene flow from twig to twig for, as has already been said, mankind at every time horizon constituted only one—polytypic—species" (1951a, p. 76). This leaves no doubt that the twigs represented have only subspecific rank.

Here there at once arises a theoretical consideration against the force of this "Entfaltungshypothese"; if there was in fact contact and gene flow between the twigs in "certainly a high degree," then a long parallel development is most improbable from the point of view of population genetics. Moreover, Remane has already asserted (1954, pp. 262, 263) that an isolated progress of the sapiens form, resting on general considerations as to the phylogenetic significance of proscopiny, is "very poorly founded." What is needed are finds which are reliably dated and which taxonomically may be unambiguously diagnosed. In the case of the present evidence adduced, Swanscombe and Fontéchevade, on which Vallois (1954a) rests his conception of a "Presapiens line" running parallel to that of the Neanderthals since at least the middle interglacial, the first requirement, reliable dating, is indeed fulfilled. Nevertheless, these "Presapiens" finds are so incomplete that their morphological and taxonomic status is in dispute. In view of the ambiguity to which the term "Presapiens," by its nature, is exposed, it must in this connection be expressly emphasized that Vallois has more precisely defined the morphological nature of his "Presapiens form" (1954a, p. 24). The diagnostically decisive criterion: "Forehead upright and completely lacking any torus" corresponds to that used above (1954a, 4B, p. 77) in the narrower definition of the species *H. sapiens*. To Vallois, therefore, "Presapiens" is synonymous with "primitive sapiens" (p. 112) or Primisapiens (Breitinger, 1955, p. 10). By this criterion of form, the occipital fragment of Swanscombe is certainly not to be definitely diagnosed as a Primisapiens form. By differential diagnosis, Swanscombe is with much greater probability to be classed as an early race of *H. neanderthalensis* (Breitinger, 1955). Of the two skull fragments from Fontéchevade from the last interglacial one, FI, is only a few centimeters in size, and not yet published in full; the larger calotte fragment, FII, was extensively affected by fire (Vallois, 1949a, p. 340), and since the lower frontal region is lacking, a definite diagnosis is scarcely possible. Evidence for the contemporaneity of representatives of Primisapiens and of Neanderthals in the Middle and Upper Pleistocene is therefore still quite indefinite.

Heberer and other authors use the term "Presapiens" without more precise definition; consequently conceptions of an independent "Presapiens" or "Neanthropine branch" remain uncertain and variable. Since his first discussion of the "Presapiens problem" (1950b, p. 152), Heberer has included the Skhul skeletons, in spite of their pronounced proscopiny, in the category "Presapiens" of the aproscopine "Neanthropines." Gieseler likewise (1955, p. 174) regards the Skhul people as "representatives of a Presapiens" while Vallois says, from his comprehensive knowledge of the Neanderthals: "We may consider the Palestine men as a highly evolved variety of Neanderthal Man; beyond this we cannot go" (Boule-Vallois, 1946, p. 400; 1952, p. 396). Since Heberer, who in 1950 (b, p. 152) still placed the Steinheim skull in the Preneanderthals, now (1955, p. 87) ranges it with the "Presapiens group," there has disappeared completely the theoretical assumption for accepting an independent "Neanthropine branch."

Whoever does not accept the splitting of the fossil hominids into two or more species can only seek to trace particular lines in the racial web of the evolving species. In theoretical approach, the "deployment" hypothesis here greatly overshoots the mark, and in the present state of known material, and the uncertainty of the concept of "Presapiens," indications for a phyletic independence of these "Neanthropines" reaching back beyond the Upper Pleistocene must remain suspect. This is also the view of von Koenigswald (1955a): "There is no ground for accepting diverse 'stems' and 'parallel evolution' on a large scale" (p. 229).

As long as hominid finds provide so scanty a basis for reasoning, it will be well to refrain from conclusions which assume a thorough analysis of biological facts. The model of phyletic evolution, marked by polytypy in a genetically open racial network, provides the investigation of the origin of our own species *H. sapiens* with plentiful deductive help, conceived and tested in paleontological research. It provides wide scope for the variability of populations, for most of which we have now the remains of only a few individuals; and at the same time it protects interpretation of the phyletic relationships, in the material now known, from incautious hypotheses which cannot stand up to new discoveries. A certain constancy in phyletic assumptions would foster the respect which the scientific meaning of this old, widely interesting problem should have in public opinion.

SUMMARY

1. Elementary principles for an agreement on problems of hominid phylogeny may be found in the principles of the new systematics relating to taxonomy and nomenclature.

2. Starting from this, the question of the origin of the species *H. sapiens* faces two alternatives: whether, in the sense of G. G. Simpson,

the mode of evolution is to be viewed as a "splitting," or a "phyletic evolution."

3. An eventual splitting into two or more contemporary hominid species is, on the basis of present knowledge, improbable.

4. The phyletic evolution of *H. sapiens* is discussed in terms of two taxonomically different propositions; following this, the recently revived hypothesis of a parallel evolution of *H. sapiens* reaching back into the Lower Pleistocene is disputed.

A Reconsideration of Some Mandibular Profiles

L. H. Wells   1958

Mandibular profiles have most often been compared by superimposing them with the alveolar planes coinciding, although the vertical axis used for registration varies. Much valuable information may certainly be obtained in this way. It may be suggested however, that equally important features are obscured or at least not clearly brought out.

In his classic memoir on "Variations in the Form of the Jaws," Sim Wallace (1927) remarked that the only really fixed point on the mandible is the articular condyle. Following Professor Arthur Thomson, he superimposed mandibles for comparison with the posterior borders of their ascending rami coinciding. When the mandible is dissected into its component parts as indicated by Washburn (1951b) it is evident that the posterior border of the ascending ramus belongs almost wholly to the angular process, which is moulded by the interaction of the internal pterygoid muscle and the superficial fibres of the masseter muscle. Consequently the direction of this border has no consistent relation either to that of the mechanical axis of the ramus or to that of the occlusal plane.

I suggest, therefore, that mandibular profiles can be compared much more satisfactorily by bringing the condylar surfaces into coincidence, but so orientating the profiles that the alveolar planes, or preferably, from a functional viewpoint, the occlusal planes, are parallel. Strictly speaking, these are not planes, but arcs of circles; their radius is however so large that they can for practical purposes be treated as planes.

FROM *the* South African Journal of Science, *1958, vol. 54, pp. 55–58, reprinted by permission of the South African Association for the Advancement of Science. This article, introduced for its methodological nature, shows how careful comparisons of essential morphological feautres (cf. articles by Le Gros Clark and Washburn, preceding) can lead to the identification of important problems and differences. Dr. Wells is Professor of Anatomy in the University of Cape Town.*

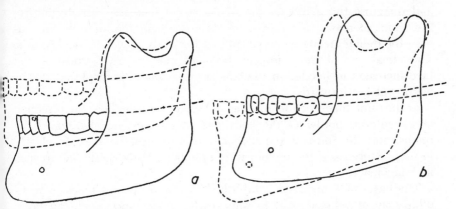

FIGURE 1. (*a*) Profiles of European and Bushman mandibles; (*b*) profiles of European and Negro mandibles (specimens in Edinburgh University Anatomical Museum).

The working of this method may be illustrated in the first place by comparing the mandibular profiles of a robust European, of a strongly prognathous Negro, and of a typically paedomorphic Bushman.

When the European and Bushman jaws are compared in this way (Figure 1a) the contrast in the height of the ramus above the occlusal plane is most striking, all the more because in these two examples the condylar-coronoid width is almost the same. So far as the mandible itself is concerned, this goes with the difference in the inclination of the ramal axis, which can be approximately indicated by a line from the anterior border of the condylar neck to the point at which the anterior border of the ramus crosses the alveolar margin. In terms of the skull as a whole, the difference in the ramal height above the occlusal plane registers the shortness or failure of downward growth of the face in the paedomorphic type (Drennan, 1931).

The Negro mandible selected for comparison (Figure 1b) has a ramus which rises slightly higher above the occlusal plane than does that of the European. The salient difference between them is that the dental arcade in the prognathic Negro is not only longer but is placed further forwards in relation to the condyle, the third molar in this jaw coinciding approximately with the second molar in the European jaw. With this forward displacement, the ramal axis is again more oblique than that of the European.

These contrasts register divergent trends in the post-natal growth of the mandible. In all three types, the juvenile ramus is short and its mechanical axis very oblique (Wells, 1931b). The Bushman's ramal axis retains this infantile oblique direction because the face does not elongate and therefore the height of the ramus is not increased. In the Negro, the ramus increases in height while its axis retains the infantile orientation; the dental arcade is thus displaced forwards as well as downwards. The ramal axis of the European becomes more nearly vertical as the face increases in height, so that the occlusal plane is displaced downwards but not forwards.

At the same time, such features as the symphyseal profiles, the direction of the inferior border of the body and of the posterior border of the ramus, and the form of the coronoid process, can be seen as clearly in these figures as if the profiles were orientated with the dental arcades in coincidence.

The bases of comparison established for these modern types of mandible may now be applied to some early human and prehuman jaws. The Mauer (Heidelberg) jaw may be taken as a starting point. When this specimen is compared with the European mandible already studied (Figure 2a), the height of the condyle above the occlusal plane proves to be practically identical. The extraordinary breadth of the ramus in the Mauer jaw is due to a very oblique ramal axis, combined with a special development of the coronoid and angular processes. The Mauer dental arcade is not only longer anteroposteriorly than that of the European, but is placed further in advance of the temporomandibular joint. In this respect the Mauer jaw agrees with that of the Negro (Figure 2b). When these two jaws are orientated as I have suggested, their ramal axes are found to be very nearly parallel. The difference in the form of the ramus is brought about entirely by the coronoid and angular processes. Compared with the Negro, the dental arcade of the Mauer jaw is both a little longer anteroposteriorly and placed a little further in advance of the temporomandibular joint.

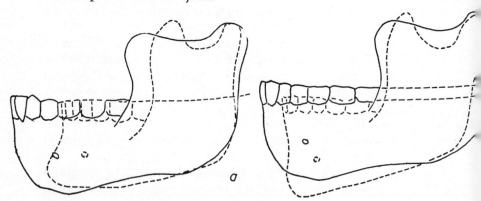

FIGURE 2. (a) Profiles of Mauer and European mandibles; (b) profiles of Mauer and Negro mandibles (Mauer mandible from cast).

Comparison of the male Pekin jaw with that of Mauer (Figure 3a) reveals some enlightening contrasts. The Pekin jaw gives the impression of possessing a tall ramus. In fact, the height of the condyle above the occlusal plane is appreciably less than that of the Mauer mandible. The appearance of height is due partly to the smaller condylar-coronoid width, and partly to the accentuated downward development of the angular process; this last feature is in marked contrast to the broadly truncated angle of the Mauer jaw. Because the ramus is shorter, its axis is more oblique than might at first be supposed. The dental arcade is very nearly the same in length as that of the Mauer jaw, but is not projected so far in front of the temporomandibular joint. Although the Pekin jaw cannot be described as paedomorphic in the same sense as the Bushman, its features lie on the paedomorphic side of those of the Mauer jaw.

Many years ago (Wells, 1931b), comparing immature mandibles of humans and apes, I noted that the Taung child shows an extraordinarily high mandibular ramus, implying a face which is remarkably elongated vertically, but projects forwards very little. The adult Australopithecine mandibles from Sterkfontein and Makapansgat are not complete enough for this comparison, but those of the larger *Paranthropus crassidens* from Swartkrans show the same great height of the ascending ramus above the occlusal plane as does the Taung specimen. This feature is emphasised by the fact that the Swartkrans ramus is narrower than that of the Mauer jaw, though broader than that of the Pekin man (Figure 3b). The axis of the ramus must therefore be much more nearly vertical than those of the Mauer and Pekin jaws. The

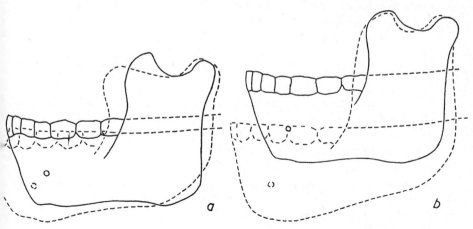

FIGURE 3. (a) Profiles of Pekin and Mauer mandibles (from casts); (b) profiles of Pekin and Swartkrans mandibles (Swartkrans from Brown and Robinson, 1952).

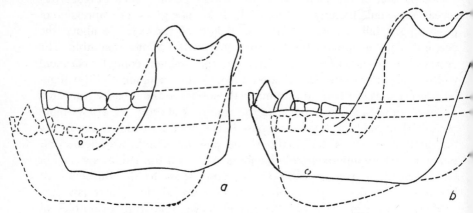

FIGURE 4. (a) Profiles of Pekin and Proconsul mandibles; (b) profiles of Proconsul and Swartkrans mandibles (Proconsul from cast).

evidence of the Taung fossil indicates that the Australopithecine ramal axis assumes this direction at an earlier developmental stage than does that of the European type of man. In the general form of the mandibular body there is a remarkable agreement between the Swartkrans and Mauer jaws (Figure 3a, b).

In view of the many features which tend to associate the Australopithecines with the Hominidae, this contrast in the form of the ascending ramus demands consideration. Is it legitimate to postulate that the ancestral Hominidae possessed the tall Australopithecine ramus with the elongated face which it implies, or did these characters develop in the Australopithecines as specialisations following their divergence from the ancestral Hominids?

A consideration of the more ancient Hominoid genus Proconsul may throw some light on this problem. For greater ease of comparison, the larger species *Pronconsul nyanzae* rather than the smaller *P. africanus* has been employed; however it appears that the two species agree fundamentally on the points with which we are concerned (Le Gros Clark and Leakey, 1951). The ascending ramus of Proconsul is also strikingly high (Figure 4a), though it is considerably more oblique than that of Paranthropus; in consequence the dental arcade protrudes further in front of the temporo-mandibular joint (Figure 4b). So far as this evidence goes, it suggests that a high ascending ramus is a feature of the earlier Hominoids. It need not therefore be regarded as an aberrant specialisation in the Australopithecines. The significant development in the Australopithecines as compared with Proconsul appears to be the much more vertical ramal axis, which is associated with a "pulling in" of the facial structure.

If this view is correct, the height of the ascending ramus, and consequently of the face, must have been dramatically reduced in the Hominidae at a stage earlier than that represented by the Pekin man. This could be interpreted as part of a process of paedomorphic modification. It also follows that if Broom and Robinson (1952) prove to be correct in restoring the mandible of *Telanthropus capensis* with a relatively low ascending ramus, it will be a strong point in favour of their view that Telanthropus is a true Hominid rather than an Australopithecine.

Interpretations of the Fossil Material

Franz Weidenreich   1949

I do not intend to enter into a detailed discussion of the new finds from Java and China which Dr. von Koenigswald has brought to this country. I only want to say that the originals not only confirm what the casts have shown but make the conclusions drawn from the study of the casts definitive. For the characteristic human features which *Meganthropus* and *Gigantopithecus* exhibit are in reality much more pronounced than they were indicated to be by the casts. Judging from the responses and comments my study of the *Sinanthropus* skull has met with in some circles, I do not dare to hope that objections to the human character of the new finds or to their relation to modern man will be overcome in the near future. There are too many people who do not take pains to check the reported anatomical details from which the conclusions have been drawn but only look over the summaries. Unless these comply with their preconceived opinions or the axioms made sacred by tradition, they refuse acknowledgment. Such an attitude is very char-

Reprinted by permission of The Wistar Institute Press from Studies in Physical Anthropology, *1:149–157 (1949), "Early Man in the Far East," ed. by W. W. Howells, a symposium originally organized by S. L. Washburn and held December 28, 1946, under the auspices of the American Anthropological Association and the American Association of Physical Anthropologists. Published by permission of the Estate of Mathilde Weidenreich and of the American Association of Physical Anthropologists. This article is a succinct statement of Dr. Weidenreich's general position on lines of evolution in the fossil men, detailed at greater length in his other writings (see especially Weidenreich, 1946). Refer also to the next article by Vallois. At his death, on July 11, 1948, Dr. Weidenreich was Research Associate at the American Museum of Natural History in New York; before this, until 1941, he had been in charge of the excavation and study of the Chou Kou Tien remains of Pekin Man, acting as director of the Cenozoic Research Laboratory of National Geological Survey of China and the Peiping Union Medical College.*

acteristic of paleoanthropology and has not changed since the first fossil man came to light. It took 50 years before Neanderthal Man was recognized as a special human form and not pushed aside as a pathological variant of modern man, and it took 40 more years before Dubois' *Pithecanthropus erectus,* originally described as a giant ape, was acknowledged as a normal-sized hominid.

J. P. Kleiweg de Zwaan has written (1940):

An explanation is due in regard to *Pithecanthropus erectus.* This subject was not included in the edition of 1923, because at the time there was still considerable reluctance to assigning a place to *Pithecanthropus* among the hominids. However, it is sufficiently well known that not only the products of nature are subject to evolution, but that also the science which investigates these phenomena is, like every science, a living thing and therefore in a state of constant change and development.

Therefore there is at least a remote chance that as a consequence of the evolution of anthropological science and scientists, *Meganthropus* and *Gigantopithecus* may be admitted to the hominid family at about 2000 A.D. This auspicious prospect relieves me from wasting my time and yours by repeating here why these fossils have to be classified as hominids and why they lie in the line of human evolution. Instead I want to emphasize more general issues which the anatomical features suggest.

These facts are: (1) The lower jaw and the teeth of *Meganthropus* are of gigantic proportions when compared with modern man. (2) The jaw and teeth of *Pithecanthropus robustus* are smaller than those of *Meganthropus* but larger than those of *Pithecanthropus erectus.* (3) The teeth of *Gigantopithecus* are not only much larger than those of the Java giant but also much larger than any teeth of living anthropoids. Among von Koenigswald's material there are some isolated teeth of the same size as those of *Meganthropus* and there is also an additional molar of *Gigantopithecus* apparently belonging to one more individual. This proves that the giant forms cannot be dismissed as accidental variants of normal-sized hominids as Le Gros Clark recently suggested. Nor is it possible to identify *Gigantopithecus* as a large orang utan as the same author does. Von Koenigswald brought with him a collection of several hundreds of fossil, subfossil, and recent orang utan teeth from both Java and China. Neither in size nor in pattern do any of these orang teeth come closer to *Gigantopithecus* than do chimpanzee or gorilla. If the morphological character of the new specimens is taken as basis for classification and the most primitive ones are put at the top, they can be ranged in the following evolutionary line: *Gigantopithecus, Meganthropus, Pithecanthropus robustus, Pithecanthropus erectus.*

Since I first had a chance to examine the *Homo soloensis* skulls in

Batavia in 1938 I have been convinced that their usual classification as Neanderthal skulls cannot be maintained. The skulls which were in very poor condition and badly neglected are now in preparation in the paleontological laboratory of the American Museum of Natural History. They show a great many characteristic features which have so far escaped observation. Of particular importance is the fact that the bases of two skulls are almost entirely undamaged. No Preneanderthalian has been recovered in this condition, and among the Neanderthalians only the left side of the Rhodesian skull is so nearly perfect. Each anatomical structure of the Soloensis skull is clear and unimpaired. All show that *Homo soloensis* is much more primitive than any of the so-called Neanderthal skulls. The cranial capacity could be measured directly with water in three skulls. In one the cranial capacity is 990 cm^3, in the second, 1040 cm^3, and in the third 1100 cm^3. All this shows that compared with *Pithecanthropus, Homo soloensis* represents an evolutionary phase which is intermediate between *Pithecanthropus* and Neanderthal Man as the latter is known from Europe. The two preserved tibiae of Soloensis, never described before—one smaller, the other very robust—reveal a general human character but seem not to exceed those of modern man in length despite the heaviness of the skulls. If we keep in mind that Java has also yielded Wadjak Man, an early modern human type which has been identified as a forerunner of the Australian bushman of today, we have before us an almost continuous line proceeding from primitive to most advanced ones. As all the phases of this line remain closely connected continuously with the Sino-Malayan fauna, they represent the Sino-Malayan human line of evolution. *Sinanthropus* obviously belongs to the same general line although he differs in some details.

These Java and China finds prove that there never was a single cradle of mankind—whether located in Asia or Africa—from whence the different phases of mankind spread over the world whenever the center produced them. There must have been several centers more or less independent of each other. Unfortunately, our knowledge of those other human lines is very poor. That of the European line to date begins with the European Neanderthalians as earlier phases are not known. As to later ones, the discovery of the Mount Carmel population of Palestine made it evident that there must be the same connection between the European Neanderthal form and the modern Upper Paleolithic type of man as exists between *Homo soloensis* and Wadjak Man. Compared with the Sino-Malayan line, the European line is very incomplete. Notwithstanding this obvious deficiency, all the theories of human evolution, particularly those concerning the origin of *Homo sapiens*, have been based only on finds on European soil. The finds of the Far East reveal that the more advanced human types which correspond to the Neanderthalians and Upper Paleolithic Man of Europe have in common only the general features characteristic of the evolutionary phase they represent. They differ in details, however, and thereby give evidence of their special differentiation. In addition, the lines demonstrate by their mere existence that evolution, at least in later phases, cannot have been brought about as a reaction to environmental influences, as for example the climate of the Ice Ages, a favored theory 40 years ago. We know now that man lived and developed under subtropical and tropical conditions as well as under arctic ones but the final result of this development was in all cases the same so far as the general human appearance is concerned.

The European line owes its prominent place in the history of paleoanthropology partly to the fact that the first human fossils were recovered from Europe and partly to the much greater weight which has been attached to geological rather than to morphological data. As far as *Homo sapiens* is concerned, unless the whole evolutionary theory is repudiated, primitive phases must, in each case, have preceded more advanced ones wherever and whenever the latter may have lived. To deny any direct connection between different phases, only because the geological data of the site where the specimens were picked up do not seem to correspond with the morphological character, is tantamount to presuming that (1) there was always only one human line all over the world and that (2) all corresponding phases must have always been synchronous, none being of longer or shorter duration, whatever the environmental conditions may have been. The facts now at hand do not lend support to such a theory. Solo man belonged to the Upper Pleistocene according to the geological evidence and the best possible dating. If this is true this type was contemporary with the Mount Carmel population of Palestine, the people of Krapina in Croatia and those of Saccopastore in Italy. Morphologically, however, Solo Man is much more primitive than any of the ones mentioned. Some of his most characteristic features have undoubtedly preceded those which the others display. The usual interpretation of those temporary discrepancies was always the same. As Europe or nearby Asia was regarded as the exclusive seat of human evolution, the time scale in which man developed was set once and for all according to the European dating. In addition, the tempo of evolution was deemed constant and definite for each phase. In consequence of this dogma, each type which did not fit, temporarily and spatially, into the scheme was excluded from the direct human line and labelled as an extinct branch. So it happened that people are still looking for ancestors of *Homo sapiens* although they have the remainders on their desks. If we, instead, realize that man has evolved from different centers in some cases, and at certain times faster, in other cases slower, all difficulties will be immediately overcome.

The possibility of the occurrence of several evolutionary types at the same time can be exemplified even by mankind of today. In each race certain individuals may have preserved primitive features to a greater or lesser extent while other individuals of the same race show more advanced traits. In some races the number of individuals marked in this way may be greater than in others.

Differences in tempo are also responsible in a certain sense for what I have called disharmonies. Features which are characteristic of more advanced phases of evolution are to be found in those types which have to be classified as primitive, judged according to their appearance on the whole. The opposite happening, namely the persistence of primitive features in generally advanced types, is a well and long known fact. It is called atavism or reversion. Both phenomena prove that evolution goes on by gradual development of novelties in an otherwise stabilized and therefore seemingly harmonious type.

Human evolution, as it appears from fossil evidences, shows a distinct tendency to proceed in a certain direction. This kind of evolution has been named orthogenesis. Now sensitive people prefer to speak of rectilinear or progressive evolution. The difference depends upon the philosophy behind the interpretation but the process itself is not involved by the way in which it is interpreted.

In speaking of different human lines I may run the risk of being misunderstood, namely that I believe in polyphyletic evolution of man, or, in other words, that man originated from different branches of the common anthropoid stem. This is not what I have in mind. All facts so far available indicate that man branched off as a unit which split afterwards, within its already limited faculties, into several lines.

This is one of the reasons why I regard all the hominids, living mankind included, as members of *one* species. But I do not intend to dwell on this point, for I deem the whole discussion of this subject unsubstantial in the present state of our knowledge. It may give satisfaction to those students who judge the morphological value of a specimen more by the label attached to it than by what it really represents. More discoveries and more facts are what we need.

Addendum

Since I first put down, and delivered, these "Interpretations," I came across an article published by Henri V. Vallois in "La Nature" (1946) in which the author touches on several questions with which I dealt. As they are of general interest I think this is the right place to discuss Vallois' views, especially as he takes issue with our views on the Asiatic giants.

The article referred to is a review of my paper "Giant Early Man From Java and South China." The facts and my interpretations drawn from them are accepted by Vallois so far as gigantism itself is concerned; neither does he seem to deny that the new forms must be ranged with the hominids. He disagrees only with my conclusions that their discovery sheds light on human evolution as a whole and, in particular, on the origin of *Homo sapiens*. According to Vallois there is not a continuous morphological line that leads from *Gigantopithecus-Pithecanthropus* to Neanderthal Man and further up to modern man, as I believe. He thinks instead that there was a multiplicity of representatives of the genus *Homo*, regardless of the geological age, and that no direct relationship has existed between the different forms. For analogy he points to the great apes in which various types have developed from Miocene to Pliocene. Chimpanzee and gorilla are the products of one of these simian branches; the orang utan is another; and man is the product of a third branch. All these represent forms which have persisted and so are still living, while others, such as the Australopithecinae, have vanished in the course of time.

One of the ancient simian branches which flourished in the southeast of Asia did continue its evolution and produced man. However, its tendency to ramify did not stop at this point. In its prehominid stage as well as in that of Neanderthal, the branch continued to differentiate. Some of the offshoots ended in actual human races, while others disappeared without leaving any descendants. The prehominids of Java and China belong to the latter category, as does Neanderthal Man. According to Vallois, such an extinction of side-branches happens even today: Tasmanians, Fuegians, and Bushmen are those sterile boughs of the human tree which "will not participate in the future development of mankind." Therefore, *Gigantopithecus*, *Meganthropus* and *Pithecanthropus* cannot be our "ancestors," but only our "cousins."

People who are repelled by the idea of any relationship between "us," that is, modern man, and those ape-like creatures such as *Gigantopithecus* and his kin, will side with Vallois and play him off against me. But Vallois' and my own views in reality differ less than his not very clear wording suggests. In each of my publications since 1938 in which I have discussed the origin of man, I pointed out that mankind of today is represented everywhere by one distinct morphological type, usually called modern man, but that it consists of different variants ("races") whose remote ancestors may not necessarily have belonged to the same primary human or hominid group. For there was certainly not *one* "Adam" and *one* "Eve" who could be claimed as progenitor by every man living today. In figure 30 of my book, *Apes, Giants and Man*, I drafted a chart representing the "Pedigree of hominids." It shows that an individual or any group of individuals belonging to a Eurasian race today is not necessarily the somatic descendant of the East Asiatic Archanthropinae. These special prehominids gave origin to other branches of modern mankind as represented by the Australian Bushmen or similar racial groups. I do not know for which living human group Vallois is the speaker when he refuses to recognize members of the Sino-Malayan stem as "our" ancestors. But I have never considered my own relationship to *Pithecanthropus* as closer than that of a first "cousin" or whatever gradation of kinship may be regarded as convenient.

On the other hand, I shall never agree with Vallois in his interpretation of almost all recovered fossil human forms as being "corpses left on the road along which humanity has differentiated" provided this means that all these forms became completely extinct without leaving any descendants to continue the line of evolution. If Neanderthal Man, for example, was not an ancestor of modern man, who was this ancestor? Vallois takes the easier way out and does not dwell on this important point. Neither does he offer any evidence on which to base his assumption of the complete extermination of all known fossil hominids. There is only one hint indicating the line of his argument, namely his reference to Tasmanians, Fuegians, and Bushmen as not partaking in the future evolution of man. Vallois apparently does not realize that human types of today, wherever they may be located, look back on a long history, as does each modern racial group. Who dares to say that those ancient types have not in the past contributed to building up the somatic constitution of individuals who may, today, be ascribed to quite a different looking racial unit? There is not the slightest doubt that Bushman and Fuegian "blood" runs through the veins of the South African colored population and through those of the South American Indians, respectively. Therefore, the chance of becoming extinct and entirely excluded from the shaping of future mankind is not greater for those races than it is for any other race. The same is certainly true for races of the past. This juggling with extinction neglects the fact that extinction is the doom of each individual. But human evolution does not depend on the destiny of one individual or one group of individuals, no matter how small or great this group may be. What we call Neanderthal Man is a widely spread evolutionary phase which may well have perished in one circumscribed territory, but have flourished, expanded, and been transmuted somewhere else, and so have given origin to *"Homo sapiens."*

The Origin of Homo sapiens

Henri-V. Vallois   1958

Although, strictly speaking, the search for the paleontological origin of *Homo sapiens* appears to lie outside the framework of this monograph, the primary aim of which is a comparative and descriptive study of the men of Fontéchevade, it is nevertheless appropriate here to a certain degree. In fact, our acquaintance with the men of Fontéchevade and with their relationships to other human remains of the Middle and Lower Pleistocene of Europe, throws a new light on the controversial problem of the precursors of *H. sapiens* in this continent, and of their relationships with the men of Neanderthal. Accordingly, a consideration and discussion of different hypotheses which have been put forward on this subject cannot be considered as superfluous.

Without going into the details of a historical survey such as may be found in the majority of studies of human paleontology, the many conceptions suggested by writers (Figure 1) may be classed under three headings:

    I. *H. sapiens* derives directly from Neanderthal man;

    II. *H. sapiens* derives from the Preneanderthals;

    III. *H. sapiens* derives from a special trunk, independent from that of the Neanderthals and Preneanderthals, the trunk of the Presapiens.

To be quite complete, one should add a fourth category for those who believe that *H. sapiens* and *H. neanderthalensis* were already separated when humanity itself became differentiated; this is the polyphyletic

Originally entitled "L'origine de l'Homo sapiens," Chapter V from La Grotte de Fontéchevade, 2me partie, Anthropologie, 1958, reprinted by permission of the author and of the Institut de Paléontologie Humaine. In this the dean of French anthropologists reviews various hypothetical patterns for the evolution of modern man, and the arguments for and against each, taking as his own view one which is at the opposite extreme from that of Weidenreich in the preceding article. Dr. Vallois has for many years been Director of the Musée de l'Homme and of the Institut de Paléontologie Humaine in Paris.

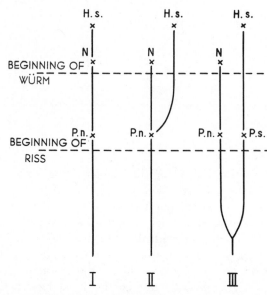

FIGURE 1. The three conceptions of the phyletic relations between *Homo sapiens* and Neanderthal Man. P. n. = Preneanderthals; P. s. = Presapiens; N. = Neanderthal Man; H. s. = *Homo sapiens*.

hypothesis. With few advocates, it has never provided convincing proofs (Vallois, 1952). I shall not consider it further.

1. The Neanderthal Hypothesis

In the beginnings of human paleontology, the idea that *H. sapiens* derives from *H. neanderthalensis* quickly recommended itself to the anthropologists. It rested on seductive arguments. In Europe, *H. sapiens* appeared in the Upper Paleolithic with an Aurignacian industry, in the second phase[1] of the Würm period. He was preceded on European soil by the bearer of Mousterian culture, *H. neanderthalensis,* and the ever more numerous discoveries following 1848, the date of the discovery at Gibraltar of the first Neanderthal man, have shown that this kind of man belonged to the end of the Riss-Würm and the first phase of the Würm. Neanderthal man was thus chronologically prior to *H. sapiens,* as well as more primitive from the cultural point of view.

In addition, study of his anatomical character soon showed that, morphologically as well, he was less advanced. Schwalbe in particular (1901), dealing with the cranium, had pointed out a whole series of traits evidently intermediate between those of Pithecanthropus and those of modern man. Following the same line later on, Weidenreich (1943b)

[1] Or possibly the third (Vallois, 1958, p. 88)

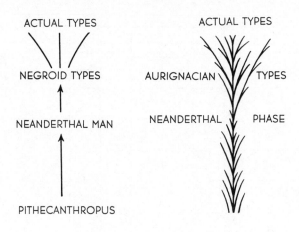

VERNEAU-1924   HRDLIČKA-1927

FIGURE 2. The origin of modern men according to the conceptions of R. Verneau, 1924 (left) and A. Hrdlička, 1927 (right).

arrived at identical conclusions in the case of Sinanthropus. Facts of a morphological nature thus seem to align themselves with those of an archeological and chronological order in suggesting that Neanderthal man might have given rise directly to *H. sapiens*. It is therefore not surprising that most of the older anthropologists were adherents of this notion. This was so, to cite only a few names among the best known, of de Quatrefages and Hamy, Hervé, Mahoudeau, and Verneau in France; Houzé, Fraipont, and Lohest in Belgium; Dubois in Holland; Huxley, Busk, and Pearson in Great Britain; Kollmann in Switzerland; Schwalbe, at least to begin with, in Germany; Gorjanović-Kramberger in Austria; Hrdlička in the United States, et cetera.

Furthermore, this hypothesis might appear in different forms. Figure 2, for example, presents two of the conceptions put forward: that of Verneau (1924), according to whom Neanderthal man gave birth directly to the Negro racial group, which the author considered as the most primitive among those of modern *H. sapiens;* and that of Hrdlička (1927), who judged Neanderthal man to be too variable to be viewed as a species, and preferred to make him a "phase" of human evolution.

Although, as will be seen below, the discovery of Piltdown, and later that of Swanscombe, dealt a serious blow to the Neanderthal hypothesis, it has nevertheless managed to retain a certain number of defenders

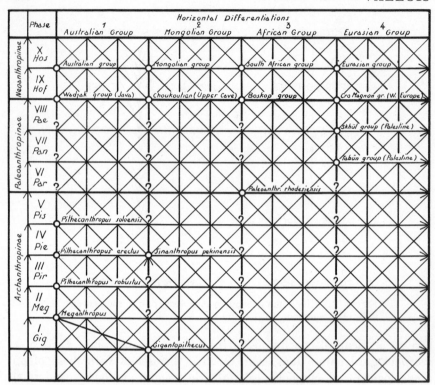

FIGURE 3. F. Weidenreich's view: development of man in four parallel phyla, which are however considerably interlaced, and of which each passes through ten successive stages.

to the present day. Weinert, for example, in a series of volumes running from 1932 to 1951, presents the evolution of the hominids as corresponding to a single line in which a *Neandertaler-Stufe* preceded the *Sapiens-Stufe*. This author, in 1955 (Weinert, 1955), and in the face of the considerable favor already accorded by this time to hypotheses other than the Neanderthal, still maintained the same opinion; believing the Swanscombe fossil to be identical to the Steinheim man, he held both to be Preneanderthals, intermediate between Pithecanthropus and Neanderthal man, the latter in turn being the direct precursor of *H. sapiens*. Roginskii (1947), adopting the same interpretation for Swanscombe man somewhat earlier, also upheld an analogous hypothesis. Quite lately it has found new defenders in Wiercinski (1956) and Dambski (1957).

Here we must make special mention of Weidenreich, also an adherent of the Neanderthal hypothesis, but with this important modification: that the transformation of *H. neanderthalensis* into *H. sapiens* took place in parallel in different areas, in several lines which were partially independent and whose evolutionary velocity might not have been the same in every case (Weidenreich, 1928, 1943a, 1947a, 1949). Although in 1928 Weidenreich dealt in this way with only two lines, one European, the other African, in 1947 he accepted four phyla (Figure 3) culminating respectively in the Australians, in the Mongolians, in the Africans, and in the whites, each of which lines would have passed through 10 "phases," 5 corresponding to the pithecanthropoids (*Archanthropinæ*), 3 to the Ne-anderthalians (*Paleoanthropinæ*), and 2 to *H. sapiens* (*Neoanthropinæ*). Many representatives of these different stages remain to be discovered, but, the author affirms, they must have existed. Precursors of *H. sapiens* at the Neanderthalian stage, known only in two phyla, one in Africa, and the other in Eurasia, are represented by Rhodesian man (third phylum) and the men of Tabun and Skhul (fourth phylum).

In drawing this up, Weidenreich leaves to one side the classic Neander-thals of the Würm of Europe, from which we may conclude that he agrees with the opinion of those who consider them to have been a sterile branch without issue; but his text is not clear on the subject (see below), and in any case this stipulation does not change the base of his argument, which holds that modern man has passed through an essentially Nean-derthalian stage. This American anthropologist has nothing to say on Swanscombe man.

Long one of the most fervent champions of the idea of a great antiquity of the *H. sapiens* (Figure 7 on page 489), A. Keith quite lately (1948), declared himself for Weidenreich's hypothesis, with the difference only that he believed that the four phyla were almost completely independent throughout the span of their evolution; the chart drawn up by Weiden-reich shows that he, by contrast, accepted the existence of many crossings and migrations.

Discussion

In spite of its indubitable interest, and in spite of the logical appear-ance given it by a concatenation of arguments based on morphology, stratigraphy, and archeology, the theory of a Neanderthal origin nonethe-less presents gross defects. In a work which appeared four years ago, I dwelt at length on these, and discussed in detail all the objections which it raises (Vallois, 1954a). I shall recapitulate the principal objections here.

a. A first group of arguments rests on *the specialization of Neanderthal man*. Marcellin Boule, above all, in his classic monograph on the man of

La Chapelle-aux-Saints (1911–1913), pointed out that, if many characters of Neanderthal man are intermediate between those of *H. sapiens* and those of Pithecanthropus (and later, it was possible to add, of Sinanthropus), and beyond them those of anthropoid apes, there were others which could not be so considered. Constituting very pronounced specializations, they placed Neanderthal man outside of any series which ends in *H. sapiens*. Such for example is the "bun-shaped" form of the occipital, the absence of canine fossae, the configuration of the nasal bones and the disposition of the piriform aperture, the orientation of the orbital openings, the lowering and widening of the ascending branch of the mandible, the orientation of the spinous processes of the cervical vertebrae, the very special structure of the external border of the scapula, the "taurodontism" of the pulp cavities[2] et cetera.

Various numerical data point in the same direction. If one compares the proportions of limb bones in apes, Neanderthal man, men of the Upper Paleolithic, and modern men (the Prehominians or pithecanthropoids are unknown in this respect), one finds that the indices calculated for the Neanderthals systematically fall outside the series. If one takes for example the humeroradial or brachial index, which expresses the length of the forearm in relation to that of the upper arm, one notes that in all the higher primates the index is high; that is to say, the forearm is relatively long. For the apes in particular, the index reaches 90 and often more. In *H. sapiens*, the forearm is short and the index is low: 76 to 80 in men of the Upper Paleolithic and many modern colored races; it is only 71 to 74 in modern Europeans. In these circumstances, one might have expected to find in the Neanderthals indices intermediate between those of the nonhuman primates and those of the Aurignacians. Actually, the mean of the different subjects measured is only 73.8; that is to say, the shortening of the forearm is as pronounced as in the majority of modern Europeans. The same thing is even more characteristic of the index which compares the length of the leg to that of the thigh, the femorotibial or crural index. This varies from 80 to 91 in the apes, has a value of 85.5 in men of the Upper Paleolithic and 80 to 82 in modern Europeans, while it falls to 76.6 in the Neanderthals. Again, a finding which shows a nonintermediate position for the last.

[2] Weidenreich, in one of his writings (1947a, p. 191), dwelt on the fact that taurodontism could not be considered as a specialization of Neanderthal man, since it is not seen in all representatives of that group and, besides, it exists in modern man. These observations are correct, but the fact remains that taurodontism is much more common in the Neanderthals than in *H. sapiens*, and that it attains a degree which is never to be seen in us, making a contrast with the marked reduction of the pulp cavities which is the rule in modern man. Without there having been an extreme difference between them, it nevertheless appears that *H. sapiens* and *H. neanderthalensis* each followed, in their main lines, a different evolution in this character.

b. Of quite a different order, a second group of objections turns on the fact of *the lack of morphological continuity between the European Neanderthals and the first Aurignacians.*

All authors agree that the Neanderthals who lived in Europe during the first period of the Würm glaciation formed a most homogeneous assemblage, and presented in a maximal degree the distinctive characters of the group. The Aurignacians who succeeded them are on the other hand unquestionably *H. sapiens.* The morphological difference between the former and the latter is very marked, and shows itself at first glance. The table below, which juxtaposes the dimensions and indices of a particularly typical Neanderthal, the La Ferrassie man, and the two oldest Aurignacians, which are thus the closest chronologically to the former (the Combe-Capelle man and one of the two "negroid" subjects from Grimaldi), well illustrate these differences[3].

Finally, to these metrical distinctions may be added important modifications in the structure of the head, resulting in effacing the supra-orbital torus, changing the form of the cranial cavity, retracting the facial complex, reducing the palatine arch and the teeth, et cetera. It is pointless to insist on the assemblage of differences thus achieved, an assemblage

TABLE

	La Ferrassie (male)[3]	Combe-Capelle (male)	Negroid from Grimaldi (female)
Maximum length	209	198	191
Maximum width	158	130	130.5
Basion height	134	139	135
Calotte height (glabella-inion)	86	104	107
Angle inion-glabella bregma	44°	58°	60°
Cranial index	75.5	65.7	68.3
Height-length index	64.1	70.2	70.6
Calotte-height index	42.1	54.4	60.1
Upper facial height	90	70 (S.)	59.5
Bizygomatic width	149	ca. 130	128
Upper facial index	60.4	53.9	46.4
Orbital index	76.6	70	72.4
Nasal index	54.6	52 (S.)	52.1
Stature	160	166 ?	159
Humeroradial index	74.3	79.2	80.1
Femorotibial index	77.5	89.8	83.9

[3] Measurements of the La Ferrassie and Grimaldi men were made directly on the originals, by me, in the latter case after correction of the deformed parts, so that they differ often considerably from those previously published by Verneau. Measurements of Combe-Capelle man are those of Klaatsch and Hauser (1910), except for those marked (S.) which are from Saller (1925).

which Klaatsch and Hauser (1910) demonstrated for Combe-Capelle man, and which appeared no less clearly in the study of the Grimaldi subjects. They are the differences which separate *H. sapiens* from *H. neanderthalensis* and which are well known. Their great interest in the present connection is that they already manifest themselves full force in those men of the Upper Paleolithic who, from their stratigraphic position, would have been the most likely to have preserved Neanderthal characters. The table shows that there are none such. Figure 4 is no less categorical.

That such modifications could have come about in the very short space of time separating the end of the Mousterian from the beginning of the Aurignacian seems practically impossible; here we have certainly the most important argument against the idea of a genetic continuity of the two groups.

Attempts have been made to minimize these objections. Weinert, for example, has declared that "it would be having far too little confidence in nature to suppose that in 5000 generations she would not have been able to transform a skull of *H. neanderthalensis* into a skull of *H. sapiens*" (1955, p. 219). If one counts thirty years for a generation, which is certainly a maximum for Upper Paleolithic man, 5000 generations represents 150,000 years. It is possible that in such a lapse of time the transformation in question might have come about, even though present genetic indications would demand a much longer period (see M. Weninger, 1956). However, between the last European Neanderthals and the first Aurignacians, there was no lapse of 150,000 years! There were at most a few thousand, and at the moment there is a tendency to agree that, at least in France, Neanderthals and Aurignacians were at one point actually contemporary. Weinert's proposition cannot be entertained.

Hrdlička (1927) attempted in much more methodical fashion to refute the preceding objections. He emphasized the selective action which the onset of a glacial period would have exercised on man: ever more difficult conditions of life, and a greater need of nourishment would have brought about an intensification of physical and mental efforts which would have allowed only the most apt subjects to survive, that is to .say those who manifested variations in the direction of *H. sapiens*. But this explanation is far from being convincing. We really know nothing of the effects of the glacial climate on man. Whereas Hrdlička supposed an effect which is stimulating and consequently progressive, Weckler, quite recently (1954), declares that life in regions subjected to glacial action had a conservative effect and prevented the diversification of Neanderthal man. Other authors write that, being of African origin, this form of man was fundamentally tied to a warm climate, and that the appearance

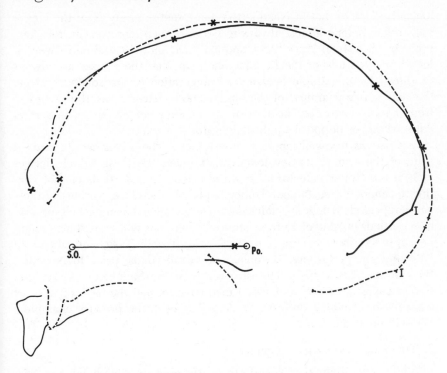

FIGURE 4. Superposition of sagittal diagrams of La Chapelle-aux-Saints (continuous line) and Combe-Capelle Man (dashed line). Orientation according to Frankfort plane; because of the position of porion in La Chapelle-aux-Saints, the two skulls have been superimposed so as to make the suborbital (S.O.) points coincide; the x-signs correspond respectively to the two nasions, the two bregmas, the two lambdas, and to the porion of Combe-Capelle Man. The very different morphology of the occipital and facial regions is to be noted. (½ natural size.)

of a glacial climate only had the consequence of bringing about his extinction.

Thus, the most contradictory hypotheses have been put forth. Furthermore, if that of Hrdlička were correct, one cannot see how climatic conditions, which would have completely transformed humanity with incredible rapidity during the Würm I—II interval, would also have abruptly ceased to act during all the rest of the fourth glaciation, so that *H. sapiens*, once having appeared, remained practically unchanged!

As to the argument, sometimes invoked, by which the later reappearance, in certain examples of *H. sapiens*, of characters of Neanderthal man is taken as proof of their phyletic relation, this was long ago put to rest. First of all, there is the fact that those subjects in which such reappearance was noted, instead of dating as they should from periods chronologically close to that of Neanderthal man, that is to say from the Upper Paleolithic, belong almost always to periods much more recent, the Neolithic or the Metal Ages. Add another fact, on which Boule dwelt at length in his study of the La Chapelle man, that these cases are always produced by the simple occasional exaggeration of an isolated feature; the actual reappearance of so fundamental character as the complete frontal torus has never been seen on a European of post-Neanderthal date, whatever period it might belong to.

It is useless to dwell longer on these facts. They demonstrate that, in spite of the arguments developed in its favor, the thesis which derives men of the Upper Paleolithic from the classic Neanderthals of that continent cannot be sustained. Understandably, therefore, various authors have appealed to less specialized forms: possibly Neanderthals or Preneanderthals outside of Europe, still unknown, but whose existence might be supposed from the finds of Staroselje, Teshik Tash, and above all Palestine; or, preferably, European Preneanderthals, prior to Neanderthals of the classic type. The discoveries of the Steinheim (1933) and the Saccopastore (1929 and 1935) men have formed the basis of this last conception, of which Professor S. Sergi has been the primary champion. We will now examine it.

2. The Preneanderthal Theory

While older than the Neanderthals, the men of Steinheim and Saccopastore, instead of, as would seem natural, being more primitive than the former in their total morphology, and thus still further removed from *H. sapiens*, are on the contrary closer to the latter in a number of traits: form of the occipital curve, absence of a torus on the same bone, disposition of the temporoparietal suture, presence of a canine fossa, et cetera. H. Weinert interpreted these likenesses by the fact of their being female crania (1936, 1944), but this explanation is certainly not acceptable. The real reason, as was first clearly shown by S. Sergi, is that the Preneanderthals, the ancestral form of the Neanderthals, had not yet reached the extreme specialization of the latter, being thus in a certain sense more generalized. For this very reason, they are found to possess, in somewhat prophetic fashion, a number of traits which are encountered in *H. sapiens*. Being primitive forms which were not absolutely differentiated in one direction or the other, and polymorphic besides, they would thus be situated at the base of both lines. Following Sergi, this conception has been skillfully defended by various anthropologists, Clark Howell and Breitinger particularly; the Russian author Jakimov also subscribes to it.

Sergi, in his first writings (1944, 1948), insisted particularly on the polytypy of the Preneanderthals, a polytypy contrasting with the extraordinary homogeneity of their Neanderthal descendants. While considering the existence of a genetic connection between the Preneanderthals and *H. sapiens* as very probable, he did not make himself explicit on this question. Instead, he made this the object of his memoir of 1953 (1953a, see also 1953b): the Swanscombe and Fontéchevade men, he said there, present a mixture of characteristics of Phaneranthropi and Palaeanthropi.[4] They approach the former in the absence of a torus, as in Fontéchevade, and in certain metrical resemblances especially evident in Swanscombe. They approach the Palaeanthropi in the following: platycephaly in general, and particularly the posterolateral expansion of the occipital region and the basal expansion of the parietal, traits which recall the relative broadening of the basal part of the cerebral cavity of the pithecanthropoids. He concludes that the men of Fontéchevade and Swanscombe should be considered as "palaeanthropiform Prophaneranthropi"; however they cannot actually be separated from the Palaeanthropi of the same period, since these in turn also possessed "phaneranthropic" characters. Both groups formed part of a great pre-Würmian nexus of humanity from which all later types were derived (Figure 5). From this we may suppose, the author suggests, that modern men had their roots not in a single type, but in several.

In more categorical fashion Clark Howell (1951, 1952) unites the assemblage constituted by the men of Steinheim, Ehringsdorf, Krapina, Saccopastore, Galilee, Mount Carmel, and Teshik Tash in one group, which he calls "progressive Neanderthals" and which he opposes to the "classic Neanderthals" of Würm I. Between these two there existed, in fact, not only the differences noted by Sergi, but a whole series of further differences detected in this meticulous comparative study by the American author. From the phyletic point of view, Dr. Howell thus arrives at the scheme represented in Figure 5, according to which *H. sapiens* derives from the progressive Neanderthals—in effect, the Preneanderthals—by the intermediate steps of the Neanderthaloids of Mount Carmel. The existence of the fossil men of Swanscombe and Fontéchevade would not be incompatible with this scheme: the author considers the first as more or less identical to Steinheim man, while the second, which in his opinion was probably equipped with a frontal torus, would constitute another progressive Neanderthal.

In support of this hypothesis, Dr. Howell points to the existence of a morphological gradient which was consistently more accentuated from east to west in the progressive Neanderthals, attaining its maximum in

---

[4] In the classification proposed by S. Sergi, *H. sapiens* is designated by the name Phaneranthropi (*Fanerantropi*), the Neanderthal men by Palaeanthropi.

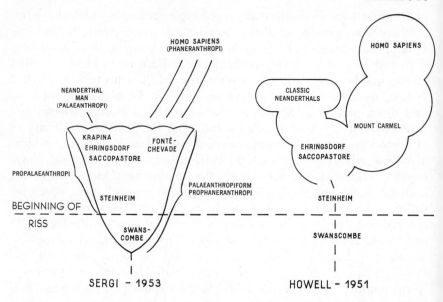

FIGURE 5. "Preneanderthal" interpretations of S. Sergi, 1953 (left) and Clark Howell, 1951 (right).

the classic Neanderthals, descendants of the western progressive Neanderthals. The simultaneous action of selective forces due to the onset and intensification of the fourth glacial period, and of the process of genetic drift, would explain the eventual appearance of these "classic Neanderthals." But the author does not dwell on the origin of *H. sapiens*, saying only that "modern man was developing further to the East."

Breitinger (1955) arrives at a practically identical conclusion in his important study of the Swanscombe cranium. Being of the opinion, as we have already seen, that this skull belongs to the same type as Steinheim, he joins the two in a single group, as a point of departure for both the Neanderthals and *H. sapiens* (Figure 6). To this group he gives the name of *Praesapiens*, considering this term to be preferable to "Preneanderthal"; used thus, however, in a sense quite different from the usual one, it runs the risk of causing confusion. Elsewhere, Breitinger uses the name *Primisapiens* for the branch formed by the fossil men of Palestine, which, deriving from his *Praesapiens*, led in turn to *H. sapiens* of the Upper Paleolithic. Since he has various objections to the interpretation of Fontéchevade man as a Presapiens (in the usual sense of the word), he considers it preferable to leave this fossil provisionally aside, unless, he adds, it is merely "a subspecific variety of the progressive Neanderthals of the same period."

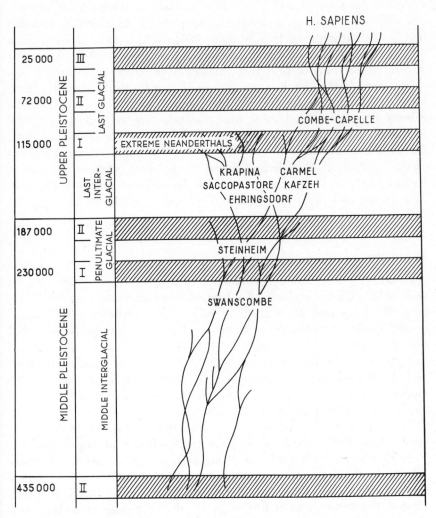

FIGURE 6. "Preneanderthal" interpretation of E. Breitinger. The figures in the left-hand column represent years.

Gieseler (1957) has lately adhered to the same hypothesis, excepting that he does not give a name to the basal type constituted by the men of Swanscombe and Fontéchevade, reserving the names Preneanderthal and Presapiens for the two groups in the Riss-Würm interglacial which are its descendants. Furthermore, enlarging the second group, he includes not only the fossils of Fontéchevade and Quinzano, as well as Kanam and Kanjera, but also the Skhul men, whose frontal torus, he feels, should not prevent them from being typical Presapiens.

Finally Jakimov (1954), like Clark Howell, to whom he refers frequently, and in spite of a declaration of principle in which he specifies that Soviet anthropologists fully share in Hrdlička's point of view, gives his opinion that the men of Swanscombe and Fontéchevade form part of a large assembly of primitive Palaeanthropi which gave birth to the classic Neanderthals in the west, and to *H. sapiens* in the east. The skeletons of Mount Carmel, Teshik Tash, and Staroselje represent, in the eastern line, transitional steps from the primitive Neanderthals to the men of the Upper Paleolithic, of whom some, such as the Kostienki fossils, still bore traces of their Neanderthal origin. The rough contemporaneity of the specialized Neanderthal forms of the west, such as the classic Neanderthals of France, and the much less typical forms of the east, such as the men of Teshik Tash and Staroselje, would be an argument in favor of this theory.

Discussion

Profiting by a systematic examination of fossils recently discovered, as well as by a careful revision of older finds, and sustained by anthropologists who have long given their attention to the problem, the Preneanderthal thesis presents a far more convincing front than the Neanderthal theory. It avoids the two essential hazards of the latter: the extreme specializations of the Würm Neanderthals, and the insufficient time period allowed these Neanderthals for their transformation into *H. sapiens*. It is, therefore, most seductive. On the other hand, it also is marked by a fundamental contradiction.

The basic idea of the theory is, in effect, that all the way from Swanscombe up to Ehringsdorf and Krapina, the fossil men of Europe and the Near East so far known without being absolutely identical, nevertheless exhibit a sufficient number of common characteristics to be united in a single assemblage: these are the progressive Neanderthals of Clark Howell, the *Praesapiens* of Breitinger (in the new sense given the word by that author), and the Prophaneranthropi related to the primitive Palaeanthropi of Sergi. But an examination of the forms thus juxtaposed shows that the group is completely artificial. I have already had occasion to point out that several of the fossil men included by Howell in his "progressive Neanderthals" appear to be, in spite of their designation, contemporaneous with the Neanderthals proper; this is very probably the case for Staroselje, Teshik Tash, and Krapina; it may also be the case, according to several authors, for Galilee and Mount Carmel. Morphologically distinct from the men of Steinheim and Swanscombe, all these fossils are thus also far removed from them chronologically; in such a case, there is nothing justifying their union with the latter.

But union becomes actually impossible, since we are now dealing with subjects of totally different structure, between the men of Swanscombe and Fontéchevade on the one side and Steinheim with its Ehringsdorf and Saccopastore descendants on the other. I have earlier dwelt at length on the numerous traits which contrast these two groups with one another. To disregard these differences, and to wish, for example, to place together Fontéchevade man, with a voluminous cranium and with no frontal torus, and Steinheim, whose dimensions are much smaller but whose torus is even more developed than in the Neanderthals proper, is to run counter to every principle of palaeontological classification. If Clark Howell, and after him Breitinger and Jakimov, have advocated such a union, it was because they were not aware of the actual morphology of these fossils, due to the too brief descriptions of the Fontéchevade men published up to the present. Sergi, who had seen the original pieces at first hand, was much more prudent. But even with his more flexible formula, the union proposed remains completely inadmissible, since the existence of certain common primitive traits cannot erase the differences, which are fundamental, and which are applicable to Swanscombe man as well. Generally contemporary with the Preneanderthals, but different morphologically, the precursors of *H. sapiens* at this period certainly constituted a distinct group.

In these circumstances, it is impossible to derive the European *H. sapiens* from the Preneanderthals of the same regions. Members of a lineage to which I have earlier given the name of Presapiens, the ancestors of modern man were already autonomous. The Preneanderthal thesis, therefore, recommends itself no more than the Neanderthal thesis and, of the three hypotheses named earlier, it is only the last, resting on the existence of the Presapiens, which remains to be considered.

3. THE PRESAPIENS THEORY

I have mentioned in the preceding chapter the ups and downs of the Presapiens idea, and how this hypothesis, whose first defenders were guided almost entirely by theoretical reasons found, seemingly with the

Piltdown discovery and then, later, actually with that of Swanscombe, the scientific arguments which it had lacked heretofore. The discovery of Piltdown has now lost all significance but, more than compensating for this, that of Fontéchevade has at last provided that crucial proof which should bring conviction (Vallois, 1949b).

It is therefore to be understood why, well before the term Presapiens had been invented and its definition rendered precise, a considerable number of phyletic trees, drawn or at least described over some forty years, showed H. sapiens originating as a distinct branch from that which led to the Neanderthal men. Separating early from a common source, the two branches were considered as following generally parallel courses over a long period. Among the authors who adopted this view, I need cite only the following, limiting myself to the most recent: Boule (1913) and Teilhard de Chardin (1951) in France; Bonarelli (1941) and A. Blanc (1954) in Italy; Pilgrim (1915), Burkitt (1921), Elliot Smith (1924), Arthur Keith (1927), and Leakey (1953) in Great Britain; Schwalbe (1923), Mollison, (1933), and Heberer (1950b) in Germany; Kälin (1952) in Switzerland; Kleiweg de Zwaan (1956) in Holland; Matiegka (1910) in Czechoslovakia; Skerlj (1950) in Yugoslavia; Broom (1934) in South Africa; McCurdy (1927), Osborn (1927), Coon (1939), Hooton (1947), Howells (1954), and Weckler (1954) in the United States, et cetera.

A few of the phyletic trees thus put forward are represented in Figure 7. Examination shows that the manner in which their authors conceived of the origin and evolution of the branch which gave rise to H. sapiens is not the same in every case. Piltdown man, as far as he was believed in, was placed sometimes directly on this branch, more often as a derivation from it, and sometimes completely outside it. All anthropologists, by contrast, agree in setting Swanscombe man and, later, Fontéchevade on the trunk which ended in H. sapiens of Europe.

Heberer, the originator of the term "Presapiens," as we have seen, or at least the one responsible for its general definition has, in a series of publications (1950b, 1951a, 1955), gradually developed the concept for which Fontéchevade man had so lately furnished proof, having immediately understood the significance of that fossil. Using the adjectives proposed by Frassetto for expressing the state of development of the frontal torus—proscopiny (presence of torus), oligoproscopiny (torus weak), aproscopiny (torus absent)—he described the evolution of hominids as corresponding to three independent branches, but deriving all three from a basal group, which was oligoproscopine, that of the australopithecines (Praeanthropini of the author). In two of these three branches the torus increased; these were the pithecanthropoids (Archan-

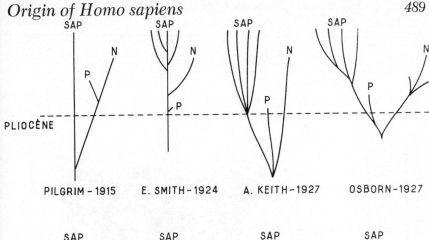

PILGRIM - 1915   E. SMITH - 1924   A. KEITH - 1927   OSBORN - 1927

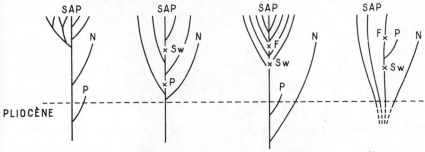

MOLLISON - 1933   HOOTON - 1947   SKERLJ - 1950   KÄLIN - 1952

FIGURE 7. Schematic representation of various phyletic trees accepting the existence of an independent Presapiens trunk. SAP = *Homo sapiens;* N = Neanderthal Man; P = Piltdown; Sw = Swanscombe; F = Fontéchevade.

thropi) and the Neanderthals (*Palaeanthropi*), both of them being proscopine. On the other hand, in the third branch the torus lessened; this is the aproscopine sapiens group (*Neanthropinæ*); this group in itself comprises two successive stages: Presapiens to begin with, sapiens proper or *Eusapiens* at the end. Figure 8 shows the several positions of the different human fossils in the classification thus set up.[5]

All of the family trees thus imagined have a logical basis. All are possible. Nonetheless all, even that of Heberer, in spite of its greater flexibility, are susceptible to the same criticism: the arbitrary portion which is made necessary by the desire, with the few fossil men in our possession, to trace complete phyletic trees and continuous lines. Another criticism is that when one examines these lines in detail, one realizes that often, in constructing them, the authors have brought together forms

[5] This diagram corresponds to the interpretation of the author in 1950; in 1955, the position of some fossils was modified, but the general form of the scheme remained the same.

Neanthropini

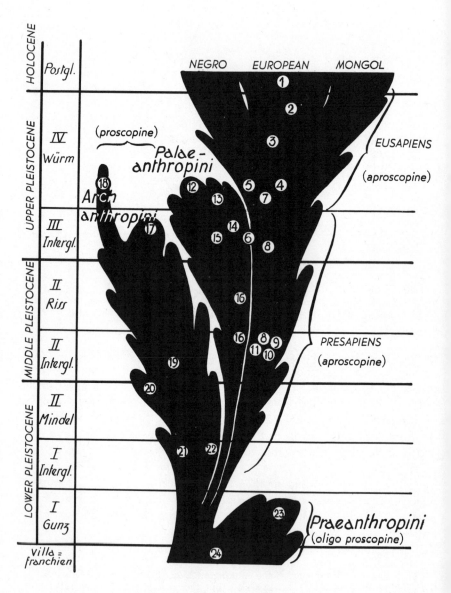

FIGURE 8.   Interpretation of G. Heberer.

belonging indifferently to Europe, Asia, or Africa. In doing this, one falls into an error which has more than once been held against paleontological trees: considering the fossils as pawns in a game of chess to be moved around as one wishes, using, to make up morphological evolutionary sequences, pieces taken indifferently from this or that continent, without being disturbed as to whether the migrations thus taken for granted might actually have occurred.

To palliate such criticisms as well as may be done, I have in Figure 9 represented the only continuous phyletic lines which may be considered as more or less certain (continuous line) or at least probable (discontinuous line). Thus, for the whole Pleistocene, four phyla appear, each of them limited to a single geographic territory: one developed in the Far East, another in Africa, and the last two in Europe.

The pithecanthropoids (*Archanthropini* of Heberer) taken together form the first phylum: Weidenreich's (1945) fine researches have in fact well shown that the Ngandong men, in spite of their superficial resemblance to the European Neanderthals, should be regarded as pithecanthropoids of large size: morphology, chronology, and geographical location thus concur in suggesting a phyletic continuity whose duration was certainly considerable, since the Ngandong men appear to be synchronous with the Mindel-Riss interglacial (Movius and von Koenigswald, 1949). It is not to be doubted that Sinanthropus, whose relationship with Pithecanthropus is evident, also belongs to this line.

The Neanderthals of Europe represent another phylum which all authors agree in carrying back as far as Steinheim man. Between these two elements, the Preneanderthals of Saccopastore and Ehringsdorf establish a recognized chronological and morphological connection. Until quite recently, it was difficult to prolong this phylum beyond Steinheim man; several hypotheses have been propounded, none of which carry a convincing argument, even the most favored, which would derive the entire Preneanderthal-Neanderthal ensemble from the Mauer man.

The discovery of the Montmaurin mandible has now brought important support to this hypothesis. In fact, this specimen, in the majority of its characteristics, occupies a situation visibly intermediate between the mandibles of the classic Neanderthals and that of Mauer. In spite of certain differences in dimension, it accommodates itself acceptably to the Steinheim skull (Vallois, 1955a). The idea, often voiced but heretofore lacking in paleontological proof, that the Mauer man forms the base of the line leading to the Neanderthals of Europe, takes on new force from this point. Thus, it is possible to trace a long phylum, parallel to that of the pithecanthropoids through a part of its course, but which, appearing later, carries further and continues to the beginning of the last glaciation.

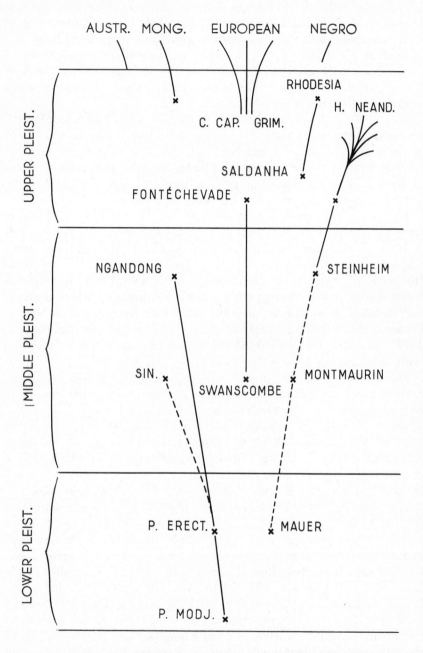

FIGURE 9. Attempt to represent present evidence on the phylogeny of fossil human groups. The length of the Lower Pleistocene is shown considerably diminished.

Still in Europe, the Presapiens, with the Swanscombe and Fontéchevade men, constitute a third phylum whose independence vis-à-vis
that of the Neanderthals and Preneanderthals has been amply demonstrated in the course of the present work. Finally, in Africa the recent
discovery of the Saldanha skull has ended the isolation which until then
had set off Rhodesian Man, together with the fragments, of uncertain
age, to which has been given the unsuitable name Africanthropus; this
allows us to discern a forth phylum, localized in South Africa and, for
the present at least, limited to the Upper Pleistocene.

What are the relations of modern *Homo sapiens* with these several
phyla?

Although all the genealogical trees so far published make use of perfectly continuous lines (cf. Figure 7), one must realize (and this is a
regrettable gap in our understanding of human paleontology) that nowhere has a direct relationship been observed in reality: the majority of
the great groups of modern *H. sapiens* may be traced into the Upper
Pleistocene but, after a relatively short course, their lineage ends without
coming in contact with the phyla of previous periods. The eventual
junctions, if junctions there be, can only be established subjectively, and
across an empty space of often considerable extent.

Outside of Europe this noncontinuity appears quite clearly. Weidenreich
(1943b) wrote that Ngandong man gave birth to Wadjak man who, in
his turn, provided the origin of the Australians and Melanesians; elsewhere he accepted that Sinanthropus was the base of the trunk from
which were derived the Chinese, and that there were to be encountered
already in Sinanthropus certain traits characteristic of the Mongoloid
races (cf. Figure 3). But these assertions were never made the object of
a systematic demonstration. Between the Ngandong men, who date from
the Mindel-Riss, and those of Wadjak, who are at most Neolithic, there
elapsed a very long period of time for which we have no fossils. Furthermore, the differences in the cranial structure are considerable. To this
must be added the relationship which appears to exist between the present Australians (essentially Carpentarian) and the Vedda of southern
India, and also the presence of Australoids in the Neolithic of Indo-China,
two facts which suggest rather that the Australians, and with them the
Melanesians, must have come from the Asiatic continent.

Furthermore, the differences between Sinanthropus and the Chinese
are such that it seems audacious indeed to affirm the existence of any
kind of ancestral relation: the few fossil crania recovered from the Upper
Paleolithic of China (Choukoutien Upper Cave; Szechwan) have in any
case a structure which is completely that of *H. sapiens,* and which
scarcely recalls Sinanthropus. Here, as in the case of the Australians and

Melanesians, a lineal descent is evidently possible, but paleontology, in the present state of our knowledge, has not yet produced any decisive evidence.

We are no better provided with documents on the origin of African *H. sapiens*. The oldest known definitely fossil Negro is Asselar man, whose age according to the latest research is only Mesolithic. With some appearance of reason, a part at least of Bushman ancestry has been traced to the Boskop fossil man, but the latter, whose geological age is not known but cannot have been very great, is himself a *H. sapiens;* he is very different from the Rhodesian Neanderthaloid, who is in turn without doubt not much older; certainly between the two there was no continuity. It has been argued that another line, leading to the same Bushman or to vanished varieties of them, started from Florisbad man, a fossil to whom recent works give an age of approximately 40,000 years, which would make it earlier than Rhodesian man. Now, the frontal torus of Florisbad man is not heavily emphasized, so that this fossil is much closer morphologically to *Homo sapiens* than is Rhodesian man. Here again the two phyla do not merge.

Finally (as we have seen in the first paragraph of this chapter), if the sapiens men of the Upper Paleolithic in Europe, represented by the two fossils of Combe-Capelle and Grimaldi, came into actual contact with the Neanderthals, once again there was no continuity. *H. sapiens* of Europe comes from another source. But here, far better than elsewhere, paleontological documents allow us to push investigation further.

It is scarcely to be doubted that the Presapiens provide the origin of sapiens man of the European Upper Paleolithic. From the morphological point of view the differences are minor, and the mutations which would have been necessary in the first to give rise to the second would have been much less considerable than those which any sort of Neanderthal would have had to undergo. Furthermore, from the chronological point of view the period of time between the middle of the Riss-Würm and the second phase of the Würm is broadly sufficient for such a transformation. The major arguments raised against a Neanderthal derivation do not exist in this case.

It is not to be denied, however, that between the men of Swanscombe and Fontéchevade on the one hand, and the first European Aurignacians on the other, there elapsed a long period. The chronological gap thus recognized cannot be attributed to an insufficiency of paleontological finds, since the same period has yielded more than a hundred fossil men all of which, without exception, are of the Neanderthal type; the discontinuity is therefore a real one. A close examination of the facts however shows that this discontinuity is not opposed to the hypothesis of a phyletic continuity.

Newly arrived in central and western Europe, the men of the Upper Paleolithic could only have come from the east; the barriers represented by the great glaciers to the north, and by the Mediterranean on the south, actually exclude any other route. Somewhere in the east, doubtless in Western Asia, and prior to the Würm, there must have existed Presapiens men who by gradual development became sapiens proper. We have seen that, in parallel fashion in Europe, the Preneanderthals were likewise becoming transformed into the classic Neanderthals. Under these circumstances one may suppose—the idea has already been put forward by Coon (1939)—that the Swanscombe and Fontéchevade men were emissaries of an Asiatic stock, coming into Europe during interglacial periods, which however were not able to maintain themselves there. One might also suppose that these same men belonged to a Presapiens group which had developed *in situ* in Europe, but which, toward the end of the last interglacial, had finally given way to the Neanderthals. In either hypothesis, the latter remained in sole possession at the beginning of the Würm. Reappearing with the second period of this glaciation, descendants of the Presapiens lost no time in taking a final revenge on their Mousterian conquerers.

Were analogous phenomena witnessed on other continents? That is to say, were the *H. sapiens* who today people them derived from a Presapiens source, either from the Asiatic stock already mentioned or from others still known? Did they on the contrary arise directly from Neanderthal or Neanderthaloid forms, according to the old classic hypothesis? We are almost entirely without evidence on which to answer. One cannot help noting, however, that in Africa Rhodesian Man does indeed seem to represent, like the European Neanderthals, the end of a phylum which left no descendants, since Florisbad man, much closer morphologically to the Sapiens type, is chronologically anterior to Rhodesian man. If, furthermore, it were to be allowed that the Kanam and Kanjera fossils, whose age is still undecided, really belong to the Middle Paleolithic, as Leakey affirms, the question would be settled in the same way as in Europe. Only new finds will tell us.

But whence came the Presapiens phylum—or possibly phyla—itself, from which *H. sapiens* was derived? In the Preneanderthal theory, separation between the Neanderthal group and the sapiens group was relatively late; it would have occurred in the Riss-Würm, from a common Preneanderthal source. The Presapiens theory carries this separation back to an earlier epoch, since it supposes that Preneanderthals and Presapiens coexisted for a given length of time. When, then, was this epoch?

Most authors are silent on the point, although in text and illustrations they allow it to be implicitly understood that in their opinion this time was still in the Pleistocene. Certain ones, however, are more explicit. The following list gives the ages which have been explicitly named[6] (see also Figure 7):

Elliot Smith (1924)	Pleistocene "relatively late"
Weckler (1954)	"Before the invention of the hand-axe" therefore before the Chellean, and consequently in the Lower Pleistocene
Heberer (1950b)	"Gunz or Villafranchian," that is to say, in the lowest Pleistocene
Broom (1934)	Pliocene or at the latest Lower Pleistocene
Pilgrim (1915)	Pliocene
Arthur Keith (1927)	Pliocene
Osborn (1927)	Pliocene
Kälin (1952)	Pliocene
Leakey (1953)	Miocene

Between these different hypotheses a choice is difficult. All that one may grant, in fact, is that the upper limit of the epoch sought does not go beyond the Mindel-Riss, since we know that at that time the two phyla were already separate. On the other hand, and without admitting to a polygenesis to which all would be opposed, its lower limit is given by the period in which humanity itself became differentiated, the Pliocene, it would seem, and probably its end. In the vast period of time thus circumscribed, we completely lack points of reference. It may fairly be noted that, without being identical, the Steinheim and Swanscombe men already exhibited a convergence. On the other hand, the Mauer mandible, if its morphological characteristics place it at the base of the Neanderthal phylum, nevertheless has teeth of a highly evolved type, such as would be perfectly suitable for the Presapiens. The point of separation of the two phyla might thus be less remote than is believed by certain of the authors mentioned above, and might correspond to the Lower Pleistocene, perhaps only to its post-Villafranchian phase. It is difficult to say more.

Although it was not explicitly formulated until after the discovery of the Fontéchevade men, the Presapiens thesis, and with it the idea that human evolution might have taken place with several branches evolving in parallel of which some, particularly that of the classic Neanderthals,

[6] It should be noted here that authors prior to 1950 considered the Villafranchian as belonging to the Pliocene, whereas there is increasing agreement today, following Haug, on placing it in the Pleistocene. Different published schemes are accordingly not exactly comparable.

became extinct without leading to modern man, has already called forth certain criticisms. Some of them, resting on erroneous interpretations of the fossil remains of Swanscombe and Fontéchevade, have been answered in the preceding chapter. There are two of a more general nature, however, about which in concluding I wish to say a few words.

Weidenreich, whose thesis as to the direct transformation of Neanderthal man into *H. sapiens* has been discussed at length above (p. 476) took exception in one of his latest works (1949) to an article (Vallois, 1946) in which, although the question of Presapiens man was not yet raised, I declared that a certain number of fossil men might have represented the termination of evolutionary branches; certain human divisions, in other words, had disappeared without extending as far as modern *H. sapiens*. In opposition to this conception the learned anthropologist wrote; "If Neanderthal Man, for example, was not an ancestor of modern man, who was this ancestor? Vallois takes the easier way out and does not dwell on this important point."

Corroborating that of Swanscombe, the Fontéchevade discovery, one year before the death of this honored anthropologist, was to give this question an answer which he did not foresee. To make the European Neanderthals the ancestors of the Upper Paleolithic Men is not to adopt, as he believed, the easiest way, but a way full of anthropological, archeological, and chronological contradictions. Quite the reverse, it is the derivation of these men from Presapiens which presents the most logical evolutionary process, and raises the fewest difficulties. Furthermore, Weidenreich long defended (1928) the idea of the parallel existence of different human branches. What a series of miracles are needed if all these branches, without exception, and after a strictly identical evolution, were to have survived until today!

Of quite a different kind, and much more tendentious in the ground which they choose for debate, are the objections of Wiercinski (1956). This author begins by opposing Polish-Soviet scholars, to which he adjoins a few other anthropologists—such as Hrdlička, Weidenreich, and Clark Howell—to the majority of western anthropologists. For the first, he says, "anthropogenesis is to be conceived as a normal evolutionary process, leading lower forms of the Pithecanthropus type to *H. sapiens* by way of Neanderthal man." The second group, on the contrary, denying the variability of the species *H. sapiens* once it was differentiated, would uphold "the antievolutionist point of view," of a precocious appearance of *H. sapiens* and his coexistence with Neanderthal Man.

Such a criticism leads one to think that its author has not read, or at least has hardly understood, the hypotheses against which he takes a stand. The Neanderthal theory could be defended in the last century, when we were acquainted with very few human fossils, for which the theory established phyletic connections which seemed logical. But for fifty years discoveries have followed one after another. As often happens in science, an early theory, put forth to explain a few facts only, no longer holds good when, the evidence having increased, one becomes aware of the breadth and complexity of the problems. The much more complete knowledge which we now have of fossil men has obliged all really unprejudiced anthropologists, whatever their philosophical attitudes may be, to abandon the Neanderthal thesis. In any case, when one reflects, could it have been otherwise? How could we suppose that the few human fossil remains which we possessed in the last century (Pithecanthropus and two or three Neanderthal men) should have sufficed to allow us to retrace, without consideration of its variations, the whole of human evolution? Really, chance would have had to be singularly kind to the excavators!

Wiercinski concludes that the non-Neanderthal theories do not conform to what we know of evolution. This opinion will seem curiously reactionary to those who have followed the progress of vertebrate paleontology since the beginning of the century.

It is now well established in fact that, in most vertebrates and notably in the mammals, the majority of groups branched out, almost from the moment of their origin, precociously provided with their essential characteristics, which proceeded to develop along parallel courses. This is called "bushlike" evolution, corresponding in general to the "adaptive radiation" of English-speaking authors; one sees the persistence of lines, side by side, often over long periods of time, of which some remain more primitive and, by consequence, much closer morphologically to the presumed ancestors of the group, while others appear very early in a more evolved state. By adaptation or by selection, each of these lines itself undergoes many modifications in the course of time; development or regression of certain characters, bifurcation or the outgrowth of lateral branches; naturally they may also become extinct. In all this an essential fact is the long parallel persistence of forms exhibiting very different degrees of evolution of which certain ones, were one not aware of their very ancient origin, might *a priori* be considered as descendants of others.

This is the same mode of evolution which one finds in fossil men. One need only glance at Figure 9 to realize, in fact, that in the same epoch, the Mindel-Riss, we encounter in the men of Ngandong, the Preneanderthals, and the Presapiens, three simultaneous lines which in earlier times we would have believed to succeed one another in time. Such a coexistence does not signify that these lines did not evolve further after their appearance, and one wonders where Dr. Wiercinski believes he has seen such a conception expressed! From Pithecanthropus to Ngandong man, from Mauer man to the classic Neanderthals, significant transformations took place, which are well known to the paleontologists. Though they were less pronounced, we have seen that changes also took place from Presapiens to modern man; and the wide racial differentiation of the latter furthermore shows to how great a degree human lines are susceptible of becoming diversified as they branch out. Far from being the denial of evolution, parallelism succeeding the bushlike radiation and the precocious appearance of the first human types lend still more significance to this evolution.

To suppose that modern man was the goal of a single phylum which, from its beginning, was modified in a single and predetermined direction, as though by a sort of predestination which could have led only to him as he now finds himself, would be to make of man a being apart. Strongly opposed to such a conception, the modern data of human paleontology teach us that the hominids became differentiated following a process identical to that which we recognize for other mammal groups, including, to be sure, other groups of primates. These put human evolution in its true place.

In bringing together the facts revealed by paleontological discoveries, the idea of Presapiens also confirms for us that human evolution has been much more complex than was originally believed.

Our genealogical tree should not be compared to a poplar which rises in a single thrust high above the ground, but rather to a bush which spreads out at once in lateral branches, many of which come to an end, others subdividing to end in turn, with only a few reaching full growth. We do not know if the totality of races living today derives from a single branch or from several, but there is no doubt that the first appearance of the type which we call *Homo sapiens* was much older than we formerly imagined. The idea, long the classical one, that all hominids should be ranged along the same phylum which, by way of Neanderthal man, was to terminate in modern men, that man, in other words, results from a simple unilinear evolution, should be abandoned from every point of view.

The Neanderthal Palaeanthropi in Italy

Sergio Sergi   1958

The Saccopastore men represent the Palaeanthropi[1] who occupied Latium during the Riss-Würm interglacial. The other Palaeanthropi who lived in Europe at the same time are represented by the finds of Krapina and Ehringsdorf. The Steinheim find stems from a previous epoch. All these are different from one another as well as from Saccopastore, and it may be asserted that Europe at that time was occupied by men of different species and races who are nowadays designated as "Neanderthals" generally, and in the broad sense of the word.

In the following time period, that is to say in the last or Würm glaciation, the Neanderthal Palaeanthropi lived in wide areas of Europe. They resemble one another extraordinarily, with respect both to their morphology and to their skull capactiy. Compare, for example, the fossil finds from Neanderthal, from La Chapelle, and Monte Circeo. The morphological and metrical homogeneity among these is great, to a degree which would be difficult to match in a series of modern skulls of the same race.

According to my view, these last constitute the actual type of the Neanderthals, and for this reason the designation "Neanderthals" will be used for them alone. For the skull from Neanderthal belongs to this

[1] Editor's note: Dr. Sergi designates the Neanderthals in the broad sense, and modern men, respectively, as "Palaeanthropi" and "Phaneranthropi" (the last signifying "visible" or here-and-now men).

Originally entitled "Die Neandertalischen Palaeanthropen in Italien, II, Diskussion und Deutung," *from* Hundert Jahre Neanderthaler, Gedenkbuch der International Neanderthal Feier, *Dusseldorf, August 26–30, 1956, published 1958, ed. by G. H. R. von Koenigswald for the Wenner-Gren Foundation for Anthropological Research. Reprinted by permission of the author and the Wenner-Gren Foundation. The author considers the significance of variation among the Neanderthals themselves for human evolution in the Upper Pleistocene. Before retiring, Dr. Sergi (himself the son of a celebrated anthropologist, Guiseppe Sergi) was Professor of Anthropology at the University of Rome.*

group. This also signifies that there existed a terminal parallel line of the great palaeanthropic complex, which succumbed during the last glaciation. In this parallel line there obtained a marked homogeneity which was the result of a progressive lessening of variability, leading to a phase of fixity—the herald of the extinction of the race. The men of Saccopastore, Krapina, and Ehringsdorf, all of whom stem from the Riss-Würm interglacial, exhibit different stages of evolution in their characteristics, and are especially differentiated from the Neanderthals of the Würm glaciation in showing a pronounced polymorphism. Some of their characteristics are of a primitive nature, for example, in Saccopastore I, the extreme platycephaly, the small cranial capacity, and, in the facial skeleton, the special morphology of the alveolar region. The two Saccopastore finds seem on the one hand to be more primitive than the Neanderthal type; they differ, however, from the other "Neanderthals" in the more highly developed architectonic structure of the skull and in the well marked bending of the base.

The progressive development of the vaulting in Saccopastore I comes about through the more open frontal angle. The curve of the occiput does not exhibit that bulging which is typical for the Neanderthals of the glacial period. The length-breadth index of the skull is higher, also. In these details, Saccopastore approaches the series from Krapina, which belongs to the same epoch. In Saccopastore I and II, the completely phaneranthropic dental volume indicates a progressive development of the face, while the Krapina specimens are macrodontic. The latter are quite variable, almost suggesting that they might stem from different races. However, a difference can also be established in the two skulls from Saccopastore, particularly in regard to their form: in Saccopastore II the occiput is evidently projecting, and in my opinion the cephalic index is also somewhat lower than that of Saccopastore I. The Ehringsdorf skull shows signs of characteristics making it appear rather as a transitional link to modern man than—corresponding to its primitive appearance—belonging to the Neanderthals. The definite elevation of the forehead and the marked curvature of the whole forward skull cap argue for a separation of this skull from the Neanderthals, while the marked occipital torus and the shallow glenoid fossae on the other hand bring it nearer to them. The Steinheim skull, of earlier date, must also be cited as a compromise between characteristics of Neanderthals and modern men. This is the more so since it exhibits a mixture of palaeanthropic and phaneranthropic peculiarities.

The hominids are distinguished by their special psychic evolution, the degree of which rests morphologically on the volume and structure of the brain. In this connection it is of course to be noted that while the hominids went through several stages of brain evolution in their different phases of development, other special characteristics also were making their appearance, such as those which made the vertical posture possible. At different levels of human evolution, brain development took place within differing limits; that is to say, brain development proceeded differently in different types, faster in some, slower in others. Simultaneously, other human traits were also transformed, each with its own tempo—one more slowly, another more rapidly, corresponding entirely to the developmental tempo of the brain. In the course of the transformation of this complicated organ, the numerous necessary changes did not follow a single definite sequence, but rather a course like that of other variations. These simultaneous transformations and mutual adaptations took place in spheres offering widely varying possibilities; in this way the development of the Palaeanthropi of Europe eventually gave rise to several types, more or less corresponding to specific adaptive needs; these in turn gave rise to later changes. The simultaneous variation of different groups may be explained through the principle of the selection of correlated changes (il principio delle variazioni coincidenti), and likewise the much more rapid development of one group as opposed to another, on the ground of different pressures in the struggle for existence. A series of incipient characteristics and tendencies culminated more quickly and fully in certain groups than in others. The typical Neanderthals of the last glaciation possessed peculiarities which appeared in the palaeanthropic group at the end of its evolution, that is to say, in the period of its decline ("paracme" of Haeckel); these peculiarities may be illustrated by the final florescence of the specific architectonic structure of the skull of the group in question.

The anterior surface of the maxillary bone appears more or less bowed in three cross sections (incurvatio horizontalis, incurvatio sagittalis, incurvatio inframalaris frontalis) in the following types: Palaeanthropus of Saccopastore, Sinanthropus (Protoanthropus), Palaeanthropus from Steinheim, and Phaneranthropus (modern man). The maxilla of the Neanderthal Palaeanthropus from Monte Circeo differs, being flat in the horizontal and frontal profiles rather than bowed, and appearing swollen (oncognatus) in the lateral profile, as in the Neanderthal Palaeanthropi of LaChapelle and La Ferrassie.

In the European Palaeanthropi of the last glaciation (Würm)—the last of the palaeanthropic series, which in my view includes only the typical Neanderthals of the nature of the specimens from La Chapelle, La Ferrassie, and Monte Circeo—these three foldings or depressions of the maxillary bone are not present; the surface appears flat in the three planes named, and above all expanded in the sagittal plane (oncognatia).

This expansion of the maxillary wall corresponds to an expansion of the maxillary sinus, and involves a changed form of the roof of the nose and of the interorbital space. I am of the opinion that these differences between the Neanderthals of the glacial period and the Palaeanthropi of the interglacial must be viewed in relation to new physiological necessities in respiration, arising from changed conditions of temperature and moisture in the environment. Morphological changes took place in the whole nasomaxillary structure (nasal fossae, maxillary sinuses, et cetera), which in the Palaeanthropi of the interglacial (Saccopastore) had been adapted to a warm, moist climate (tropical forest) and which, broadly speaking, had approximated a Negroid type. In the Neanderthals, the original architecture of the nose region of this Negroid type (eurrinia) was morphologically modified, in order to be adjusted to functional necessities and to assure vitality and survival.

In considering functional traits suggested by the study of morphology as determined by jaw muscle attachment, certain ones found in Circeo III appear predominant, that is, those which depend on the inner and outer pterygoid muscles, and are thus related to grinding movements. These functional studies allow speculations as to the nature of the food being masticated, and thus, in particular, as to the nature of the food of the Neanderthals. It should be mentioned at once that the jawbone is deficient in calcium, while the magnesium content is high.

From its characteristics, the Circeo III mandible appears to be a typical representative of the type of the large-skulled Neanderthals of the Würm. This is what the Circeo I skull indicates; just as this was found to resemble La Chapelle and La Ferrassie, so the Circeo III jawbone finds its greatest morphological similarities with the same specimens and manifests, also like them, the same functional details with relation to the chewing mechanism. Again, like the Circeo I skull before it, the jawbone of Circeo III substantiates the great homogeneity of the species, and its fixity, which developed in the period just before its extinction, and which follows a progressive lessening of its variability.

Brain sizes were extraordinarily enlarged; the brain volume is greater than that of those human races possessing a distinctly large brain (euencephales, aristencephales). The Neanderthals of the last glaciation are a race in which the brain had its own early progress, whereas the development of the skull appears as though it were late and inadequate. Thus, there appeared an absolute lack of balance between the individual organs. A harmony in development is one of the prerequisites for effective further progress.

In the Saccopastore and Circeo finds, Italy has furnished evidence that different types of Palaeanthropi lived in Europe, belonging to different epochs. Saccopastore is a man of the last interglacial; Circeo is a man from the following Würm glaciation. In the interglacial, there prevailed an extensive polymorphism, represented by different lines branching off. Among these we may find the forerunners of this or that phaneranthropic race. In the cold period, there survived one dying branch, that of the type of the Neanderthals with a large skull volume. Both of the types found in Italy are extinct; while one—the Circeo type—disappeared without any legacy to the Phaneranthropi, the Saccopastore man exhibits, although in primitive guise (that is, consonant with his general form and period) an approach to the line of evolution of the Phaneranthropi, or modern man.

If a definite genetic relationship between Palaeanthropi and Phaneranthropi is admissible, the idea which comes to mind is a connection with man of Saccopastore.

Using Dobzhansky's dynamic conception of species, according to which species and race constitute a continual biological process of transformation, population genetics can furnish an indication as to how fossil remains of the European Palaeanthropi may be viewed from the standpoint of microevolution. We must separate species and races (varieties) according to the dynamic principle, which in itself supplies no sharp division between the absolute categories of living forms (genus, species, and varieties). However, the best evidence for this dynamic principle is the mutability and variability of types found in the series of the European Palaeanthropi, and the distribution of this polymorphism with respect to time and space. In fact, it is in just this way that we may begin to determine the actual trends in the characteristics of the species. In phylogenetic problems, human fossils constitute phenotypes of geographically and ecologically differing populations. In order to distinguish and classify them, it is necessary to have a comparative analysis which, at least theoretically and hypothetically, permits some impression as to systematic positions. The difficulty of exactly defining races and their subdivisions in the Palaeanthropi is multiplied by the extreme rarity of the finds. That is what we are faced with: an insufficient number of individuals for consideration as typical representatives of a group. The criterion of genetics must be viewed as basic for a systematics of fossil remains, although it cannot be applied by the methods of modern genetics. Unfortunately, however, even this criterion can only give artificial results, since the concrete information is insufficient, although necessary for a positive solution of the problem. Not only do we lack experimental information from the area of physiology, which we have when treating of living beings, but also the objective facts themselves are incomplete; they are based on parts of the body of an individual, and this often permits only inadequate deductions as to the morphological organization of the whole. In order to undertake a classification, we must first determine the differentiating characteristics which we use in the identification of types. In speaking of characteristics, there is no certainty as to their value and significance, since the word "characteristic" itself is used with "elastic meaning" (Osborn). Moreover, when we think in rigorous genetic terms, we do not know how to identify with genetic units something which, on the one hand, we denote as a "characteristic," but which, on the other hand, we select empirically and subjectively. We are ignorant of their genetic persistence, because the factors on which they depend, and with which they are connected, are of a more or less complex nature. Out of this grows the double meaning of the word "characteristic," which is often conceived of in the proper genetic sense, but also often used to denote some morphological and physiological entity, of a kind which is more or less complex relative to its genetic background.

The rarity of fossil finds, then, creates an extreme difficulty for a complete understanding; over and above this, however, particular characteristics of each find must be considered as probable only; thus limited, they permit only a probable explanation of evolution. The types considered are examples of a "rising fluctuation," by means of which we are able to explain the dynamics of the development of species and their differences; their variety must correspond to local mutations taking place at limited genetic centers. The diversity of these different forms was promoted by the success and the spread of the species in the course of its "acme," that is, during the time of its florescence. This increased vitality manifested itself in various ways, and not in individual series alone. Progress was not regular, since it is brought about by "different and varying" opposing forces, so that, genetically, characteristics are combined in different ways, or are diminished, or disappear entirely, or are changed into unrecognizable latent forms, which under other circumstances may once more be restored to their original value.

Consequently, the basic prerequisite for the evolution of a species with vital potentialities is an original diversity of forms. In the beginning, the strength of adaptation is the greater the broader is the possibility of variation, and the broader the degree of geographical expansion. In this way, I would explain the great polymorphism, that is, the marked variability of form, in the Palaeanthropi of the interglacial, in the course of their enormous expansion in the Old World. On the other hand, I must regard the great fixity and homogeneity of the surviving forms of the last glacial as the sign of decline and extinction. Saccopastore man belongs to the first named type, Circeo man to the latter.

Before this final series of the palaeanthropic cycle, marked by very limited variability, there were already in existence representatives of a third human cycle, corresponding to present-day forms (Phaneranthropi). We still do not know—and in view of the small number of specimens in our hands today it is not possible to know—at what moment the phaneranthropic series arose, and where this had its origin and development. Its genetic relation to extinct forms at various points in time has not become clear; it appears, however, that these relationships have left traces in a few living ethnic groups; and if these traces are not simply an expression of a process of hybridization, they might well be an indication of great age; venerable survivors of different proto-phaneranthropic types.

The extraordinary development of the great phaneranthropic complex in the post-Pleistocene, its almost unimaginable rise, coincided with the final extinction of the Palaeanthropi. Forerunners of an earlier phase, of uncertain duration, had already heralded the beginning of the phaneranthropic cycle; this phase was to attain its high point in the Holocene. Only a few series belonging to a given cycle of hominization overlap with the beginning of the following, while the greater part are replaced by neotenomorphic or gerontomorphic stages. The pattern of rhythmic cycles in which various series have arranged themselves in the course of human evolution appears to reflect a variety of diverse biotypes and ecotypes of humanity, correlated with the changes from glacial to interglacial periods. The glacial phases are reflected in the evolution of culture simultaneously with the morpho-physiological evolution of the hominids. The physical and psychic evolution of mankind must therefore be regarded, in all its different aspects, as connected with, and regulated by, the geological events of the Pleistocene.

Morphological Position of the «Prophaneranthropi» (Swanscombe and Fontéchevade)

Sergio Sergi   1953

On numerous occasions finds held to be contemporary with, or older than, those of the *Palaeanthropi* have been attributed to fossil *Phaneranthropi* (*Homo sapiens fossilis*). The greater part of the material described by the various authors at different times and in different circumstances need not be taken seriously into consideration. Only those pieces of evidence which Vallois united in the *Praesapiens* group need be discussed; they have a stratigraphical and chronological position that has been ascertained but their morphological diagnosis is still discussed and uncertain owing to the insufficiency of the fragments. These are the Swanscombe and Fontéchevade remains.

THE SWANSCOMBE MAN (Swanscombe Committee, 1938)

Occipital (1935) and parietal (1936) discovered in the Barnfield gravel (Kent) by Marston.

The observations which I made on the cast of the Swanscombe skull bone (a cast which I owe to the courtesy of Professor Trevor) and the comparisons which I was able to make with the Circeo skull lead me to note an appreciable convergence between them, both as to dimensions and morphology, especially in the parietal bones, which I will briefly

FROM the Actes du Congrès International du Quaternaire (*INQUA*), pp. 651–665, *reprinted by permission of the author and of INQUA. The article has also appeared as "I profanerantropi di Swanscombe e di Fontéchevade," in* Rendiconti dell'Accademia Nazionale dei Lincei, *1953, serie Viii, vol. 15, pp. 601–608; this version has been used by the editor for minor editorial changes in the author's English translation. The paper presents another variant among possible interpretations of the relations of later fossil men, but is also included for reasons of method: Professor Sergi's use of special contour tracings and of ratios derived from them to render, graphically and numerically, morphological comparisons which are more usually left to observation and verbal description.*

outline. The convergences are connected with the measurement of the basion-bregma height, the position of the principal lambda, the position of the inion, the biasteric diameter, the location of the asteria, and the form and position of the parietal. These convergences can easily be noted by superimposing the relevant craniograms, and particularly the oblique frontal-sagittal-asteric craniograms. I have used this last name to indicate a section corresponding to a plane cutting the skull obliquely through the bregma, the basion, and one of the asteria (either the right or the left). (Figure 1). The contours of this craniogram reflect the trend of the curve of the inner wall of the skull cavity, provided that the section does not show any particular protuberances in the corresponding outer wall which could alter or hide the inner curve. In *Palaeanthropus* this section has a typically elliptic, narrow, and prolonged form (lenticular type section) which shows immediately the characteristic flattening of the skull vault (platycephaly). In a craniogram divided into quadrants, one notes from the basion-bregma line and the trace of the normal lambda plane to this line, that in *Palaeanthropus* the area of the upper left quadrant (frontal and parietal) is more reduced than in *Phaneranthropus* while, on the contrary, the area of the near lower quadrant (occipital quadrant) in the first is considerably more extended than in the second (see Figure 2). In its entirety, the whole general structure of the Swanscombe skull portion which has been preserved recalls the form of the Neandertal *Palaeanthropi*, especially on account of the large extension of the occipital region backwards, downwards, and laterally and for the marked degree of platycephaly. (Figures 3, 4, 5, 6, 7.) Thus, as in the Neandertals, the greater distance of the asteric angle of all the parietal bones from the median plane, and the consequent increase in the diameter of the biasteric width, is the evidence of the expanding force, in the lateral direction, of the occipital region. To the sublambda expansion in the occipital direction below the horizontal plane which lies on the level of the lambda there corresponds the flattening of the upper part (supralambda) of the parietal bone, i. e., the platycephalic parietal which corresponds to the zone where the force of expansion has made itself felt in a lesser degree. The occipital expansion and the platycephaly is shown in Swanscombe combined with architectural conditions which are common to the Neandertal *palaeanthropi* (Sergi, 1944). And like these, it is also likely that the frontal bone, which is lost, would probably have possessed a *torus*, a possibility not excluded by Morant and recently admitted without reserve by Breitinger (1952). But this cannot be categorically stated because, as Ashley Montagu notes on the subject of the Wallbrook skull, a frontal bone without a supraorbital margin might occur combined with an unusual thickness in the bones of the vault of the skull. The Swanscombe man is not a *Phaneranthropus*, in

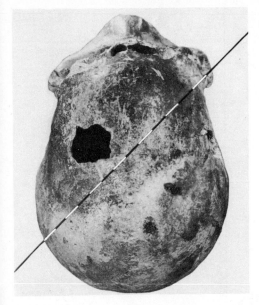

FIGURE 1. The Saccopastore I *Palaeanthropus* photographed in the vertical norma, oriented on the basion-bregma vertical axis. The dashed line indicates the section, corresponding to the oblique left basion-bregma-asterion plane.

other words, he is not yet *Homo sapiens* but more a Palaeanthropic form, a forerunner of the *Phaneranthropi*, a *Prophaneranthropus*.

THE FONTÉCHEVADE MAN (Vallois, 1949a)

In August of 1947, the daughter of Henry Martin, who discovered the La Quina remains, found a small fragment of a human frontal bone (Fontéchevade I) at a depth of 2.6 m. amid prehistoric deposits in the Fontéchevade Cave (Charente), and a little later, the vault of another human skull (Fontéchevade II). The strata from which they derived have been classified as belonging in the Riss-Würm interglacial and contained Palaeolithic implements of the Tayacian type and a warm and temperate fauna characterized by *Rhinoceros Merckii, Dama* sp. *Cuon, Testudo graeca*. The stratigraphic position is not contested and it is the first time that such ancient human remains have been found in France. So states Vallois (1949a) to whom we owe the comments on the material. Fontéchevade II is represented by the left parietal, the upper half of the right, and the upper part of the frontal bone. Some other tiny fragments belong to the right parietal and the occipital. The bones are remarkably thick (from 7 to 9 mm.) as in the Swanscombe skull. The sutures are largely obliterated so that Vallois judges the age to have been between 40 and 50 years. The median sagittal contour for a large part of the parietal appears very flat. The curve of the frontal bone which has been preserved is more pronounced. In the rear norma the walls of the parietal are curved laterally, starting from the median

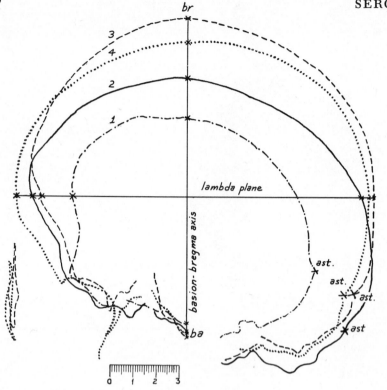

FIGURE 2. Oblique craniogram bregma (br); basion (ba); asterion (ast) of: (1) Chimpanzee, (2) Saccopastore I, (3) modern Roman brachymorphic, (4) modern Roman dolichomorphic. The craniograms are superimposed on the basion-bregma axis and on the lambda plane. One can note: (a) the gradual heightening of the vault of the skull above the lambda plane from the chimpanzee to present-day man and the corresponding reduction below the lambda plane corresponding to the lower occipitoparietal quadrant; (b) lenticular section of Saccopastore, typical in the *Palaeanthropi* (Sergi, 1944).

plane until they reach the greatest distance (154 mm) a little below and from there they turn inwards. Vallois holds that the missing part of the frontal bone must have been of the same type as that of living man, i. e., without the *torus* which characterized the Neandertals. He draws the confirmation for his opinion from the fragment of frontal bone of Fontéchevade I which consists of the glabella of the frontal bone without a trace of the *torus*. The most striking feature which divides Fontéchevade from *Phaneranthropus* is the width, at the level of the asterion, such as is found in the Swanscombe skull and as occurred in the Neandertal *Palaeanthropus*. These conditions are combined with the lowness of the skull (*platycephaly*). Vallois concludes that the structure of the brain

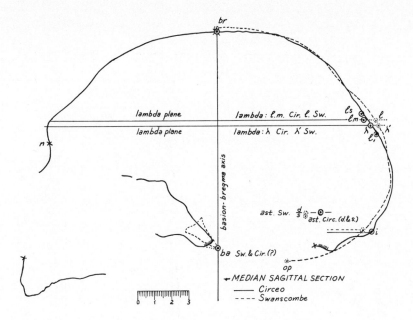

FIGURE 3. Median sagittal contour of the Swanscombe and Mt. Circeo skulls, superimposed on the basion-bregma axis with lambda planes parallel. Note the similarity.

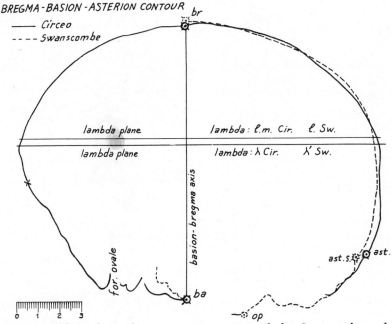

FIGURE 4. Oblique basion-bregma-asterion contour of the Swanscombe and Mt. Circeo skulls, superimposed on the basion-bregma axis with lambda planes parallel. Note the similarity.

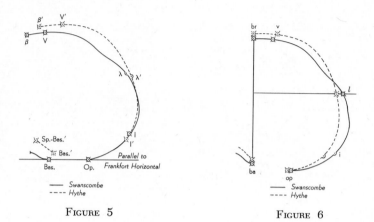

FIGURE 5

FIGURE 6

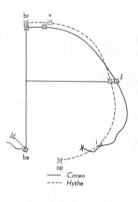

FIGURE 7

FIGURE 5. Sagittal contour of the Swanscombe skull and the Hythe (Kent) medieval female type skull superimposed on the Frankfort horizontal claimed by Morant for Swanscombe as corresponding to the basion opisthion horizontal. This orientation is unsuitable. Reprinted by permission from G. M. Morant, "The Form of the Swanscombe Skull," *J. Royal Anthropological Institute of Great Britain and Ireland.*

FIGURE 6. The sagittal contour of the Hythe type superimposed on Swanscombe on the basion-bregma axis and the lambda plane, compared with Figure 5, emphasizes the great differences which result from the different orientations adopted. The orientation on the basion-bregma axis shows the gap between Swanscombe and the Hythe type and the Swanscombe-Circeo similarity.

FIGURE 7. The sagittal contour of the Hythe type superimposed on Mt. Circeo on the basion-bregma axis and the lambda plane, compared with Figure 5, emphasizes the great differences which result from the different orientations adopted. The orientation on the basion-bregma axis shows the gap between Swanscombe and the Hythe type and the Swanscombe-Circeo similarity.

case is not the same as the one of present-day man, although as sharing the above-mentioned absence of the *torus* in the glabellar region. After having examined the fragment of Fontéchevade II in the Musée de l'Homme with Vallois' kind permission, I am also of the opinion that it has a different morphology from present-day man's without at all excluding that it could have suffered some artificial posthumous deformation. The Fontéchevade skull differs from *Phaneranthropus*, i. e., present-day man, particularly by the exceptional biasteric width, the considerable lowering of the skull vault, and the very low position of the diameter of the maximum width. These three facts are the manifestation of the particular posterior-lateral expansion of the occipital region as is shown by the bregma-asterion curve, as I drew it from the original in Paris in May 1951 (Figure 11). In Fontéchevade, the evolutionary thrust of the cranial cavity took place in the occipital direction as happened in *Palaeanthropus,* differently from the *Phaneranthropi,* among which the evolutionary thrust was directed towards the vault.

Fontéchevade is not a *Phaneranthropus* (*Homo sapiens*) but a form not far from the *Palaeanthropi*—it is a Palaeanthropic form—i. e., *Prophaneranthropus.*

The palaeanthropic form typology of the Swanscombe and Fontéchevade skulls, somewhat summarily treated owing to the limited time available, can be highlighted from an examination of the basion-bregma-asterion perigram (see Figures 8, 9, 10, 11, 12). In this section, where the basion-bregma height is taken as the vertical axis and the lambda plane as the horizontal one, I have considered the perpendicular from the asterion to the basion-bregma axis which I have termed *asterion apostasy* (distance from the asterion) and the perpendicular from the farthest point from the basion-bregma curve (which I have named *gonation* or knee) to the basion-bregma axis which I designate as *gonation apostasy.* The gonation (*go* in the figures) corresponds to a folding back of the parietal and marks the maximum lateral expansion of the bone in the plane in question. I then determined the percentage ratio of each of the two apostasies (asterion apostasy and gonation apostasy) to the basion-bregma height. These two ratios I have called respectively, *asterion apostasy index* and *gonation apostasy index.* And finally I have taken into consideration the angle of the bregma-asterion curve with the lambda plane, i. e., the slope of the whole parietal bone in the oblique basion-bregma-asterion section, and the angle of the segment of the curve above the lambda plane (paralambda-bregma point segment). The value of this angle determines the degree of elevation of the skull vault above the lambda plane in the above-mentioned oblique section.

The measures shown on the craniograms which I made on the cast of

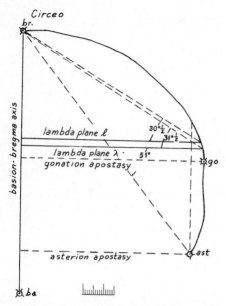

FIGURE 8. Basion-bregma-asterion section of Mt. Circeo skull (contours taken on original).

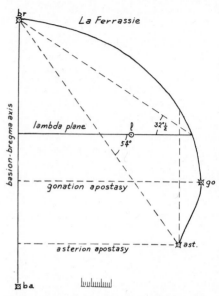

FIGURE 9. Basion-bregma-asterion section of La Ferrassie skull (contours taken on original).

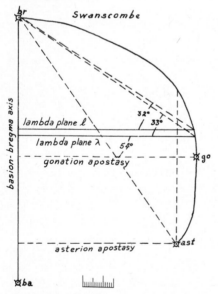

FIGURE 10. Basion-bregma-asterion section of Swanscombe skull (contours taken on a cast).

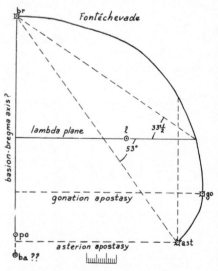

FIGURE 11. Basion-bregma-asterion section of Fontéchevade skull. The basion is presumed to be 10 mm below the porion as taken by Vallois (Vallois, 1949a, Figure 4) (contours taken on original).

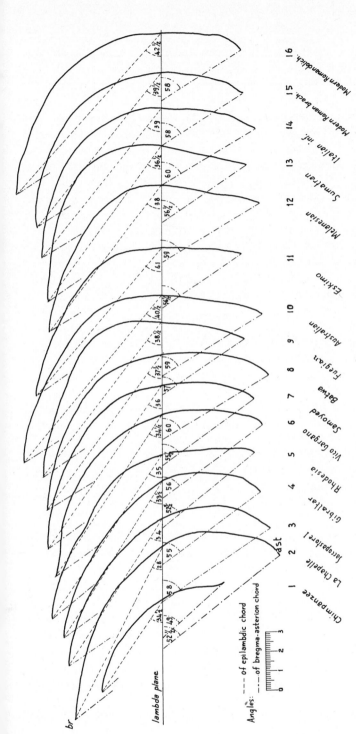

FIGURE 12. Bregma-asterion curve in the basion-bregma-asterion plane. Above the horizontal (lambda plane) are the angles formed by this with the epilambdic chord; below, the angles with the bregma-asterion chord. 1. Chimpanzee. Inst. Anthrop. Rome (3253); 2. La Chapelle, Mus. Paleont. Paris; 3. Saccopastore I, Inst. Anthrop. Rome; 4. Gibraltar, Royal College of Surgeons, London; 5. Rhodesia, British Museum, London; 6. Ancient Vico Gargano; 7. Samo-

yed, Inst. Anat., Oxford (Aus. 20972); 8. Pygmy (Batwa), Inst. Anat., Oxford (Af. 30, 1.H.A.); 9. Fuegian, Inst. Anthrop. Rome; 10. Australian, Inst. Anat., Oxford; 11. Eskimo, Inst. Anat., Oxford (Am. 10) 844; 12. Melanesian, Inst. Anthrop. Rome (904); 13. Sumatra, Inst. Anthrop. Rome (2626); 14. Italian inf. I. Inst. Anthrop. Rome (394); 15. Modern Roman brachycephalic (skull index 84); 16. Modern Roman dolichocephalic (skull index 70).

the Swanscombe skull and on the Fontéchevade original have been compared with those of craniograms of a group of *Palaeanthropi,* and those of a group of *Phaneranthropi* belonging to widely diverse human types (see table).

In the table the measurements and the relevant indexes are listed, and the skull series are given according to the decreasing value of the asterion apostasy index. With this arrangement, the skulls fall into three distinct groups: the first comprises all the *Palaeanthropi* with the highest values; the second, intermediate, Swanscombe and Fontéchevade, the *Prophaneranthropi* with values very near to those of the first group; and the third takes in all the *Phaneranthropi* with much lower values. This classification reflects the corresponding morphological position already noted in the Swanscombe and Fontéchevade skulls. Two subgroups can be distinguished in the *Phaneranthropi,* the first with higher values, the second with lower. The first subgroup comprises extremely low skulls, platycephalic, with a chamaetapeinocephalic index. To these belong two extreme human types, the Samoyed, markedly brachycephalic, the Batwa, typically dolichocephalic, and two Italian skulls of an archaic human type with a very sloped frontal bone and parapalaeoanthropic occipital formation, which I will have the opportunity of mentioning in another article. The same classification is reproduced in a diagram (Figure 14) which reveals at a glance the situation of these three different groups. The basion-bregma height values and asterion apostasies listed in comparative tables emphasize the reciprocal situation of the skulls examined (Figure 13).

From the table (column 6) it can also be seen that the epilambda parietal angle of inclination in the oblique section is smaller in *Palaeanthropus* and *Prophaneranthropus* and greater in *Phaneranthropus.* The particular significance of the strong lateral oblique occipital formation accompanied by the marked lowering of the lateral epilambda curve can be noted. It is a morphological condition which characterized the Swanscombe and Fontéchevade *Prophaneranthropi* giving them something in common with the *Palaeanthropi.*

The morphological position of Swanscombe man and Fontéchevade man in comparison with other Pleistocene fossil humans is somewhat uncertain at the present point of our knowledge since the material is limited to segments of the brain case, while nothing is known of the face, which has an enormous value in distinguishing the types. The fact that the skulls are incomplete also leads to different opinions. Avoiding any speculations that might prejudice the objective evaluation of what can be deduced from the material, it may be stated that these fossils partly fit into both the Palaeanthropic and Phaneranthropic categories, the

TABLE

	Axis. Basion-bregma height (mm)	Asterion apostasy from axis (mm)	Asterion apostasy index 100 (Sergi, 1944; Swanscombe Committee, 1938)	Gonation apostasy from axis (mm)	Gonation apostasy index 100 (Vallois, 1949a; Swanscombe Committee, 1938)	Inclination angle of the epilambda segment of the bregma-asterion curve
PALAEANTHROPI						
Circeo	123	82	66	89	72	30°½–31°½
Rhodesia	128	85	66	88	68	35°
Saccopastore I	109	70	64	82	75	34°
La Chapelle	129	84	64	97	74	28°?
Gibraltar	120	75	62	84	70	33°½
La Ferrassie	132	82	62	94	71	32°½
PROPHANERANTHROPI						
Fontéchevade	117??	82	64??	95	74	33°½
Swanscombe	125	78 (80)	62	88	70	32°–33°
PHANERANTHROPI						
Samoyed	126	77	61	85	67	36°
Vico Gargano	125	76	60	86	68	34°½
Batwa	114	69	60	81	71	37°½
Calabrese	129	77	59	87	67	34°–39°
Roman brachy.	124	69	55	79	63	39°
Italian inf.	121	66	54	77	63	39°
Fuegian	133	73	54	81	60	38°½
Eskimo	133	73	54	76	57	41°
Roman dolich.	136	73		83	61	42°
Melanesian	126	68	53	76	60	38°
Australian	143	76	53	85	59	40°½
Sumatran	128	67	52	79	61	36°½

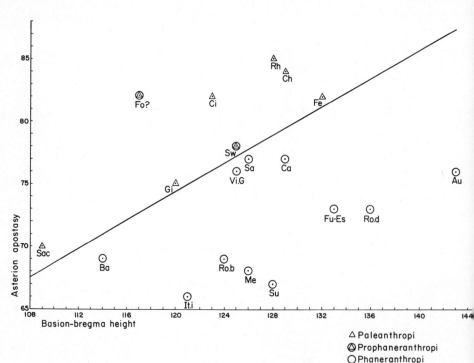

FIGURE 13. *Palaeanthropi:* Ci = Circeo; Rh = Rhodesia; Sac = Saccopastore; Ch = La Chapelle; Gi = Gibraltar; Fe = La Ferrassie. *Prophaneranthropi:* Fo? = Fontéchevade; Sw = Swanscombe. *Phaneranthropi:* Sa = Samoyed; Vi.G = Vico Gargano; Ba = Batwa; Ca = Calabrese; Ro.b = Roman brachy.; It.i = Italian inf.; Fu = Fuegian; Es = Eskimo; Ro.d = Roman dolich.; Me = Melanesian; Au = Australian; Sū = Sumatra.

features approaching the Palaeanthropic being of a generally architectural nature. I think that, up to now, these have been underestimated. They are the platycephaly, the posterior-lateral expansion of the occipital region, and the basal expansion of the parietal bones. The skull is still in a primitive condition, which is shown by the accentuated development of its base, a primitive condition which is found in different degrees in *Palaeanthropus* and more markedly in *Sinanthropus.*

On the other hand, the characters approaching *Phaneranthropus* can be found in certain regional morphological features of the skull, for example in the frontal bone on account of the absence of the *torus* (Fontéchevade) and also in the metrical characters and comparisons between them which fall within the area of the variability of the Phaneranthropic type (Swanscombe, according to Morant). However, the comparison with Palaeanthropic type skulls shows that some of these metric values

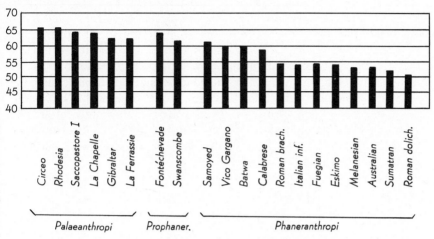

FIGURE 14. Values of the asterion apostasy index.

are the same in both groups. One fact which has not yet been satisfactorily explained is the remarkable thickness of the bones of the vault of the skulls under examination. Until the day we know something about the missing parts of the skulls, particularly the face, we shall not be able to make any definite categorical statement concerning the attributes of the type in question.

However, the Swanscombe and Fontéchevade evidence is the oldest which approaches the present form since they show characteristics which share a morphology which is not so far from that of the *Phaneranthropi* without its being possible to identify them with these latter, to which they could be genetically related.

At the present moment (Vallois, 1949a and others) there is a tendency to separate the Swanscombe and Fontéchevade remains absolutely and completely from the whole Palaeanthropic picture so as to consider it as an independent phyletic line.

From the opposite point of view, one must take into due consideration those Palaeanthropic-form characteristics that have come to light in examining these finds and which suggest a more or less intimate relationship with the *Palaeanthropi* (Sergi, 1944).

On account of their incompleteness, one cannot say how much they may be considered as an intermediate form between the *Protoanthropi* and the *Palaeanthropi* on the one side and the *Phaneranthropi* on the other, as they can no more be considered as forms which are independent from the latter than they can be considered as independent from the *Palaeanthropi*.

If *Palaeanthropus palestinensis,* which possesses both Palaeanthropic and Phaneranthropic features, is placed alongside these forms and if we also recall the pre-Würm, pre-Neanderthal forms of Steinheim and Saccopastore, which have phaneranthropic-form features, it seems clear today that the present hominids must trace their origins and roots not to a single type or a common forerunner, but to more than one; following this line of thought, perhaps in the future it may be possible to classify the aggregate of the forms which appeared immediately after and constituted the different types of *Phaneranthropi* which led directly to the Holocene hominids, in other words the latter already had more than one type of precursor in the remoter Pleistocene.

The Pattern of Evolutionary Development of the Genus Homo

J. S. Weiner   1958

Fifty years ago, that is at the mid-centenary after the Darwin-Wallace announcement, palaeontologists could find solid cause for satisfaction with the extent to which the evidence available to them afforded verification of the evolutionary hypothesis as applied to Man. Darwin himself, through sheer lack of material, could make no reference in the "Origin" to human fossils and even at the time of the "Descent" the disputes over the "type" Neanderthal fossil had hardly begun to abate. Yet by 1908 the fossil record of Man's past, while not abundant, was in a phylogenetic sense quite impressive and coherent. In *H. sapiens* (modern and prehistoric), in *H. neanderthalensis,* and in *Pithecanthropus* from Java, three striking stages (Figure 1) were discernible in an apparently simple evolutionary sequence—a sequence which led back chronologically and morphologically and pointed clearly to a still earlier small brained apelike ancestor as postulated long before on the indirect arguments of comparative primatology, by Darwin, Huxley, Haeckel, and others.

This simple linear series, Java man—Neanderthal man—Sapiens man, based on relatively few specimens, was no doubt far too close to simple prediction to be true. The first two stages were strictly speaking discontinuous "morphospecies"—the representatives of Java and Neander-

FROM the South African Journal of Medical Science, 1958, vol. 23, pp. 111–120, reprinted by permission of the author and of the Witwatersrand University Press. (Figure 2 is from Man in the Primitive World. 1949 copyright, by E. A. Hoebel. Figures 3 and 4 are new versions, substituted by Dr. Weiner for those published originally.) This is the substance of a paper read at the XVth International Congress of Zoology (Darwin-Wallace Centenary), in London, 1958. A final opinion of the relations of modern man to fossil forms, taking account of certain views of the nature of species. Dr. Weiner, a one-time student of Professor Dart, is Reader in Physical Anthropology at Oxford University.

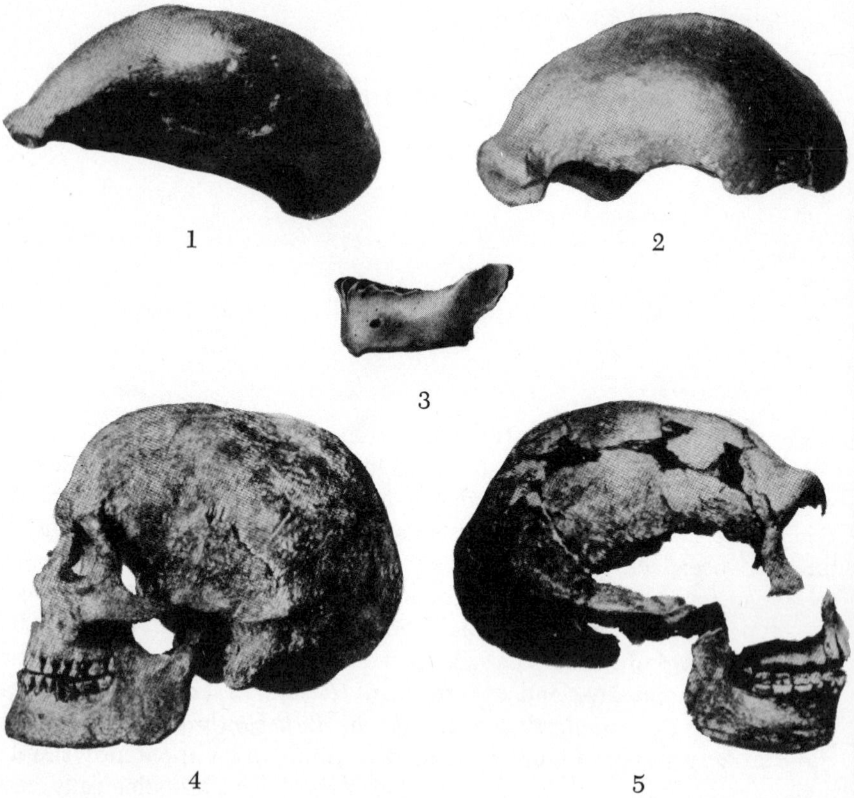

FIGURE 1. The main fossil evidence on human evolution available 50 years ago. 1, Java man; 2, Neanderthal man from Dusseldorf; and 4, Sapiens man (Cro-Magnon) from Grimaldi caves. The jaw, 3, is a Neanderthal specimen from La Naulette and 5 is a Neanderthal skull from Spy. Darwin makes mention in *The Descent of Man* only of the Dusseldorf and La Naulette specimens.

thal man were of very restricted provenance and even the polytypic sapiens species gave little evidence of a smooth gradation with the antecedent forms. It remained a presumption only that the phylogeny had passed through these stages in this particular linear series, though the late Dr. Weidenreich for one never did abandon this scheme and tried in the main always to adapt it to all the subsequent evidence. To do this, however, became increasingly difficult in face of the complexities of the accumulating fossil material. In fact, until a few years ago, it was really not possible to put forward a genealogical scheme for the tool-making Hominidae which was entirely free of contradictory or question-able features. An example, but not atypical, is shown in Figure 2. A major cause was the need to accommodate the Piltdown remains, but

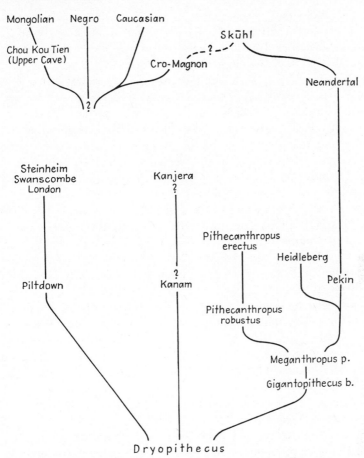

FIGURE 2. A "probable phylogenetic tree of fossil man" to illustrate the complexities of human evolutionary relationships on the evidence available 10 years ago. The 2nd edition (1957) of this valuable text book shows clearly how many of these difficulties have now been resolved. Reprinted by permission from *Man in the Primitive World*, by E. A. Hoebel. Copyright, 1949. McGraw-Hill Book Company, Inc.

this was by no means the only source of difficulty. The factors which rendered the simplicity of the Weidenreich scheme inadmissible may be listed as follows: (1) The finding of new and distinctive regional varieties—Solo (Ngandong) man in Java, and Rhodesian man, neither easy to equate with sapiens or Neanderthal. (2) The discovery of forms intermediate between Neanderthal and modern man, notably those from Steinheim, Ehringsdorf, Mount Carmel (as well as Djebel Kafzeh). (3) Some of these intermediate forms with clearly marked sapiens features, like Mount Carmel, were nearly contemporaneous with Neanderthal;

some, like Steinheim, were much *earlier* than "classical" Neanderthal man. (4) If Galley Hill, the Kanam jaw, the Swanscombe material, or the Fontéchevade skull was accepted as admissible evidence, it seemed possible that a *fully* developed sapiens form was in existence *before* Neanderthal man. For this and the preceding reasons, it became impossible to believe that sapiens developed from Neanderthal man. (5) Arguments based on certain important finds were far less conclusive than many protagonists would admit. Thus Swanscombe was in an incomplete condition and the provenance of the Kanam jaw a matter of some uncertainty, while Fontéchevade still remains undecided. This left much room for arbitrariness in drawing up genealogies since different investigators often came to quite different conclusions on the status of these disputed remains. (6) To add to the difficulties, each succeeding find was almost invariably given quite distorted or exaggerated taxonomic evaluation. Even fragmentary finds were accorded, usually without proper zoological definition, specific or even generic status. *Meganthropus, Sinanthropus,* and even the recent *Atlanthropus* (known from the jaw) were deemed to merit generic status equivalent to *Pithecanthropus,* whereas species or even subspecies distinction is probably all that is involved. *Homo* was split into innumerable taxonomic "binomial" species, e. g., *H. kanamensis, H. steinheimensis,* etc., or new genera created, e.g. *Palaeanthropus palistinensis.* (7) Last, but not least, there obtruded the strange case of *Eoanthropus dawsoni;* in the hominid genealogy, Piltdown man could be interpreted variously as an aberrant form without descendants, the ancestral form of *H. sapiens* or even a fairly late creature without any certain ancestral stock.

If we are able today, as I believe we are, a hundred years after the Darwin-Wallace pronouncement, to view the human palaeontological record once again as a coherent phylogeny, based now on a not inconsiderable array of fossil recoveries, it is because in the last five to ten years, many of the difficulties noted above have become better understood and most of the contradictions eradicated. More rigorous dating methods, introduced by Oakley, have eliminated anomalous specimens like Piltdown and Galley Hill, and recently the Kanam jaw, from their position of presumed antiquity.

A revolt against unprincipled taxonomic designations is beginning to make itself felt and many extravagant titles have failed to establish themselves. A great impetus to the cause of a sane hominid systematics has been given by Sir Wilfrid Le Gros Clark's book (1955). In this, he deals effectively with many of the large, generally ill-appreciated problems of taxonomic analysis, including such topics as the unnecessary multiplication of genera and species, the quantitative assessment of taxonomic relationships, the pitfalls introduced by convergent and parallel evolution, the meaning of primitive, generalised and specialised characters and the significance of the geochronological record in phylogenetic interpretation. In the light of this examination and the principles he adumbrates, Le Gros Clark discusses the phylogeny of the Hominidae, and as an outcome provides "model" generic and specific definitions for the Hominidae. However belated in the history of human palaeontology, this appraisal should help to remove the reproaches so justly leveled at the human palaeontologist by G. G. Simpson: "The peculiar fascination of the primates and their publicity value have almost taken the order out of the hands of sober and conservative mammalogists and have kept, and do keep, its taxonomy in a turmoil. Moreover, even mammalogists who might be entirely conservative in dealing, say, with rats are likely to lose a sense of perspective when they come to the primates, and many studies of this order are covertly or overtly emotional."

For the purposes of this paper, namely an examination of the phylogeny of *Homo* and the place of the Swanscombe skull in it, there seem to me two matters in particular deserving of further consideration; these may be regarded as corollaries to the principles adumbrated by Le Gros Clark. The first concerns the need to formulate quite explicitly a method of dealing with the problem so obtrusive in hominid palaeontology, the treatment of apparently important specimens of disputed, ambiguous or uncertain morphology. This problem has been discussed elsewhere (Weiner, 1957). In summary, the proposition advanced may be stated as follows: Schemes of hominid evolution should be built up in the first place on the basis of material well attested morphologically and chronologically; the probable or possible status of disputed or difficult specimens should then be assessed in the light of such schemes. If the specimen is consistent with the general theory, the balance or probability would seem to lie with the interpretation which best fits all the material; if the specimen will not conform to the theory it may be possible to revise the theory. If this is not possible, it would then seem to emphasize still more the uncertainty of the specimen in question.

Needless to say, this common-sense approach has been prompted by experience of the Piltdown puzzle where schemes which were based on an *a priori* judgment of the status of the "fossil" invariably led to marked inconsistencies. Indeed, the anomalous position of Piltdown man had long been a notorious fact, and became a major reason for questioning the interpretation placed on it and finally for doubting the specimen itself.

At the present time, there are in particular three fossil finds which, for various reasons, lend themselves to alternative interpretations—they are the Kanam jaw fragment, the Heidelberg jaw, and the Swanscombe calvarial fragments. The authenticity of these is, of course, not in doubt. In the case of Swanscombe and Heidelberg, the fossil material is insufficient in amount for final anatomical judgment; in the case of Kanam, not only is the fragment small, but the dating of the specimen has been the subject of dispute.

In the paper already referred to, a scheme of hominid evolution was sketched and in the light of this, the claim for Kanam "man" as a lower Pleistocene early sapiens form appeared rather unlikely; if Kanam man was accorded a status of high antiquity, the resulting phylogenetic scheme could be shown to be internally inconsistent. Thus, the outcome of using a general theory based on reliable material is to strengthen the dubiety already adhering to the antiquity of the specimen. It is interesting that Oakley has recently brought forward evidence of chemical dating which does not favour the alleged antiquity of the specimen.

The second corollary concerns the need to apply more deliberately and rigorously in hominid taxonomy some of the concepts and conclusions which have emerged from what has come to be called the "New Systematics." The fact is that the hominid fossil record now demands a taxonomy of *continuity* and the designation of the species categories within the hominid genera must reflect that situation.

When we put on one side material of ambiguous or uncertain status, we are left with a Pleistocene series in which an overlapping succession is clearly discernible. Chronologically, there seems to be overlapping between *Pithecanthropus* and early forms of *Homo*, between these and Neanderthal, and between Neanderthal and Sapiens. Equally striking is the morphological continuum which pervades these groups. This cannot be elaborated here, but two main trends are quite clear (Figure 3). There is a general trend of enlargement of the brain case and a second trend characterised by increasing evidence of sapiens characters, e.g., in the jaw and forehead. Enlargement (without "sapienization") gives us the Neanderthal line, so that classical Neanderthal may be regarded as the enlargement of *Pithecanthropus*. The sapiens trend combined with enlargement is shown in the Steinheim—Ehringsdorf—Mount Carmel sequence. Rhodesian man may be characterised as an "enlargement" of Steinheim man.

The whole sequence of tool-using hominids thus approximates to a continuous and plexiform lineage (or "gens") with Neanderthal, Rhodesian, and "modern" man as "terminators." As Cain (1954, p. 107) points out, it is in a sequence of this sort that an approach to the actual process of past evolution becomes recognizable. Here we have a species problem very different from that of 50 years ago. "As soon as any gens

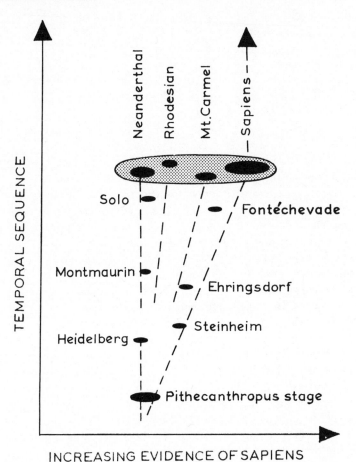

FIGURE 3. A "lineage" scheme to show the continuum, temporal, and morphological, as well as the main trends of differentiation, apparent in the human palaeontological evidence at present available.

showing considerable alteration in morphology with time can be constructed from the available evidence, then the problem of breaking it up into species becomes acute" (Cain, p. 112) . . . "anyone may claim at any time that several successive transients with binomial names really did not differ so greatly as to deserve specific rank. They should be considered only as chronological subspecies. The limits of both subspecies and species within a gens are equally arbitrary." (Cain, p. 113). It is necessary therefore to be careful in human palaeontology as to which of several possible meanings is given to the term "species." Where particular specimens remain isolated or sparse, a "species" status will almost be inevitable, purely for lack of intermediates. The "species" is, in fact, a "morphospecies" as defined by Cain (p. 52). Rhodesian man approximates to this status though it must be admitted that with the finding of the Hopefield calvarium its range in time and space is considerably extended though its morphological connections and antecedents remain undetermined. On the other hand, sapiens and Neanderthal both call for species categorization of a very different order.

Le Gros Clark's taxonomic analysis has led him to a position where *H. sapiens* is more accurately regarded as a "chronospecies" or "palaeospecies" rather than a "terminator" "neospecies." The fact that forms like Steinheim and Ehringsdorf exhibit a progressive tendency towards sapiens implying a *loss* of *Pithecanthropus* or Neanderthal features, has persuaded Le Gros Clark that they are more correctly thought of as "early sapiens." Viewed in this light, *H. sapiens* does approximate to the concept of the chronospecies as elaborated (for example) by Neville George (George, 1956) who writes "The chronospecies is composed of transient populations each of which at its moment of time was a biospecies as geographically, ecologically and functionally variant as now-living biospecies. In its full expression, the chronospecies is an integrated phyletic succession of biospecies." Of the transients in *H. sapiens* we have not only modern races and varieties, prehistoric communities of late Pleistocene times, but also the Mount Carmel population which, taken along with Djebel Kafzeh and the Krapina group, point to a fairly wide ranging distribution of early emergent sapiens communities. Whether any of these at any one level collectively constitute a transient "biospecies" or subspecies seems of little moment. As Cain say, "the limits of both subspecies and species within a gens are equally arbitrary." Even though the earliest sapiens are represented by very few specimens, there is no taxonomic difficulty in describing *H. sapiens* as a chronospecies, with a space of some 100-200,000 years, polytypic both in time and space with subspeciation and race differentiation proceeding at all stages to greater or lesser degrees.

What of Neanderthal man? On the accepted view of classical Neanderthal man as a "terminator" within the plexiform lineage of *Homo*, a claim for phyletically specific status could be advanced on the following grounds: (a) Classical Neanderthal groups are sufficiently homogeneous as well as morphologically distinct from both early and late sapiens to qualify without doubt as a "morphospecies"; (b) but classical Neanderthal populations had a fairly wide range in time and space while maintaining their distinctiveness; their distinctiveness is, in fact, emphasized by their disappearance and replacement by sapiens man. The aggregation of Neanderthal populations has claim therefore at least to a "biospecies" status.

The question which remains is whether the Neanderthal has been developed as a "biospecies" by a relatively rapid process of speciation as a "side" branch of the *H. sapiens* chronospecies or whether it is really the product of a fairly long separate development from *Pithecanthropus* and approximates to a "chronospecies" itself.

Although most authorities, including Le Gros Clark, take the former view, it seems to me that this issue still remains open. Reasons have been given elsewhere (Weiner, 1957) why a separate line of development remains a possibility. It may well be, however, that as more finds come to light we shall have to admit an even closer morphological continuum between Neanderthal, Rhodesian, Steinheim, and Sapiens. Thus, the new Shanidar skull is pronouncedly Neanderthal, far more than Steinheim, yet it seems, like Rhodesian, to possess an occipital region of sapiens aspect. Thus it is quite likely that the distinctiveness which on either view is attributed to Neanderthal and Sapiens, may, in due course, seem unduly exaggerated if more intermediates come to light. In this case (Figure 4) the genus *Homo* would correspond to the chronospecies and Neanderthal and Sapiens would appear merely as distinctive subspecies, each with an array of local geographical races.

In summary, I believe we are on respectable taxonomic ground in specifying sapiens as a chronospecies of *Homo* and Neanderthal man as a distinctive biospecies within the plexiform phyletic lineage *Homo*.

Swanscombe Man

The Swanscombe remains consist only of the rear part of the brain case —the intact occipital bone and the left parietal, both discovered in 1935, and the right parietal discovered a few years ago. The dating methods which helped in the radical reassessment of Piltdown man, Galley Hill, and Kanam, have confirmed the antiquity of this, the oldest British hominid, as dating from the second interglacial. In geological terms, it is not very different in age from Steinheim man. Because of the incompleteness of the material, it is not possible to reach a firm verdict on the morphology of the skull. It is clear enough that the occipital and parietal are not to be attributed to the Neanderthal line, and that morphologically the material must be attributed to the *Homo sapiens* chronospecies as defined above. But in itself, Swanscombe cannot be used as primary evidence for the phylogeny of *Homo* as various authors have attempted to do. The ambiguity is such that it could be argued, as was the case with Kanam, that the whole skull was sapiens and that *H. sapiens* was in existence from an extremely early date. This would require a considerable alteration in our views on the phylogeny of man, but no such revision seems called for on the basis of the actual evidence, confined as it must

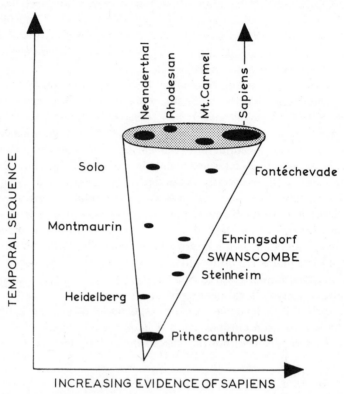

FIGURE 4. The phyletic lineage of "*Homo*" to show the probable place of Swanscombe man on present evidence.

be to the incomplete Swanscombe material. The fact is, that metrical analysis (Weiner and Campbell, to be published) shows that even in Steinheim, Skhul, and Tabun, the occipital and parietal fall very close to sapiens limits. In accordance with the principle adumbrated above and so well vindicated in the case of Piltdown or Kanam, Swanscombe does not demand or justify any departure from the scheme (Figure 4) based on the evidence as a whole, and this principle can be extended to the case of the Heidelberg jaw and Montmaurin jaw. Both of these can be attributed, without straining the evidence, to the *Pithecanthropus*-Neanderthal line of development.

SUMMARY

A brief survey is given of the progress, over the last 100 years, of our understanding of the phylogeny of the genus *Homo*. The simple evolutionary series Java man—Neanderthal man—Sapiens man, established first just 50 years ago, was in itself a powerful validation of Darwin's views on human evolution adumbrated when practically no fossil evidence was available. The accumulation of fossil material in relative abundance over the last 50 years has revealed the total inadequacy of this simple linear sequence; the analysis of the phylogeny of *Homo* has in fact been attended by many difficulties and inconsistencies. The main causes of these are considered. Emphasis is placed on the need to apply rigorously the principles of the "New Systematics" to the field of human palaeontology. Proposals are made for a method of dealing with apparently important specimens (e.g., Swanscombe or Kanam) which are at the same time of disputed morphology or chronology. On the basis of the phylogenetic principles discussed, it is claimed that at the present time a coherent and consistent scheme of the phylogeny of *Homo* can be put forward and the taxonomic status of the various species of *Homo* evaluated.

Note added by author:

The ideas sketched in this paper may perhaps be thought of as constituting a "spectrum" theory of the phylogenesis of *Homo*. According to this "spectrum" theory there would exist at any one time, in different areas, from the Steinheim-Swanscombe stage onwards, aggregates or groups of the genus *Homo*, some exhibiting tendencies towards the well-developed Neanderthal variety, others with strong tendencies towards *Homo sapiens* and others again the "intermediates," showing a mosaic of Neanderthal and sapiens features. These groups would tend to be relatively small-brained on the average in the early stages, large-brained in the later stages. In due course they would emerge in the last phases of the Pleistocene as "classical" Neanderthal, Rhodesian Man, Solo Man, and, eventually, the "modern" varieties of *Homo*, with only the latter surviving and spreading.

From the Steinheim-Swanscombe stage onwards one can therefore discern temporally, as well as spatially, a succession or spectrum of the various groupings that constitute the genus *Homo*.

Bibliography

Abel, O., 1927, *Lebenbilder aus der Tierwelt der Vorzeit* (Jena: Fischer).

—— 1931, *Die Stellung des Menschen im Rahmen der Wirbeltiere* (Jena: Fischer).

Adloff, P., 1932, "Das Gebiss von *Australopithecus africanus* Dart. Einige ergänzende Bemerkungen zum Eckzahnproblem," *Z. Anat. Entwickl. Gesch.* 97:145–156.

—— 1939, "Die südafrikanischen fossilen Menschenaffen und der Ursprung des menschlichen Gebisses," *Anthrop. Anz.* 16:72–76.

Allee, W. C., A. E. Emerson, O. Park, T. Park, and K. P. Schmidt, 1949, *Principles of animal ecology* (Philadelphia: Saunders).

Allison, A. C., 1954, "Notes on sickle cell polymorphism," *Ann. Hum. Genet.* 19:39–51.

Arambourg, C., 1950, "Traces possibles d'une industrie primitive dans un niveau villafranchien de l'Afrique du Nord," *Bull. Soc. préhist. franç.* 47:348–350.

—— 1955a, *La genèse de l'humanité* (4th ed.; Paris: Presses Universitaires de France).

—— 1955b, "A recent discovery in human paleontology. *Atlanthropus* of Ternifine (Algeria)," *Amer. J. Phys. Anthrop.* n.s. 13:191–201.

Asdell, S. A., 1946, *Patterns of mammalian reproduction* (Ithaca, N.Y.: Comstock).

Ashton, E. H., M. J. R. Healey, and S. Lipton, 1957, "The descriptive use of discriminant functions in physical anthropology," *Proc. Roy. Soc. (London)* B 146:552–572.

Balout, L., 1955, *Préhistoire de l'Afrique du Nord* (Paris: Arts et Métiers Graphiques).

Barbour, G. B., 1949a, "Ape or man," *Ohio J. Sci.* 49:129–145.

—— 1949b, in *The fourth yearbook of physical anthropology, 1948*, ed. G. W. Lasker and F. P. Thieme (New York: Viking Fund), pp. 22–39.

Barnes, A. S., 1939, "The differences between natural and human flaking on prehistoric flint implements," *Amer. Anthrop.* 41:99–112.

—— 1943, "High-angle edge flaking of flint," *Nature* 152:477.

Barth, F., 1950, "On the relationships of early primates," *Amer. J. Phys. Anthrop.* n.s. 8:139–149.

Bartholomew, G. A., Jr., 1952, "Reproductive and social behavior of the northern elephant seal," *Univ. Calif. Publ. Zool.* (Berkeley) 47:369–472.

Bartholomew, G. A., Jr., and J. B. Birdsell, 1953, "Ecology and the protohominids," *Amer. Anthrop.* 55:481–498.
Bartholomew, G. A., Jr., and H. C. Caswell, Jr., 1951, "Locomotion in kangaroo
rats and its adaptive significance," *J. Mammalogy* 32:155–169.
Bates, M., 1953, "Human ecology," in *Anthropology today: an encyclopedic
inventory*, ed. A. Kroeber (Chicago: Univ. of Chicago Press), pp. 700–
713.
Beer, G. de, 1954, "Archaeopteryx and evolution," *Advanc. Sci.*, no. 42,
pp. 1–11.
Bennejeant, M. C., 1936, *Anomalies et variations dentaires chez les primates*
(Paris: Vallier).
Benninghoff, A., 1925, "Spaltlinien am Knochen, eine Methode zur Ermittlung
der Architektur platter Knochen," *Verh. anat. Ges. (Jena)* 34:189–206.
Suppl. to *Anat. Anz.* 60.
Berg, L. S., 1926, *Nomogenesis or evolution determined by law* (London:
Oxford Univ. Press).
——— 1940, "Classification of fishes, both recent and fossil," *Trav. Inst. zool.
Acad. Sci. URSS*, vol. 5, pt. 2.
Birch, L. C., 1955, "Selection in *Drosophila pseudoobscura* in relation to
crowding," *Evolution* 9:389–399.
Black, D., P. Teilhard de Chardin, C. C. Young, and W. C. Pei, 1933, "Fossil
man in China: the Choukoutien cave deposits with a synopsis of our
present knowledge of the late Cenezoic in China," *Mem. Geol. Surv.
China A*, no. 11.
Black, G. V., 1902, *Descriptive anatomy of the human teeth* (4th ed.;
Philadelphia: White).
Blochwelder, R. E., and L. E. Hoyme, 1955, "Statistics, experiment and the
future of biology," *Sci. Monthly* 80:225–229.
Blumenbach, J. F., 1775, "Versuch natürlicher Ordnungen der Säugthiere,"
Göttingische Anz. gelehrten Sachen Aussicht kön. Ges. Wiss. 2:1257–1259.
——— 1779, 1791, *Handbuch der Naturgeschichte* (1st and 4th eds.;
Göttingen: Dieterich).
——— 1808, *De l'unité du genre humain et de ses variétés* (tr. from Latin in
3rd ed.; Paris: Allut).
Bluntschli, H., 1913, "Die fossilen Affen Patagoniens und der Ursprung der
platyrrhinen Affen," *Anat. Anz.* 44:33–43.
Bodenheimer, F. S., 1938, *Problems of animal ecology* (London: Oxford
Univ. Press).
Bohlin, B., 1946, "The fossil mammals from the Tertiary of Tabun-buluk,"
Rep. Sino-Swed. Sci. Exped. N.W. Prov. China 6, no. 4.
——— 1951, "Some mammalian remains from Shih-ehr-ma-ch'eng, Hui-
hui-p'u area, western Kansu," *Rep. Sino-Swed. Sci. Exped. N.W. Prov.
China 6*, no. 5.
Böker, H., 1935, *Einführung in die vergleichende biologische Anatomie der
Wirbeltiere* (Jena: Fischer).
Bolk, L., 1913, "Über die Obliteration der Nähte am Affenschädel, zugleich ein
Beitrag zur Kenntnis der Nahtanomalien," *Z. Morph. Anthrop.* 15:1–206.
——— 1926, *Das Problem der Menschwerdung* (Jena: Fischer).
Boule, M., 1911–1913, "L'homme fossile de la Chapelle-aux-Saints," *Ann.
Paléont.* 6:109–172; 7:85–192; 8:1–67.
——— 1921, 1946, 1952, *Les hommes fossiles* (Paris: Masson).

Boyden, A. A., 1953, "Fifty years of systematic serology," *Syst. Zool.* 2:19–30.

Brain, C. K., C. van Riet-Lowe, and R. A. Dart, 1955, "Kafuan artifacts in the post-australopithecine breccia at Makapan," *Nature 175*:16.

Breitinger, E., 1952, "Zur Morphologie und systematische Stellung des Schädelfragments von Swanscombe," *Homo* 3:131–133.

———— 1955, "Das Schädelfragment von Swanscombe und das 'Praesapiens-problem,' " *Mitt. anthrop. Ges. Wien 84–85*:1–45.

———— 1957, "Zur phyletischen Evolution von *Homo sapiens*," *Anthrop. Anz.* 21:62–83.

Breuil, H., 1948, "Ancient raised beaches and prehistoric civilisations in South Africa," *S. Afri. J. Sci. 44*:61–74.

Bronowski, J., and W. M. Long, 1951, "Statistical methods in anthropology," *Nature 168*:794–795.

———— 1952, "Statistics of discrimination in anthropology," *Amer. J. Phys. Anthrop.* n.s. *10*:385–394.

Broom, R., 1949, "Discoveries from South Africa," *Lond. Ill. News,* Sept. 10, p. 378.

———— 1950a, *Finding the missing link* (London: Watts).

———— 1950b, "The genera and species of the South African fossil ape-man," *Amer. J. Phys. Anthrop.* n.s. *8*:1–13.

Broom, R., and J. T. Robinson, 1949, "A new mandible of the ape-man *Plesianthropus transvaalensis*," *Amer. J. Phys. Anthrop.* n.s. *7*:123–127.

———— 1950, *Further evidence of the structure of the Sterkfontein ape-man* Plesianthropus, Transvaal Museum Memoir 4 (Pretoria).

———— 1952, *The Swartkrans ape-man,* Paranthropus crassidens, Transvaal Museum Memoir 6 (Pretoria).

Broom, R., and G. W. H. Schepers, 1946, *The South African fossil ape-men: the Australopithecinae,* Transvaal Museum Memoir 2 (Pretoria).

Burkitt, M. C., 1956, "Some early prehistoric cultures south of the Sahara," *Scientia 91*:304–308.

Burt, W. H., 1943, "Territoriality and home range concepts as applied to mammals," *J. Mammalogy 24*:346–352.

———— 1949, "Territoriality," *J. Mammalogy 30*:25–27.

Buxton, L. H. D., 1938, "Platymeria and platycnemia," *J. Anat. (London)* 73:31–36.

Buxton, L. H. D., and G. M. Morant, 1933, "The essential craniological technique," *J. Roy. Anthrop. Inst. Gt. Brit. Ireland 63*:19–47.

Cain, A. J., 1954, *Animal species and their evolution* (London: Hutchinson Univ. Library).

Calhoun, J. B., 1952, "The social aspects of population dynamics," *J. Mammalogy 33*:139–159).

Camp, C. L., 1949, in *The fourth yearbook of physical anthropology, 1948,* ed. G. W. Lasker and F. P. Thieme (New York: Viking Fund), pp. 22–39.

Campbell, T. D., 1925, *Dentition and palate of the Australian aboriginal* (Adelaide: Hassell).

Carpenter, C. R., 1934, *A field study of the behavior and social relations of howling monkeys,* Comparative Psychology Monographs 10 (Baltimore: Johns Hopkins Press), pp. 1–168.

———— 1940, *A field study of the behavior and social relations of the gibbon,* Comparative Psychology Monographs 16 (Baltimore: Johns Hopkins Press), pp. 1–212.

———— 1941, "The menstrual cycle and body temperature in two gibbons (*Hylobates lar*)," *Anat. Rec.* 79:291–296.

———— 1942, "Societies of monkeys and apes," *Biol. Symp.* 8:177–204.

Carter, G. S., 1951, *Animal evolution* (London: Sidgwick and Jackson).

Castetter, E. F., and W. H. Bell, 1942, *Pima and Papago Indian agriculture,* Inter-American Studies 1 (Albuquerque: Univ. of New Mexico Press).

Clark, J. D., 1958, "The natural fracture of pebbles from the Batoka Gorge, and its bearing on the Kafuan industries of Africa," *Proc. Prehist. Soc.* n.s. 24:64–77.

Colbert, E. H., 1949, "Some paleontological principles significant in human evolution," in *Early man in the Far East. Studies in Physical Anthropology,* ed. W. W. Howells (Philadelphia: American Association of Physical Anthropologists), I, 103–147.

Cole, La Mont C., 1951, "Population cycles and random oscillations," *J. Wildlife Management* 15:233–252.

Collias, N. E., 1944, "Aggressive behavior among vertebrate animals," *Physiol. Zool.* 17:83–123.

Collias, N. E., and C. Southwick, 1952, "A field study of population density and social organization in howling monkeys," *Proc. Amer. Phil. Soc.* 96: 143–156.

Coon, C. S., 1939, *The races of Europe* (New York: Macmillan).

Coon, C. S., S. M. Garn, and J. B. Birdsell, 1950, *Races* (Springfield, Ill., Thomas).

Cope, E. D., 1882, "An anthropomorphous lemur," *Amer. Naturalist* 16:73–74.

———— 1885, "The Lemuroidea and the Insectivora of the Eocene period of North America," *Amer. Naturalist* 19:457–471.

———— 1896, *The primary factors of organic evolution* (Chicago: Open Court).

Crawford, O. G. S., 1921, *Man and his past* (London: Oxford Univ. Press).

Cummins, H., 1946, "Dermatoglyphics of the gorilla," *Amer. J. Phys. Anthrop.* n.s. 4:262–263; abstract.

Cuvier, G., 1805, *Leçons d'anatomie comparée* (Paris: Baudouin).

Dahlberg, A., 1949, "The dentition of the American Indian," in *Physical anthropology of the American Indian,* ed. W. S. Laughlin (New York: Viking Fund), pp. 138–176.

Dambski, J., 1957, "Wspolczesne poglady na jednosc rodzaju ludzkiego" (Vues actuelles sur l'unite de l'espèce humaine), *Przegląd antropologiczny* 23:160–181.

Darling, F. F., 1937, *A herd of red deer* (London: Oxford Univ. Press).

———— 1938, *Bird flocks and the breeding cycle* (Cambridge, Eng.: Cambridge Univ. Press).

Dart, R. A., 1925, "*Australopithecus africanus:* the man-ape of South Africa," *Nature* 115:195–199.

———— 1948a, "The Makapansgat proto-human *Australopithecus prometheus,*" *Amer. J. Phys. Anthrop.* n.s. 6:259–284.

———— 1948b, "A (?) promethean *Australopithecus* from Makapansgat Valley," *Nature* 162:375–376.

———— 1949a, "The first pelvic bones of *Australopithecus prometheus,*" *Amer. J. Phys. Anthrop.* n.s. 7:255–257.

———— 1949b, "The predatory implemental technique of *Australopithecus,*" *Amer. J. Phys. Anthrop.* n.s. 7:1–38.

———— 1949c, in *The fourth yearbook of physical anthropology, 1948*, ed. G. W. Lasker and F. P. Thieme (New York: Viking Fund), pp. 22–39.

———— 1957a, *The osteodontokeratic culture of* Australopithecus prometheus, Transvaal Museum Memoir 10 (Pretoria).

———— 1957b, "The Makapansgat australopithecine osteodontokeratic culture," *Proc. Third Pan-Afr. Congr. on Prehistory,* Livingstone, 1955, pp. 161–171.

———— 1958, "Bone tools and porcupine gnawing," *Amer. Anthrop.* 60:715–724.

———— 1960, "The bone tool manufacturing ability of *Australopithecus prometheus,*" *Amer. Anthrop.* 62:134–143.

Darwin, C., 1859, *On the origin of species by means of natural selection or the preservation of favored races in the struggle for life* (London: Murray).

———— 1871, *The descent of man and selection in relation to sex* (London: Murray).

Deevey, E. S., Jr., 1951, "Recent textbooks of human ecology," *Ecology* 32:347–351.

Descartes, R., 1637, *Discours de la méthode* (Leyden: Maire).

Dietz, V. H., 1944, "A common dental morphotropic factor, the Carabelli cusp," *J. Amer. Dent. Assoc.* 31:784–789.

Dingler, H., 1941, *Von der Tierseele zur Menschenseele* (Leipzig: Heling).

Dobzhansky, T., 1937, 1951, *Genetics and the origin of species* (1st and 3rd eds.; New York: Columbia Univ. Press).

———— 1944, "On species and races of living and fossil man," *Amer. J. Phys. Anthrop.* n.s. 2:251–265.

———— 1947, "Adaptive changes induced by natural selection in wild populations of *Drosophila,*" *Evolution* 1:1–16.

———— 1949, "Observations and experiments on natural selection in *Drosophila,*" in *Proc. Int. Congr. Genet.,* 8th Congr., Stockholm, ed. G. Bonniers and R. Larsson (Lund: Berlingska Boktryckeri), pp. 210–224.

———— 1950, "Evolution in the tropics," *Amer. Scientist* 38:209–221.

———— 1954, "Evolution as a creative process," in *Proc. Int. Congr. Genet.,* 9th Congr., Como, ed. G. Montalenti and A. Chiarugi, 1:435–439. Suppl. to *Carylogia 6.*

———— 1955, *Evolution, genetics and man* (New York: Wiley).

———— 1956, *The biological basis of human freedom* (New York: Columbia Univ. Press).

———— 1957, "Genetic loads in natural populations," *Science* 126:191–194.

———— 1958, "Genetics of natural populations. XXVII. The genetic changes in populations of *Drosophila pseudoobscura* in the American Southwest," *Evolution* 12:385–401.

Dobzhansky, T., and G. Allen, 1956, "Does natural selection continue to operate in modern mankind?" *Amer. Anthrop.* 58:591–604.

Drennan, M. R., 1931, "Pedomorphism in the pre-Bushman skull," *Amer. J. Phys. Anthrop.* 16:203–210.

Duckworth, W. L. H., 1904, "Variations in the crania of *Gorilla savagei,*" in *Studies from the Anthropological Laboratory, the Anatomy School, Cambridge* (Cambridge, Eng.: Cambridge Univ. Press), pp. 41–50.

Edinger, Tilly, 1948, "Evolution of the horse brain," *Geol. Soc. Amer. Mem.* 25:1–177.

Ehrenberg, K., 1938, "*Austriacopithecus*, ein neuer menschenaffenartiger Primate aus dem Miozän von Klein Hadersleben bei Poysdorf in Niederösterreich (Nieder-Donau)," *S.-B. Akad. Wiss. Wien, math. nat. Kl.*, Abt. I, *147*:71–110.

Eickstedt, E. von, 1959, "Stammesgeschichte des Seelischen," in *Die Evolution der Organismen*, ed. G. Heberer (2nd ed.; Stuttgart: Fischer), pp. 1192–1242.

Elftman, H., and J. Manter, 1935a, "Chimpanzee and human feet in bipedal-walking," *Amer. J. Phys. Anthrop. 20*:69–79.

———— 1935b, "The evolution of the human foot, with especial reference to the joints," *J. Anat.* (London) *70*:56–67.

Errington, P. A., 1946, "Predation and vertebrate populations," *Quart. Rev. Biol. 21*:144–177, 221–245.

Evans-Pritchard, E. E., 1940, *The Nuer: a description of the modes of livelihood and political institutions of a Nilotic people* (London: Oxford Univ. Press).

Ferembach, D., 1953, "Affinités et mode de vie de *Limnopithecus macinnesi* Le Gros Clark and Leakey," *C.R. Acad. Sci.* (*Paris*) *236*.

Fiedler, W., 1956, *Übersicht über das System der Primaten. Primatologia*, ed. H. Hofer, A. H. Schultz, and D. Starck (Basel: Karger), I, 1–266.

Fischer, E., 1936, "Die gesunden körperliche Erbanlagen," in E. Baur, E. Fischer, and F. Lenz, *Menschliche Erblehre und Rassenhygiene* (4th ed.; Munich: Lehmann), vol. I.

Fisher, Edna M., 1939, "Habits of the southern sea otter," *J. Mammalogy 20*:21–36.

Fisher, R. A., 1930, *The genetical theory of natural selection* (Oxford: Oxford Univ. Press).

———— 1948, *Statistical methods for research workers* (10th ed.; Edinburgh: Oliver & Boyd).

Ford, E. B., 1937, "Problems of heredity in Lepidoptera," *Biol. Rev. Cambridge Phil. Soc. 12*:461–503.

———— 1938, "The genetic basis of adaptation," in *Evolution*, ed. G. R. de Beer (London: Oxford Univ. Press), pp. 43–55.

Forsyth Major, C. J., 1881, "Beiträge zur Geschichte der fossilen Pferde, inbesonders Italiens," *Schweiz. Pal. Ges. Abh. 7*:1–153.

Gates, R. R., 1948, *Human ancestry from a genetical point of view* (Cambridge, Mass.: Harvard Univ. Press).

Gehlen, A., 1950, *Der Mensch. Seine Natur und seine Stellung in der Welt* (4th ed.; Bonn: Athenäeum).

George T. N., 1956, "Biospecies, chronospecies and morphospecies," in *The species concept in palaeontology*, ed. P. C. Sylvester-Bradley (London: Systematics Assoc.), publ. no. 2, pp. 122–137.

Gieseler, W., 1955, "Zur Herkunft des *Homo sapiens*," *Aus. der Heimat 63*:166–175.

———— 1957, "Die Fossilgeschichte des Menschen," in *Die Evolution der Organismen*, ed. G. Heberer (2nd ed.; Stuttgart: Fischer), pp. 951–1109.

Glaesmer, E., 1910, "Die Beugemuskeln am Unterschenkel und Fuss bei den Marsupialia, Insectivora, Edentata, Prosimiae und Simiae," *Morph. Jb.* (Leipzig) *41*:149–336.

Gregory, W. K., 1916, "Studies on the evolution of the primates," *Bull. Amer. Mus. Nat. Hist. 35*:239–355.

———— 1920, "On the structure and relations of *Notharctus,* an American Eocene primate. Studies on the evolution of the primates, part III," *Mem. Amer. Mus. Nat. Hist.* 37:841–859.

———— 1922, *The origin and evolution of the human dentition* (Baltimore: Williams & Wilkins).

———— 1927a, "How near is the relationship of man to the chimpanzee-gorilla stock?" *Quart. Rev. Biol.* 2:549–560.

———— 1927b, "The origin of man from the anthropoid stem—when and where?" *Proc. Amer. Phil. Soc.* 66:439–463.

———— 1928, "Were the ancestors of man primitive brachiators?" *Proc. Amer. Phil. Soc.* 67:129–150.

———— 1934a, "A half century of trituberculy, the Cope-Osborn theory of dental evolution," *Proc. Amer. Phil. Soc.* 73:169–317.

———— 1934b, *Man's place among the anthropoids* (Oxford: Clarendon Press).

———— 1939a, "Fossil man-apes of South Africa," *Nature* 143:25–26.

———— 1939b, "The South African man-apes and the origin of the human dentition," *J. Amer. Dent. Assoc.* 26:558–564.

———— 1949, "The bearing of Australopithecinae upon the problem of man's place in nature," *Amer. J. Phys. Anthrop.* n.s. 7:485–512.

———— 1951, *Evolution emerging. A survey of changing patterns from primeval life to man,* 2 vols. (New York: Macmillan).

Gregory, W. K., and M. Hellman, 1923, "Notes on the type of *Hesperopithecus haroldcookii,*" *Am. Mus. Novitates,* no. 53.

———— 1926, "The dentition of *Dryopithecus* and the origin of man," *Anthrop. Papers Amer. Mus. Nat. Hist.* 28:1–123.

———— 1939, "The dentition of the extinct South African man-ape *Australopithecus (Plesianthropus) transvaalensis* Broom. A comparative and phylogenetic study," *Ann. Transvaal Mus.* 19:339–373.

Gregory, W. K., M. Hellman, and G. E. Lewis, 1937, "Fossil anthropoids of the Yale-Cambridge India Expedition of 1935," *Carnegie Inst. Wash. Publ.* 495:1–27.

Gusinde, M., 1948, *Urwaldmenschen am Ituri: Anthropo-biologische Forschungsergebnisse bei Pygmäen und Negern im östlichen Belgisch-Kongo aus den Jahren 1934/35.* (Vienna: Springer).

———— 1949, *Die Twa-Pygmäen in Ruanda. Forschungsergebnisse im tropischen Afrika aus dem Jahre 1934* (Vienna-Mölding: Missionsdruckerei St. Gabriel).

Haeckel, E., 1866, *Generelle Morphologie* (Berlin: Reiner).

———— 1896a, *The evolution of man,* 2 vols. (New York: Appleton).

———— 1896b, *Systematische Phylogenie. III. Systematische Phylogenie der Wirbeltiere* (Berlin: Reiner).

———— 1898, *The last link* (London: Black).

Haldane, J. B. S., 1956, "Can a species concept be justified?" in *The species concept in palaeontology,* ed. P. C. Sylvester-Bradley (London: Systematics Assoc.), publ. no. 2, pp. 95–96.

Hatt, R. T., 1932, "The vertebral columns of ricochetal rodents," *Bull. Amer. Mus. Nat. Hist.* 63:599–738.

Haug, H., 1958, *Quantitative Untersuchungen an der Sehrinde* (Stuttgart: Thieme).

Haxton, H. A., 1947, "Muscles of the pelvic limb. A study of the differences between bipeds and quadrapeds," *Anat. Rec.* 98:337–346.

Heberer, G., 1950a, "Haeckel und die sog. 'Affenabstammung' des Menschen," *Naturw. Rundschau* 3:13–20.

───── 1950b, "Das Präsapiens-Problem," in *Die moderne Biologie,* Festschrift für Hans Nachtsheim, ed. H. Grüneberg and W. Ulrich (Berlin: F. Peters), pp. 131–162.

───── 1951a, "Grundlinien der pleistozänen Entfaltungsgeschichte der Euhomininen," *Quartär* 5:50–78.

───── 1951b, "Der phylogenetische Ort des Menschen," *Studium Generale* 4:1–14.

───── 1952a, "Fortschritte in der Erforschung der Phylogenie der Hominoidea," *Ergebn. Anat. Entwickl.-Gesch.* 34:499–637.

───── 1952b, "*Oreopithecus bambolii* Gervais und die Frage der Herkunft der Cercopithecoidea," *Z. Morph. Anthrop.* 46:1–107.

───── 1955a, "Die geographische Verbreitung der fossilen Hominiden (ausser Eusapiens) nach neuerer Gruppierung," *Naturw.* 42:85–90.

───── 1955b, "Wandlungen in der Lehre von der Abstammung des Menschen während der letzten 50 Jahre," *Kosmos (Swed.)* 51:304–308.

───── 1955c, "Fortschritte in unserer gegenwärtigen Kenntnis der Herkunftsgeschichte des Menschen," *Naturw. Rundschau* 8:373–379.

───── 1956, *Die Fossilgeschichte der Hominoidea. Primatologia,* ed. H. Hofer, A. H. Schultz, and D. Starck (Basel, S. Karger), I, 379–560.

───── 1958a, "Lebten in Südchina 'Riesenaffenmenschen?' " *Kosmos (Swed.)* 54:283–285.

───── 1958b, "Das Tier-Mensch-Übergangsfeld," *Studium Generale* 11:341–352.

───── 1958c, "Zum Problem der additiven Typogenese," in *Systematics Today,* Uppsala Univ. Årsskr. 6, pp. 40–47.

───── 1960, "*Zinjanthropus boisei* und der Status der Prähomininen (Australopithecinae)," *Zool. Jb. Syst.* 88:91–106.

Hellman, M., 1918, "Observations on the form of the dental arch of the orangs," *Int. J. Orthodont.* 4:1–15.

───── 1928, "Racial characters in human dentition," *Proc. Amer. Phil. Soc.* 67:157–174.

Hill, W. C. O., 1957, *Primates II. Haplorhini: Tarsioidea* (Edinburgh: University Press).

Hofstadter, R., 1955, *Social Darwinism in American thought* (Boston: Beacon).

Hooijer, D. A., 1951, "Questions relating to a new large anthropoid ape from the Mio-Pliocene of the Siwaliks," *Amer. J. Phys. Anthrop.* n.s. 9:79–94.

───── 1957, "The correlation of fossil mammalian faunas and the Plio-Pleistocene boundary in Java," *Proc. kon. ned. Akad. Wet. B,* 60:1–10.

Hooten, E. A., 1931, 1946, *Up from the ape* (1st and rev. eds.; New York: Macmillan).

Hopwood, A. T., 1933a, "Miocene primates from British East Africa," *Ann. Mag. Nat. Hist.* 11:96–99.

───── 1933b, "Miocene primates from Kenya," *J. Linn. Soc. London, Zool.* 38:437–464.

Howell, F. C., 1951, "The place of Neanderthal man in human evolution," *Amer. J. Phys. Anthrop.* n.s. 9:379–416.

───── 1952, "Pleistocene glacial ecology and the evolution of 'classic Neandertal' Man," *Southwestern J. of Anthrop.* 8:377–410.

───── 1955, "The age of the australopithecines of southern Africa," *Amer. J. Phys. Anthrop.* n.s. 13:635–662.

———— 1960, "European and Northwest African Middle Pleistocene hominids," *Curr. Anthrop. 1*:175–232.

Hrdlička, A., 1927, "The neanderthal phase of man," *J. Roy. Anthrop. Inst. Gt. Brit. Ireland 57*:249–274.

———— 1930, "The skeletal remains of early man," *Smithsonian Misc. Colls.*, no. 83.

———— 1935, "The Yale fossils of anthropoid apes," *Amer. J. Sci. 29*:34–40.

Hubrecht, A. A. W., 1897, *The descent of the primates* (New York: Scribners).

———— 1902, "Furchung und Keimblattung bei *Tarsius* spectrum," *Verh. kon. Akad. Wet. 8*:1–96.

Hürzeler, J., 1947, "*Alsaticopithecus leemanni* nov. gen. spec., ein neuer Primate aus dem unteren Lutetien von Buchsweiler im Unterelsass," *Ecl. Geol. Hel. 40*:343–356.

———— 1948, "Zur Stammesgeschichte der Necrolemuriden," *Schweiz. pal. Ges. Abh. 66*, no. 3.

———— 1949a, "Neubeschreibung von *Oreopithecus bambolii* Gervais," *Schweiz. pal. Ges. Abh. 66*, no. 5.

———— 1949b, "Uber die europäischen Apatemyiden," *Verh. Schweiz. Naturf. Ges. 129*:140–141.

———— 1954, "Zur systematischen Stellung von Oreopithecus," *Verh. Naturf. Ges. (Basel) 65*:88–95.

———— 1958, "*Oreopithecus bambolii* Gervais. A preliminary report," *Verh. Naturf. Ges. (Basel) 69*:1–48.

Huxley, J. S., 1942, *Evolution, the modern synthesis* (New York: Harper).

Huxley, T. H., 1860, "Darwin on the origin of species," *Westminster Rev. 73*:541–570.

———— 1863, *Evidence as to man's place in nature* (London: Williams & Norgate).

———— 1864, "Further remarks upon the human remains from the Neanderthal," *Nat. Hist. Rev. 4*:429–446.

———— 1876, *Lectures on evolution* (reprinted 1931; New York: Thinker's Library).

———— 1906, *Man's place in nature* (London: Everyman's Library).

Illiger, J. K. W., 1811, *Prodomus systematis mammalium et avium* (Berlin: Salfeld).

Jakimov, V. P., 1954, "Problema sootnocheniia iskopaemik lioudeï sovremennogo i neandertal'skogo tipov," *Sovietskaia Etnografiia 3*:57–62.

Jepsen, G. L., 1934, "A revision of the American Apatemyidae and the description of a new genus, *Sinclairella*, from the White River Oligocene of South Dakota," *Proc. Amer. Phil. Soc. 74*:287–305.

———— 1949, "Selection, orthogenesis and the fossil record," *Proc. Amer. Phil. Soc. 93*:479–500.

Jepson, G. L., G. G. Simpson, and E. Mayr (eds.), 1949, *Genetics, paleontology and evolution* (Princeton: Princeton Univ. Press).

Jonge-Cohen, E. de, 1932, "Maximal-, Minimal- und Mittelwerte der mesiodistalen Dimensionen der postkaninen Zähne des menschlichen Gebisses," *Z. Anat. Entwickl. Gesch. 99*:324–337.

Jones, F. Wood, 1918, *The problem of man's ancestry* (London: Soc. for Promoting Christian Knowledge).

———— 1920, *Principles of anatomy as seen in the hand* (London: Churchill)

———— 1923, *The ancestry of man* (Brisbane: Gillies).

—— 1929a, "The distinctions of the human hallux," *J. Anat. (London)* 63:408–411.

—— 1929b, *Man's place among the mammals* (New York: Longmans Green).

—— 1944, *Structure and function as seen in the foot* (London: Ballière, Tindall & Cox).

—— 1948, *Hallmarks of mankind* (Baltimore: Williams and Wilkins).

Joysey, K. A., 1956, "The nomenclature and comparison of fossil communities," in *The species concept in palaeontology*, ed. P. C. Sylvester-Bradley (London: Systematics Assoc.), publ. no. 2, pp. 83–94.

Kälin, J., 1949, "Zum Vergleich von Menschenfuss und Anthropoidenfuss insbesondere vom Berggorilla (*Gorilla beringei* Matschie)," *C.R. 13ᵉ Congr. Internat. Zool. (Paris)*, pp. 331–333.

—— 1952, "Die ältesten Menschenreste und ihre Stammesgeschichtliche Deutung," in *Historia Mundi*, ed. F. Kern (Berne: Franke), I, 33–98.

—— 1955, "Zur Systematik und evolutiven Deutung der höheren Primaten," *Experientia* 11:1–17.

Kaplan, B. A., 1948, "The fourth summer seminar in physical anthropology," in *The fourth yearbook of physical anthropology, 1948*, ed. G. W. Lasker and F. P. Thieme (New York: Viking Fund), pp. 22–39.

Keith, A., 1891, "Anatomical notes on Malay apes," *J. Straits Branch Roy. Asiat. Soc.* 23:77–94.

—— 1923, "Man's posture: its evolution and disorders," *Brit. Med. J.* 1:451–454, 499–502, 545–548, 587–590, 624–626, 669–672.

—— 1925, *The antiquity of man* (2nd ed.; London: Williams & Norgate).

—— 1934, *The construction of man's family tree* (London: Watts).

—— 1940, "Fifty years ago," *Amer. J. Phys. Anthrop.* 26:251–267.

—— 1948, *A new theory of human evolution* (London: Watts).

Kennedy, K. A. R., 1960, "The phylogenetic tree: an analysis of its development in studies of human evolution," *Kroeber Anthrop. Soc.* 23:7–53.

Kermack, K. A., 1956, "Species and mutations," in *The species concept in palaeontology*, ed. P. C. Sylvester-Bradley (London: Systematics Assoc.), publ. no. 2, pp. 101–103.

Kern, H. M., and W. L. Straus, 1949, "The femur of *Plesianthropus transvaalensis*," *Amer. J. Phys. Anthropol.* n.s. 7:53–77.

Kettlewell, H. B. D., 1956, "Further selection experiments on industrial melanism in *Lepidoptera*," *Heredity* 10:287–301.

King, W., 1864, "The reputed fossil man of the Neanderthal," *Quart. J. Sci.* 1:88–97.

Klaatsch, H., 1910, "Die Aurignac-Rasse und ihre Stellung im Stammbaum der Menschheit," *Z. Ethnol.* 42:513–577.

—— 1923, *The evolution and progress of mankind*, Eng. trans. (New York: Stokes).

Klaatsch, H., and O. Hauser, 1910, "*Homo aurignacensis* Hauseri, ein paläontologischer Skelettfund aus dem ersteren Aurignacien der Station Combe-Capelle, bei Montferrand, Périgord," *Prähist. Z.* 1:273–388.

Kleiweg de Zwaan, J. P., 1940, "Introduction, in Anthropologische Bibliographie van den Indischen Archipel en van Nederlansch West-Indië," suppl., by A. J. van Bork-Feltkamp, *Mededeel. Afdeel. Volkenkunde Kol. Inst.*, extra ser. no. 3 (Leiden: Britt).

Knauer, S., 1916, "Ursachen und Folgen des aufrechten Ganges des Menschen," *Anat. Hefte*, Abt. 2, Ergebn., 22:1–155.

Koenigswald, G. H. R. von, 1948, "Remarks on the lower canine of *Plesianthropus transvaalensis* Broom," in *Robert Broom Commemorative Volume* (Cape Town: Royal Society of South Africa), spec. publ. 159.

―――― 1950, "Fossil hominids from the Lower Pleistocene of Java," *Rep. 18th Int. Geol. Congr., 1948*, pt. 9, pp. 59–61.

―――― 1955a, *Begegnungen mit dem Vormenschen* (Jena: Diederichs).

―――― 1955b, "Remarks on *Oreopithecus,*" *Riv. Sci. preist. 10*:1–3.

―――― 1957a, "Bemerkungen zum Gebiss der Australopithecinen," *Anthrop. Anz. 21*:54–61.

―――― 1957b, "Remarks on *Gigantopithecus* and other hominoid remains from Southern China," *Proc. Kon. Ned. Akad. Wet. B 60*:53–159.

Kraft, G., 1948, *Der Urmensch als Schöpfer* (Tübingen: Matthiesen).

Krogh, C. von, 1959, "Die Stellung des Menschen im Rahmen der Primaten," in *Die Evolution der Organismen,* ed. G. Heberer (2nd ed.; Stuttgart: Fischer), pp. 917–920.

Krzywicki, L., 1934, *Primitive society and its vital statistics* (London: Macmillan).

Kurtén, B., 1959a, "The age of the Australopithecinae," *Stockholm Contrib. Geol. 4*:9–22.

―――― 1959b, "New evidence on the age of Peking man," *Vertebrata Palasiatica 3*:173–175.

Kurth, G., 1957, "*Oreopithecus bambolii,* ein Hominide von der Wende Miozän/Pliozän," *Naturw. Rundschau 9*:57–61.

―――― 1958, "Neue Befunde zu *Oreopithecus bambolii* Gervais," *Naturw. Rundschau 11*:420–426.

Lack, D., 1945, "The Galapagos finches (Geospizinae), a study in variation," *Occas. Papers Calif. Acad. Sci. 21*:1–151.

Lamarck, J. B. de, 1809, 1869, *Philosophie zoologique* (Paris).

Leakey, L. S. B., 1945, "A Miocene anthropoid mandible from Rusinga, Kenya," *Nature 152*:319–320.

―――― 1951, *Olduvai Gorge* (Cambridge, Eng.: Cambridge Univ. Press).

―――― 1959, "A new fossil skull from Olduvai," *Nature 184*:491–493.

Le Double, A. F., 1903, *Traité des variations des os du crâne de l'homme* (Paris: Vigot).

―――― 1906, *Traité des variations des os de la face de l'homme* (Paris: Vigot).

Le Gros Clark, W. E., 1934, *Early forerunners of man* (London: Ballière, Tindall & Cox).

―――― 1936, "The problem of the claw in primates," *Proc. Zool. Soc. London 1936*, pp. 1–24.

―――― 1947a, "The importance of the fossil Australopithecinae in the study of human evolution," *Sci. Prog. 35*:377–395.

―――― 1947b, "Observations on the anatomy of the fossil Australopithecinae," *J. Anat. (London) 81*:300–334.

―――― 1948a, "African fossil primates discovered during 1947," *Nature 161*:667–669.

―――― 1948b, report of paper, "Miocene finds in East Africa," in *The third yearbook of physical anthropology, 1947,* ed. G. W. Lasker and J. L. Angel (New York: Viking Fund), pp. 18–20.

―――― 1948c, report of paper, *Abstr. Proc. Geol. Soc. London,* no. 1445, p. 9–10.

―――― 1949a, 1954a, *History of the primates* (4th ed.; Brit. Mus. Nat. Hist.).

—— 1949b, "New palaeontological evidence bearing on the evolution of the Hominoidea," *Quart. J. Geol. Soc. Lond.* 105:225–264.

—— 1950, "Hominid characters of the Australopithecine dentition," *J. Roy. Anthrop. Inst.* 80:37–54.

—— 1954b, "The antiquity of *Homo sapiens* in particular and of the Hominidae in general," *Sci. Prog.* 42:377–395.

—— 1955, *The fossil evidence for human evolution* (Chicago: Univ. of Chicago Press).

—— 1958, "Bones of contention," *J. Roy. Anthrop. Inst.* 88:131–145.

Le Gros Clark, W. E., and D. P. Thomas, 1951, "Associated jaws and limb bones of *Limnopithecus macinnesi*," *Fossil mammals of Africa* (London: Brit. Mus. Nat. Hist.), no. 3.

Lerner, I. M., 1954, *Genetic homeostasis* (New York: Wiley).

Lewis, G. E., 1934, "Preliminary notice of new man-like apes from India," *J. Amer. Sci.* 27:161–179.

Linnaeus, C., 1758, 1759, *Systema naturae per regna tria naturae* (10th ed.; Stockholm: Laurentius Salvius), vol. I.

Loth, E., 1931, *Anthropologie des parties molles* (Paris: Masson).

Lowe, C. van Riet, 1952, "The Pleistocene geology and prehistory of Uganda, part II," *Geol. Surv. Uganda Mem.*, no. 6.

Ludwig, W., 1954, "Die Selektionstheorie," in *Die Evolution der Organismen*, ed. G. Heberer (2nd ed.; Stuttgart: Fischer), pp. 662–712.

Luria, S. E., and M. Delbruck, 1943, "Mutations of bacteria from virus sensitivity to virus resistance," *Genetics* 28:491–511.

MacCurdy, G. G., 1924, *Human origins. A manual of prehistory*, 2 vols. (New York: Appleton).

McGregor, J. H., 1938, "Human origins and early man," in *General anthropology*, ed. F. Boas (Boston: Heath), pp. 24–94.

MacInnes, D. G., 1943, "Notes on the East African Miocene primates," *J. E. Afr. Uganda Nat. Hist. Soc.* 17:141–181.

Mackintosh, N. A., and J. F. G. Wheeler, 1929, "Southern blue and fin whales," *Discovery Rep.* 1:257–540.

Mahalanobis, P. C., D. N. Majumdar, and C. R. Rao, 1949, "Anthropometric survey of the United Provinces, 1941," *Sankhyā* 9:89–324.

Martin, R., 1928, *Lehrbuch der Anthropologie* (2nd ed.; Jena: Fischer).

Mason, R. J., 1961, "The earliest tool-makers in South Africa," *S. Afr. J. Sci.* 57:13–16.

Matthew, W. D., and W. Granger, 1915, "A revision of the Lower Eocene Wasatch and Wind River faunas," *Bull. Amer. Mus. Nat. Hist.* 34:429–483.

Mayr, E., 1942, *Systematics and the origin of species* (New York: Columbia Univ. Press).

—— 1944, "On the concepts and terminology of vertical subspecies and species," *Nat. Res. Council Bull.* 2:11–16.

—— 1948, "The bearing of the new systematics on general problems. The nature of the species," *Advanc. Genet.* 2:205–237.

—— 1949, "Speciation and systematics," in *Genetics, paleontology and evolution*, ed. G. L. Jepsen, E. Mayr, and G. G. Simpson (Princeton: Princeton Univ. Press), pp. 281–298.

—— 1951, "Taxonomic categories in fossil hominids," *Cold Spr. Har. Symp. Quant. Biol.* 15:109–117.

―――― 1953, "Comments on evolutionary literature," *Evolution* 7:273–281.

―――― 1958, Review of *"Die Evolution der Organismen,"* *Science* 127:193.

―――― 1959, "Darwin and the evolutionary theory in biology," in *Evolution and anthropology: a centennial appraisal,* ed. Betty J. Meggers (Washington, D.C.: Anthrop. Soc. of Washington), pp. 1–10.

Midlo, C., 1934, "Form of hand and foot in primates," *Amer. J. Phys. Anthrop.* 19:337–389.

Midlo, C., and H. Cummins, 1942, "Palmar and plantar dermatoglyphics in primates," *Amer. Anat. Mem.,* no. 20 (Philadelphia: Wistar Inst. of Anat. and Biol.).

Miller, Ruth A., 1945, "The ischial callosities of primates," *Amer. J. Anat.* 76:67–91.

Mivart, St. G., 1873a, *Man and apes* (London: Hardwicke).

―――― 1873b, "On *Lepilemur* and *Cheirogaleus,* and on the zoological rank of the *Lemuroidea,"* *Proc. Zool. Soc. London 1873,* pp. 484–510.

Mohr, C. O., 1947, "Table of equivalent populations of North American small mammals," *Amer. Midland Naturalist* 37:223–249.

Moir, J. R., 1927, *The antiquity of man in East Anglia* (Cambridge, Eng.: Cambridge Univ. Press).

Mollison, T., 1910, *Die Körperproportionen der Primaten,* Habilitationsschrift. Univ. Zürich (Leipzig: Engelmann).

―――― 1911, "Die Körperproportionen der Primaten," *Morph. Jb.* 42:79–304.

―――― 1933, *Phylogenie des Menschen,* vol. III of *Handbuch der Vererbungswissenschaft,* ed. E. Baur and M. Hartmann (Berlin: Bornträger).

Montagu, M. F. A., 1933, "The anthropological significance of the pterion in the primates," *Amer. J. Phys. Anthrop.* 18:159–336.

―――― 1943, "The mesethmoid-presphenoid relationships in the primates," *Amer. J. Phys. Anthrop.* n.s. 1:129–140.

―――― 1945, *An introduction to physical anthropology* (Springfield, Ill.: Thomas).

Moody, P. A., 1953, *Introduction to evolution* (New York: Harper).

Morant, G. M., 1938, "The form of the Swanscombe skull," *J. Roy. Anthrop. Inst.* 68:67–97.

Morton, D. J., 1922, 1924, "Evolution of the human foot," *Amer. J. Phys. Anthrop.* 5:305–336; 7:1–52.

Mottl, M., 1957, "Bericht über die neuen Menschenaffenfunde aus Oesterreich, von St. Stefan im Lavanttal, Kärnten," *Carinthia II* 67:39–84.

Movius, H. L., 1949, "The lower palaeolithic cultures of southern and eastern Asia," *Trans. Amer. Phil. Soc.* n.s. 38:329–420.

Napier, J. R., 1959, "The problem of brachiation among the primates with special reference to *Proconsul,"* *Ber. 6. Tag. dtsch. Ges. Anthrop.,* p. 187.

Napier, J. R., and P. R. Davis, 1959, "The fore-limb skeleton and associated remains of *Proconsul africanus,"* *Fossil Mammals Afr.* 16:1–78.

Narr, K., 1956, "Der Urmensch als Natur- und Geistwesen," *Saeculum* 7:243–288.

Nice, Margaret M., 1941, "The role of territory in bird life," *Amer. Midland Naturalist* 26:441–487.

Nissen, H. W., 1951, "Social behavior in primates," in *Comparative psychology,* ed. C. P. Stone (3rd ed.; New York: Prentice-Hall), pp. 423–457.

Noback, C. V., 1936, (1) "Note on menstruation in the gorilla," and (2) "Note on gross changes observed in the external genitalia of the female just before, during and after menstruation," *Amer. J. Phys. Anthrop.* *21*, suppl. 9; abstract.

Noble, G. K., 1939, "The experimental animal from the naturalist's point of view," *Amer. Naturalist* 73:113–126.

Nuttall, G. H. F., 1904, *Blood immunity and blood relationship* (Cambridge, Eng.: Cambridge Univ. Press).

Oakley, K. P., 1949, 1950a, 1958, *Man the toolmaker* (London: Brit. Mus. Nat. Hist.).

——— 1950b, "New evidence on the antiquity of Piltdown man," *Nature* *165*:379–382.

——— 1951, "A definition of man," *Sci. News 20*:69.

——— 1954a, "Dating of australopithecines of Africa," *Amer. J. Phys. Anthrop.* n.s. *12*:9–27.

——— 1954b, "Early man in Africa," *S. Afr. Arch. Bull.* 9:64–68.

——— 1955a, "Dating the australopithecines," *Proc. Third Pan-Afr. Congr. on Prehistory*, pp. 155–157.

——— 1955b, "Earliest use of fire," *Proc. Third Pan-Afr. Congr. on Prehistory*, pp. 385–386.

——— 1956a–1957, "Dating fossil men," *Mem. Proc. Manchester Lit. Phil. Soc. 98*:75–94.

——— 1956b, "The earliest fire-makers," *Antiquity 30*:102–107.

——— 1956c, "The earliest tool-makers," *Antiquity 30*:4–7.

——— 1957, "Tools makyth man," *Antiquity 31*:199–209. (See also p. 422 of this volume.)

Oakley, K. P., and P. V. Tobias, 1960, "The Kanam jaw," *Nature 185*:945–947.

Obermaier, H., 1924, *Fossil man in Spain* (New Haven: Yale Univ. Press).

Olson, E. C., 1943, "The vertebrates," MS on deposit in library of Chicago Nat. Hist. Mus.

——— 1944, "Origin of mammals based upon cranial morphology of the therapsid suborders," *Spec. Papers Geol. Soc. Amer.* 55, 136 pp.

Orford, M., 1934, "The pelvis of the Bush race," *S. Afr. J. Sci. 31*:586–610.

Osborn, H. F., 1927, "Recent discoveries relating to the origin and antiquity of man," *Science 65*:481–488.

Owen, R., 1868, *On the anatomy of vertebrates, vol. III: Mammals* (London: Longmans, Green).

Patterson, B., 1954, "The geologic history of non-hominid primates in the old world," in *The non-human primates and human evolution*, ed. J. A. Gavan (Detroit: Wayne Univ. Press), pp. 13–31.

Pearson, K., and J. Bell, 1919, *A study of the long bones of the English skeleton* (Drapers' Co. Res. Mem., Biometric Series X, XI; London: Cambridge Univ. Press), pt. I: "The femur of man with special reference to other primate femora."

Pearson, O. P., 1948, "Metabolism and bioenergetics," *Sci. Month. 66*:131–134.

Pei, W. C., 1934, "Report on the excavation of the Locality 13 in Choukoutien," *Bull. Geol. Soc. China 13*:359–367.

——— 1956, "New material of *Gigantopithecus* teeth from South China," *Acta Pal. Sinica 4*:477–490.

——— 1957, "Discovery of *Gigantopithecus* mandibles and other material in Liu-Cheng District of Central Kwangsi in South China," *Vertebrata Palasiatica 1*:65–71.

Pennant, T., 1793, *History of quadrupeds* (London: White), vol. I.

Pilgrim, G. E., 1915, "New Siwalik primates and their bearing on the question of the evolution of man and the Anthropoidea," *Rec. Geol. Surv. India* 45:1–74.

Piveteau, J., 1957, *Primates. Paléontologie humaine,* vol. VII: *Traité de paléontologie.* (Paris: Masson).

Randall, F. E., 1943–44, "The skeletal and dental development and variability of the gorilla," *Hum. Biol. 15*:236–254, 307–337; *16*:23–76.

Rao, C., 1948, "The utilization of multiple measurements in problems of biological classification," *J. Roy. Statist. Soc. B 10*:159–203.

Raven, H. C., 1936a, "Comparative anatomy of the sole of the foot," *Am. Mus. Novitates,* no. 871.

—— 1936b, "Genital swelling in the female gorilla," *J. Mammalogy 17*:416.

—— 1950, "Regional anatomy of the gorilla," in *The anatomy of the gorilla,* ed. W. K. Gregory (Henry Cushier Raven Memorial Volume; New York: Columbia Univ. Press), pp. 115–188.

Ray, J., 1693, *Synopsis methodica animalium quadrupedum et serpentini generis* (London: Smith and Walford Soc.)

Regnault, F., 1894, "Suture lacrimo-éthmoidale," *Bull. Soc. d'Anthrop. Paris* [4]5:413–419.

—— 1902, "Suture orbito-fronto-maxillaire," *Bull. et Mém. Soc. anat. Paris* [6]4:479–483.

Remane, A., 1921, "Beiträge zur Morphologie des Anthropoidengebisses," *Arch. Naturgesch. 87*:1–179.

—— 1924, "Einige Bemerkungen zur Eckzahnfrage," *Anthrop. Anz. 1*:35–40.

—— 1927a, "Art und Rasse," *Verh. Ges. Phys. Anthrop. 2*:2–33.

—— 1927b, "Studien über die Phylogenie des menschlichen Eckzahnes," *Z. Anat. Entwickl. Gesch. 82*:391–481.

—— 1952a, *Die Grundlagen des natürlichen Systems, der vergleichenden Anatomie und der Phylogenetik* (Leipzig: Geest & Portig).

—— 1952b, "Methodische Probleme der Hominiden-Phylogenie. I," *Z. Morph. Anthrop. 44*:188–200.

—— 1954, "Methodische Probleme der Hominiden-Phylogenie. II. Möglichkeiten der Verwandtschaftsforschung innerhalb der Hominiden," *Z. Morph. Anthrop. 46*:225–268.

—— 1955, "Ist *Oreopithecus* ein Hominide?" *Akad. Wiss. Lit. math.-nat. Kl.* (Mainz) *12.*

—— 1956a, "Methodische Probleme der Hominidenphylogenie. III. Die Phylogenie der Lebensweise und die Entstehung des aufrechten Ganges," *Z. Morph. Anthrop. 48*:28–54.

—— 1956b, "Paläontologie und Evolution der Primaten, besonders der Nicht-Hominoiden," in *Primatologia,* ed. H. Hofer, A. H. Schultz, and D. Starck (Basel: Karger), I, 267–378.

Rensch, B., 1957, *Die stammesgeschichtliche Sonderstellung des Menschen* (Cologne and Opladen: Westdeutscher).

Richter, R., 1948, *Einführung in die zoologische Nomenklatur durch Erläuterung der internationalen Regeln* (2nd ed.; Frankfurt a.M.).

Rickenmann, E., 1957, *Beiträge zur vergleichenden Anatomie, insbesondere des Beckens bei Catarrhinen* (Basel: Karger).

Robinson, J. T., 1952a, "The australopithecine-bearing deposits of the Sterkfontein area," *Ann. Transvaal Mus.* 22:1–19.

────── 1952b, "Some hominid features of the ape-man dentition," *Offic. J. Dent. Assoc. S. Afr.* 7:102–113.

────── 1953a, "*Meganthropus*, australopithecines and hominids," *Amer. J. Phys. Anthrop.* n.s. 11:1–38.

────── 1953b, "The nature of *Telanthropus capensis*," *Nature* 171:33.

────── 1953c, "Note on the skull of *Proconsul africanus*," *Amer. J. Phys. Anthrop.* n.s. 7:12.

────── 1953d, "*Telanthropus* and its phylogenetic significance," *Amer J. Phys. Anthrop.* n.s. 11:445–501.

────── 1954, "The genera and species of the Australopithecinae," *Amer. J. Phys. Anthrop.* n.s. 12:181–200.

────── 1955, "Further remarks on the relationship between *Meganthropus* and australopithecines," *Amer. J. Phys. Anthrop.* n.s. 13:429–445.

────── 1956, *The dentition of the Australopithecinae*, Transvaal Museum Memoir 9 (Pretoria).

────── 1958, "The Sterkfontein tool-maker," *Leech* 28:94–100.

────── 1960, "The affinities of the new Olduvai australopithecine," *Nature* 186:456–458.

────── 1961, "The australopithecines and their bearing on the origin of man and of stone tool-making," *S. Afr. J. Sci.* 57:3–13.

Robinson, J. T., and R. J. Mason, 1957, "Occurrence of stone artifacts with *Australopithecus* at Sterkfontein," *Nature* 180:521–524.

Roginskii, I. I., 1947, "K voprosoo drevnosti tcheloveka sovremennogo tipa; mesto svanscombskogo tcherepa v sisteme hominid" (La question de l'ancienneté de l'homme actuel; la place du crâne de Swanscombe dans le système des Hominidés), *Sovietskaia Etnografiia*, no. 3, pp. 33–40.

Rust, A., 1956, *Artefakte aus der Zeit des* Homo heidelbergensis *in Süd- und Norddeutschland* (Bonn: Habelt).

Saban, R., 1956, 1957, "Les affinités du genre *Tupaia* Raffles après les caractères morphologiques de la tête osseuse," *Ann. Paleont.* 42:169–224; 43:1–44.

Schaaffhausen, D., 1861, "On the crania of the most ancient races of man," trans. G. Busk, in *Nat. Hist. Rev.* (April), from *Müller's Archiv* (1858), pp. 453ff.

Schinz, H. R., 1827, *Naturgeschichte und Abbildungen der Säugethiere* (Zürich: Bürkli).

Schlosser, M., 1911, "Beiträge zur Kenntnis der oligozänen Landsäugetiere aus dem Fayum (Agypten)," *Beitr. Paläont. Geol. Öst.-Ungarn Orients* 24:51–167.

Scholander, P. F., R. Hock, V. Walters, and L. Irving, 1950, "Adaptation to cold in arctic and tropical mammals and birds in relation to body temperature, insulation, and basal metabolic rate," *Biol. Bull.* 99:259–271.

Schreber, J. C. D., 1775, *Die Säugethiere in Abbildungen nach der Natur mit Beschreibungen* (Erlangen: Walther).

Schultz, A. H., 1924, "Growth studies on primates bearing upon man's evolution," *Amer. J. Phys. Anthrop.* 7:149–164.

────── 1925, "Studies on the evolution of human teeth," *Dent. Cosmos* 67:935–947, 1053–1063.

────── 1926, "Fetal growth of man and other primates," *Quart. Rev. Biol.* 1:465–521.

———— 1927, "Studies on the growth of *Gorilla* and of other higher primates with special reference to a fetus of *Gorilla*, preserved in the Carnegie Museum," *Mem. Carnegie Mus. 11*:1–87.

———— 1929, "The technique of measuring the outer body of human fetuses and of primates in general," *Contr. Embryol. Carnegie Inst. Wash.* 20:213–257.

———— 1930, "The skeleton of the trunk line and limbs of higher primates," *Hum. Biol. 2*:303–438.

———— 1931, "Man as a Primate," *Sci. Month.* 33:385.

———— 1933a, "Chimpanzee fetuses," *Amer. J. Phys. Anthrop.* 18:61–79.

———— 1933b, "Die Körperproportionen der erwachsenen catarrhinen Primaten, mit spezieller Berücksichtigung der Menschenaffen," *Anthrop. Anz.* 10:154–185.

———— 1933c, "Observations on the growth, classification and evolutionary specialization of gibbons and siamangs," *Hum. Biol.* 5:212–255, 385–428.

———— 1934a, "Inherited reductions in the dentition of man," *Hum. Biol.* 6:628–631.

———— 1934b, "Some distinguishing characters of the mountain gorilla," *J. Mammalogy* 15:51–61.

———— 1935a, "Eruption and decay of the permanent teeth in primates," *Amer. J. Phys. Anthrop.* 19:489–581.

———— 1935b, "The nasal cartilages in higher primates," *Amer. J. Phys. Anthrop.* 20:205–212.

———— 1936, "Characters common to higher primates and characters specific for man," *Quart. Rev. Biol.* 11:259–283, 425–455.

———— 1937, "Proportions, variability and asymmetries of the long bones of the limbs and the clavicles in man and apes," *Hum. Biol.* 9:281–328.

———— 1938, "Genital swelling in the female orang-utan," *J. Mammalogy* 19:363–366.

———— 1940, "Growth and development of the chimpanzee," *Contr. Embryol. Carnegie Inst. Wash.* 28:1–63.

———— 1941a, "Growth and development of the orang-utan," *Contr. Embryol. Carnegie Inst. Wash.* 29:57–110.

———— 1941b, "The relative size of the cranial capacity in primates," *Amer. J. Phys. Anthrop.* 28:273–287.

———— 1942a, "Conditions for balancing the head in primates," *Amer. J. Phys. Anthrop.* 29:483–497.

———— 1942b, "Morphological observations on a gorilla and an orang of closely known ages," *Amer. J. Phys. Anthrop.* 29:1–21.

———— 1944, "Age changes and variability in gibbons," *Amer. J. Phys. Anthrop.* n.s. 2:1–129.

———— 1947, "Variability in man and other primates," *Amer. J. Phys. Anthrop.* n.s. 5:1–140.

———— 1949, "Ontogenetic specialization of man," *Arch. d. Julius Klaus-Stiftung* 24:197–216.

———— 1950a, "Morphological observations on gorillas," in *The anatomy of the Gorilla*, ed. W. K. Gregory (Henry Cushier Raven Memorial Volume; New York: Columbia Univ. Press), pp. 227–254.

———— 1950b, "The physical distinctions of man," *Proc. Amer. Phil. Soc.* 94:428–449.

———— 1951, "The specializations of man and his place among the catarrhine primates," *Cold Spr. Harb. Symp. Quant. Biol.* 15:37–52.

────── 1953, "Man's place among the primates," *Man* 53:7–9.

────── 1955, "The position of the occipital condyles and of the face relative to the skull base in primates," *Am. J. Phys. Anthrop.* n.s. *13*:97–120.

────── 1956, "Postembryonic age changes," in *Primatologia*, ed. H. Hofer, A. H. Schultz, and D. Starck (Basel: Karger), I, 887–964.

────── 1957a, "Die Bedeutung der Primatenkunde für das Verständnis der Anthropogenese," *Ber. 5. Tag. dtsch. Ges. Anthrop.*, pp. 13–28.

────── 1957b, "Past and present views of man's specializations," *Irish J. Med. Sci. August 1957*, pp. 341–356.

────── 1960, "Einige Beobachtungen und Masse am Skelett von *Oreopithecus* im Vergleich mit anderen catarrhinen Primaten," *Z. Morph. Anthrop.* *50*:136–149.

Schultz, A. H., and W. L. Straus, Jr., 1945, "The numbers of vertebrae in primates," *Proc. Amer. Phil. Soc.* 89:601–626.

Schwalbe, G., 1923, "Die Abstammung des Menschen und die ältesten Menschenformen," in *Die Kultur der Gegenwart*, pt. 3, sec. 5: Anthropologie, ed. G. Schwalbe and E. Fischer (Leipzig: Teubner), pp. 223–338.

Schweitzer, A., 1947, *An anthology*, ed. C. R. Joy (Boston: Beacon).

Sears, P., 1950, *Charles Darwin, the naturalist as a cultural force* (New York: Scribner).

Seltzer, C. C., 1937, "A critique of the coefficient of racial likeness," *Amer. J. Phys. Anthrop.* 23:101–109.

Sergi, S., 1944, "Craniometria e craniografia del primo Paleantropo di Saccopastore," *Ric. Morf. 20–21*:1–60.

────── 1948, "Il cranio del secondo Paleantropo di Saccopastore," *Palaeontographica italica* 42:25–64.

────── 1953a, "I Profanerantropi di Swanscombe e di Fontéchevade," *Atti Accad. Lincei, 350,* [8]*14*:601–608.

────── 1953b, "I Profanerantropi di Swanscombe e di Fontéchevade," *Riv. Antrop. 40*:65–72.

────── 1953c, "I tipi umani più antichi," in *Le razze e i popoli della terra*, ed. R. Biasutti (2nd ed.; Turin: VTET), I, 69–133.

Shaw, J. C. M., 1931, *The teeth, the bony palate and the mandible in Bantu races of South Africa* (London: Bale and Danielsson).

Simpson, G. G., 1926, "Mesozoic mammals, IV: The multituberculates as living animals," *Amer. J. Sci.* [5]*11*:228–250.

────── 1935, "The Tiffany fauna, Upper Paleocene. II. Structure and relationships of *Plesiadapis*," *Amer. Mus. Novitates*, no. 816, pp. 1–30. "III. Primates, Carnivora, Condylarthea, and Amblypoda," *Amer. Mus. Novitates*, no. 817, pp. 1–28.

────── 1937, "The Ft. Union of the Crazy Mountain Field, Montana, and its mammalian faunas," *U.S. Nat. Mus. Bull.* 169:1–277.

────── 1940, "Studies on the earliest primates," *Bull. Amer. Mus. Nat. Hist.* 77:185–212.

────── 1944, *Tempo and mode in evolution* (New York: Columbia Univ. Press).

────── 1945, "The principles of classification and a classification of mammals," *Bull. Amer. Mus. Nat. His.* 85:1–350.

────── 1947, "Holarctic mammalian faunas and continental relationships during the Cenozoic," *Bull. Geol. Soc. Amer.* 58:613–687.

────── 1949, *The meaning of evolution* (New Haven: Yale Univ. Press; 1950, London: Oxford Univ. Press).

────── 1951a, "Some principles of historical biology bearing on human origins," *Cold Spr. Harb. Symp. Quant. Biol. 15*:55–66.

────── 1951b, *Horses* (London: Oxford Univ. Press).

────── 1953, *The major features of evolution* (New York: Columbia Univ. Press).

Simpson, G. G., C. S. Pittendrigh, and L. H. Tiffany, 1957, *Life: an introduction to biology* (New York: Harcourt, Brace).

Sim Wallace, J., 1927, *Variations in the form of the jaws* (London: Ballière, Tindall & Cox).

Skerlj, B., 1950, *Razvoj cloveka. Antropogeneza* (Ljubljana: Univ. Ljubljana Inst. Antrop.).

Smith, G. E., 1924, *Essays on the evolution of man* (Oxford: Oxford Univ. Press).

Sperino, G., and A. Bovero, 1896, "Sulla sutura metopica basilare o frontile-basilare nel cranio umano," *G. Accad. med. Torino* [4]*2*:409–446.

Stebbins, G. L., Jr., 1949, *Variation and evolution in plants* (New York: Columbia Univ. Press).

Steward, J. H., 1938, *Basin-plateau aboriginal sociopolitical groups* (Washington, D.C.: U.S. Govt. Printing Office).

Straus, W. L., Jr., 1929, "Studies on primate ilia," *Amer. J. Anat. 43*:403–460.

────── 1930, "The foot musculature of the highland gorilla (*Gorilla beringei*), *Quart. Rev. Biol. 5*:261–317.

────── 1940, "The posture of the great-ape hand in locomotion, and its phylogenetic implications," *Amer. J. Phys. Anthrop. 27*:199–207.

────── 1941a, "Locomotion of gibbons," *Amer. J. Phys. Anthrop. 28*:354–356.

────── 1941b, "The phylogeny of the human forearm extensors," *Hum. Biol. 13*:23–50, 203–238.

────── 1942a, "The homologies of the forearm flexors: urodeles, lizards, mammals," *Amer. J. Anat. 70*:281–316.

────── 1942b, "Rudimentary digits in primates," *Quart. Rev. Biol. 17*:228–243.

────── 1946, "The hand and foot musculature of catarrhine primates—a phylogenetic survey," *Amer. J. Phys. Anthrop.* n.s. *4*:263; abstract.

────── 1947, "The riddle of man's ancestry," *Amer. J. Phys. Anthrop.* n.s. *5*:243; abstract.

────── 1948a, "The humerus of *Paranthropus robustus*," *Amer. J. Phys. Anthrop.* n.s. *6*:285–311.

────── 1948b, "The limb bones of australopithecines," *Amer. J. Phys. Anthrop.* n.s. *6*:237–238; abstract.

────── 1949, "The riddle of man's ancestry," *Quart. Rev. Biol. 24*:200–223.

────── 1955, "Closing remarks," in *The non-human primates and human evolution*, ed. J. A. Gavan (Detroit: Wayne Univ. Press), pp. 126–134.

────── 1957, "Hunters or hunted?" *Science 126*:1108.

Straus, W. L., Jr., and G. B. Wislocki, 1932, "On certain similarities between sloths and slow lemurs," *Bull. Mus. Comp. Zool. 74*:43–56.

Swanscombe Committee of the Royal Anthropological Institute, "1938 report on the Swanscombe skull," *J. Roy. Anthrop. Inst. Gt. Brit. Ireland 68*:17–98.

Systematics Association, 1956, *The species concept in palaeontology* (London).

Teilhard de Chardin, P., 1916–1922, "Les mammifères de l'éocène inférieur français et leurs gisements," *Ann. Paléont. Paris 10*:171–176; *11*:1–116.

────── 1952, "On the zoological position and evolutionary significance of australopithecines," *Trans. N.Y. Acad. Sci.* [2]*14*:208–210.

Thenius, E., 1958a, "Tertiärstratigraphie und tertiäre Hominoidenfunde," *Anthrop. Anz.* 22:66–77.

—— 1958b, "Zum Skelettfund von Oreopithecus von Toskana," *Öst. Hochschul-Z. 10,* no. 19, pp. 3–4.

Thomson, A., 1890, "The orbito-maxillary frontal suture in man and the apes, with notes on the varieties of the human lachrymal bone," *J. Anat. Physiol.* n.s. 4:349–357.

Tindale, N. B., 1949, "Large biface implements from Mornington Island, Queensland and from South Western Australia," *Rec. S. Aust. Mus.* 9:157–166.

Trevisan, L., 1949, "Lineamenti dell' evoluzione del ceppo di elefanti eurasiatici nel Quaternario," *Ric. Sci. 19*:105–112.

Trouessart, E. L., 1897, *Catalogus mammalium tam viventium quam fossilium* (Berlin: Friedländer), fasc. 1.

Turner, W., 1886, "Report on the human crania and other bones of the skeletons collected during the voyage of H.M.S. Challenger, in the years 1873–1876," in *Report of the scientific results of the voyage of H.M.S. Challenger, during 1873–1876,* ed. C. W. Thompson and J. Murray (London: H. M.'s Stationary Office), part I, "The crania," in vol. 10 (1884), part II, "The bones of the skeleton," in vol. 16 (1886).

Vallois, H. V., 1946, "Les nouveaux Pithécanthropes et le problème de l'origine de l'homme," *La Nature,* no. 3123, pp. 367–370.

—— 1949a, "The Fontéchevade fossil man," *Amer. J. Phys. Anthrop.* n.s. 7:339–362.

—— 1949b, "L'Origine de l'*Homo sapiens,*" *C.R. Acad. Sci. (Paris)* 228:949–951.

—— 1952, "Monophyletism and polyphyletism in man," *S. Afr. J. Sci.* 49:69–79.

—— 1954a, "Neanderthals and Praesapiens," *J. Roy Anthrop. Inst. Gt. Brit. Ireland 84,* pt. 2, pp. 111–130.

—— 1954b, "L'Oréopithèque, hominidé tertiaire primitif?" *L'anthropologie* 58:349–351.

—— 1955a, "La mandibule humaine prémoustérienne de Montmaurin," *C.R. Acad. Sci. (Paris)* 240:1577–1579.

—— 1955b, "Ordre des Primates," in *Traité de zoologie 17,* ed. P. Grasse (Paris: Masson), II, 1854–2206.

—— 1956, "Nouvelles recherches sur l'Oréopithèque," *L'Anthropologie* 60:364–367.

—— 1958, "La Grotte de Fontéchevade," Deuxième Partie, *Anthropologie.*

Verneau, R., 1924, "La race de Néanderthal et la race de Grimaldi; leurs rôles dans l'humanité," *J. Roy. Anthrop. Inst. Gt. Brit. Ireland* 54:211–230.

Visser, J. B., 1946, 1947, "De Wortelvariaties van de postcanine onderelementen van het menschelijk gebit," *T. Tandheelk.* 53, no. 11; 54, no. 1.

Waddington, C. H., 1953a, "The evolution of adaptations," *Endeavour 12*:134–139.

—— 1953b, "Genetic assimilation of an acquired character," *Evolution* 7:118–126.

Warren, S. H., 1940, "Geological and prehistoric traps," *Essex Nat.* 27:13–19.

—— 1948, "The Crag Platform: its geology and archaeological problem," *S. E. Nat. Antiq.* 53:48–52.

Washburn, S. L., 1942a, "Skeletal proportions of adult langurs and macaques," *Hum. Biol. 14*:444–472.

——— 1942b, "Technique in primatology," *Anthrop. Briefs,* no. 1, p. 6.

——— 1946, "The sequence of epiphysial union in the opossum," *Anat. Rec.* 95:353–364.

——— 1947, "The relation of the temporal muscle to the form of the skull," *Anat. Rec.* 99:239–248.

——— 1949, "Sex differences in the pubic bone of Bantu and Bushman," *Amer. J. Phys. Anthrop.* n.s. 7:425–432.

——— 1951a, "The analysis of primate evolution with particular reference to the origin of man," *Cold Spr. Harb. Symp. Quant. Biol.* 15:67–77.

——— 1951b, "The new physical anthropology," *Trans. N.Y. Acad. Sci.* [2]:*13*:298–304.

——— 1953, "The strategy of physical anthropology," in *Anthropology today,* ed. A. L. Kroeber (Chicago: Univ. of Chicago Press) pp. 714–727.

——— 1957, "The hunters or the hunted?" *Amer. Anthrop.* 59:612–614.

Washburn, S. L., and V. Avis, 1958, "Evolution of human behavior," in A. Roé and G. G. Simpson, *Behavior and evolution* (New Haven: Yale Univ. Press), pp. 421–436.

Washburn, S. L., and B. Patterson, 1951, "Evolutionary importance of the South-African 'Man-apes,'" *Nature* 167:650–651.

Watson, D. M. S., 1951, *Palaeontology and modern biology* (New Haven: Yale Univ. Press).

Weber, M., 1927–28, *Die Säugetiere* (2nd ed.; Jena: Fischer).

Weckler, J., 1954, "The relationships between Neanderthal Man and *Homo sapiens,*" *Amer. Anthrop.* 56:1003–1025.

Weidenreich, F., 1913, "Über das Hüftbein und das Becken der Primaten und ihre Umformung durch den aufrechten Gang," *Anat. Anz.* 44:497–513.

——— 1921, "Der Menschenfuss," *Z. Morph. Anthrop.* 22:51–282.

——— 1928, "Entwicklungs- und Rassetypen des *Homo primigenius,*" *Natur und Museum* 58:1–13, 51–62.

——— 1937, "The dentition of Sinanthropus pekinensis," *Palaeont. Sinica* n.s. *101*:1–180.

——— 1940, "Some problems dealing with ancient man," *Amer. Anthrop.* 42:375–383.

——— 1941, "The brain and its role in the phylogenetic transformation of the human skull," *Trans. Amer. Phil. Soc.* n.s. *31*:321–442.

——— 1943a, "The 'Neanderthal Man' and the ancestors of *Homo sapiens,*" *Amer. Anthrop.* 45:39–48.

——— 1943b, "The skull of *Sinanthropus pekinensis;* a comparative study on a primitive hominid skull," *Palaeont. Sinica* n.s. D *10,* no. 127, pp. 1–229.

——— 1945, "Giant early man from Java and South China," *Anthrop. Papers Amer. Mus. Nat. Hist.* 40:5–134.

——— 1946, *Apes, giants and man* (Chicago: Univ. of Chicago Press).

——— 1947a, "Facts and speculations concerning the origin of *Homo sapiens,*" *Amer. Anthrop.* 49:187–203.

——— 1947b, "The trend of human evolution," *Evolution* 1:221–236.

——— 1949, "Interpretations of the fossil material," in *Early man in the Far East. Studies in Physical Anthropology,* ed. W. W. Howells (Philadelphia: American Association of Physical Anthropologists), I, 149–158.

Weiner, J. S., 1957, "The evolutionary taxonomy of the Hominidae in the light of the Piltdown investigation," in *Selec. Papers Fifth Int. Congr. Anthrop. Ethnol. Sci.,* pp. 741–752.

Weiner, J. S., K. P. Oakley, and W. E. Le Gros Clark, 1953, "The solution of the Piltdown problem," *Bull. Brit. Mus. Nat. Hist.* 2:141–146.

Weinert, H., 1925, "Die Ausbildung der Stirnhölen als stammesgeschichtliches Merkmal: Eine vergleichend-anatomische Studie mit einem Atlas der Stirnhöhlen und einem neuen Messzirkel zur Ermittelung der inneren Schädelmasse," *Z. Morph. Anthrop.* 25:243–357, 365–418.

―――― 1932, 1944, *Ursprung der Menschheit* (Stuttgart: Enke).

―――― 1936, "Der Urmenschenschädel von Steinheim," *Z. Morph. Anthrop.* 35:463–518.

―――― 1944, "Altsteinzeitliche Forschungen in Italien. Ergebnisse und Probleme," *Z. Morph. Anthrop.* 41:87–125.

―――― 1955, "Die Neandertaler-Gruppe und die 'Praesapiens' Funde," *Forsch. Fortschr.* 29:219.

Weitzel, K., 1949, "Neue Wirbeltiere (Rodentia, Insectivora, Testudinata) aus dem Mitteleozän van Mersel bei Darmstadt," *Abh. Senckenberg naturforsch. Ges.*, no. 489, pp. 1–24.

Wells, L. H., 1931a, "The foot of the South African native," *Amer. J. Phys. Anthrop.* 25:185–289.

―――― 1931b, "Growth changes in the Bushman mandible," *J. Anat.* (*London*) 66:50–63.

Weninger, M., 1956, "Die Bedeutung der zurfälligen Aenderungen der Allelenfrequenz (Random drift) für die Stammes- und Rassengeschichte des Menschens," in *Novant' anni delle leggi mendeliane*, ed. L. Gedda (Rome: Ist. Gregorio Mendel), pp. 416–424.

Werth, E., 1918, "Parapithecus, ein primitiver Menschenaffe," *S.-B. Ges. Naturforsch. Freunde Berlin 1918*, pp. 327–345.

―――― 1928, *Der fossile Mensch* (Berlin: Bornträger).

Wiercinski, A., 1956, "Zagadnienie wystepowanìa form *Homo sapiens* we wczesnym i srodkowym plejstocenie" (Le problème de l'apparition des types d'*Homo sapiens* aux Pleistocènes inférieur et moyen), *Przeglad antropologiczny* 22:267–285.

Wilder, B. G., 1911, "Preliminary note upon a brain of about one-half the average size," *J. Nerv. Ment. Dis.* 38:95–97.

Winge, H., 1941, *The interrelationships of the mammalian genera. II. Rodentia, Carnivora, Primates*, ed. S. Jensen, R. Spärck, and H. Vølsoe (Copenhagen: Reitzels-Sandal). Eng. trans.; contains trans. of paper of 1895 on Primates.

Wolff, T., 1906, "Beiträge zur Anthropologie der Orbita," diss. Zürich.

Woo Ju-Kang, 1957, "*Dryopithecus* teeth from Keiyuan, Yunnan Province," *Vertebrata Palasiatica* 1:25–31.

Woollard, H. H., 1925, "The anatomy of Tarsius spectrum," *Proc. Zool. Soc. London 1925*, pp. 1071–1184.

Woollard, H. H., and A. Harpman, 1938, "Note on the internal architecture of the mandible," *J. Anat.* (*London*) 72:575–578.

World Health Organization, 1957, *Effect of radiation on human heredity* (Geneva: WHO).

Wright, S., 1934, "Polydactylous guinea pigs," *J. Hered.* 25:359–362.

―――― 1949a, "Adaptation and selection," in *Genetics, paleontology and evolution*, ed. G. L. Jepsen, E. Mayr, and G. G. Simpson (Princeton: Princeton Univ. Press), pp. 365–389.

―――― 1949b, "Population structure in evolution," *Proc. Amer. Phil. Soc.* 93:471–478.

Yerkes, R. M., 1939, "Social dominance and sexual status in the chimpanzee," *Quart. Rev. Biol. 14*:115–136.

Zapfe, H., 1951, "Die Pliopithecus-Funde aus der Spaltenfüllung von Neudorf an der March (CSR)," *Verh. geol. Bundesanst. Wien,* suppl. C, pp. 126–130.

————— 1959, "The skeleton of *Pliopithecus (Epipliopithecus) vindobonensis* Zapfe and Hürzeler," *Amer. J. Phys. Anthrop.* n.s. *16*:441–458.

Zapfe, H., and J. Hürzeler, 1957, "Die Fauna der miozänen Spaltenfüllung von Neudorf an der March (CSR), Primates," *S.-B. Öst. Akad. Wiss. math.-nat. Kl.,* Abt. I, *166*:113–123.

Zeuner, F. E., 1952, *Dating the past* (3rd ed.; London: Methuen).

Zuckerman, S. 1932, *The social life of monkeys and apes* (London: Kegan Paul).

————— 1933, *Functional affinities of man, monkeys, and apes* (New York: Harcourt, Brace).

————— 1952, "Discussion of 'The australopithecines and their evolutionary significance,' by J. T. Robinson," *Proc. Linn. Soc. London 163*:200–203.